ELEMENTS

OF

PHYSIOLOGICAL PSYCHOLOGY

ELEMENTS

OF

PHYSIOLOGICAL PSYCHOLOGY

*A TREATISE OF THE ACTIVITIES AND NATURE
OF THE MIND*

FROM THE PHYSICAL AND EXPERIMENTAL POINTS OF VIEW

(THOROUGHLY REVISED AND RE-WRITTEN)

BY

GEORGE TRUMBULL LADD, LL.D.

EMERITUS PROFESSOR OF MORAL PHILOSOPHY AND METAPHYSICS IN YALE UNIVERSITY

AND

ROBERT SESSIONS WOODWORTH, PH.D.

PROFESSOR OF PSYCHOLOGY IN COLUMBIA UNIVERSITY

ILLUSTRATED

CHARLES SCRIBNER'S SONS

NEW YORK CHICAGO BOSTON

PREFACE

It is now nearly a quarter of a century since the appearance of the first edition of this treatise, which attempted to gather within the limits of a single volume the main results of the then modern study of psychology from the physiological and experimental points of view. It was at that time (1887) the only work of its kind in English; and so far as the author was aware, it was the only work in any language, with the sole exception of Professor Wundt's *Grundzüge der physiologischen Psychologie*, which was then in its second edition. The task involved in any such attempt was even so long ago exceedingly large and difficult. But the prompt favorable response given to its accomplishment, not only in this country, but also from abroad, was on this account all the more unexpectedly gratifying.

During the interval since the first edition, many trained and skilled workmen have assiduously devoted themselves to the solution of the various subordinate problems involved in the study of mental life and mental development with the carefully guarded methods prescribed by modern science. Much light has been thrown on these problems, their nature and their probable solution; while many new ones or new aspects of old problems have been uncovered and are still awaiting future investigation. And there is no prospect that this process will come to an end. But it is just this fact which evinces in an unmistakable way the vitality of the science of psychology, as it does the vitality of all the other forms of human knowledge. On the other hand, it is entirely safe to say that neither the extravagant hopes nor the extravagant fears of twenty-five years ago, with reference to the results of the so-called "new psychology," have been verified. The fundamental problems with regard to the nature of man's mind and its relations to the organism, its place in the scale of development and its destiny, remain essentially unchanged.

v

Those acquainted with the first edition will notice several important changes on comparing with it the present revised edition. Of these changes perhaps the most important may be summed up in the fact that, of the two editions, this is much the most distinctly *physiological*. The reason for this change is chiefly the following: While many excellent volumes and articles have meantime appeared to give the results of *experimental* psychology, more strictly so-called, comparatively little has been published, of a worthy character, which could be brought under the head of *physiological* psychology. with any strict application of this latter term. With the same end in view, two entire chapters—one on THE PLACE OF THE NERVOUS MECHANISM IN THE ANIMAL KINGDOM, and the other on THE DEVELOPMENT OF THE NERVOUS SYSTEM IN THE INDIVIDUAL—have been added to Part I, and all the other chapters of this part have been carefully rewritten and in most cases considerably expanded. The new chapters on THE LOCALIZATION OF CEREBRAL FUNCTIONS have been transferred to it. In this way the aim has been to give a compact and complete summary of the nervous mechanism in its relations to mental life. The hope has also been indulged that the book might thus be made more useful to students of physiology and medicine, who, in the opinion of the authors, ought to know far more than they now do about the science of psychology as approached from the physiological point of view.

The subjects more definitely falling under the head of experimental psychology have, however, by no means been neglected. Indeed, so far as these are connected with the functions of the organs of sense, and with the measurement of all sorts of reactions to all kinds of stimuli, they are themselves distinctly physiological in their character and in their conclusions. And even when the students of experimental psychology attempt the more difficult problems connected with the mental functions involved in memory, association, thinking, and learning, they can not possibly quite separate themselves from the closely allied physiological problems. On the other hand, the problems which are attacked and more or less successfully handled by the most purely experimental methods are available and important data for the student of the same phenomena from the physiological point of view. While, then, Part II has not been correspondingly extended, it, too, has been revised with equal thoroughness, with the intention of making it a fairly complete but succinct treatment of similar data as regarded from a somewhat changed point of view. In all this, however, the controlling purpose of the book has never been lost out of sight, which is to summarize what modern science knows, or reasonably conjectures, about the correlations existing between the nervous mechanism and the mental life of man.

The other principal change which will be noted is the great reduction made in the Third Part of the book. This has been partly on account of economy of space. But it has been chiefly due to the fact that the author of the first edition has, since its appearance, expressed his views on the more distinctly speculative questions involved, in a series of monographs.[1] The two chapters to which this part has been reduced—to summarize them in a single word—simply maintain the contention that the study of ultimate psychological problems, from the physiological and experimental points of view, finally leaves them in essentially the same condition as that in which it finds them; and this position is that of a naive and so-called "common-sense" dualism, as distinguished from the metaphysical theories of parallelism, materialism, or subjective idealism. To this dualism, neither psychology nor physiology and physics have anything to oppose on scientific grounds. The settlement of *these* questions, then, if they are to be settled at all, must be relegated to philosophy.

While, as has already been stated, the entire subject has been studied afresh and the book rewritten throughout, it has been all the more gratifying to find that as candid and objective a reconsideration of his own views as it is easily practicable for any student to give, did not seem to require essential modifications in any of the psychological theories advanced by the first edition on alleged scientific grounds. But if the same candidly critical reception is accorded to this edition which was so happily experienced by its predecessor, it will be all that can be justly asked—perhaps more than, under existing circumstances, can be reasonably expected.

The authors of this edition wish to make general acknowledg-

[1] Especially "Philosophy of Mind" (1895), and "A Theory of Reality" (1899).

ment of obligations to the many authorities whom they have consulted and without whose assistance, of course, the book could never have been written. So far as was practicable, they have endeavored to mention them by name, either in the text or in the foot-notes. But they desire to make special mention in this place of their obligations to the writers and publishers of the neurological journals and treatises from which so many of the figures illustrating the anatomy of the nervous system have been borrowed.

During the progress in preparation of this edition, the author of the first edition found that his obligations to Professor R. S. Woodworth could be justly discharged only by placing his name upon the title-page as its joint author. And this act of justice was cheerfully rendered.

GEORGE TRUMBULL LADD.

NEW HAVEN, *May*, 1911.

PREFACE TO THE FIRST EDITION

THERE can be no doubt that an important movement in psychology has arisen in recent times through the effort to approach the phenomena of mind from the experimental and physiological point of view. Different students of psychological science will estimate differently both the net result already reached by this effort and the promise of further additions to the sum of our knowledge from continued investigation of the same kind. Some writers have certainly indulged in extravagant claims as to the past triumphs of so-called Physiological Psychology, and in equally extravagant expectations as to its future discoveries. On the other hand, a larger number, perhaps, have been inclined either to fear or to depreciate every attempt to mingle the methods, laws, and speculations of the physical sciences with the study of the human soul. These latter apparently anticipate that some discovery in the localization of cerebral function, or in psychometry, may jeopard the birthright of man as a spiritual and rational being. Or possibly they wish to regard the soul as separated, by nature and with respect to its modes of action, from the material body in such a way as to render it impossible to understand more of the one by learning more about the other.

As a result of some years of study of the general subject, I express with considerable confidence the opinion that there is no ground for extravagant claims or expectations, and still less ground for any fear of consequences. In all cases of new and somewhat rankly growing scientific enterprises, it is much the better way to waive the discussion of actual or possible achievements, as well as of welcomed or dreaded revelations of new truth, and proceed at once to the business on hand. It is proposed in this book to follow this better way. It will be the task of the book itself to set forth the assured or alleged results of Physiological Psychology; and this will be done at every step with such degree of assurance as belongs to the evidence hitherto attainable upon the particular subject discussed. With declamation, either in attack or defence of the "old psychology," of the "introspective method," etc., one may dispense without serious loss.

The study of the phenomena of consciousness by the method here proposed necessarily requires some acquaintance with a considera- ble circuit of sciences which are not usually all alike closely allied. The number of scholars who can form opinions with equal freedom and confidence in all of these sciences is very small. Moreover, since all *psycho-physical* laws are supposed—as the very term indi- cates—to govern the correlations of phenomena of consciousness with phenomena of the nervous system, a peculiar mystery belongs to much of the domain within which psycho-physical science is compelled to move. These facts may fitly, on the one hand, excite caution in the writer; and, on the other hand, excuse him for many inevitable failures to set forth with perfect definiteness and confidence the conclusions he has to propose. Much will be said that must be accepted as provisional, as only probably true. Much room must also be made for conjecture and speculation. What is most important, however, is that conjecture should not be put forth as ascertained fact, or speculation as unquestioned law.

It would have been a great assistance to me if I had had more predecessors in the path which I am to take. But with the excep- tion of Wundt's masterly work (*Grundzüge der physiologischen Psychologie*, second edition in 1880), no one book has attempted to cover, even in a summary way, the entire ground. The number of monographs, however, which have dealt with individual ques- tions subordinate to, or part of, the main inquiry is very great. These two facts also render the attempt at a general survey of Physiological Psychology for readers of English both peculiarly attractive and peculiarly difficult. I can only indulge the hope that I have done something toward breaking this path and render- ing it easier and more secure, both for myself and for others, in the future.

The investigators and authors to whom I am under obligations for material upon the various questions discussed, or statements made, in this book are by no means all mentioned by name. Of course, much of what is said on the structure of the nervous system, and on the phenomena of sensation and perception, has already become part of that general fund of facts and laws which belongs alike to all students of the subject. But by quoting certain authorities in the text, and by a few (in· comparison with the number which might have been cited) references in foot-notes, I have connected some of the discoveries and views of modern psycho-physical science with their authors. These may serve somewhat as guide to those persons who wish to pursue such studies still further.

I am under particular obligations to Dr. James K. Thacher, Professor of Physiology in the Yale Medical School, for valuable assistance in that description of the Nervous Mechanism, its structure and functions, which the First Part of the book contains. If I have escaped the mistake of assuming to teach more than is really known upon this subject, it has been in large measure due to his friendly and skilful guidance. Valuable assistance has also been received from Russell H. Chittenden, Professor of Physiological Chemistry, and Charles S. Hastings, Professor of Physics—both of the Sheffield Scientific School.

The method and arrangement of the book have been chosen so as to fit it for use, both as a text-book by special students of the subjects of which it treats, and also by the general reader who is interested in knowing what results have been reached by the more modern—and even the latest —psycho-physical researches.

GEORGE T. LADD.

YALE UNIVERSITY, NEW HAVEN, *February,* 1887.

TABLE OF CONTENTS

PAGE

INTRODUCTION 1–10

PART FIRST

THE NERVOUS MECHANISM

CHAPTER I

THE PLACE OF THE NERVOUS SYSTEM IN THE ANIMAL KINGDOM...... 13–35

§ 1, Necessity of the Comparative Method.—§ 2, Primary Division of Animals.—§§ 3–4, Description of the Amœba.—§ 5, Specialization of Receptors and Effectors.—§§ 6–8, Nerve-Net Type of Nervous System.—§§ 10–11, Segmented Type of Nervous System.—§ 12, Centralized Type of Nervous System.—§§ 13–15, Nerve-Centres of Vertebrates.—§ 16, Structure of the Cerebellum.—§ 17, The Mid-Brain.—§ 18, Inter-Brain and End-Brain.—§ 19, Development of the Cortex.—§§ 20–21, Relation of Size to Intelligence.—§ 22, Essential Function of Nervous Tissue.

CHAPTER II

THE DEVELOPMENT OF THE NERVOUS SYSTEM IN THE INDIVIDUAL...... 36–62

§§ 1–2, Reproduction in Unicellular Organisms.—§ 3, Formation of the Neural Groove.—§ 4, Constitution of the Neural Tube.—§§ 5–6, Growth of Nerve Axons and Fibres.—§ 7, Formation of the Spinal Cord.—§§ 8–9, Growth of the Five Brain Vesicles.—§§ 10–11, Development of the Cortex.—§§ 13–14, The Twelve Pairs of Cranial Nerves.—§§ 15–16, Factors in Growth of the Nervous System.—§ 17, Function of the Myelin Sheath.—§§ 18–20, Variations in Weight of Human Brain.

CHAPTER III

GROSS STRUCTURE OF THE NERVOUS SYSTEM........................ 63–96

§ 1, Importance of Relation between Nervous Elements.—§§ 2–3, Differentiation of Nervous Function.—§ 4, Distinction of Sympathetic and Cerebro-Spinal.—§ 5, Membranes of Brain and Spinal Cord.—§§ 6–7, Columns and Commissures of the Cord.—§§ 8–9, White and Gray Matter of the Cord.—§§ 10–11, Nerve-Fibres and Nerve-Cells in the Cord.—§ 12, Different Aspects of the Encephalon.—§ 13, Twelve Pairs of Cranial Nerves.—§§ 14–

15, Internal Structure of Brain-Stem.—§§ 16–18, Continuations of the Brain-Stem.—§§ 19–21, Structure and Relations of Inter-Brain.—§ 22, The Cerebellum.—§§ 23–24, Tracing and Naming of Nerve-Tracts.—§§ 25–27, Nerve-Tracts and Their Connections.—§ 28, Principal Motor Pathway.—§§ 29–35, Systems of Nerve-Centres and Connections.

CHAPTER IV

PAGE

ELEMENTS OF THE NERVOUS STRUCTURE............................ 97–116

§§ 1–2, Development of the Nervous Elements.—§ 3, Structure of the Nerve-Fibre.—§ 4, Size of Different Nerve-Fibres.—§ 5, Constitution of the Gray Matter.—§ 6, Size and Shape of Nerve-Cells.—§§ 7–8, Internal Structure of Nerve-Cells.—§ 9, Arrangement of Nerve-Cells.—§ 10, Structure and Office of the Dendrites.—§ 11, Nerve-Cells of the Cerebellum.—§ 12, Structure and Function of the Axon.—§ 13, The Neurone Theory.—§14, The Neuroglia Cells.

CHAPTER V

CHEMISTRY OF THE NERVOUS SYSTEM 117–126

§§ 1–2, General Chemistry of Brain and Nerves.—§ 3, Chief Chemical Elements of Brain.—§§ 4–5, The Lipoids of the Nervous Substance.—§ 6, Non-Fatty Substances in Brain.—§ 7, Cholesterin.—§§ 8–11, The Phosphorized Lipoids in the Nervous Substance.—§ 12, Specific Chemistry of Nervous Elements.

CHAPTER VI

THE NERVES AS CONDUCTORS..................................... 127–144

§§ 1–2, Most General Function of the Nerves.—§ 3, Methods of Experimentation.—§ 4, Excitability of the Nerve.—§ 5, The Laws of Du Bois-Reymond.—§ 6, The Refractory Period.—§ 7, Speed of the Nervous Current.—§ 8, Alterations in Conductivity of Nerves.—§ 9, Double Conduction of the Nerves.—§ 10, Nature of the Process Conducted.—§ 11, Phenomena of Fatigue.—§ 12, The Current of Action.—§§ 13–14, Electrotonic Changes in Nerves.—§ 15, The Core Model or Core Conductor.—§§ 16–17, The Current of Rest.—§ 18, Theories of Nervous Function.

CHAPTER VII

REFLEX FUNCTIONS OF THE NERVOUS SYSTEM 145–174

§§ 1–2, Nature of Reflex Arc.—§ 3, Instinctive and Simple Reflexes.—§§ 4–5, Automatic Action of Nervous Centres.—§§ 6–7, The Ganglionic Reflexes.—§ 8, Reflexes of the Skeletal Musculature.—§§ 9–12, Local Reflexes of the Spinal Cord.—§§ 13–14, Reflexes of the Cerebellum.—§ 15, Reflexes of the Medulla.—§ 16, Influence of Cerebrum on Lower Centres.—§§ 17–18, Nervous Mechanism of Reflexes.—§§ 19–20, Phenomena of Inhibition.—§§ 21–22, The Refractory Period.—§ 23, Diphasic Impulses.—§ 24, Latent Time of Nervous Reflexes.—§§ 25–26, Intensity and Extent of Reflexes.—§§ 27–28, Facilitation of Reflexes.—§§ 29–30, Interference of Reflexes.—§ 31, General Characteristics of Reflex Action.

CHAPTER VIII

PAGE

END–ORGANS, OR RECEPTORS, OF THE NERVOUS SYSTEM 175–212

§§ 1–3, Function of End-Organs in the Nervous System.—§§ 4–5, End-Organs of Smell.—§§ 6–7, End-Organs of Taste.—§§ 8–9, End-Organs of Touch.—§ 10, The Pacinian Corpuscles.—§§ 11–12, Structure of the Eye-Ball.—§ 13, Refracting Media of the Eye.—§ 14, Muscles of the Eye-Ball.—§ 15, The Problem Before the Organ of Vision.—§ 16, Indices of Refraction.—§ 17. Mechanism of Accommodation.—§ 18, The Stimulus of Vision.—§§ 19–20, Nervous Elements of the Retina.—§ 21. The Yellow Spot and the Blind-Spot.—§ 22, Office of the Rods and Cones.—§ 23, Chemical Changes in the Retina.—§ 24, General Description of the Eye.—§ 25, Three Principal Parts of the Ear.—§ 26, Structure of the Middle Ear.—§ 27, Office of the Tympanum.—§ 28, The Eustachian Tube.—§ 29, Structure of the Internal Ear.—§ 30, Distribution of the Auditory Nerve.—§ 31–32, The Organ of Corti.—§ 33, Theory of Sympathetic Vibration.—§§ 34–36, Function of the Semicircular Canals.—§ 37, End-Organs of Motion.

CHAPTER IX

THE CEREBRAL HEMISPHERES AND THEIR FUNCTIONS.............. 213–234

§§ 1–4, The Problem of Cerebral Functions.—§ 5, Evidence from Comparative Anatomy.—§§ 6–7, Evidence from Removal or Injury.—§ 8, The Problem Stated.—§ 9, General Description of Cerebral Hemispheres.—§ 10, Principal Divisions of the Cortex.—§ 11, Projection and Association Fibres.—§§ 12–13, Nervous Elements of the Cortex.—§ 14, History of the Investigation.—§ 15, The Three Lines of Evidence.—§ 16, The Method of Extirpation.—§ 17, Evidence of Human Pathology.—§ 18, Evidence from Histology.—§ 19, Summary of the Situation.

CHAPTER X

THE CEREBRAL HEMISPHERES AND THEIR FUNCTIONS [Continued]....235–274

§ 1, The Work of Fritsch and Hitzig.—§§ 2–3, Localization in the Brains of Monkeys and Anthropoid Apes.—§ 4, Paralyses of the Motor Area.—§§ 5–7, Definition and Function of the Motor Area.—§ 8, Restitution of Motor Functions.—§§ 9–11, The Somesthetic Area.—§ 12, The Visual Area.—§§ 13–14, Phenomena of Psychical Blindness.—§ 15, The Auditory Centre.—§§ 16–17, Centres of Smell and Taste.—§ 18, The So-called "Silent Areas."—§ 20, Results of Injuries to the Occipital Lobe.—§ 21, To the Temporal Lobe.—§§ 22–23, To the Parietal Lobe.—§§ 24–25, Disturbances of Speech Functions.—§§ 26–29, Discussion of Broca's Speech Centre.—§ 30, Localization of a Writing Centre.—§§ 31–33, Functions of the Frontal Lobe.—§ 34, Summary of the Results.—§§ 35–38, Cell-Layers in the Cortex.—§§ 39–40, Histological Mapping of the Cortex.—§§ 41–43, Grouping of Functions in the Cortex.

CHAPTER XI

PAGE

MECHANICAL THEORY OF THE NERVOUS SYSTEM................... 275–293

§§ 1–3, Machine-like Nature of the Organism.—§§ 4–5, Significance of Chemical Constitution.—§§ 6–7, Arrangement of the Nervous Elements. § 8, Equilibrating of Different Parts.—§§ 9–10, Imperfect Character of Present Theory.—§§ 11–12, Theory of Specific Energies.—§§ 13–15, Mechanism of the Nerve-Centres.—§§ 16–17, Function of the Nerve-Cells.— §§ 18–19, Significance of the Synapse.—§ 20, Rival Metabolic Theories.— §§ 21–23, Review of the Evidence.

PART SECOND

CORRELATIONS OF THE NERVOUS MECHANISM AND MENTAL PHENOMENA

CHAPTER I

THE QUALITY OF SENSATIONS................................... 297–323

§§ 1–3, Changes in Points of View.—§§ 4–5, Classification of the Sensations.—§§ 6–7, Need of Further Analysis.—§ 8, The So-called Simple Sensation a Fiction.—§ 9, Questions Requiring an Answer.—§ 10, Bearing of the Specific Energy of the Nerves.—§§ 11–12, Stimuli of Olfactory Sensations.—§§ 13–15, Analysis of Olfactory Sensations.—§ 16, Stimuli of Gustatory Sensations.—§§ 17–18 Analysis of Gustatory Sensations.—§ 19, Chemical Stimulus of Sensations of Taste.—§§ 20–21, General Nature of Auditory Sensations.—§ 22, Characteristics of Musical Sounds.—§ 23, The Pitch of Musical Sounds.—§ 24, Sensitiveness of the Ear to Differences of Pitch.—§ 25, And Purity of Interval.—§ 26, Means of Judging Musical Sounds.—§ 27, Nature of the "Clang."—§ 28, Sounds Used in Music.— §§ 29–30, Theory of Consonance and Dissonance.—§ 31, The Difference-Tone.

CHAPTER II

THE QUALITY OF SENSATIONS [Continued]........................324–352

§ 1, Intricacy of Visual Sensations.—§ 2, Stimulus of Visual Sensations. —§ 3, Local Values of the Retina.—§ 4, The General Problem of Visual Sensations.—§ 5, The Spectral Color-Tones.—§ 6, Relative Brightness of Color-Tones.—§ 7, Composite Nature of Ordinary Colors.—§ 8, Number of Colors Distinguishable.—§§ 9–12, Theory of Complementary Colors.— §§ 13–14, Phenomena of Color-Blindness.—§§ 15–16, Negative and Positive After-Images.—§ 17, Phenomena of Contrast.—§§ 18–21, Theories of Color Vision.—§ 22, Symbolic Representation of Visual Sensations.— §§ 23–24, Sensations of the Skin.—§ 25, Nature of Temperature Stimuli.— §§ 26–27, Sensations of Pain.—§ 28, The So-called Muscular Sense.—§ 29, Labyrinthic Sensations.—§ 30, Visceral or Organic Sensations.—§ 31, Summary of Evidence for the Specific Energy of the Nerves.

CHAPTER III

PAGE

THE QUANTITY OF SENSATIONS 353-379

§§ 1-2, Distinction of Quantity from Quality.—§§ 3-4, Unscientific Form of Ordinary Usage.—§§ 5-6, Character of the Quantitative Problems. —§ 7, Method of Determining the Limits.—§ 8, Methods of Determining the Least Perceptible Difference.—§§ 9-11, Weber's Law and Fechner's Formulas.—§§ 12-13, The Perception of Weight.—§ 14, Sensitiveness to Light Pressure.—§ 15, Discriminations of Temperature.—§§ 16-17, Sensitiveness of Acoustic Perception.—§ 18, Least Perceptible Difference in Intensity of Tones.—§§ 19-20, Quantitative Discriminations of Sight.—§ 21, Weber's Law Applied to Visual Sensations.—§ 22, Perceptible Minimum of Sensations of Light.—§ 23, Extensive Sensations of Light.—§§ 24-25, Intensity of Gustatory Sensations.—§ 26, Intensity of Sensations of Smell.— § 27, Review of Weber's Law.—§§ 28-29, Explanations of Weber's Law.— § 30, Fechner's Intepretation of the Phenomena.—§ 31, Summary of Results.

CHAPTER IV

PRESENTATIONS OF SENSE, OR SENSE-PERCEPTIONS 380-412

§ 1, Artificial Character of Simple Sensations.—§ 2, Necessity of Analysis.—§§ 3-4, Nature and Stages of Sense-Perception.—§ 5, Necessity of Mental Synthesis or Fusion.—§§ 6-7, Nativistic and Empiristic Schools.— § 8, Nature of a Spatial Series.—§ 9, Nature of the Local Signs.—§ 10, Stages of Sense-Perception.—§ 11, Activity of Higher Faculties.—§ 12, Perceptions of Smell.—§ 13, Perceptions of Taste.—§ 14, Perceptions of Hearing.— §§ 15-18, Localization of Sounds.—§§ 19, Construction of the Field of Touch.—§§ 20-22, Explanation of Weber's "Sensation-Circles."—§§ 23-25, The "Two-Point Threshold."—§ 26, Sensuous Basis of Discrimination.— § 27, Mixed and Tangled Skin-Sensations.—§§ 28-29, Localization of Temperature.—§ 30, Nature of the Muscular Sense.—§§ 31-32, Judgments of Bodily Movements.—§ 33, Co-operation of Eye with Hand.—§ 34, Feelings of Double Contact.

CHAPTER V

PRESENTATIONS OF SENSE, OR SENSE-PERCEPTIONS [Continued]..... 413-469

§ 1, Special Difficulties of Visual Perceptions.—§§ 2-3, Data of Visual Perceptions.—§§ 4-5, Formation of the Retinal Field.—§ 6, Statement of the Problem.—§ 7, Values of Different Retinal Sensations.—§ 8, Muscles of the Eye-Ball and Its Movements.—§ 9, The Law of Listing.—§ 10, Effects of Accommodation.—§§ 11-13, Conditions of Binocular Vision.—§ 14, Visual Perception of Depth.—§§ 15-16, Visual Perception of Distance and Size.—§ 17, Visual Perceptions of Motion.—§§ 18-19, Judgment in Errors of Sense.—§ 20, Geometrical Optical Illusions.—§ 21, Central Factor in Illusions.—§ 22, Illusions of Angles.—§ 23, Illusions of Areas.—§ 24, Theories of Visual Illusions.—§ 25, The Central Theories.—§ 26, The Dynamic Theory.—§ 27, The Confusion Theory.—§ 28, Binocular Mixing and Contrast of Colors.—§§ 29-30, Upright and Inverted Vision.—§ 31, Inferences from Errors of Sense.—§ 32, General Conclusions as to Theory of Vision.—§ 33, Influence of Eye-Movements on Space Perception.— § 34, Graphic Records of Eye-Movements.—§§ 35-36, Speed of Eye-Movements.—§ 37, Value of Objective Measurements.—§§ 38–39, Development of Visual Perception.—§ 40, Relations of Visual and Muscular Perception.— § 41, Perception as an Achievement of Mind.

CHAPTER VI

PAGE

TIME–RELATIONS OF MENTAL PHENOMENA 470–499

§§ 1–2, Experiments in Reaction-Time.—§ 3, Simple Reaction-Time. —§ 4, Inertia of the End-Organs.—§ 5, Measurement of Smallest Intervals. —§ 6, The Point of Starting.—§§ 7–8, Variations in Reaction-Time.—§ 9, Effect of Increasing Intensity.—§ 10, Character of Reacting Movement.— § 11, Influence of Central Conditions.—§ 12, The Three Periods.—§ 13, Wundt's Analysis.—§ 14, So-called Sensorial and Muscular Reactions.— § 15, Complex Reactions.—§§ 16–18, Reaction with Discrimination.—§ 19, Discernment of Intensities.—§§ 20–22, Associative Reaction-Time.—§§ 23– 24, Amount of Conscious Process Involved.—§§ 25–26, General Character of Reaction-Time.

CHAPTER VII

FEELING, EMOTION, AND EXPRESSIVE MOVEMENTS 500–541

§§ 1–2, Variable Conceptions of the Nature of Feeling.—§§ 3–4, Difficulties of Analysis.—§ 5, Methods of Investigation.—§ 6, Physiological Theories of Feeling.—§ 7, Kinds of Feeling.—§ 8, Pleasantness and Unpleasantness. —§ 9, Induced Electrical Changes.—§§ 10–11, Other Theories of Feeling. —§ 12, General Classification of the Feelings.—§ 13, Changeable Characteristics of all Feeling.—§§ 14–15, Pleasureable and Painful Tone of Feeling. —§ 16, Forms of Common Feeling.—§§ 17–18, Feeling-Tone of Sensations.— § 19, Mixtures of Feeling.—§§ 20–22, Nature of the Emotions.—§ 23, Peripheral Theory of the Emotions.—§ 24, Teleological Value of the Emotions.—§ 25, The Intellectual Feelings.—§§ 26–27, The Æsthetic Feelings. —§ 28, Nature of the Sentiments.—§§ 29–30, Dynamogenic Effects of the Emotions.—§ 31, Automatic and Ideo-Motor Movements.—§§ 32–33, Phenomena of Fatigue.—§§ 34–35, Causes of Fatigue.—§ 36, The Kinds of Fatigue.—§ 37, The Refractory Period.

CHAPTER VIII

MEMORY AND THE PROCESS OF LEARNING 542–592

§ 1, Memory as Recognitive, Inexplicable.—§§ 2–3, Processes Involved in Memory.—§ 4, Learning Among Invertebrates.—§ 5, Learning Among Vertebrates.—§ 6, Process of Selection in Learning.—§ 7, Adjustment of Psycho-physical Mechanism.—§ 8, Learning by Trial and Error.—§§ 9–10, Learning by Ideas.—§ 11, Solution of Mechanical Puzzles.—§ 12, Acquirement of Skill.—§§ 13–14, Analysis of Feats of Skill.—§ 15, The Rate of Improvement by Practice.—§ 16, Relation of Consciousness to Learning. —§§ 17–19, Transference of Learning—§§ 20–21, Processes of Memorizing. —§ 22, Methods of Studying Memory.—§ 23, The Curve of Forgetting.— §§ 24–25, Forming of Association.—§ 26, The Psycho-physical Mechanism.— §§ 27–28, The Culture of Memory.—§§ 29–31, Phenomena of Reproduction. —§ 32, Inhibition of Reproductive Processes.—§ 33, Phenomena of Perseveration.—§§ 34–35, Varieties of Association.—§§ 36–37, Recall with Recognition.—§ 38, The Guarantee of Memory.

CHAPTER IX

PAGE

THE MECHANISM OF THOUGHT 593–625

§§ 1–2, Logical Terms Inadequate.—§ 3, Perception as a Form of Reaction.—§ 4, The Process of Abstraction.—§ 5, The Span of Attention.—
§§ 6–7, Shifting and Fluctuation of Attention.—§ 8, The Direction of Attention.—§ 9, Development of Abstract Concepts.—§ 10, The Nature of
Comparison.—§ 11, The Psychology of Reasoning.—§ 12, Reasoning as
Search for Premises.—§ 13, Immediate and Mediate Reasoning.—§§ 14–15,
Correlations of Mechanism and Mental Life.—§§ 16–18, Cerebral Conditions
of Consciousness.—§ 19, The Mechanism of Attention.—§ 20, The Power
of Varied Reaction.—§§ 21–22, Physiology of Local Signs.—§§ 23–25,
Cerebral Action in Memory.—§§ 26–28, The Mechanism of Associations.—
§§ 29–30, Physiology of the Higher Units.—§§ 31–33, Collecting and Distributing Mechanisms.—§ 34, Limitations of all Explanation.

PART THIRD

THE NATURE OF THE MIND

CHAPTER I

GENERAL RELATIONS OF BODY AND MIND 629–667

§§ 1–2, The Metaphysical Problem Proposed.—§ 3, Nature of Uncritical Dualism.—§ 4, Reality of Correlations.—§§ 5–7, The Brain as "Seat"
of the Mind.—§§ 8–10, The Brain as "Organ" of the Mind.—§ 11, The
Conception of a Bond Between Brain and Mind.—§ 12, The Body as the
Tenement of Mind.—§§ 13–14, The Conception of Product as Applied to
the Case.—§§ 15–16, Reciprocal Influence of Body and Mind.—§§ 17–18,
General Objections to Causal Theory.—§§ 19–20, Analysis of Conceptions.
—§§ 21–23, Conservation of Cerebral Energy.—§ 24, Some Kind of Causal
Relation Necessary.—§ 25, Necessity of a Further Hypothesis.—§ 26, The
Three Processes Involved.—§§ 27–29, The Conception of Development
Necessary.—§ 30, Mental Condition of the Embryo.—§ 31, Earliest Develop-
ment of the Child.—§ 32, Development of the Adult.—§ 33, The Changes of
Old Age.—§ 34, Argument from Phenomena of Decay.—§ 35, Peculiarly
Mental Elements.—§ 36, Peculiarly Mental Operations.—§ 37, The Con-
clusion Drawn.

CHAPTER II

REALITY AND UNITY OF THE MIND 668–687

§§ 1–2, Nature of the Claims Discussed.—§ 3, Conceptions of Reality
and Unity Expounded.—§ 4, Unity as Involving Plan.—§§ 5–6, Reality
and Unity of Mind, not Merely Phenomenal.—§§ 7–8, The Activity of
Apperception.—§§ 9–11, Mental Unity not Atomic.—§§ 12–13, The Distinction of Ego and Non-Ego.—§§ 14–15, Mind as Unifying Actus.—§ 16,
Mind not a Static Unity.—§§ 17–18, The Spirituality of Mind.—§§ 19–20,
Mind as a Unity of Growth.—§§ 21–22, Limits of Physiological Psychology.

INDEX OF AUTHORS 689

INDEX OF SUBJECTS 694

PHYSIOLOGICAL PSYCHOLOGY

INTRODUCTION

§ 1. A clear conception of *Physiological Psychology* requires some knowledge of the nature and methods of those two sciences, the results of whose investigations it endeavors to combine. These sciences are Psychology and Physiology—the latter being understood so as to include also various applications of the general theory of physics to the functions of the animal organism. But as the form taken by this compound term would itself seem to indicate, the two do not stand upon precisely the same level in effecting this combination, whether we consider the end that science desires to reach, or the means that it employs to reach the end. For the noun ("psychology") in the compound term may be said more particularly to define this end; while the adjective ("physiological") defines the character of the means which it is proposed especially to employ. Hence "Physiological Psychology" can scarcely claim to be an independent science; it is rather to be regarded simply as psychology approached and studied from a certain—the so-called "physiological"—side or point of view. It is necessary, then, in the first place, to define what we understand by the science of psychology.

§ 2. Perhaps the most common definition of psychology, until recent times, has regarded it as "the science of the human soul." If this definition had always been taken only in a provisional way, and with the implied confession that it is the business of psychology itself to demonstrate the existence of "the soul," and to show how such an entity is needed to explain the phenomena of consciousness, then little valid objection could have been made to it. But such has by no means been the case. Objections have, therefore, been more or less fitly and forcefully urged against this definition as ordinarily employed. It has been said that clearly we have no right to *assume* any such entity as the soul; and it has even been claimed, especially of late, that there may be a "psychology without a soul," and, indeed, that this kind of psychology is alone worthy of being considered truly scientific. Further objection to the same definition has been made in other quarters, because it

1

seems to regard the question as settled, whether there may not be more than *one* subject (or "ground") of the manifold phenomena called psychical. Recent researches into so-called "subconsciousness" as involving *mental* processes which go on "below the threshold," and theories of double and triple selves, have served further to confuse or discredit the time-honored concept of a soul, or mind, as a permanent and quasi-independent entity. It would be aside from the course of our inquiries to consider these objections in detail at this time. They may all be, for the present, excluded by stating the course of procedure which the study of psychology from the physiological point of view seems to us plainly to recommend.

Accordingly, it will serve our purpose best to define our science, in at least a preliminary way, by ascribing to it a certain more or less definite sphere of phenomena. We shall, therefore, consider psychology as that science which has for its primary subject of investigation all the phenomena of human consciousness, or of the sentient life of man. If the term "sentience" be employed as preferable to consciousness, it must be understood as equivalent to consciousness in the broader sense of the latter word. This definition, or rather description, plainly implies an acquaintance experimentally with certain phenomena that cannot, strictly speaking, be defined. These are the phenomena of consciousness; and one result of all our subsequent investigations will be to show us that consciousness and its primary phenomena can never be defined.

Nevertheless it would be very inconvenient, not to say impossible, to begin and continue the investigation of psychical phenomena, using only roundabout phrases through fear of implying the real existence of some spiritual entity called the Soul or the Mind. In some sort there cannot be any description, much less any scientific study, of the phenomena of consciousness without employing some word like these. In all languages, and in the constant everyday use of them all, men in stating and describing the phenomena of their own sentient life make the distinctions involved in such terms as "I" and "me," and place in a kind of contrast with them such other terms as "thou" and "he" or "it." In all the earlier part of this treatise the word "mind" will, therefore, be employed simply as the equivalent of the *subject* of the phenomena of consciousness. In other words, whatever all men mean by the word "I" (the empirical *ego* of philosophy), whenever they say *I* think, or feel, or intend this or that; and whatever they understand others to mean by using similar language—thus much, and no more, we propose at first to include under the term "mind." This term is preferred to the word "soul," in part out of concession to the prejudices to which reference has already been made, and in part because it seems to admit of the handling which it is proposed to give to it subsequently, with more freedom from entangling alliances with ethical, social, and religious ideas. In brief, we wish to begin and continue our investigation, as far as possible, upon purely scientific grounds.

§ 3. In accordance with what has already been said concerning the nature of psychology, we may define *Physiological* Psychology as the science which investigates the phenomena of human consciousness with the "physiological" point of view and method of approach; or, remembering the cautions which have already been expressed, we may say that it is the science of the human mind as investigated by means of its relations to the human physical organism. A more accurate definition, however, requires that something further should be said concerning the nature and method of that science which furnishes the adjective to our compound term. Human Physiology is the science of the functions (or modes of the behavior) of the human physical organism. As studied at present it implies an acquaintance with the fields of gross and special microscopic anatomy (histology), of embryology and the general doctrine of development, of biology,—including the allied phenomena of plant life,—of molecular physics and chemistry as related to the structure and action of the bodily tissues; and of other forms of kindred knowledge. It is only a relatively small part of this vast domain, however, with which Physiological Psychology has directly to deal; for it is only a part of the human organism which has any direct relation to the phenomena of consciousness. As will appear subsequently, it is with the nervous system alone that our science has its chief immediate concern. Indeed it might be described— though in a still somewhat indefinite, but more full and complete way—as the science which investigates the correlations that exist between the structure and functions of the human nervous mechanism and the phenomena of consciousness; and which derives therefrom conclusions as to the laws and nature of the so-called mind, or subject of these phenomena.

§ 4. Physiology is compelled, from its very nature as a physical science, to regard the nervous system as a *mechanism*. Physiological Psychology, inasmuch as it relies so largely upon physiology for its data and method and points of view, is also required to consider this system in the same way. Those unique relations in which the structure and functions of the nervous substance of the body stand to the phenomena of mental life cannot deter the investigator from assuming toward it the so-called mechanical point of view. Physiology presents psychology with a description of this nervous substance as a vast and complex system of material molecules, which are acted upon by different forms of the energy of nature outside (external stimuli), and by intimate changes in the contiguous molecules of the other substances of the body (internal stimuli); and which behave as they do on account of the influences thus received, as well as on account of their own molecular constitution and arrangement. But all this is the description of a material mechanism. Indeed, it is only as falling under this general conception that these molecules admit of any scientific treatment at all.

Whatever is to be said further upon the conception of the nervous system as a mechanism must appear in its proper place in the order adopted for the discussion of the general subject. *Physiological* Psychology, however, can scarcely establish itself at all unless it is willing to receive from the proper one of the two sciences which enter into it the conclusions at which this science has arrived as the result of the most successful modern researches.   As far as the nervous system admits of being subjected at all to scientific treatment, for the purpose of attaining a more complete knowledge of the nature of its functions, it is necessarily considered as a complex molecular mechanism.   We shall, then, receive, in a grateful and docile manner, all that the noble science of human physiology has to teach us, under the guidance of the conception of a mechanism, both directly concerning the manner in which the nervous matter of the human body performs its wonderful functions, and more indirectly concerning the relations in which these functions stand to the facts and the development of man's mental life.

§ 5. The remark just made introduces the truth that there are many *indirect* relations, which need investigation, between the phenomena of human consciousness and the constitution and functions of the human nervous organism.   Indeed, a large portion of this treatise will make little use of explanations derived directly from the facts and laws of anatomy, histology, and physiology.   The entire Second Part falls more properly under the head of Psychophysics or Experimental Psychology, than under Physiological Psychology, strictly so called.   Still all investigators are convinced that the phenomena of sensation, reproduction in the form of memory or imagination, association of ideas, and thought-processes, so far as they have any basis or correlate in the physical world, are either immediately or indirectly dependent upon the structure and functions of that mechanism which human physiology investigates. Only, in the great majority of cases, we have as yet no knowledge of precisely how this mechanism behaves, so interior, hidden, and subtle are its relations to mental phenomena.   After making this confession, we are only complying with a fairly well-established usage in giving the title "*Physiological* Psychology" to the entire treatise.

§ 6. Physiological Psychology—it is by this time apparent—partakes of the nature and methods of two sciences that differ widely from each other. One is a science which involves introspection; for it is only by the method of introspection that the actual and present facts of human consciousness can be reached. The other is a physical science, and involves external observation to determine the external facts of the structure, development, and functions of a physical mechanism. Two sets of phenomena must then be examined in their relations to each other, and, so far as possible, the laws (or permanent modes) of these relations pointed out. It is due to this fact, in part, that both the peculiar difficulties and the peculiar interest and value of psycho-physical researches are so great.

In every science a beginning is first made by ascertaining and comparing together all the important phenomena; the laws, or regular modes of the occurrence of the phenomena in relation to each other, are then investigated; and finally, certain conclusions are drawn concerning the nature and significance of those real beings which reason compels us to assume as permanent subjects of the different classes of phenomena. In its effort to establish itself upon a scientific basis, Physiological Psychology has no choice but to follow essentially the same method of procedure. In its case, however, as has already been remarked, the phenomena which are to be ascertained and compared belong to two orders that obviously differ greatly from each other; and the laws which it is sought to discover are laws which maintain themselves between these two orders of phenomena. It has already been said that the phenomena of the nervous system, like all physical phenomena, consist in changes in the constitution and mutual relation of material masses and molecules; and that the psychical phenomena are states of consciousness, constantly shifting modes of the behavior of that subject which we have agreed—as much as possible without involving any premature assumptions—to call the Mind. Still the above-mentioned two orders of phenomena are obviously to a large extent related to each other; they may, in fact, be said to be *correlated* in a unique manner. The constant forms of this correlation constitute the laws for the discovery of which Physiological Psychology undertakes its special researches. It endeavors to bring the two orders of phenomena face to face, to look at them as they stand thus related to each other, and, as far as possible, to unite them in terms of a uniform character, under law.

§ 7. It might seem that simply to attempt the accomplishment of so difficult and complicated a task as that just described should satisfy all legitimate demands. And, again, we remind ourselves that no little protest has of late been made against any introduction of metaphysics, whether in the form of assumptions or conclusions, into the science of psychology; especially when this science is studied from the physiological and experimental points of view. And has it not just been agreed that metaphysical assumptions shall prejudice as little as possible our statement of psychological facts and laws? But our science, like every other science, has the right to form and announce conclusions as to the real nature of the subject-matter which it investigates, if these conclusions seem to follow legitimately from its discussions of phenomena and laws. It has even a right to indulge in well-founded and reasonable speculation. Such things are not necessarily objectionable when indulged in by any of the more purely physical sciences. Indeed, there is not one of these sciences which would not look comparatively bare and unattractive if wholly stripped of its more or less questionable inferences, its metaphysical assumptions, its guessings and speculations.

§ 8. The remarks immediately foregoing serve to indicate what are the principal divisions of this work. The First Part will consist of a description of the structure and functions of the Nervous System. In order that this system in man's case may be the better understood, the first two chapters give a brief description of its place in the developmental series. As has already been said, this system will be considered under the conception of a mechanism, and as far as possible without much direct or indirect reference to the phenomena of consciousness as determined by introspection. An important exception may seem to be made in the case of the chapters which treat of the "Localization of Cerebral Function"; and which thus bring forward the relations that have recently been established in fact between the conditions and activities of the supreme nervous centres and the phenomena of conscious sensation and volition.

Again, reference is constantly made throughout this Part to the phenomena of automatic and reflex action of the nervous system as a whole; and so of necessity to certain correlated mental phenomena. But such topics seem indissolubly connected with a satisfactory description of the nervous mechanism; and to introduce them here avoids much otherwise necessary repetition.

The Second Part discusses more particularly the relations which exist between the quality, quantity, combination, and order of succession in time, of the various stimuli which act upon the nervous system, and the kind, magnitude, composite result, and time-relations of the mental phenomena. Hence the significance of the term *psycho-physics*. As Physiological Psychology is ordinarily and legitimately treated, it includes these more specially psycho-physical researches.

Besides the foregoing groups, or classes, certain observations which have more or less of scientific confirmation and value, may be made regarding the physical basis of the feelings and volitions controlling the bodily members, and of the higher faculties of memory, association of ideas, etc.

The Third Part will fitly introduce, at the close of the psycho-physical researches, the briefest possible presentation of such conclusions as may be legitimately gathered, or more speculatively inferred, concerning the nature (considered as a real being) of the human mind. The justification of the order and extent of the entire discussion, and especially of the Third Part as a whole, has already been given to some extent; the rest must be left to the progress and result of the discussion itself.

§ 9. It has already been said that the peculiarity of Physiological Psychology, considered as a branch of the general science of mind, consists largely in the method of its approach to its subject. Attention must now be more specifically called to this method as necessarily partaking of the methods of the two sciences whose researches it undertakes to combine. The method of physiology, which is in general that of external observation as employed in all the physical sciences, should be applied only when supplemented by the many delicate and accurate instruments of observation now at command, and guarded and checked by that accumulation of experience concerning the best ways of studying nature and concerning her ways of working which the whole body of such sciences has made. On the other hand, the method of psychology has ordinarily been defined as solely the method of introspection or self-consciousness. These two methods are obviously very different. It would not be strange, then, if the science which finds it necessary to combine the two should experience some special difficulty. This difficulty has, however, more often been exaggerated than explained and (what is quite possible) for the most part removed.

Our present purpose does not require that we should examine at length the question whether the introspective method is the only one possible in psychology. Scarcely more is necessary than the statement of the bearing of this question upon the inquiries it is proposed to make. There should in general be no mystery or arrogant assumption about the use of such words as "science" and "scientific method." Science is nothing but knowledge—real, verifiable, and systematic. Scientific method is nothing but the way of arriving at such knowledge. Now, although Physiological Psychology brings the investigator face to face with some of the most interesting and distinctive mysteries, it is not, as a science, to be regarded as especially mysterious. Inasmuch as its specific business is to ascertain and combine, under definite laws, two widely differing classes of facts (facts of the human nervous mechanism and facts of human consciousness), it is, of course, compelled, first of all, to ascertain both kinds of facts. The phenomena of consciousness, *as primary facts*, can be *ascertained* in no other way than in and by consciousness itself. There is no way of directly examining consciousness but the way of being conscious one's self. On the other hand, it is perfectly obvious to students of psychology and of its history (on grounds which need not be stated here) that the *scientific treatment* of the facts of consciousness can never be, to any satisfactory extent, accomplished by introspection alone. For psychology, in order to make valid its claim to be a science, must not merely display the alleged facts of individual mental experience; it must treat these facts analytically, must resolve them into their ultimate factors, and trace the stages of their development from what is simpler to what is more complex; it must also show on all sides their connections and causes, thus placing the phenomena of the mind as much as possible in interaction with the rest of the world.

The following statements will, accordingly, be found to hold good concerning the method of Physiological Psychology. It must employ faithfully the methods distinctive of both the two sciences which it endeavors to combine. Facts as to the structure and functions of the nervous mechanism, and as to the effect upon it of various kinds of physical energy acting as stimuli, must be ascertained by external observation. The primary facts of consciousness must be ascertained from consciousness itself; or, since they have already been for a long time subjected to this form of observation, and tabulated, compared, and classified, they may be accepted from the science of introspective psychology. Care must be taken, however, to make sure that all alleged psychical facts are really facts; but upon this point, again, there is no other way of making sure than in and through consciousness. The final result of research will doubtless be, not only to supplement and explain, but also to modify and correct, the previous statements of psychological science as to its laws and inferences. But here, as in other scientific research, we shall be obliged to work our way through many mistakes, obscurities, and other obstacles, progressively nearer the complete and verifiable knowledge of the truth.

§ 10. What has already been indicated will become more evident in the course of the following investigations—namely, that we are seldom or never able to proceed directly with the work of comparing the immediate physical antecedents or consequents of the mental phenomena with these phenomena themselves, and so of drawing conclusions at once as to the laws by which the two classes of facts are connected. Such immediate antecedents and consequents are hid in the inexplorable recesses of the living and molecularly active brain. It is seldom, indeed, that our direct observation can approach within the tenth, or it may be within the hundredth, remove of what goes on in these recesses. We are obliged to examine the physical phenomena from a greater distance and in a more indirect way. For example, physics can inform us what combinations of what wave-lengths of the vibration of ether fall on the eye when a certain form of conscious sensation, which we call "yellow" or "red" or "blue," arises; physiology can locate the nervous elements of the retina upon which the waves fall, can conjecture something as to the chemical changes there produced, and trace doubtfully the paths along which the resulting nervous impulses rise to the brain and diffuse themselves over certain of its areas; psycho-physics can tell approximately the relations in which the varying quantities of the stimulus stand to the resulting degrees of the sensations. But in all this we are still at a great distance from the enjoyment of those opportunities which would seem necessary to make the science of Physiological Psychology as comprehensive and exact as could readily be wished. As a rule, certain kinds and amounts of physical energy, more or less definitely measurable, are known to be acting on the *peripheral* parts of the body, and the next series of observed facts is the emergence in consciousness of a psychical experience quite unlike all kinds of physical energy. To be sure, Fechner's [1] conception of psycho-physics is that it treats those "physical activities which are the bearers (*Träger*) or conditions of the psychical, and accordingly stand in direct functional relation with them"; or again, "psycho-physics is an exact doctrine of the relations of function or dependence between body and soul—of the universals that lie between the bodily and spiritual, the physical and psychical world." But the course of investigation will make clear the fact that of such physical activities we have little or no assured knowledge; although we have the best of grounds for believing that such activities exist, and that they stand in important relations under law with the facts of the conscious psychical life.

§ 11. If the correctness of the remarks last made be admitted, the inquiry may be raised: What justification has this so-called science of Physiological Psychology for the large claims which it has made of late; and, indeed, what right has it to exist as a special

[1] *Elemente d. Psychophysik*, pp. 8 and 10 (Leipzig, 1860).

discipline at all? The full answer to the call for self-justification must be made by the actual achievements of the science itself.

The history of modern investigation, and the conclusions of the modern science of man, both physical and psychological, emphasize the necessity of studying his nature and development as that of a living unity. Such science shows man to be at the head of a series of physical and psychical existences; he cannot be understood as he is, in his whole nature and in his place within nature at large, without taking both sides of this living unity into account. For man is known to himself as body *and* mind—and not as bodiless spirit or a mindless congeries of moving molecules. That the structure and functions of the body, especially of the nervous mechanism, and the activities of the mind, are extensively and intimately correlated, is a fact beyond all doubt. It is the particular task of Physiological Psychology to show in what manner, and to what extent, such correlation exists. Moreover, there are few questions more interesting, from a philosophical and an ethical point of view, than such as the following: What is the nature of mind, considered in the light of its correlations with the body? and, Do the so-called physiological and the so-called psychical phenomena belong to one subject, or to more than one? But these and similar questions can be scientifically answered only by giving a speculative treatment to the conclusions of psycho-physical investigation.

In brief, it may be said that introspective psychology, important as its results have been, and indispensable as its method is, has shown its incompetency to deal with many of the most interesting inquiries which it has itself raised. On the other hand, psychology as pursued by the experimental and physiological method has already thrown a flood of fresh light upon many of these inquiries. We may affirm with Wundt,[1] without fear of successful contradiction: "Psychology is compelled to make use of objective changes in order, by means of the influences which they exert on our consciousness, to establish the subjective properties and laws of that consciousness." On this fact and on the real achievements of the method we confidently rest its claims to serious and permanent consideration.

[1] Art., "Ueber psychophysischen Methoden," *Philosophische Studien* (1881), Heft 1, p. 4.

PART FIRST

THE NERVOUS MECHANISM

CHAPTER I

THE PLACE OF THE NERVOUS SYSTEM IN THE ANIMAL KINGDOM

§ 1. It is essential to the development of a physiological psychology that the part played by the nervous system in animal life and the manner of its working should be understood, as far as present knowledge permits. As has already been explained in the Introduction, we wish to study man's mental life in its relation to the nervous system and, in general, to the life of the organism; we wish to understand the functions of the nervous system in their relations to mental phenomena. In such a study, the *comparative* method should prove of much assistance. For both the nervous structures and the mental activities of man are so enormously complex that the discovery of their relations is of necessity a very difficult task. If, however, we turn to animals of a lower grade, with much less complexity of nervous organization and functions, we may hope to glean some facts, of a fundamental sort, regarding the most general relation of structure to behavior. We should, at the outset of such a study, lay aside for the time our psychological preoccupation with such complex mental performances as imagination, reasoning, and will, and limit ourselves to an objective examination of the simpler behavior of lower types of animal which present little indication of these complex activities. We should, at the same time, banish any preconceived notion, founded on human experience, that the nervous system is essentially the servant, or the organ, of mental life, and look for its primary function in animals that possess the most rudimentary nervous structures, and for its increase in function with increase in the complication of its structure. We shall, of course, be unable to present in this book a full account of the comparative anatomy of the nervous system and of the behavior of different classes of animals—both of which studies have been zealously prosecuted of late years—but must limit ourselves to a brief sketch.

§ 2. The primary division of animals distinguishes two classes: the protozoa and the metozoa. The protozoa are described as "unicellular"; while the metozoa are composed of a number, usually a great multitude, of cells. A "cell," in the biological sense, is a microscopic bit of semi-fluid matter, bounded either by a definite membrane or at least by a "surface of separation," which has the important property of resisting free diffusion of dissolved substances. Though cells will live either when immersed in the water or else, as in higher animals, when bathed in the fluids of the body, substances dissolved within the cell do not freely pass out; nor do dissolved substances from without freely pass in, through the surface of the cell. There is, of course, much interchange of materials between the inside and the outside of the cell; such interchange, however, is not free, but selective. Certain substances can pass in, others out. No property of the cell is more necessary to its life than this; for, if the cell boundary interposed no barrier to free diffusion, the cell would promptly lose its individuality and be merged in the surrounding medium. The semi-fluid matter of the cell, called "protoplasm," consists of a large proportion of water, in which are dissolved salts of sodium, potassium, and calcium, as well as the highly complex compounds of carbon, nitrogen, hydrogen, oxygen, and sulphur, which are called proteins. Other organic compounds, and other salts, may also be present. Within this mass of protoplasm is a smaller mass called the nucleus, which appears to be more nearly solid than the protoplasm, and which has a somewhat different chemical composition, inasmuch as its protein contains phosphorus, in addition to the other elements mentioned. Some cells, indeed, have no nucleus, but these do not possess the power of reproducing their kind, and it is doubtful if they should be regarded as true cells, in the full sense of the word. The nucleus, the protoplasm, and the surface of separation, may therefore be regarded as the essential parts of every living cell.

§ 3. As an example of a unicellular animal we may take the *amœba*, a minute spherical creature, which lives in stagnant water, feeding on the organic matter contained in the water. It maintains its own chemical composition, which is different from that of the water; it takes in organic matter from the water, changes or "assimilates" it, and so grows; and it excretes waste products. Besides these distinctly chemical processes, it shows the phenomenon of reproduction. When it has grown to a sufficient size, it divides into two "daughter cells," each of which is an amœba. It has further the power of motility; its movements being of two opposed sorts, one consisting in the bulging outward of some part of its surface into a temporary arm or branch, while the other consists in the drawing in of these temporary arms and the resumption of the spherical shape. Certain stimuli cause it to exhibit one of these movements, and other stimuli cause it to exhibit the other. A bit of food in its neighborhood, that sends out particles through the water, acts as a stimulus to the putting forth of a branch; the amœba bulges out on the side toward the food, and then slowly flows into the protruding arm, thus advancing toward the food. When the bit of food is reached, two or more arms bulge out around it, and unite on the further side, enclosing the food within the amœba's body. On the other hand, a sudden contact with a solid body, or a jar to the water, acts as a stimulus to the drawing in of the temporary arms (see Fig. 1).

Such is animal behavior when observed and described in its lowest terms. If we leave aside the chemical and reproductive activities of the amœba, we may say that its behavior exhibits the powers of motility, irritability or sensitivity, and conductivity. "Ir-

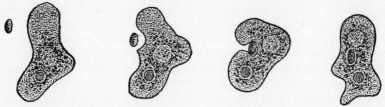

FIG. 1.—The Amœba. (Verworn.) Four stages in the ingestion of a food particle.

ritability" refers to the fact that the animal moves in response to forces acting on it; these forces do not actually move the animal, as the current of the water moves it, but they arouse its inherent power of motion. A force acting to arouse an inherent power of an animal is called a stimulus; and the movement so aroused is called a response or "reaction" to stimulus. The stimulus may be said to "discharge" the movement, as the blow of a trigger discharges a cartridge. "Conductivity" refers to the fact that the part of the animal's body which moves need not be the same as the part which receives the stimulus; there must, therefore, be a conduction or transmission of the excitement through the body. The stimulus acts directly on one side of the body, which responds by bulging outward; but the response spreads to remoter parts, till all of the protoplasm is in motion. It is not the external stimulus which is transmitted, but some sort of activity lying within the body itself.

§ 4. In the amœba there are no organs to take care of the different functions; no part of the protoplasm, more than any other, is specially concerned with digestion, or with motion, or with receiving stimuli, or with conduction. There is a complete absence of division of labor, of specialization or differentiation of parts. Every part of the surface can receive stimuli and be thrown into activity by the stimuli; every part of the protoplasm can conduct the excitation to adjoining parts; and every part can respond by motion.

On the other hand, the progress from lower to higher types of animal is marked, not only by increase in size, but by increasing specialization of the parts. Every multicellular animal begins its individual life as a single cell. This divides into two; and the daughter cells divide in their turn, and so on, as will be more fully described in the following chapter. The many cells generated in this manner remain adherent to one another; and as their multiplication proceeds, it is seen that they begin to manifest characteristic differences one from another. They differ both in visible appearance and also in their powers. Comparatively few retain full reproductive power, so as to be capable of giving rise to a new individual. Some groups of cells become specialized in their chemical powers, and produce powerful digestive fluids. Others become specialized in the power of motion and develop this power to a much higher degree than that possessed by the amœba. Some groups of cells, lying for the most part on the surface of the animal's body, become specialized in the line of irritability; that is to say, they become highly sensitive to specific stimuli, such as contact and jarring, or light, or certain chemical substances. Still other groups of cells develop to a high degree the power of conduction. The cells which have specially developed powers of receiving stimuli are called "receptors"; those with special powers of conduction may be called "conductors"; and those with special powers of movement, along with others which respond to stimuli with chemical or (in certain species of animals) electrical effects, are called "effectors." The receptors form the essential part of the sense-organs; the conductors of the nerves; and the effectors of the muscles and other organs which produce effects of importance to the animal.[1]

§ 5. In a general way, the specialization both of receptors and also of effectors, in different orders of animals, keeps pace one with the other. Where, on the one hand, the receptors are adapted to a great variety of stimuli, the effectors are, on the other, numerous and capable of a great variety of effects. Perhaps, on the whole, in the lower forms of animal life, the development of effectors keeps

---

[1] The use of the term "receptors" in place of the more familiar "sense-organs" is justified by the fact that a sense-organ, such as the eye or ear, contains many accessory structures in addition to the sensitive cells which receive the stimuli; and by the further consideration that "sensation" properly implies consciousness; and we do not know, or wish to imply, that all animals provided with receptors are conscious; while on the other hand we do know, in the case of human beings, that many stimuli acting on receptors in the internal organs, and producing reactions, do not give rise to distinguishable sensations. The use of the term "effectors" is justified by the frequent need of including under a single term glands and other organs which, as well as muscles, often execute the animal's response to a stimulus.

somewhat ahead of the development of receptors. Every effector cell is a receptor as well, to this extent, at least, that it can be aroused by the direct application to it of what are called the "general stimuli," such as mechanical jars, sudden changes of temperature, electric shocks, and certain chemical agents. In sponges, which are regarded as the lowest, or least differentiated, among the metazoa, there are two sorts of motor cell, one of which, lying along the sides of the pores that run in from the exterior of the sponge, is provided with vibratile hairs or "cilia"; these, continually lashing inward, produce currents of the sea water in through the pores to the interior cavity of the sponge. The other motor cells form a ring or "sphincter" around the mouth of the cavity at the top of the sponge, and by contracting close the mouth and check the circulation of water through the sponge. This occurs in response to stimuli applied directly to the sphincter. But the cilia in the pores are not checked in their activity by this stimulus when thus applied; they still continue to lash the water, though without effect, since the outlet is closed. The sponge, then, shows some specialization of effectors, but little if any of receptors, and none of a conducting mechanism which would

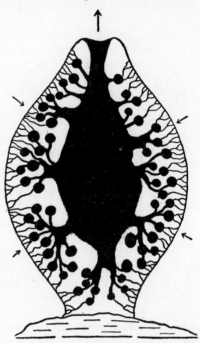

FIG. 2.—Diagram of a Sponge. (Parker.) The narrow pores on the side are lined with cilia, lashing the water inward; the large opening at the top is surrounded by the sphincter.

bring the cilia into harmonious action with the sphincter. In other words, the sponges possess no nervous tissue, and show no conduction from one cell or group of cells to another; in general, they exhibit an almost complete lack of co-ordination (see Fig. 2).

§ 6. A nervous system is met in its most elementary form in the cœlenterates, of which the jelly-fish may be taken as an example. The body of the jelly-fish may be roughly described as consisting of the "umbrella," which lies uppermost in the usual position of the jelly-fish, and is a gelatinous mass, with no power of sensitivity or motility. The motor organs lie partly in a circular band which is attached around the rim of the umbrella, and partly in the tentacles which hang down at intervals from the rim, and in the mouth stalk suspended from the centre of the animal. As to sense-organs, the tentacles are sensitive, and so is the circular band; and specialized receptors of several kinds are arranged at intervals around the rim. There is also a simple form of nervous system, lying principally in the circular band, and composed of a special form of cells with long slender branches. The uniting or "anastomosing" of each cell with the branches of neighboring cells forms a network which extends all through the circular band around the rim, and also into the tentacles. Branches of this "nerve-net" pass to the specialized receptors along the rim, and to all parts of the sensitive surface and to all parts of the muscular tissue (see Fig. 3). Thus every receptor and every muscle-cell is connected with the nerve-net, and all parts of the net are mutually connected, so that the net forms a universal medium of connection between receptors and effectors. The internal structure of the cells and branches forming the nerve-net

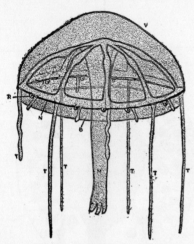

Fig. 3.—The Jelly-Fish (schematic). (Bethe.) V, umbrella; B, circular band, containing N, the ring of nervous tissue; R, receptor; T, tentacle; M, mouth stalk.

is highly specialized, the principal feature being the presence of fine fibrils—"neurofibrils"—extending along the branches from one cell to another or from one branch into another.

§ 7. To understand the function of the nerve-net in these animals, their behavior under natural and experimental conditions should be briefly considered. The swimming action of the jelly-fish consists of rhythmical contractions of the musculature in the circular band, all portions of which act in unison. This rhythmical movement is aroused by influences proceeding from the specialized receptors in the rim, for if these are all cut off the movements cease. They do not cease, if all but one are cut off, but remain the same, no matter which one has been retained. This fact shows an absence of specialization in the reactions to different receptors. Any small portion of the body, containing a receptor along with some of the muscle and nerve-net, will execute the same rhythmic movements, showing that any part of the nerve-net can do the same sort of work as the whole net. If all but one of the special receptors are removed, and then a further cut is made through the circular band on one side of the remaining receptor, the whole band will even then execute its rhythmic movements; and it makes no difference on which side of the receptor the division is made. This shows that the conduction is equally good in both directions. Moreover, even if many cuts are made part-way through the circular band, in such a manner as to leave the band of a zig-zag shape, the rhythmic contractions will still spread from the remaining receptor throughout the band, provided only that the divisions are not complete. This shows that the conduction can go around corners and in every direction through the circular band. That it is the nerve-net which supplies the means of conduction is shown by experiments in which a complete separation is made between two parts of the muscular tissue, without division of the

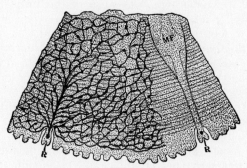

FIG. 4. — The Nerve-Net (somewhat schematic). (Bethe.) *R*, receptor; *M F*, part of circular band free from muscle.

nerve-strands connecting the two parts; the conduction is not interfered with so long as the nervous connections are left (see Fig. 4).

One further fact should be brought forward to complete the description of the conductive process. If a tentacle is gently stimulated by lightly touching it with a glass rod, it responds by a slight muscular contraction confined to the part touched. If the touch is a little heavier, the muscular reaction involves a larger part of the tentacle. If the touch reaches the intensity of a slight blow, the whole tentacle responds; and if the blow is made stronger and stronger, the reaction spreads to other tentacles, to the foot, and finally to the swimming muscles.[1]

§ 8. The facts have now been presented with sufficient detail to permit of a proper conception of the nervous system of the jellyfish and other cœlenterates. Anatomically, it is a diffuse network, continuous throughout, and connected with all receptors and with all motor organs. Experiment shows it to have no functional centre, all parts of it being equivalent. It conducts alike in all directions, and serves to bring about a general contraction of the mus-

[1] See A. Bethe, *Allgemeine Anatomie und Physiologie des Nervensystems*, 1903, p. 110.

culature when any receptor is excited. The observations on the
tentacles, however, show a stronger conduction to neighboring than
to more distant parts; inasmuch as the spread of the reaction occurs only within narrow limits when the stimulus is feeble, and extends more and more widely as the strength of the stimulus is increased. *Universal and indiscriminate conduction, limited only by
a dying out of the influence conducted with the distance traversed, is
the characteristic of this simplest type of nervous system.*

§ 9. This cœlenterate type of nervous system may be called the
"nerve-net type," because of the branches connecting the nerve-
cells; it is also called the "diffuse type," because of its being spread
widely through the epithelium, and also because of its diffuse conduction. The first distinct sign of centralization is met in the nervous system of the flatworms. In them a large proportion of the
nerve-cells is located in two bunches or ganglia, situated at the forward or mouth end of the animal. The centralization here is far
from complete; for many nerve-cells lie diffusely at the surface, and
these cells are united by their branches into a network, as in the
jelly-fish. In mollusks the condition is much the same as in the flatworms; although rather more concentration into ganglia is visible.
The nerve-net is still complete enough to make possible co-ordinated contractions of the muscles of the whole body, even after the
removal of the "centres" or ganglia. The significance of the central system is seen, however, from the fact that reactions of parts distant from the point of stimulation are much more prompt when the
ganglia are intact than when they are removed. The essential
point of advantage in the ganglionic system of these creatures appears to be that the ganglia can be connected with the muscles and
receptors by long strands of nerve, and not simply by the short
branches which connect the cells of the nerve-net. These long
strands thus afford more rapid conduction between distant parts
than is provided by the net.

§ 10. In contrast with the diffuse nerve-net of the cœlenterates,
and the partially modified net of the flatworms and mollusks, the
nervous system of the higher, segmented worms or *annelids*, and of
the arthropods (crabs, insects, etc.) and vertebrates, may be called
a *centralized system*. Nerve-nets are not indeed entirely absent
from these higher forms of animal life; they persist in certain secluded and protected situations, such as the walls of the blood-vessels, heart, stomach, and intestines of vertebrates, including man.
But the receptors of the external surface of the body, by which it
is brought into relation with its environment, and the muscles that
move the body or its parts and so produce external effects, are no
longer, in these higher forms, connected with each other by a diffuse

net of anastomosing nerve-cells. Instead, the receptors are connected by long fibres with masses of nerve-cells lying along the
middle line of the body (these animals all being bilaterally symmetrical), and the muscles are likewise connected by similar fibres
with the central masses of cells. The fibres which connect the centres with the receptors and effectors are characterized by fibrils
running lengthwise within them, and are true nerve-fibres, as in the
nerve-net. Such fibres, however, do not anastomose with each other

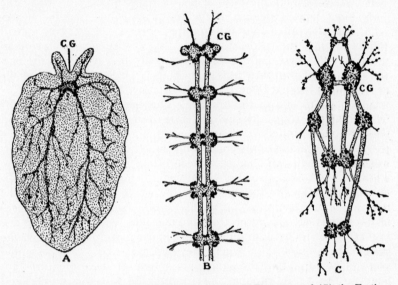

FIG. 5.—Diagram of the Nervous Systems of (A) the Flatworm, of (B) the Earthworm, and (C) the Mollusk. (Bethe.)   CG, cerebral ganglion.

outside of the centres, but, where they are gathered into the
bundles which are called *nerves*, each maintains its individuality,
somewhat as the wires bound together in a telephone cable
remain separated from each other. Connections between the
fibres from receptors and those to effectors are made only in the
centres.
  Further: the manner of communication within the centres themselves differs from that observed in the nerve-net. In the nerve-net,
the branches of different cells unite; in the nerve-centres, there seems
to be no union of the branches of different cells; at least, this is true
of all the stouter branches. If there is any real continuity between
different cells in the nerve-centres, it must be due to passage from
one to another of extremely fine strands—extremely fine even as
tested by the highest powers of the microscope. But the very fine

fibrils, which course through the nerve-cells and along their branches, would seem, from the observations of some good authorities, to have a certain independence, and to pass freely from one nerve-cell to another, forming between the cells an exceedingly tenuous and intricate network, a network of much more delicate strands than those which form the nerve-net. The existence of such an extra-cellular network of fibrils has been made out, with some probability, in worms and perhaps in crabs; in vertebrates, however, it has not been demonstrated to the satisfaction of those best qualified to judge; and many authorities are disposed to believe that no complete continuity exists between the different cells, but only a close con-tiguity of their fine branches. The evidence on this point will be presented in a later chapter on the nerve-cell. Whatever may be the truth of this difficult question, there is no doubt that the path of communication existing in the centres of the higher animal forms —including the worms—is less diffuse and indiscriminate than that which obtains in the primitive nerve-net. There is less of wide-spread distribution of the influence coming from a receptor to all the musculature. In other words, the influence is confined within narrower limits, and accordingly more specialization and greater variety of movements result. This is one cardinal feature of the centralized form of a nervous system. Another is the existence of long fibres, which afford quicker connection between distant parts of the body than occurs through the primitive nerve-net.

§ 11. From these general considerations we may turn to a brief sketch of the nervous system and behavior of the annelids, taking as a simple example the earthworm (see Fig. 5). Like other anne-lids, and like the arthropods and vertebrates as well, the body of the earthworm is built on a segmental plan, the segments succeeding one another along the length of the animal, and being visible, in the earthworm, in the ringed appearance of the animal's surface. Each segment, except at the front and back ends of the worm, is much like every other, and each is fairly complete in itself. Each has a ring of muscle, little protruding bristles which are of use in locomotion, and a set of simple sense-organs. From the sense-organs and from the muscles nerve-fibres run to pairs of ganglia within the segment, one of each pair lying on the right and one on the left. The nerve-fibres connecting with the receptors are branches of the receptive cells; those connected with the muscles are branches of cells lying within the ganglia. Connections within the ganglia are formed, as above described, between the fibres from the receptors and those issuing to the muscles; and thus a local reflex path is provided, by means of which stimuli affecting the receptors of the segment arouse activity in the muscles of that segment (see Fig. 6).

Local reflexes can be obtained from single segments cut out of a worm of this species.   But the segments are not entirely independent

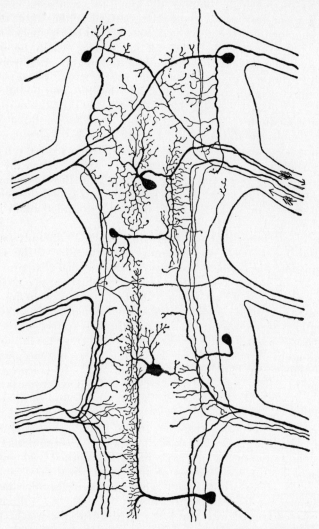

FIG. 6.—Nerve-Cells and Fibres in Ganglia of the Earthworm. (Retzius.)
Only a few out of many cells and fibres are shown.   A motor fibre
is indicated by an outward-pointing arrow, and a sensory fibre by
an inward-pointing arrow.

of one another, nor are their ganglia without mutual connections.
Between each ganglion and that of the segment next in front or be-

hind is a strand of nerve-fibres; so that the ganglia form a connected chain extending along the worm near its ventral or under surface. The nerve-fibres which compose the longitudinal strands connecting the ganglia are, for the most part, derived neither from the receptor cells nor from the nerve-cells which send out branches to the muscles, but from another class of nerve-cells, which lie in the ganglia and send their branches in a longitudinal direction from one ganglion to the next or to the next but one or two.   These central fibres connect neighboring ganglia with each other, and by the series of them in successive ganglia the whole chain is made a continuous conducting medium.   There are also a few much longer fibres, which connect distant ganglia directly with each other.   At the forward end of the worm there is somewhat of a departure from the regular segmental scheme; a ring of nervous tissue extends from the foremost pair of ganglia around the gullet and joins these ganglia to a single ganglion lying on the dorsal side, which is called the cerebral ganglion or "brain."   In the earthworm this so-called brain is not highly developed.

Experiment shows that the chain of ganglia is the only path of communication between the receptors and effectors of the worm. If the ganglia of a segment are cut out, that segment is paralyzed: its muscles no longer respond to stimuli applied to any receptor, and its own receptors, on being stimulated, give rise to no reaction in any part of the body.   If the longitudinal cord connecting the ganglia is severed at any point, no stimulus applied to the part of the worm forward of the break arouses any response in the part lying behind the break; and *vice versa;* the waves of muscular contraction that sweep backward over the animal in its creeping, stop at the point where the cord is severed, and all co-ordination between the front and rear parts is abolished.   We find in the earthworm three main classes of movement: (1) local reflexes, which can be carried out by the receptors, effectors, and connecting nerve-fibres of a single segment; (2) slowly moving waves of muscular contraction, the impulse to which is probably transmitted from segment to segment by the short fibres of the longitudinal cord, and (3) sudden jerks of the whole worm, which are probably due to conduction along the few long central fibres.

§ 12. As compared with the lowly earthworm, the higher forms of annelid, and crustaceans and insects, while preserving the same general type of segmented nervous system, show a superior nervous development in many respects.   There is an increase in the number of cells in the ganglia, which is partly to be explained by the greater complexity of the sensory and motor apparatus.   There is a still greater increase in the amount of branching of the nerve-cells within the ganglia, which probably means a higher organization of the connections between fibres. There is a great increase in the number of long fibres within the ganglion chain, and a high development of the cerebral ganglion. Both of the last-mentioned changes are to be interpreted in the light of the development of the head, which in the earthworm is not much of an affair, but which becomes richly equipped with various organs in crabs and insects. The head is first of all the mouth end of an animal, and as such it is natural that it should go first in locomotion, and that it should have a certain predominance over the rest of the body. Around the mouth are developed motor organs to serve it, and sense-organs concerned with the finding and testing of food; and thus the importance of the head is progressively increased.

The nervous connections must keep pace with the development of receptors and effectors, and thus it is that the cerebral ganglion grows in size, and becomes more and more dominant over the ganglia lying behind. It is, further, to be expected that such highly specialized receptors as the eye should appear in this same region. The eye is the type of a "distance receptor"; its importance lies in the fact that it is excited by objects at a greater or less distance from the surface of the body. With the appearance of distance receptors comes a great increase in the range of the environment that can be reacted to; and thus the life of the animal comes to be largely dominated by these organs. Since the distance receptors are located in the head, the importance of the cerebral ganglion and its connections is still further increased; and to this is to be ascribed, not only the increase in the size of the ganglion, but the increase in the number of long fibres leading backward from it, and bringing distant muscles into quick communication with the sense-organs of the head.

§ 13. The vertebrates—fishes, amphibia, reptiles, birds, and mammals—are, like annelids, crustaceans, and insects, built on a segmental plan, the segmentation appearing clearly in the vertebral column or backbone. The nervous system in vertebrates shows some of the segmental origin, in the regular succession of the nerves which issue, a pair at each vertebra, along the length of the trunk. The central organs of vertebrates are located inside the vertebræ and skull, i. e., in the spinal cord and brain, and these show very little sign of segmentation. In fact, one of the characteristics of the vertebrate nerve-centres is their visible continuity and absence of apparent segmentation. It is much as if the ganglia of the annelid's nerve-chain had grown together into a continuous cord. A second difference between the vertebrate nervous system and that of the annelids, etc., is seen in the position of the spinal cord. The nerve-chain of invertebrates lies near the ventral surface, the digestive tract lying above it, while in the vertebrates the cord lies near the dorsal surface and above the digestive tract. The cerebral ganglion of the earthworm, it will however be remembered, lies dorsal to the mouth, and this corresponds to the brain of vertebrates.

A third point of difference between the vertebrate and invertebrate systems concerns the location of the cells, the branches of which connect the receptors with the centres. In invertebrates, it is the receptive cells, lying at the periphery, the branches of which pass into the centres; but in vertebrates the receptor cells do not themselves provide the fibres for their connections, but are supplied by fibres which grow out from special ganglia that lie close to the spinal cord and brain, and are enclosed in the same bony covering. The receptive cells of the sense of smell form an exception, and send branches of their own into the brain, preserving the invertebrate condition. The nerve-fibres in vertebrates very commonly show a more complicated structure than in invertebrates, in that the branch of the nerve-cell becomes enveloped by a sheath of "myelin," a fat-like substance the significance of which is not quite clear, but will be discussed in a later chapter. On the whole, and with exceptions, the nerve-centres of vertebrates may be considered as more advanced in development than those of invertebrates; and this is seen especially in the richer provision of long fibres connecting distant parts of the system.[1]

§ 14. The nerve-centres of vertebrates may be considered as consisting of (1) a fundamental system, comprising the cord and the brain-stem, and (2) accessory organs developing as outgrowths of the brain-stem, the chief of these being the cerebellum and the cerebrum. The development of the accessory structures is very unequal in different forms of vertebrate animals;—the size of the cerebellum being closely related to the animal's powers of locomotion, and the size of the cerebrum with his powers of learning new and specific adaptations. The fundamental system is, on the other hand, fairly constant throughout the vertebrate series. This is especially true of the spinal cord, the size of which seems to depend almost wholly on the size of the animal, i. e., on the bulk of the receptor and effector organs with which it is connected. Thus, though the brain of an ox is much smaller than that of a man, the spinal cord of the former is both longer and thicker.

The fundamental system (compare Fig. 7), as most clearly seen in the spinal cord, consists of the above-mentioned sensory ganglia, the cells of which provide fibres connecting the receptors of the trunk

[1] The following treatment of the vertebrate nervous system is based mostly on L. Edinger, "Vorlesungen über den Bau der nervösen Zentralorgane," Band 2, *Vergleichende Anatomie des Gehirns* (Leipzig, 1908).

and limbs with the spinal cord; of nerve-cells lying within the cord, branches of which pass out to the muscles and other effector organs; and of numerous central units— cells whose branches do not extend beyond the centres, but run up or down or across from one side of the cord to another, and so bring its different parts into connection. Most of these central fibres are short; but there are some sets of long ones, which are present in all vertebrates, and which connect the cord directly with the brain stem.

§ 15. The brain-stem shows the same basal characteristics as the cord, but its structure is greatly complicated by the presence of the important receptors which are located in the head, and connected with this part of the central system. Where a given set of receptors is highly developed and much used, the part of the brain-stem which receives fibres from it is itself highly developed. The receptors of the vertebrate head can be, though only roughly, indicated by mentioning the human nose, eye, ear, mouth, and facial skin. Of

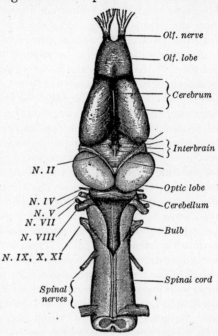

FIG. 7.—Nerve-Centres of the Frog. (Ecker-Wiedersheim-Gaupp.) The brain and upper part of the cord are shown from the dorsal side.

these, the development of the eye is perhaps the most equal throughout the vertebrates. The sense of smell is much more important in some forms than in others, and the associated parts of the brain are correspondingly unequal. The skin of the face, especially of the snout, and of the front of the mouth and nose, is much more important as a receptive surface in some species of animals than in others; and the "trigeminus" nerve, which supplies the cutaneous receptors of the face, varies correspondingly. The ear of land-living forms is the representative of a much more extensive system of receptors in fishes, which is excited by vibrations and currents in the water; this constitutes the so-called "lateral line" system, the incoming fibres from which give rise to a considerable expansion of the brain-stem at their place of entrance. Again, the sense of taste in man is provided with a comparatively slight outfit; but in fishes it has an extensive system of chemo-receptors, which lie not only within the mouth and throat, but on the external surface of the head and even of the trunk; and these receptors also, being connected with a certain region of the brain-stem, are the occasion of a complex local development in that region. Thus it comes about that the brain-stem in vertebrates is not only larger, but less uniform in size than the spinal cord.

Another difference between these two parts of the fundamental nervous system lies in the more extensive development, within the brain-stem, of the short central fibres, which connect the neighboring parts of the system. The impressions received by the various sense-organs of the head are so important in regulating the vital functions of the animal that it is but natural to find extensive paths of communication leading from the nerves of these senses in various directions. The impressions received by the internal ear (and by the lateral line in fishes) are important in governing locomotion and preserving equilibrium, and in maintaining the "tone" and readiness for action of the muscles. The sense of taste is important in regulating digestion. The impressions made on receptors in the lungs—the nerve-fibres of which also enter the brain-stem—are important in breathing. The "centres" for the digestive organs, and for respiration and the closely allied function of circulation, are located in the brain-stem; and one of the important centres for locomotion is located there as well. (By a so-called "centre" is to be understood, anatomically, a set of connections between incoming and outgoing fibres, by which receptors can influence the right effectors. Such connections are largely provided by the central fibres, which accordingly abound in the region concerned with the vital functions.)

The brain-stem, like the cord, does not belong wholly to the fundamental system, but is invaded by fibres belonging to the accessory systems of the cerebrum and cerebellum. In the higher mammals, the fundamental system is quite overgrown by fibres belonging to these accessory systems. These are long fibres, in contrast with the short interconnections of the fundamental system. The higher the development of the accessory organs, the greater is the proportion of long fibres in the brain-stem and the cord; and the more the fundamental system retires into the background. No doubt, however, it always remains fundamental; it is played upon by the accessory organs, between which and the effectors it always intervenes (compare Fig. 8).

§ 16. As already stated, the cerebellum varies in size according to the locomotor powers of the animal, so that within closely related groups, such as the lizards, the tortoises, or the eels, those species which are active swimmers have a much larger development of this organ than those which crawl. Birds, with their high powers of locomotion in three dimensions, have a large cerebellum; in mammals also this organ is large—in man specially large, perhaps on account of his upright position and the special demands which this entails on the muscles for locomotion and the maintenance of equilibrium.

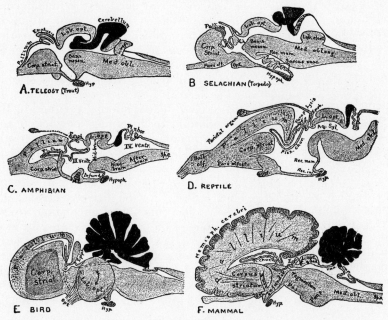

FIG. 8.—Longitudinal Sections through the Brains of Different Classes of Vertebrates. (Edinger.) The cerebellum is represented in black.

The cerebellum receives fibres, directly or indirectly, from a large share of the receptors of the whole body, including the head. The fibres which conduct outward from the cerebellum run mostly to groups of cells in the brain-stem; and the fibres from these groups which belong to the fundamental connecting or co-ordinating system, undoubtedly spread the influence of the cerebellum to the cells which directly control the muscles. The development of the cerebellum is not, however, entirely independent of that of the cerebrum, since in mammals there is a mass of fibres coming from the cerebrum and making connections with the cerebellum; and a large addition to the cerebellum, on each side, seems to result from this connection with the cerebrum.

§ 17. Before we pass to the other principal accessory organ, the cerebrum, we should pause to recognize the existence of the increased development, which occurs in vertebrates near the forward end of the brain-stem, in the part called the mid-brain. This part reaches a great size in many vertebrates, and is in fact the best-developed part of the brain in fishes and amphibia; in reptiles and birds as well it is very prominent. The most elementary fact regarding this part is that it receives fibres from one of the most important of all receptors, the eye; and that it, in turn, sends out motor fibres to the muscles of the eye. The swollen portions of the brain-stem which lie on the back of the mid-brain are accordingly called, except in mammals, the "optic" lobes. The fibres of the optic nerve here terminate in close connection with large collections of variously formed cells, some of which send forth only short branches, and serve to afford rich connections within this mass of cells, while others send out long fibres that run in large measure downward to the lower parts of the brain-stem, and to the cord, and thus carry the influence of the eye to effectors throughout the body. But the optic lobes are not exclusively concerned with the eye; for fibres can be traced to them also from the cord and brain-stem; by this means they receive impressions from the other sense-organs of the body, and especially from the ears. Thus the optic lobes come to be a general receiving and distributing centre; and in animals which have not developed the cerebrum to any great extent, the optic lobes are probably the dominant part of the whole nervous system.

§ 18. The part of the brain-stem which lies next forward of the mid-brain is called the inter-brain or thalamus; it is constantly present throughout the vertebrate series, but varies greatly in extent; and in mammals it is quite definitely an adjunct of the cerebrum, since it contains masses of cells which are relay stations in the pathways of impressions from all the receptors to the cerebrum. Thus, the principal connections of the eye, which in other vertebrates are almost exclusively with the optic lobes, become in mammals mostly transferred to the thalamus, from which fibres run to the cortex of the cerebrum. But besides this cerebral part of the thalamus, there is in all forms of vertebrates a more primitive system of cells and fibres, connecting largely with the portion of the brain still further forward (the olfactory region). The thalamus is not, however, the direct or immediate centre of smell; and in fact its significance is difficult to discover. The thalamus has several gland-like offshoots, and in some of the lower vertebrates, some of these appear to act as sense-organs. The "parietal organs," which are offshoots of the thalamus, appear in some forms to serve as eyes, which are fairly well developed, though not by any means as highly developed as the eyes customarily so called. It is possible that this part of the brain-stem is primitively, like the mid-brain, the local centre for certain sense-organs which in most vertebrates have gone out of function; and that later, the thalamus was taken possession of, so to speak, by the adjoining cerebrum.

What lies forward of the thalamus is called the fore-brain or end-brain. It consists of two parts: (1) the basal portion, which belongs to the fundamental system of the brain-stem, and (2) the expansions to the side and back, which form the greatest part of the whole brain in mammals, but in many lower vertebrates are of very small dimensions. The basal portion of the fore-brain is again readily divisible into two parts: the "corpus striatum," and the olfactory lobe and bulb. The striatum, which lies very near the thalamus, is, probably, closely related to it in function, though we must admit that on this point our knowledge is far from complete. The function of the olfactory bulb, which lies at the very front of the whole organ, is clear from its direct connection with the incoming fibres from the olfactory receptors in the nose. And the olfactory lobe, further, is directly connected with the bulb, and must also be regarded as part of the olfactory system. A portion of it, however, receives fibres from the skin of the face and mouth, and is perhaps, as suggested by Edinger,[1] a centre for the "oral sense," which in animals that use the snout or tongue as an exploratory organ, must be of much service in directing their behavior. There is no doubt that, as the mid-brain is primarily the central mechanism of the eye, the fore-brain is primarily the local centre for the sense of smell. In the fishes, it seems to be little else; only the basal portion develops, the dorsal remaining (except for one small portion) a mere membrane, without nerve-cells or fibres in it. In amphibia, however, the dorsal portion, called the "pallium" or mantle, begins to show nervous structures, and in reptiles, this is still more markedly the case; in birds more yet; and in mammals the pallium completely overshadows the primitive basal structures of the fore-brain. In amphibia the nerve-cells of the pallium are irregularly arranged, but, beginning with the reptiles, there is a true bark, or "cortex," on the outer surface of the pallium, consisting of cells arranged in a definite fashion, and with an extraordinary richness of fine branches.

§ 19. At its first appearance, in reptiles, the cortex is, to judge from its fibre connections, an adjunct of the primary olfactory and oral sense-centres which lie in the adjacent basal portion of the fore-brain. This oldest part of the pallium is called the "archi-pallium," in distinction from the "neo-pallium," the connections of which are

[1] L. Edinger, op. cit., p. 261.

with more distant parts of the brain-stem and cord (see Fig. 9). In birds, the connections with the optic lobes become prominent; and in mammals, through the intermediary of the thalamus, the cortex comes into connection with all the receptors of the body, and also sends outgoing fibres further and further back along the

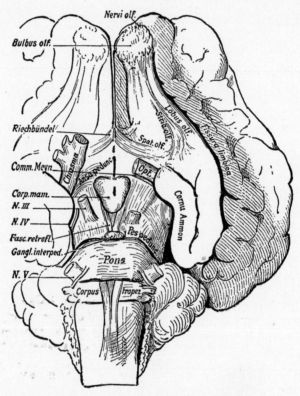

FIG. 9.—Archipallium and Neopallium in the Brain of the Calf. (Edinger.)   In the right half of the figure, the archipallium (unshaded) is separated from the partially shaded neopallium by the fissura limbica.

brain-stem and cord, thus assuming control over more and more of the fundamental system.   With the increase in the neopallium, the older, olfactory portion of the cortex is left behind near the base and median line of the cerebrum, while the neopallium spreads to the sides, and upward, forward, and backward.   The archipallium still forms a distinguishable portion of the brain, even of man, and is probably still concerned, as in reptiles, with smell and related senses.

Among the mammals, the advance of the brain from the lower to the higher forms consists in the development of the neopallium. This advance is marked by the increase of the extent of the cortex, by the growing richness of cells and their fine branches within the cortex, and by the increase of long fibres connecting different parts of the cortex with each other and with the cord, the brain-stem, and the cerebellum. The increase in total extent of the cortex is provided for partly by expansion of the skull and partly by the folding of the surface of the brain into "fissures," which are few in the lower mammals, but numerous in many of the higher forms. The increase of long fibres in the higher forms is as marked as the increase in the extent of the cortex. It will be recalled that, even among the worms, an advance in organization was marked by an increase in the long central fibres, bringing distant parts of the system into direct connection. This same principle appears in comparing the brains of different vertebrates. Man, of all vertebrates, possesses the greatest proportion of long fibres, both those leading into or out of the cerebrum, and those connecting its own non-adjacent parts. In particular, the supply of fibres connecting the right with the left hemispheres of the cerebrum shows a great advance from lower mammals to higher, and in man the cross connection between the hemispheres, called the "corpus callosum," is a prominent feature of the brain.

§ 20. In a general way, the intelligence of different vertebrates is somewhat proportional to the size of their brains, and especially to their development of cerebral cortex. We have, indeed, as yet no accurate measures of the intelligence of different animals, with the exception of a few which have been subjected to experimental test. The monkey is more intelligent than the cat or dog, as tested by the speed of learning or the number and variety of associations formed.[1] The chimpanzee and other man-like apes seem to be superior to the smaller monkeys; and the primates, in general, seem to surpass most other animals. Some mammals which possess markedly large brains, and high cortical development—such as the seal, porpoise, walrus, and whale—are little known as respects their behavior and intelligence.

One thing is reasonably certain: the brain-weight of a species, or of a breed, is partly dependent on the size of the body. Larger breeds have larger brains, but the *relative* size of the brain is greater in the smaller breeds. There is apparently a purely somatic factor in the determination of brain development, and this factor must be allowed for before the true relation between brain-size and intelli-

[1] Thorndike, "The Mental Life of the Monkeys," *Psychol. Rev.*, Monogr. Suppl. 15, 1901.

gence can be seen. Suggestions have been made toward the determination and elimination of this somatic factor, but there are still many elements of uncertainty in the calculation.

The following table of approximate brain-weights and body-weights of mammals is selected from the much more extensive tables of Warnecke.[1]

	Brain-Weight in Grams	Body-Weight in Grams
Mouse	0.4	20
Squirrel	6	400
Cat	30	3,500
Beaver	35	20,000
Kangaroo	65	45,000
Monkey (macaque) . . .	100	5,000
Dog (very large) . . .	120	46,000
Sheep	130	50,000
Lion	220	120,000
Seal	300	26,000
Bear	400	200,000
Gorilla	400	90,000
Moose	435	200,000
Cow	450	175,000
Porpoise	500	55,000
Hippopotamus	580	1,750,000
Horse	600	300,000
Giraffe	680	530,000
Man	1,400	70,000
Elephant	5,000	2,500,000
Whale	7,000	70,000,000

§ 21. Within the order of primates, we find a large range of brain-size, the cerebrum of the common tailed monkeys (e. g., macacus rhesus) weighing about 80–100 grams, that of the anthropoid apes (chimpanzee, gorilla, orang-outang) running to about 400 grams, while that of man averages about 1,400 grams. Remains of extinct forms of primates, showing a cerebral development intermediate between that of the gorilla and that of man, have been unearthed in only a few cases; and there has been considerable difference of judgment regarding the interpretation to be made of these intervening forms. On the whole, it seems allowable to recognize at least one intermediate form between the anthropoid apes and man as he exists to-day. This intermediate form (Pithecanthropus

[1] *Journal f. Psychol. u. Neurol.*, 1908, XIII, 355. A collection of brain-weights of birds, by the same author, is to be found in the same journal, 1907, IX, 93.

erectus), as represented by a single specimen found in Java,[1] is reckoned with the apes rather than with man, but has a skull capacity, as well as other anatomical peculiarities, that separate him from existing apes, and indicate a brain-weight of perhaps 600–700 grams. The paucity of the evidence, however, must continue to throw doubt on the conclusion.

A considerable number of specimens of great antiquity have been unearthed, which are undoubtedly the relics of the human species. In regard to skull capacity, these oldest surviving specimens of inhabitants of Europe do not differ much, if any, from the present inhabitants. In countries like Egypt, also, in which skulls are found representing several thousand years of history, there is no sign of an increase in brain-size. Among existing races, there are racial differences in the average brain-weight; but these differences are small compared with the wide range of variation between individuals of the same race. For example, the average brain-weight of negroes is perhaps two ounces less than that of Europeans; but the difference between individuals of either race may amount to as much as twenty-five ounces. It should be added that the differences in mental capacity of different races appear much smaller to the ethnologist, who knows different races, than they appear to those members of any race who, not having studied other races scientifically, judge in accordance with race prejudice and pride rather than in an objective manner. Even this difference may be chiefly due to the fact that, in the more highly civilized races, the large amount and variety of the educative processes develops (that is, occasions a growth in size of) many of the nerve elements which continue relatively undeveloped in the less civilized races.

§ 22. A review of the foregoing sketch of the varieties of the nervous system in the animal kingdom leaves no doubt that *the most elementary and essential function of nervous tissue is to provide lines of conduction between receptors and effectors.* No other possible function of the nervous system would have any biological utility without this. The progress from the diffuse nerve-net of the jellyfish to the highly organized system of mammals is marked, first by centralization; second, by the appearance of numbers of central or co-ordinating cells; third, by the dominance of the system by the receptors of the head; and fourth, by an increase in the plasticity or modifiability of the system, or of certain parts of it. Conduction, co-ordination, integration, and "learning" (this word in a figurative sense) may be assigned as the functions of the nervous system; and it is probable that, from the stand-point of inner mechanics, all of these are specializations of the primary function of conduction.

[1] Discovered and described by E. Dubois.

CHAPTER II

THE DEVELOPMENT OF THE NERVOUS SYSTEM IN THE INDIVIDUAL [1]

§ 1. The study of the growth of the nervous system in embryonic life and childhood is useful in two ways: it throws some light on the functions of the various parts, and it is of great aid in gaining clear conceptions of the highly complicated structure of the central organs. These organs first appear in relatively simple forms and relations, and develop gradually in complexity; an understanding of the simpler facts of the embryonic brain is thus a good point of starting for the study of its fully developed condition.

In unicellular organisms reproduction consists simply in division. The adult, full-grown cell divides into two cells of half its size, which may be called young cells, or " daughter cells"; and these in their turn grow and subsequently divide. In all but the simplest forms of living beings, there exists a differentiation among the numerous cells that compose the body; most of them form organs which, from the stand-point of reproduction and the perpetuation of the species, are accessory, and simply serve to provide favorable conditions of life for the relatively few cells which preserve the reproductive power. These reproductive cells alone are capable of producing daughter cells which can grow into new individuals. In plants and animals which show the distinction of sex, the reproductive cells are of two sorts, usually (in animals) located in separate individuals, male and female. The reproductive cells for the female animal give rise to cells called eggs or ova; while those of the male give rise to spermatozoa. In some low forms the ova are capable of developing into new individuals without aid from the spermatozoa; but in most cases, and always in vertebrates, the ovum does not develop far unless it has fused with a spermatozoon. The fusion of these two cells, the ovum from the female individual and the spermatozoon from the male, is called fertilization; and the ovum which has fused with a spermatozoon is called a fertilized ovum. Leaving aside as unessential for our purpose

---

[1] This chapter is based principally on the work of His, *Die Entwickelung des menschlichen Gehirns*, 1904; and on the treatment by O. Strong, in Bailey and Miller's "Textbook of Embryology," 1909, pp. 454–572.

the very curious changes which occur in these two cells in preparation for their fusion, we will take our start with the fertilized ovum, which may properly be called a new individual at the very earliest stage of its life, and which promptly begins to develop itself.

§ 2. As has already been said, the fertilized ovum, itself a single cell, proceeds to divide into two,[1] which, however, do not separate, but remain in contact with each other. Each of these daughter cells, after growing in size, again divides into two; and this process is repeated time after time, and for a while with considerable regularity, so that the young individual consists successively of one cell, two cells, four, eight, sixteen, and thirty-two. The details of this process differ, however, in different orders of animals, and in all the regular doubling of the number of cells is broken up after a few divisions by the beginning of the differentiation among the daughter cells and their unequal rates of growth and division.

A process preliminary to this propagation of cells by division may be noticed briefly at this point. When a cell is on the point of dividing into two, the nucleus can be seen to separate into smaller bodies, the number of which is constant for any given sort of cell. In preparation for their fusion, both ovum and spermatozoon extrude part of their nuclear matter, and at the time of fertilization, each has only half of the number of so-called "chromosomes" appropriate to the animal in question. Thus the fertilized ovum, which consists of both ovum and spermatozoon, contains exactly the full number of chromosomes appropriate to the species. When the fertilized ovum divides into two cells, half of its chromosomes go to each cell, and half of each half is from the original ovum, half from the spermatozoon. The same thing is true of the succeeding generations of "daughter cells." Thus each parent is equally represented, not only in the fertilized ovum, but in each cell of the successive generations of cells that result from repeated division.

§ 3. At first the cells of the mass resulting from repeated cleavage of the ovum adhere compactly together, presenting somewhat the appearance of a mulberry. Later, spaces appear between some of the cells, and a cavity is formed inside the mass. Then the cells

---

[1] The very early stages in the development of the human embryo have not been actually observed, but as those mammals which have been studied resemble each other in essential points at this stage, it is inferred that the beginnings of human development do not differ much from the general mammalian condition. The earliest human embryos so far available seem to be of about two weeks' growth. Within this period they have increased in size from 0.2 millimetre (or $\frac{1}{125}$ of an inch, the diameter of the ovum) to a length of some two millimetres. They have become elongated and cylindrical, and show the beginnings of head and trunk, and distinct rudiments of several organs, among which are the brain and spinal cord.

lining the cavity become differentiated from those of the exterior surface, and a third group of cells sprouts in between the two layers, so that there are formed, in all, no fewer than three "germ layers." Of these, the exterior layer is called the *ectoderm*, the inner layer the *entoderm*, and the intervening layer the *mesoderm*. From this very early stage of development on, these three layers retain their individuality. The entoderm forms the epithelial wall of the throat, gullet, stomach, and intestines, and also of the windpipe and lungs; it gives rise also to the glands which connect with these organs, including the liver and pancreas. The mesoderm gives rise to the bones and connective tissues, to the muscles, the heart and blood-vessels, and to the kidneys and the sex glands. The ectoderm gives rise to the outer layer of the skin and of the mucous membrane of the mouth and nose, to the appendages of the skin, such as hair and nails, to the essential portions of the sense-organs, and to the nervous system. It appears strange, at first thought, that the nerve-centres, which lie so far to the interior and are enclosed in bone, should develop from the superficial layer of the embryo, but the early stages in the development of the nervous system make this clear.

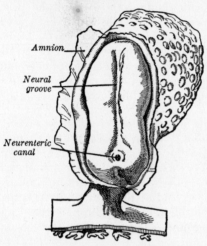

Amnion

Neural groove

Neurenteric canal

FIG. 10.—Dorsal View of a Two Weeks' Human Embryo. (Von Spee.) The future head end is above in the figure. The "neurenteric canal" is an early communication between the neural tube and the rudimentary intestine. Magnified 20 diameters.

Early in the development, when the embryo is less than two weeks old—age being reckoned from time of fertilization—there appears a shallow groove (see Fig. 10) extending lengthwise along what may be called the back of the embryo. This groove is formed by an inbending of the ectoderm, and is called the *neural groove*. The groove increases in depth, its edges arch together over the top, and, where they meet, grow together, thus transforming the groove into a tube—a hollow tube of ectoderm lying beneath the surface of the embryo, and later separated widely from this surface by the ingrowth of mesoderm between it and the superficial ectoderm. This is the so-called *neural tube*, and it is the rudiment of the nervous system, which, in fact, always retains the fundamental characteristic of a tube. The lower portion of the tube gives rise to the spinal cord, the walls of which become so thickened that the small central cavity remaining in adult life and called the central canal is very inconspicuous. The upper portion of the tube develops into the brain; and here the form of a tube is still more concealed, by fold-ings, swellings, or out-growths of the tube, and great but irregular thick-enings of the wall. The central cavity persists, how-ever, and appears in the adult brain in the form of spaces of various shape, called the ventricles. It is of great assistance in gain-ing a conception of the complicated structure to bear in mind the fact that *the brain is primarily a tube* (compare Fig. 11).

§ 4. The nerves which connect the brain and cord with the muscles and sense-organs, arise partly as outgrowths of the neu-ral tube, and partly from that portion of the ecto-derm which formed the lips of the neural groove and which was left out-side when the groove closed to form the tube. This portion of the ecto-derm is called the neural crest, and it is quickly overgrown by the adja-cent ectoderm, and so comes to lie beneath the surface of the em-bryo, and close to the neural tube, one strip at the right side of the tube and one at the left. This part of the ectoderm gives rise to the sensory nerves and to part, at least, of the sympathetic nervous system; while the neural tube itself gives rise to the motor nerves and to the brain and cord.

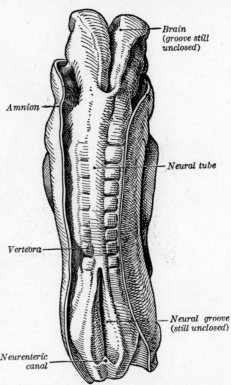

FIG. 11.—Dorsal View of a Human Embryo, Some-what More Advanced than the Preceding. (Eter-nod.) About ⁵⁰⁄₁. The neural groove has closed to a tube in the middle of its extent, but is still open at the cerebral and lumbar ends.

The neural tube, when first formed, does not as yet constitute a nervous tissue; its cells are not nerve-cells, but are still in an unspecialized condition.   The process by which this tube of undiffer-entiated cells becomes a cord of nervous tissue is as follows.   In the wall of the tube next to the cavity or "lumen" some cells be-come reproductively active, and divide, giving rise to daughter cells, which move away toward the outside of the wall, but stop midway, and proceed to change their form, sending out branches that

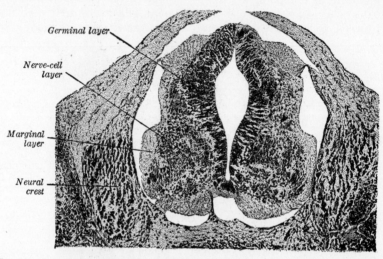

Germinal layer

Nerve-cell layer

Marginal layer

Neural crest

Fig. 12.—Cross Section of the Neural Tube and Crests of a Human Embryo of about Five Weeks.   (His.)   The dorsal side is uppermost in the figure.   Many facts which are men-tioned in the text can be observed in this figure.   The three layers of the tube are readily distinguished: the germinal layer, next to the lumen of the tube, is dark with its closely packed cells.   The nerve-cell layer, outside of this, is more loosely packed, while the mar-ginal layer is free from cells.   The fact that the nerve-cell layer develops to the sides, and not directly in the mid-ventral and mid-dorsal lines, is evident.   Commissural axons, crossing at the mid-ventral line, can be observed; also axons passing into and out of the tube in the dorsal and ventral roots.   The neural crest is clearly distinguished from the surrounding tissues in the left side of the figure.   A streaky appearance in the crest indi-cates the direction of the growing axons toward the dorsal root.   Within the tube, close to the entrance of the dorsal root, is seen the rudiment of the dorsal column which is composed of the axons which enter by the root.

unite with branches of other similar cells.   In this way a network of minute fibres is formed.   These cells, again, are not nerve-cells, nor is this tissue of fibres true nervous tissue; it is a framework or scaffolding; it is the rudiment of the supporting tissue of the nerve-centres, which in its fully developed form is called *neuroglia*.   Al-ways the growth of this supporting framework precedes the appear-ance of nerve-cells in any region of the centres.   The neuroglia strengthens the texture of the nerve-centres.   In later life, it "pro-liferates" or multiplies wherever injury or degeneration of the ner-vous tissue tends to produce vacant spaces.   The neuroglia, growing into the spaces, fills them. When the true nerve-cells begin to grow, the network of neuroglia serves to guide them into their places.

The nerve-cells originate in the same manner as the neuroglia cells. At the same portion of the tube, namely the layer next to the lumen, cells divide, giving rise to daughter cells which migrate outward to the middle of the wall. Here they stop, perhaps because checked by a dense layer of neuroglia fibres, and here they proceed to develop peculiarities which mark them as nerve-cells.

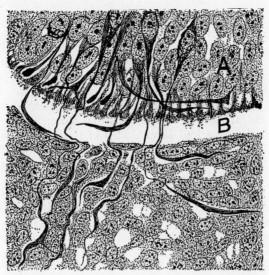

Fig. 13.—The Growing Axon. (Cajal.) From the embryo of a duck. *A* is the neural tube, the letter being placed about at the junction of the nerve-cell and the marginal layers; *B*, the space immediately surrounding the tube.

The wall of the neural tube thus comes to consist of three layers, the inner or germinal layer, where the process of cell-division is active, and where the young nerve-cells originate; the outermost or marginal layer, which is free from nerve-cells; and a middle or nerve-cell layer, in which the nerve-cells are developing (see Fig. 12).

§ 5. The first visible step in the specialization of the nerve-cell is the appearance of a few fine fibrils, the beginning of the "neurofibrils," which later develop into an extensive system within the cell and its outgrowths. The next step of importance is the appearance of a branch, which grows out from the cell toward the marginal layer. The growing end of this branch then becomes enlarged into a cone which seems to press its way between other cells and into the meshes of the neuroglia net, and so the branch elongates. The name given to this branch of the cell is the "axis cylinder process," or, more briefly, the *axon*. The axon itself branches, but not very richly; its branches are usually short and at right angles to its own course. The branches of the axon are known as *collaterals*. While the axon is pushing its way farther and farther from the cell body, the latter is developing its internal system of fibrils; and it presently puts forth, on the side opposite to the axon, other branches, quite different from the axon, more richly branched, branched in many cases much like a tree, and hence called *dendrites* (compare Fig. 13).

Leaving further description of the cell body and dendrites to a later page, let us return to the axon, and endeavor to follow its development. In most parts of the neural tube, the axon emerges from the layer of nerve-cells into the marginal layer, which thus becomes a layer of axons. Its further course differs much in different cases. In the case of a very important group of cells, which lie on the ventral [1] side of the neural tube, the axon passes straight out through the marginal layer and into the surrounding tissues; there it grows into a developing muscle, and, as with the general growth of the body the muscle comes to lie further and further from the neural tube, the axon continues to elongate. In this manner it comes to connect some small portion of the muscle with the spinal cord. This axon is a motor nerve-fibre, and its cell, which lies back in the ventral portion of the neural tube, is a motor nerve-cell. Later this cell will send "nerve impulses" down along the axon, arousing a portion of the muscle to action. As the motor nerve-cells are numerous and near together, their axons emerge from the tube in bundles or "rootlets," which come together to form "roots." These roots, emerging from the ventral side of the tube, are the ventral or motor roots of the spinal nerves (see Fig. 14).

There are also dorsal or sensory roots. These are formed, not by outgrowth of axons from cells in the tube, but by the growing into the tube of axons from outside cells that lie in the two strips which are formed from the neural crest, on the right and the left of the tube and toward its dorsal side. Cells within these strips develop in much the same way as the nerve-cells within the tube; except that each of the former sends out two axons, one of which grows toward the periphery of the body and connects with some sense-organ, while the other grows toward and penetrates the neural tube. The axon which grows toward the periphery, with others from near by, forms a dorsal root; this dorsal root soon joins the ventral root from the

---

[1] "Ventral" means on the side toward the animal's ventrum or belly; and "dorsal," the corresponding word, means on the side toward the dorsum or back.

adjacent part of the tube, and the two together form one of the spinal
or cranial nerves.

The nerves come off in pairs, on the right and left sides of the
tube. The two strips which gave rise to the sensory cells and to
their axons become compacted into two rows of "ganglia," or
bunches of nerve-cells, which lie on the dorsal roots, and are called

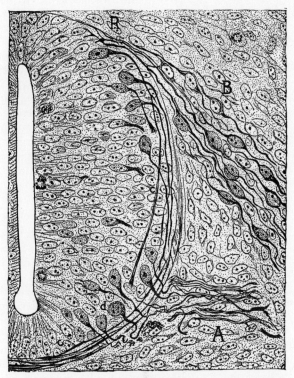

FIG. 14.—Axons Growing in Different Directions. (Cajal.) From
the spinal cord of an embryonic chick. *A*, ventral root; *B*,
spinal ganglion and dorsal root; *R*, bifurcation of dorsal root
axons on entering the cord; *d*, cell giving rise to ventral root
axon; *c, c*, commissural axons.

spinal ganglia. The cells within these ganglia, which at first sent
out an axon in each direction, later take a place to one side of their
axons, and then withdraw to some distance from them, retaining
connection by a single strand; in their fully developed form they appear to have but a single axon, which, however, speedily divides
into two. These ganglion cells put out no dendrites; but that one
of their axons which penetrates the neural tube splits in the marginal

layer into an ascending and a descending branch; it also sends off collaterals to the neighboring motor nerve-cells.

Not all of the nerve-cells in the tube send axons out to form motor

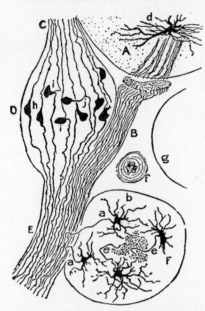

fibres. The axons of many of them, on reaching the marginal layer, simply turn upward or downward within it, while still others pass horizontally around through the marginal zone, and cross in its ventral portion to the other side of the tube. By this contrivance the right and left halves of the tube are connected. These connections are, therefore, called "commissural fibres," and their crossing-place at the mid-ventral line is called the "ventral commissure."

§ 6. The axons thus far described may now be grouped into three classes: (1) the "ventral root axons," which arise from cells in the ventral part of the tube and pass out, as motor fibres, connecting the tube with muscles; (2) the "dorsal root axons," which arise from cells in the spinal ganglia, and by their two axons, connect the tube with sense-organs; and (3) the "central axons," which lie wholly within the tube, and connect one part of it with another (compare Fig. 15).

FIG. 15.—Development of the Nerve-Cells of the Spinal Ganglia. (Cajal.) The drawing is from an embryo chick. *A* is the spinal cord, containing *d*, a motor nerve-cell, from which issues an axon; this with other similar axons emerges from the cord into *B*, the ventral root (the connection between this root and the cord has been accidentally broken in this section). *C* is the dorsal root, consisting of axons which issue from the spinal ganglion *D*. Axons issuing from this ganglion in the opposite direction join those of the ventral root, to form *E*, a spinal nerve. Within the spinal ganglion are seen cells which are still bipolar, *h;* others, *i*, which are becoming transformed into unipolar cells; and others, as *j*, which are already distinctly unipolar. *F* is a sympathetic ganglion, showing cells with axons, *a*, which join the spinal nerve, and others with axons, *e*, which do not join this nerve, but which, as a matter of fact, pass up or down in the "sympathetic chain."

There is still a fourth class of axons to be added. Some of the cells in the neural crest, instead of remaining near the dorsal part of the tube and sending axons into it, migrate in a ventral direction and develop into nerve-cells; but these send out only a single axon, which passes to some of the organs of the interior of the body—the stomach, intestines, pancreas, salivary glands, heart, and blood-vessels—and enters into connection with muscular or glandular tissue

there. Such are the visceral or "sympathetic" nerve-fibres; and
their cell bodies are gathered in the ganglia of the "sympathetic
system," some of which lie in two rows close to the backbone on its
ventral side, while others are scattered among the internal organs.
These axons and their cell bodies, it will be noted, are entirely outside of the neural tube. They do not, however, remain unconnected with it; for certain cells exist in the lateral portions of the
tube, which send out axons through the ventral roots to the sympathetic ganglia.

§ 7. We are now in a position to understand the process by which
the lower part of the neural tube becomes the spinal cord. We have
first the three layers of the wall, the germinal layer next the lumen,
the nerve-cell layer in the middle, and on the outside the marginal
layer, which becomes the axon layer. Later, the axons receive
sheaths of a white "medullary" substance called "myelin"; and
thus the axon layer becomes "white matter"; the white matter of
the cord lies in the marginal layer. The nerve-cell layer, on the
contrary, does not acquire much of this medullary substance, but
retains its light-gray or watery color, and is therefore called the
"gray matter." Thus the gray matter of the cord is surrounded
by white matter. Meanwhile the germinal layer decreases in thickness, since the cells in it divide, one after another, giving rise to
neuroglia and nerve-cells, which migrate outward; in this way the
germinal layer finally becomes reduced to a single thickness of cells
lining the cavity of the tube. The other two layers on the contrary increase greatly in thickness—the cell layer by receiving
new cells from the germinal layer, by growth in size of the cells already present in it, by growth of the dendrites of these cells, and by
the incoming of the terminations of axons into the cell layer. The
axon layer increases by the constant growth of new axons into it
from the adjoining part of the cell layer, and by the elongation of
axons from the marginal layer above and below. The thickening
of the cell and axon layers is not, however, uniform all around the
tube; in particular, the mid-ventral and mid-dorsal portions do not
develop cell layers of much thickness; since their cells migrate
mostly to the right and to the left. At the mid-ventral line, therefore, we find in the developed cord, first, a thin layer of gray matter
next to the central canal, then a thin layer of white, consisting of
fibres crossing from one side of the cord to the other (the ventral
commissure), and then a deep groove or fissure, the "ventral
fissure," which runs lengthwise of the cord between the swollen
walls of the adjacent parts of the tube. In the dorsal mid-line, there
is a thin layer of gray matter, and then a thin sheet of neuroglia,
the "dorsal septum," which has resulted from the narrowing of

the cavity to a slit, and the subsequent growing together of its side walls.

The gray matter is most abundant in the ventral half of the cord, which contains the cell bodies of the motor axons. These bodies are especially numerous at the levels of the shoulders and loins, where the nerves to the arms and legs originate. The dorsal half of the gray matter is thinner in these parts, for the reason that the cell-bodies of the sensory axons, instead of lying within the cord, are in the spinal ganglia outside of the cord. From the ventral half of

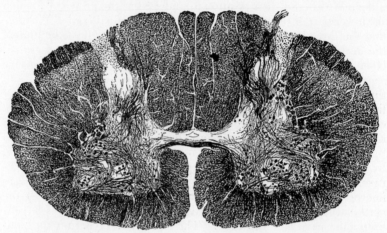

FIG. 16.—Cross Section of a Child's Spinal Cord. (Marburg.) Magnified 8 diameters. The stain employed to bring out the features of the cord has darkened the nerve-fibres and therefore the white matter, and left the gray matter light. The ventral side of the cord lies below in the figure. The cracks, showing white in the figure, are produced in the process of preparing the section, but doubtless represent natural lines of cleavage, determined by the course of neuroglia fibres.

the gray matter emerge the motor roots; and into the dorsal half enter the sensory roots. Thus at these two places, the gray matter approaches nearest the surface of the cord, forming the ventral and dorsal "horns" of the gray matter. Between these horns, and continuous with them, lies a middle or lateral portion of the gray matter. The cells in the lateral portion and in the dorsal horn give rise to central axons, which do not emerge from the cord, but turn upward or downward in the marginal layer. Many central axons come also from the ventral horn (see Fig. 16).

The main principle to be borne in mind in studying the marginal or axon layer—later the white matter of the cord—is that an axon entering it from the gray matter usually turns up or down very promptly, and thus starts its longitudinal course near to the gray matter. As it elongates itself, whether upward or downward, it is crowded outward by axons emerging at the level which it has reached. The further it goes, the more is it crowded toward the outer surface of the cord. There is, however, one striking exception to this general rule. Most of the axons from the "motor area" of the brain, which grow down into the cord late in its development (during the fifth month of foetal life), instead of lying at the very outside of the cord, bore their way through the midst of the lateral strand of white matter. With this and a few other exceptions, the axons which lie near the gray matter are near their cell bodies, while those which lie toward the outside of the cord are far from their place of origin. For this reason, that portion of the white matter which lies next the gray is called the "ground bundle," while the portions further out are composed in large measure of definite groups or "tracts" of axons connecting distant portions of the cord and brain. Many of the axons in the ground bundle never extend far from their cells, but turn back into the gray matter and so connect neighboring levels of the cord. From comparative study of the nervous systems of various orders of animals, it is

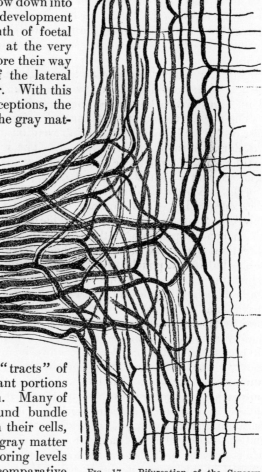

Fig. 17. — Bifurcation of the Sensory Root Fibres, at Their Entrance to the Cord. (Cajal.)

believed that these short axons of the ground bundle represent a primitive and universal system of connections within the nerve-centres; while the long axons of the tracts represent a later and higher development.

The sensory axons entering by the dorsal roots bifurcate into ascending and descending branches, and these, like other axons, entering the marginal layer, lie at first near to their point of entry (compare Fig. 17). As they grow upward (the downward branches remain short) they are subsequently crowded away from the region of the dorsal roots by other similar axons. They therefore turn into the marginal layer on the dorsal side of their roots, i. e., toward the mid-dorsal line; and they become still further crowded toward this line by the fresh fibres entering higher up the cord. In this manner a thick column of sensory axons is formed between the dorsal roots and the mid-dorsal line; and at each level of the cord, those axons which lie nearest the mid-dorsal line have come from farthest down the cord, while those which lie nearest the roots have come from near by.

The dorsal column of white matter is clearly marked off from the rest of the white matter by the intervention of the dorsal roots and the dorsal horn of the gray matter. The remainder of the white matter is less completely divided by the ventral horn and roots into a lateral and a ventral column.

§ 8. The brain is formed from the forward or headward end of the neural tube. In the human embryo of two weeks' growth the tube shows at this end a considerable degree of complication. A sharp bend appears in it, the front end being bent in the ventral direction. In front of this "cephalic flexure" the tube expands somewhat into a pouch or vesicle, and behind into another vesicle which tapers downward into the spinal part of the tube. Just before and behind the flexure are two shallow transverse grooves which mark off a third vesicle between the other two. These three primary brain vesicles, appearing thus early in the individual's life, are constant throughout all the vertebrates, and represent the fundamental divisions of the brain. Already, however, a division of the foremost vesicle by another shallow transverse groove is visible in the human embryo; and a little later a backward bend within the hindmost vesicle makes it convenient to regard this vesicle, also, as subdivided. Thus there are five vesicles out of which the various parts of the brain are developed. They are called, from before backward, the end-brain, the inter-brain, the mid-brain, the hind-brain, and the after-brain or medulla; or, in Greek derivatives, the *telencephalon* ("encephalon" meaning brain), the *diencephalon*, the *mesencephalon*, the *metencephalon*, and the *myelencephalon*.[1] Of these five

---

[1] "Myel" is the Greek derivative equivalent to the Latin "medulla," which means marrow. The spinal cord was called the "spinal marrow," or medulla spinalis; and the enlarged extension of the cord at the base of the cranial cavity was known as the medulla oblongata. Recently, the name "medulla spinalis" has been little used, and "medulla" has come to mean the medulla oblongata. The latter is also, most briefly, designated as the "bulb."

the after-brain develops into the medulla; the hind-brain develops into the pons and cerebellum; the mid-brain consists largely of the corpora quadrigemina, and the inter-brain of the optic thalamus; while the end-brain develops into the cerebrum. The eye, which is embryologically a part of the brain, first appears as a pouch bulging outward at about the junction of the inter-brain and end-brain; its permanent attachment is to the thalamus (compare Fig. 18).

In the lowest part of the medulla the conditions which affect the external form of the parts do not differ essentially from those present in the cord; the walls of the neural tube thicken greatly, leaving a small cavity in the centre. A little further up, however, the dorsal wall, without growing in thickness, increases greatly in width, and lies as a mere skin, containing no nerve-cells, over the expanded cavity, which here is called the "fourth ventricle of the brain."

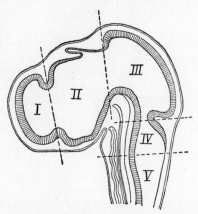

Forward of this, the dorsal wall becomes enormously thickened, forming the cerebellum. Still further forward, in the mid-brain, the dorsal wall maintains a moderate thickness, and swells into two hills on each side, the *corpora quadrigemina*. The cavity of the neural tube here

Fig. 18.—Brain of a Developing Chick. (Mihalkovics.) The numbers indicate: *I*, the end-brain; *II*, the inter-brain; *III*, the mid-brain; *IV*, the hind-brain; *V*, the after-brain or bulb, tapering downward into the cord.

remains small, and forms the "aqueduct" connecting the fourth with the third ventricle. It is in the inter-brain that the aqueduct expands into the third ventricle; and here again the dorsal wall of the tube becomes a broad, thin membrane, folded into the ventricle and carrying blood-vessels with it. As the cerebral hemispheres undergo their enormous growth, the cavity expands with them, and remains connected with the third ventricle by two small openings, the foramina of Munro. Within the hemispheres, the cavities are known as the lateral ventricles; in the numbering they count as the first and second. Thus, in spite of all its bendings and thickenings, *the neural tube remains a tube*, and its lumen is continuous from the lateral ventricles, through the foramina of Munro, the third ventricle, the aqueduct, and the fourth ventricle, with the central canal of the cord. This cavity is filled with a lymph known as the cerebro-spinal fluid.

§ 9. In the end-brain of the two-weeks-old embryo, certain parts can be distinguished which retain their identity throughout the later development (compare Fig. 19). The ventral wall, on each side of the middle line, shows a slight swelling, which becomes pronounced at the age of four weeks, and later grows forward and is entered

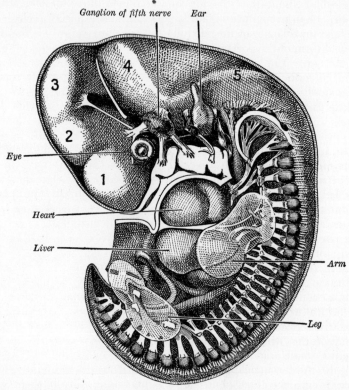

Ganglion of fifth nerve   Ear

Eye

Heart

Liver

Arm

Leg

Fig. 19.—Human Embryo of About Four Weeks. (Streeter.) 1, 2, 3, 4, 5, the brain vesicles; continuous with 5, the spinal cord can be followed down, close beneath the ectoderm, to the posterior extremity. The spinal ganglia show as round, dark masses, connected by (light) rootlets with the cord, and on the other side connected with the nerves, which also show light. The rudiments of arm and leg show as transparent masses, and a group of nerves can be seen entering each.

by axons of cells lying in the upper part of the nasal cavity. This is the olfactory lobe. Its forward end swells into the olfactory bulb, which receives the axons from the nose and contains nerve-cells whose axons in turn pass back through the hinder part of the lobe (the olfactory tract) to other parts of the brain. Just lateral to the ventral portion of the end-brain out of which the olfactory lobe is formed, there appears, at four weeks, a shallow furrow, which indicates the future position of the mass of gray matter in the base of the hemispheres known as the corpus striatum. The dorsal half of the end-brain shows, even at two weeks, a slight swelling, which grows rapidly. This is called the "brain-mantle," or "pallium," and it gives rise to the great bulk of the cerebral hemispheres. The pallium is the part of the nervous system whose complex development characterizes the higher mammals, and especially man.

In comprehending the general shape of the cerebral hemispheres, there is one fact of prime importance. The great increase in size of this part of the neural tube does not proceed by further extension of its length, from its end forward. The middle of the forward end does not itself grow, but remains as a fixed limit, or so-called "lamina terminalis," which is a membrane without nervous functions. The growth of the end-brain may, therefore, be described as primarily lateral; and then, within each lateral half, forward, backward, and upward, as well as to the side. One result of this method of growth is the division of the swelling pallium into right and left hemispheres—a division which appears very early in the growth of the embryo. Accompanying this is the enlargement of the cavity which forms the lateral ventricles, and which extends forward and backward within each hemisphere. The backward growth of the hemispheres causes them to overlap the thalamus and mid-brain, and finally, in the human species, the cerebellum as well. The corpora striata grow forward and backward with the pallium, and overlap the thalamus so as to appear, in the adult brain, rather to the side of the thalamus than in front of it. A vertical or "frontal" section through the midst of the brain shows, at the exterior surface, the cortex; next this the white matter of the hemispheres; then the corpus striatum; and in the centre the thalamus.

§ 10. As the hemispheres grow forward, backward, and upward from their place of attachment to the inter-brain, each of them comes to present a two-lobed appearance, somewhat like that of a bean, the notch corresponding to the point of attachment. The front and rear lobes grow at first downward, and then toward each other, making the notch deeper; the wall above the notch grows out and overhangs it. Thus is formed a fissure, the "fissure of Sylvius," the first and principal landmark on the lateral surface of the hemisphere. The part in front of this fissure is the frontal lobe, and that behind and below it is the temporal lobe. The surface within the fissure, which is considerable, is clearly visible at the fourth month of fœtal life, but becomes partly concealed at the seventh month, by the overgrowth of the frontal and temporal lobes; in the fully developed brain it is wholly concealed, and from its secluded position is called the "island." Both the Sylvian fissure and the longitudinal fissure which separates the hemispheres are visible during the second month; in the succeeding months many other fissures appear, till the surface becomes thickly seamed with them.

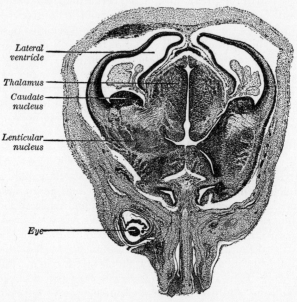

Lateral ventricle

Thalamus

Caudate nucleus

Lenticular nucleus

Eye

FIG. 20.—Frontal Section of the Fore-brain of an Eleven Weeks' Embryo. (His.) The skull as well as the brain is shown, and, on the left side of the figure, the eye. Gray matter appears dark, and white matter light; the skull also appears light, and the ventricular spaces, or cavity of the neural tube, appear white. There is also a clear space between the skull and the brain. The two largest and nearly equal spaces are the lateral ventricles; each is surrounded by the pallium, except below, where it is bounded by the dark rounded mass of the caudate nucleus, a part of the striatum. On the left side of the figure, the caudate nucleus is wholly separated by a white mass of fibres from another, less dark nucleus, the lenticular, which also is part of the striatum. The mass of fibres separating these two parts of the striatum is the internal capsule, and the fibres connect the pallium with the thalamus. The thalamus appears as two nearly semicircular masses of gray matter, separated by a median cleft, which is the third ventricle, part of the cavity of the tube. On the right side, thalamus and striatum are not yet joined by the crossing fibres. The pallium is thickest at its junction with the striatum; it shows three layers, the germinal layer (dark) next the lateral ventricle, a light fibre-layer next, and on the outside another dark layer of cells, the cortex. The lowermost part of the brain, in the figure, is olfactory. Into each lateral ventricle extends a membrane, which is a part of the wall of the tube doubled inward and carrying blood-vessels.

The development of neuroglia, nerve-cells, and axons in the brain proceeds in essentially the same manner as in the cord. The germinal cells, which by division give birth to cells destined to grow into neuroglia and nerve-cells, in the brain as in the cord, lie next to the cavity of the neural tube. The primitive neuroglia framework is first formed; after which the cells that migrate from the germinal layer into the middle or cell layer begin to take on the characteristics of nerve-cells. Thus there appear in the developing cortex of the cerebrum the same three layers as in the cord: the germinal layer inside, then the nerve-cell layer, and, outermost, the marginal layer. But there is one marked difference between the cord and the cortex. The axons of the nerve-cells, instead of issuing from the cell layer into the marginal layer, go from their cells in the opposite direction, toward the germinal layer. Before reaching this, they turn to the side; and so form a layer of axons between the cell layer and the inner cavity or ventricle. Thus it is that the white matter of the hemispheres lies inside the gray, instead of outside as in the cord. From its position on the outside, the gray matter of the hemispheres has been named the "bark" or "cortex." The first nerve-fibres to appear in the white matter of the cerebrum do not arise from the cortex, but come into the hemispheres from below. They arise from cells in

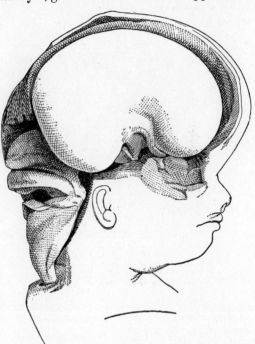

FIG. 21.—Brain of an Embryo of About Three Months. (His.) Inter-brain and mid-brain are already concealed by the pallium; the cerebellum and bulb are shown; also, through the fissure of Sylvius, some of the olfactory region can be seen.

the thalamus, and break through the corpus striatum, dividing its gray matter into two principal masses, and forming the "internal capsule" between them. From here they pass into the adjoining wall of the hemisphere, and run along in it, between the germinal and nerve-cell layers. The axons from the thalamus are sensory: they come from groups of nerve-cells, which are connected with the nervous apparatus of sight, hearing, and touch; and they terminate in areas of the cortex which come thus to be chiefly concerned with the corresponding senses.

§ 11. The cortex develops late in comparison with other parts of the nervous system. Nerve-cells begin to appear here at about the beginning of the third month of fœtal life, or more than a month later than in the cord (compare Fig. 20). The appearance of the axons and dendrites of the cortical cells is also late, and indeed the cortex is by no means fully developed at birth. The specialization of the pallial wall into a nervous structure, with gray cortex and underlying white matter, begins at a definite part of the wall; namely, where it joins the corpus striatum, or at the junction of the pallial

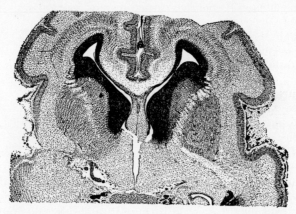

FIG. 22.—Frontal Section of the Brain at the End of the Fourth Month. (His.) The callosum appears clearly. At each side of the figure a depression in the wall of the hemisphere indicates the fissure of Sylvius.

outgrowth with the main stem of the neural tube. From here, the development of a cortex spreads up over the lateral surface, and finally over the top down into the median fissure between the hemispheres. Near the bottom of this fissure the cortex ends, leaving a narrow strip of the wall free from the usual covering of gray matter. The exposed strip of white matter of the right hemisphere is in close proximity to that of the left, and at a later stage the two strips grow together in the central portion of their extent, and thus the white matter of the two hemispheres becomes continuous. Axons, in vast numbers, here cross over from one hemisphere to the other, bringing the two into functional connection. This bridge between the hemispheres is the *corpus callosum* (see Fig. 22).

§ 12. In the cerebellum, the process of inner growth is essentially the same as in the cerebrum. Here, too, the axons of the cells which have reached the nerve-cell layer pass inward, and not toward the marginal layer, so that the gray matter lies on the surface and the white matter inside. Possibly the axons take the inner course because, in outgrowths of the tube such as the cerebrum and cerebellum, this is the shortest path to the fundamental centres of the tube proper. The external location of the gray matter, further, favors the spreading out of its great mass into a thin layer readily accessible at all points to axons coming from without. In the cerebellum also, as in the cerebrum, there are, besides the cortex, other collections of nerve-cells lying in the basal part near to its attachment. The cerebellum resembles the cerebrum also in its late development; in man its nervous structures are far from complete at birth.

§ 13. The brain-stem cannot be properly understood without reference to the nerves which issue from it. These are called the cranial nerves, and there are twelve of them on each side, designated by numbers and also by names more or less expressive of their distribution and function. The list comprises:

I. The olfactory.

II. The optic.

III. The oculomotor. This is the principal motor nerve to the eye; it innervates the muscle of accommodation, and also four of the six muscles which move the eyeball.

IV. The trochlear. This is the motor nerve to the "trochlear" or superior oblique muscle of the eyeball.

V. The trigeminal, so called because it promptly splits into three branches, which, between them, supply the skin of the face, and the sensitive surfaces of the eyeball, nose, and front of the mouth, with sensory axons. The fifth pair is thus the nerve of "touch" for the whole face. It also contains motor axons in smaller quantity; these innervate the muscles of mastication.

VI. The abducens, the motor nerve to the external rectus muscle of the eyeball, which rolls the eye to the side.

VII. The facial. This is the main motor nerve of the face, and controls the muscles of facial expression. It also includes a small and distinct bundle of sensory fibres, which come from the taste-buds of the front portion of the tongue.

VIII. The auditory. This again consists of two distinct portions, both sensory, one of which is connected with the cochlea of the inner ear, the organ of hearing, and the other with the remainder of the inner ear, which apparently has to do, not with hearing, but with sensations of movement and posture.

IX. The glosso-pharyngeal, or sensory nerve to the back of the tongue and to the throat, including the taste-buds in this region.

X. The so-called vagus, in allusion to its wide or wandering distribution. It contains both sensory and motor fibres between the central organs and the larynx, windpipe, lungs, gullet, stomach, pancreas, upper part of intestine, and heart. The outgoing fibres to the heart can be called "motor" only in a loose sense, since their action is confined to the slowing or stoppage of the heart-beat.

XI. The spinal accessory, a motor nerve to some of the muscles at the back of the neck which participate in head movements.

XII.   The hypoglossal, the motor nerve of the tongue.

Of these twelve pairs of nerves the first consists of axons arising from cells in the olfactory mucous membrane of the upper part of the nose, these cells being the peripheral organs of smell, and being derived from the ectoderm.   They thus represent a primitive condition of the sensory nerves (compare p. 26), in which the sensitive cells located in the periphery have sent axons to the centre, instead of being supplied by axons growing out from the centre or from ganglia located near the centre.   The axons of the olfactory nerve enter the brain at the olfactory bulb, as previously described.

§ 14. The optic nerve also is peculiar in its origin, but in a different way.   Both this nerve and the retina of the eye arise as an outgrowth of the neural tube; they are, therefore, properly to be reckoned as a part of the brain.   Besides the rods and cones, which are specialized nerve-cells sensitive to light, the retina contains many nerve-cells similar to those found in the nervous centres; and some of these send their axons back through the optic nerve.   The nerves from the right and left eyes meet at the base of the brain in the optic "chiasm" or crossing.   Here many of the axons cross to the other half of the body; and after crossing, the nerves proceed and enter the thalamus.

The nerve of the inner ear is somewhat peculiar in its mode of development, in that its ganglion lies within the ear itself; and besides, the cells in this ganglion retain their "bipolar" form.

The remaining cranial nerves develop in the same manner as the spinal nerves.   Their sensory axons arise from ganglia, analogous to the spinal ganglia, which lie on the roots of the nerves; and their motor axons grow out from cells in the tube.

§ 15. The process of development, as well as the final structure, of the brain-stem is highly complicated, and it will be sufficient for our purposes to mention one general principle which is of considerable aid in understanding the whole matter.   We make a distinction between the more and the less primitive structures contained in any part.   The more primitive include (1) the nerves entering or leaving the part, (2) the groups of cells connected with these nerves, and (3) the fibres which link together these groups of cells.   These, taken together, form the local mechanism of the part.   Less primitive, in relation to any particular region, are fibres which grow into it from other parts of the neural tube, and also any cells developed locally but having connection with fibres from other parts. Now since the local mechanisms of any part develop in advance of the less primitive structures, these accordingly grow over the primitive structures, here as in the spinal cord. Thus the order of development helps toward an understanding of the position of the numerous structures which are found within the brain-stem. All along the neural tube, it is the ventral side which develops first; and accordingly we find, in the adult condition of the brain-stem, that the most primitive structures lie on the ventral side of the ventricles, and close to them. In the bulb, as was previously said, the dorsal side of the neural tube merely expands into a membrane. The lateral wall of the tube, however, gives rise to many nerve-cells, and these, developing later than the ventral portion, are less primitive and more related to distant parts of the system. Many of these lateral cells migrate in a ventral direction, and settle in positions ventral to the original ventral cells; and the fibres which in immense numbers grow into the bulb from above and below, pass on either the ventral or the lateral side of the primitive structures. Thus it finally comes about that the bulb contains, close beneath the ventricle, a rather small central mass devoted to the local mechanisms, and giving rise to the local nerves; while enclosing this mass on the sides and below is the large mass of cells and fibres which are less local in character. The development of the pons and mid-brain proceeds along the same lines as that of the bulb, except that in the mid-brain there is an important development of the dorsal wall of the tube, which gives rise to the corpora quadrigemina.

§ 16. The factors in the growth of the nervous system, as thus far mentioned and applied, are (1) the production of young nerve-cells from the germinal cells at the lumen of the tube; (2) the migration of these young nerve-cells away from the lumen; and (3) the outgrowth and prolongation of the axon. The first of these factors is only temporary in its action; the reproductive activity in the germinal layer comes to an end at different times in different parts of the brain and cord, but in the cortex of the cerebrum, where it starts latest and is longest continued, it ceases during the fourth month of foetal life. It is probable that all the nerve-cells which will finally belong to the individual adult are formed at this early period in embryonic development. The migration of young nerve-cells is also in the main a temporary phenomenon. The lengthening of the axon, on the contrary, is continued for a long time, and the growth of the dendrites of the cell is also a slow and long-continued process. Many of the young nerve-cells remain throughout foetal life and even much longer in an undeveloped state. Many of them never develop. It appears that undeveloped nerve-cells in the cortex can be made to grow by stimuli affecting the region where they lie and arousing neighboring cells to activity—in other words, by experience and education. For example, Donaldson,[1] on examining the brain of Laura Bridgman, who became blind and deaf when a baby of less than two years, found those parts of the cortex which are normally connected with the eye and ear to be under-developed, and to contain an unusual number of undeveloped nerve-cells. The growth of the gray matter, after the production of new nerve-cells has ceased, results from the growth of the cells and especially of their dendrites; from the coming-in of axons from the white matter to branch and terminate in the gray matter; and from the continued growth of the neuroglia framework.

The increase of the white matter in the nervous system is due in part to the lengthening of axons and the advent of new axons from the developing cells in the gray. It is also partly due to a growth in thickness of the individual axons. But it is very largely due to another factor which has barely been mentioned thus far. The axon becomes invested with a sheath of "myelin," a mixture of fat-like substances; and the volume of this sheath, at first small, increases gradually till it often becomes much greater than the volume of the axon which it invests. Whether this myelin is secreted by the axon, or by neuroglia cells, is not yet determined. The myelinization of an axon does not occur as soon as the axon has made its appearance, but there is often a considerable interval during which the axon remains without any sheath. In general, those bundles of axons which develop early also acquire myelin early, and those bundles which appear late become myelinated late. Thus, for example, the ventral and dorsal root axons and the short axons of the ground bundle become myelinated early; while the latest of all, in the spinal cord, are the long descending axons which come from cells in the cerebral cortex. Within the cerebrum, the first axons to appear are those from the thalamus, and these also, after an interval of several months, are the first to become myelinated. The inward-growing or sensory axons of the cerebrum develop before the outward-growing or motor; and these in turn before the numerous "association" axons which extend from one part of the cortex to another.

§ 17. The function of the myelin sheath, to which we shall return in a later chapter, is not definitely known; but it seems reasonable to suppose that it has some function, and that therefore the axon itself does not become fully functional till it has become envel-

[1] *American Journal of Psychology*, 1890, III, 293. *Growth of the Brain*, 1898, p. 240.

oped by its sheath. It was an easy inference that a given bundle of axons, and the connected portions of gray matter, did not become functional at all till these axons were myelinated; and on this basis it seemed possible to assert (so Flechsig[1]) that, within the cortex, the sensory portions first became functional, then the motor, and later still the remaining and presumably more intellectual parts. It has, however, been shown by Watson[2] that in the white rat, co-ordinated reflex action, requiring the use of both sensory and motor axons and also their central connections, occurs promptly at birth, though no myelinization whatever has so far taken place; and further that the rat is capable of forming and retaining definite associations at an age when its cortex, which is in all probability concerned in such learning, is entirely unprovided with myelinated connections. The case of the rat, therefore, seems conclusive against the view that orderly function is impossible before the advent of myeliniza-tion. On the other hand, von Bechterew reports[3] that sharply localized response to electrical stimulation of small portions of the nerve-centres occurs only after myelinization has set in; and Held[4] found that opening one eye of a new-born animal whose eyes do not naturally open for some time after birth causes the central connections of this eye to become myelinated earlier than those of the other eye. We may, perhaps, conclude that, in some cases at least, function is possible without myelin; but that actual function-ing stimulates the deposition of the myelin, which in turn in some way assists function. There is also evidence to show, in the case of the human species, that control of the muscular system which we call "voluntary" requires to make use of myelinated nerve-tracts.

§ 18. The weight of the human brain at birth averages about 380 grams, or 13 ounces. This is about one-eighth of the weight of the entire body. During childhood and youth, other organs rapidly outstrip the brain, so that at maturity the brain weighs but one-fiftieth of the entire body. The spinal cord at birth weighs one one-hundredth as much as the brain, and at maturity one-fiftieth. In other words, the growth of the brain is carried further in fœtal life than the growth of the other organs. This is true as re-gards size, but not, perhaps, as regards the minute details of struct-ure which count for so much in the functions of the nerve-centres.

[1] Flechsig, Gehirn und Seele, 1896.
[2] J. B. Watson, Animal Education, 1903, pp. 115 ff.
[3] W. v. Bechterew, Die Leitungsbahnen im Gehirn und Rückenmark, 1899, p. 104.
[4] Cited from Edinger, Vorlesungen über den Bau der nervösen Zentralorgane, 1904, p. 32.

The increase of the brain's weight occurs mostly in childhood, as is seen from the following figures:

At birth,	the weight of the brain averages . . .	380 grams
At one year,	" " " " " " . . .	945 "
At two years,	" " " " " " . . .	1,025 "
At three years,	" " " " " " . . .	1,100 "
At four years,	" " " " " " . . .	1,300 "

After the age of four, the human brain continues to increase more slowly, reaching 1,400 grams at from eight to ten years; after which it gains in weight scarcely at all. According to some series of measurements, however, the maximum weight is reached at fifteen, after which age a very gradual decrease sets in. There is no doubt that there is uniformly some decrease after the age of fifty-five; and in old age, there is often a marked shrinking in its weight. The above figures apply to the brain of males. In the female, the weight at birth is nearly the same as in the male; the increase during childhood is somewhat less, and the adult weight averages about 150 grams less than for the male. In proportion to the total weight of the body, however, the female brain is as heavy as that of the male; or it may be slightly heavier. Brain-weight also depends to some extent on stature; distinctly tall individuals averaging about 2 per cent. more than distinctly short individuals.

It should be noted, however, that the figures quoted above are gross averages, and that there is much variation. The extreme range, if idiots are excluded, is from 1,000 to perhaps 1,900 grams; 90 per cent. of males lying between the limits 1,200 and 1,600 grams, and 60 per cent. between 1,300 and 1,500. Most of the individuals whose brains have been weighed on autopsy, and have thus formed the basis for scientific study,[1] have been inmates of workhouses and similar public institutions; they therefore represent the poorer and less successful portion of the population. There is some evidence that the more prosperous and successful portion have, on the average, somewhat heavier brains, and that the growth of their brains is longer continued. This evidence is derived from the post-mortem weight of the brains, sometimes of men who were so eminent for mental ability that the examination was desired in the interests of science, and sometimes of men who realized the

---

[1] The figures given have been taken from Donaldson, who, in his work on *The Growth of the Brain*, 1898, has brought together the results of the most reliable series of measurements by various authorities, and subjected them to careful analysis. The brain-weights given for the ages from six to sixteen are derived from the measurement of so few individuals that it has not seemed worth while to attempt to trace the full curve of growth. The main outlines, however, as given in the text seem fairly reliable.

value to science of such an examination, and therefore directed
that their brains should be made available for study. As a result,
there are now on record the brain-weights of about one hundred
men of more or less eminence. The average of these is about
1,470 grams, which is two to four per cent. above the average of
workhouse inmates. They range from 1,200 to 2,000 grams,
overlapping the range of ordinary men to such an extent that it
would clearly be impossible to draw any conclusion, from the mental
achievements of an individual, as to his brain-weight, or *vice versa*.
A few well-known names may be cited from the list:[1]

Cuvier, naturalist	1830 grams
Thackeray, novelist	1658 "
Siemens, physicist	1600 "
Daniel Webster, statesman	1518 "
Chalmers, theologian	1503 "
Agassiz, naturalist	1495 "
De Morgan, mathematician	1494 "
Gauss, mathematician	1492 "
Broca, anthropologist	1484 "
Grote, historian	1410 "
Bertillon, anthropologist	1398 "
Liebig, chemist	1352 "

The average of this group of certainly eminent minds is above
that of the whole number of more or less eminent men. But the
correlation between eminence and brain-weight is, at the best, far
from close.

§ 19. The question of decrease of brain-weight with advanced age
can be examined in the light of the evidence from the lists of "eminent" men, who may be taken as at least representing the more
intellectual part of the population. As few young men are included
in the lists, it will be necessary to group all not older than fifty-five
together.   The averages for the different ages come out as follows:

No. of Individuals	Ages	Av. Brain-Weight
32	25–55	1482
33	56–65	1492
24	66–75	1448
15	76–89	1389

In view of the wide variation of the individual cases, so small a
difference as that between the first and second age-groups must not

[1] These data are quoted from E. A. Spitzka, "A Study of the Brains of Six
Eminent Scientists," etc., in *Transactions of the American Philosophical Society*,
Philadelphia, 1907.   In this paper he has brought together all previous records
of the brain-weight of eminent men.

be taken to mean that the brain-weight of this class of men increases beyond the age of fifty-five; it is conceivable that it should do so, but the data are not sufficient to show it. There is, however, some indication that the brain-weight does not start to decrease much before sixty-five. The measurements of the less favored and in-tellectual classes show[1] a loss of about 50 grams from the age of fifty-five to that of sixty-five, and an equal loss in the succeeding decade of life. It is probable, therefore, that the brain reaches a greater size in the more intellectual classes, and maintains its weight longer. The differences in size are, however, too small to serve as a measure of the differences between men in intellectual ability. We must conceive the growth of the brain which takes place after the age of eight to consist for the most part in the development of very minute structures, such as the dendrites and the fine terminations of axons. These structures are individually so small that a vast increase in their number would make but a small impression on the total weight of the brain.

§ 20. *It is the cerebrum which we should expect to show most de-velopment after early childhood, because it is probably this part of the nervous system which is chiefly concerned with learning, educa-tion, and all individual acquisitions.* More definitely, the develop-ment to be expected would occur in the cortex, and in the axons connecting its various parts. That such development does take place is not merely to be expected; but it seems to be demonstrated by microscopical study. Already mentioned are the observations tending to show an increase in the number of developed nerve-cells (with their dendrites) as the result of use. There are other obser-vations showing an increase of the myelinated axons and branches of axons traversing the cortex. The axons which enter the cortex from the white matter below are found to penetrate further and further into the cortex, or at least to become myelinated further and further, as the individual advances toward maturity. Axons and their collaterals which traverse the cortex in directions parallel to its surface, both in the outer or marginal layer and in two or more layers in the midst of the nerve-cells, also increase greatly in myeliniz-ation as late as the thirtieth year of life, and probably later still. This growth in complexity of organization of the cortex appears sufficient, so far as the evidence goes, to be paralleled with the increasing com-plexity of mental capabilities which occurs during early life.[2]

---

[1] See Donaldson, *The Growth of the Brain*, 1898, p. 325.

[2] See Watson, op. cit., p. 103; Kaes, *Archiv für Psychiatrie und Nervenkrank-heiten*, 1894, XXV, p. 695; Donaldson, *Growth of the Brain*, 1898, p. 241; Edinger, *Vorlesungen über den Bau der nervösen Zentralorgane*, 7th ed., 1904, vol. I, p. 335

CHAPTER III

GROSS STRUCTURE OF THE NERVOUS SYSTEM [1]

§ 1. Regarded as isolated, and as possessed only of those properties which belong to all living matter of the peculiar chemical constitution and structural form which are described by the word "nervous," the nerve-fibres and nerve-cells are of great interest to physiological and psycho-physical researches. But in their normal position and activity they are always combined into organs, which are then arranged in a symmetrical whole. Thus combined they are dependent upon each other for the parts which they play in the entire system. The condition and function of each element are thus determined by the condition and function of the rest. One part of this system excites another, or modifies the excitation received from another. We are, therefore, unable to isolate perfectly any one of these elements, and so study its normal functions apart. It is, indeed, possible to dissect out a nerve with a muscle attached, to keep it alive for a time, and thus to inquire what an isolated nerve will do. In this way many of the most important discoveries in the general physiology of the nerves have been made. But every nerve is itself a compound of nervous elements which have been placed for purposes of experiment under abnormal conditions. The action of the nerve-cells, even when gathered into small masses called ganglia, is not easily open to direct inspection. Moreover, when different tracts of nerves, or different regions in the central organs where ganglion-cells abound, are partially isolated by being laid bare for the direct application of stimulus, just so far as they are separated from the system they are in abnormal condition and show abnormal results; and just so far as they are normal in condition and function they are still connected with the system. It is the mutual condition and reciprocal action of the elements, when combined into this totality, which constitute the nervous mechanism. To describe in brief outline the gross structure of this mechanism is the purpose of this chapter.

[1] Among the very numerous and excellent treatments of the anatomy of the nervous centres, reference may be made to Edinger, *Vorlesungen über den Bau der nervösen Zentralorgane*, 7th ed., Leipzig, 1904; Schäfer and Symington, "Neurology," in Quain's *Anatomy*, 11th ed., London, 1909; O. S. Strong, in Bailey's *Textbook of Histology*, New York, 1910.

§ 2. It will be of great service toward understanding such a description if it is begun under the guidance of some appropriate idea. Nerve-fibres and nerve-cells exist in enormous numbers within the human nervous system, and are combined in different proportions to make the different organs of this system. The significance of the combination appears only in the light of reflection upon the amount and kind of work which is to be done. The most general office of the nervous mechanism may be said to be that of "concatenating" all the functions of the living body in accordance with the complex internal and external conditions to which it is subject. But in the case of any of the higher animals, and especially in the case of man, this one office requires the doing of a quantity and variety of work that are proportionate to the complexity of these conditions. How shall such a quantity and variety of work be done? The actual arrangement of the elements of this system, in the exercise of their reciprocally conditioned activities, is the solution of the problem. As in all very complex questions of this sort, so this particular problem is solved by a wise division of labor.

The manner in which the human nervous mechanism is developed as a response to the before-mentioned problem has already been made clear in its general outlines, especially as applied to the lower forms of animal life. Even the simple protoplasmic speck called an amœba may be considered as a living molecular mechanism. Minute and almost structureless as it appears, the amœba is really composed of a great number of molecules that are undergoing constant change; and, as we have seen, it is capable of exercising several wonderful functions that do not belong to any non-living collection of molecules. Most important for our present purpose is the fact that the amœba is irritable and automatic. With these properties the molecular mechanism of this small bit of protoplasm, under the stimulus of changes in the pressure and temperature of its medium, and in accordance with the unknown laws of its internal self-originating changes, solves the problem of constant readjustment which its environment presents to it.

§ 3. Let it be supposed that the same problem becomes more complicated, and the animal structure which is to solve it correspondingly complex. The metabolic function of the animal may then be assigned to a separate system of structures; and the closely related secretory and excretory functions as well. The reproductive function may then also acquire its own peculiar organs. The muscles perform movements in masses because they retain in an eminent degree the "amœboid" contractility. But the property of being irritable and automatic becomes the special endowment of the nervous system. All these different systems, in order that they may be moved in united masses, are then adjusted to a mechanical framework (of indifferent value so far as really vital changes are concerned) of cartilage, bone, etc.

But the eminently irritable and automatic system of molecules called nervous must also undergo a further differentiation of function. In the structureless protoplasm of the amœba, the external molecules are, of course, the ones primarily to be affected by the external stimuli. It is with the internal molecules, on the other hand, that the changes called "automatic" begin. But the continual flux of its protoplasmic substance indicates that, in its simplest form, any of the molecules of the animalcule may in turn act either as irritable or as automatic. The primary differentiation of this substance by the so-called "surface of separation" (see p. 14) points, however, to a division of labor.

We have already seen that, in the somewhat higher forms of animal life, we come upon an increased differentiation of parts into "receptors," "conductors," and "effectors" (see p. 16), and a corresponding further division of labor. When a somewhat complicated nervous mechanism appears in the ascending scale of animal development, the idea which lies at the base of this rudimentary differentiation of the system calls for these three kinds of nervous substance: (1) superficial cells susceptible to external stimuli; (2) central and eminently automatic cells, also susceptible to internal stimuli; (3) a strand of irritable protoplasm connecting the two. In order that the more highly organized animal may exercise "a will of its own," certain of its muscle-fibres must be placed under the control of the central and automatic cells. In order, also, that the entire muscular system may feel the reflex influence of external stimuli, and so, by co-ordinated contractions, adapt the organs of the body to the changes of its environment, the muscle-fibres must be indirectly connected with such superficial cells as are sensitive to these stimuli. The nervous system, therefore, in its most fundamental form consists of these three sets of contrivances with their respective functions: (A) sensitive cells upon the surface of the body; (B) central cells that are both automatic and modifiers and distributers of sensory impulses; (C) connecting tracts, or strands, that can convey the nervous impulses either centripetally from A to B, or centrifugally from B to the contractile muscular tissues of the body.

Higher developments of this triple-formed fundamental type of a nervous system are reached by further differentiations of A, B, and C. If various kinds of stimuli are to act upon this system, then the sensitive cells upon the surface (A) must be modified into various external organs of sense. The terminations of the centrifugal

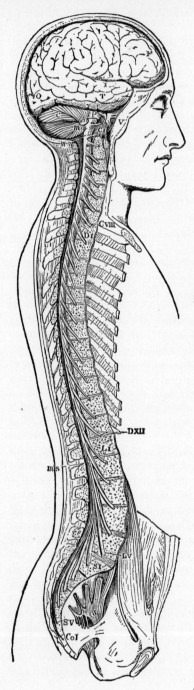

FIG. 23.—View of the Cerebro-spinal Axis. (After Bourgery.) ⅓. The right half of the cranium and trunk has been removed, and the roots of the spinal nerves dissected out and laid on their several vertebræ. *F, T, O,* cerebrum; *C,* cerebellum; *P,* pons Varolii; *mo,* medulla oblongata; *m s, m s,* upper and lower extremities of the spinal marrow. *CI* to *CVIII* are cervical nerves; *DI* to *DXII,* dorsal; *LI* to *LV,* lumbar; *SI* to *SV,* sacral; *CoI,* coccygeal.

or motor nervous strands may also be variously modified so as to connect with and control the contractile tissue of many sets of muscles. The central cells may be variously grouped and arranged, with functions more or less localized, so as to receive, modify, and distribute, in manifold ways, the different sensory impulses. Other such central cells may become more particularly related to the phenomena of conscious sensation and volition.

Such a highly developed nervous system will then consist of the following parts: (A) End-organs of Sense, like the skin, the eye, and the ear; (A^1) End-organs of Motion, like the so-called motor end-plates; (B) Central Organs, like the various peripheral and sporadic ganglia, the spinal cord, and brain, in which may come to exist (b) certain portions more distinctively automatic, (b^1) certain others more concerned in receiving and distributing reflexly the sensory impulses, and (b^{11}) still others more particularly connected with the phenomena of consciousness; and (C) Conducting Nerves, which will be either (c) centripetal, afferent, and sensory, or (c^1) centrifugal, efferent, and motor, designed to connect the central organs and the end-organs.

§ 4. The nerves and ganglionic masses of nervous matter in the human body are arranged in two great systems, the Sympathetic and the Cerebro-spinal. The Sympathetic Nervous System consists of a pair of nervous cords, situated one on each side of the spinal column; of three main plexuses, situated in the cavities of the thorax and abdomen; of a great number of smaller ganglia, lying in relation to the viscera of the same cavities, and widely distributed over the body, especially in connection with the vascular system; and of a great multitude of fine distributory nerves. Each of the two cords comprises a number of ganglia united by intermediate nerves. In the other regions of the spinal column the number of these ganglia equals that of the vertebræ (sacral 5, lumbar 5, thoracic or dorsal 12), but in the neck (cervical) there are only 3. From this gangliated cord a communicating and a distributory series of nerve-branches are derived. By the communicating branches the two systems are brought into close anatomical and physiological relation, and a kind of double interchange takes place between them. The distributory branches of nerves in the sympathetic system bring the gangliated cord into connection with the blood-vessels and viscera of the body. The involuntary muscles in the coats of these vessels and in the walls of the viscera are thus related, and through the sympathetic fibres brought into connection with the cerebro-spinal axis. The three main plexuses referred to are collections of nerve-cells and a dense plexiform arrangement of nerve-fibres. One of them is situated at the base of the heart, to which it gives off branches that wind around that organ and penetrate its muscular substance; another is placed at the upper part of the abdominal cavity, and gives origin to numerous plexiform branches that supply the viscera of the abdomen; the third is in front of the last lumbar vertebra, and supplies the vaso-motor nerves and nerves of the muscular coats and mucous membranes of the various organs in that region of the body. Further details in the anatomy of the sympathetic nervous system are of little interest to psycho-physical studies. To such studies it is

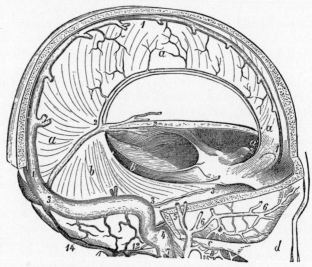

Fig. 24.—The Cranium Opened to Show the Falx Cerebri and Tentorium Cerebelli, and the Places of Exit for the Cranial Blood-vessels. (Schwalbe.) *a, a,* Falx; *b, b,* the tentorium; 3, 3, Sinus transversus, and 2 to 3, Sinus rectus, receiving from in front the Vena magna Galena; 4, internal jugular vein; 5, superficial temporal vein; and 6, middle temporal vein.

of great interest, however, to know that this system forms a bond between the sensations, emotions, and ideas which have their physical basis in the molecular condition of the cerebro-spinal centres, and those various organs in the thoracic and abdominal regions whose condition is so closely related to such psychical states.

§ 5. The Brain and Spinal Cord are the great centres of the cerebro-spinal system. These bodies are situated in the bony cavity of the skull and spinal column. They have three Coverings or Membranes, the innermost one of which is directly united with the surface of the nervous substance, and sends numerous processes into

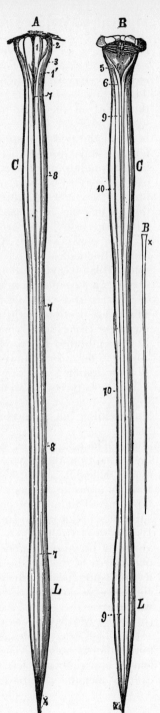

Fig. 25.—*A*, Ventral, and *B*, Dorsal, View of the Spinal Cord and Medulla Oblongata. *B*¹ the Filum terminale, which has been cut off from *A* and *B*. 1, Pyramids of the medulla, and 1¹, their decussation; 2, olives; 3, lateral strands of the medulla; 4¹, calamus scriptorius; 5, the funiculus gracilis; and 6, the funiculus cuneatus; 7, the ventral and 9, the dorsal, fissures; 8, the ventro-lateral impression; 10, dorso-lateral groove. *C*, the cervical, and *L*, the lumbar, enlargements of the cord.

69

its interior. (1) The *Dura Mater,* which is the membrane lying next to the wall of the bony cavity, is tough, white, fibrous, and of structure somewhat different in the cranial from the spinal cavity. Three processes of the dura mater divide—only incompletely—the cavity of the skull into two symmetrical halves and into an upper and lower space: (*a*) the *falx cerebri,* a sickle-shaped process between the two hemispheres of the large brain; (*b*) the *falx cere-belli,* a similar process between the two lateral lobes of the cerebellum, or small brain; and (*c*) the *tentorium cerebelli,* an arched process over the cerebellum separating it from the back portions of the large brain. The membrane lying next inward is called (2) *Arachnoid;* this membrane is transparent and of delicate connective tissue. The space below this surface is called *subarachnoid;* the subarachnoid or cerebro-spinal fluid, which fills the intercommunicating compartments into which this space is divided by bundles of delicate areolar tissue, is alkaline and poor in albumen. (3) The *Pia Mater* is a vascular membrane, a minute network of fine branches of arteries and veins held together by delicate connective tissue. These ramifications of the blood-vessels in the pia mater are on their way to or from the nervous substance of the spinal cord and brain. The membrane, therefore, closely invests this substance, being, however, more intimately attached to the cord than to the brain. The pia mater is well supplied with nerves.

By these three membranes the nervous masses of the cerebro-spinal system are protected, held together and in place with a soft and yielding but sufficiently firm pressure, and nourished by the blood.

§ 6. The Spinal Cord, or *Medulla Spinalis,* extends in the vertebral canal from the aperture in the cranial cavity (*foramen magnum*), above which it is continuous with the medulla oblongata, downward to opposite the body of the first lumbar vertebra, where, after tapering off, it is spun out into a slender thread of gray nervous substance (*filum terminale*) that lies in the axis of the sacral canal. Its length is from fifteen to eighteen inches; its weight, when divested of membranes and nerves, about an ounce, or not far from one-fiftieth of that of the brain. It is nearly cylindrical in shape, its front and back surfaces being somewhat flattened; it has two considerable enlargements of its girth—an upper (cervical), from which arise the nerves that supply the upper limbs; and a lower (lumbar), which supplies the lower limbs with nerves.

§ 7. The external structure of the spinal cord requires us to notice the fissures which almost completely divide it for its whole length into right and left (lateral) halves, and are, therefore, fitly called "median"; of these fissures (a) the one in front (anterior or ventral[1] median) is somewhat broader than (b) the one behind (posterior or dorsal median). The ventral fissure is penetrated by the pia mater, carrying blood-vessels; the dorsal fissure is not a genuine fissure, but a wall or septum of neuroglia.

Each of these symmetrical and nearly half-cylindrical halves of the cord is subdivided by the lines of entrance of the dorsal and ventral nerve-roots into three *columns:* (a) the ventral, which lies between the ventral fis-

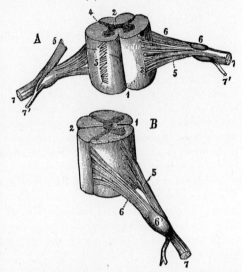

sure and the ventral root; (b) the dorsal, which lies between the dorsal fissure and the dorsal root; and (c) the lateral column, which lies at the side of the cord between the other two columns. The line of division between the lateral and ventral columns is not perfectly sharp, because the fibres of the ventral roots emerge over a considerable width of the surface.

The Commissures of the spinal cord are two bands of nervous matter which unite its halves, thus preventing it from being completely separated by the fissures. The one in front, at the bottom of the ventral median

FIG. 26.—*A*, Ventral, and *B*, Lateral, View of a Portion of the Cord from the Cervical Region. $\frac{2}{1}$. (Schwalbe.) 1, ventral median, and 2, dorsal median, fissures. At 3 is the ventro-lateral impression, over which spread the ventral roots (5). The dorsal roots (6), with their ganglion (6[1]), arise from the dorso-lateral groove, and uniting with the ventral roots form the compound nerve (7).

fissure, is composed of transverse nerve-fibres and is called (a) the *ventral white commissure;* the one behind, at the bottom of the dorsal fissure, is (b) the *dorsal gray commissure.* The gray commissure is nearly twice as large as the white, except at the cervical and lumbar enlargements of the cord, where the white is larger.[2] Along its whole length the gray commissure encloses a circular or

---

[1] There is a certain advantage in the use of "ventral" and "dorsal" in place of the common words "anterior" and "posterior." The advantage lies in the fact that ventral and dorsal apply with equal fitness to all animals, whether they have the erect position or not. It is convenient also, in some parts of the brain, to speak of anterior in the sense of "rostral" or "toward the mouth."

[2] See Henle, *Anatomie des Menschen*, text, p. 309.

elliptical canal (*central canal*), the vestige of the cavity of the embryonic neural tube. The gray commissure consists for the most part of extremely fine nerve-fibres devoid of medullary sheath; while the white commissure is composed of medullated fibres. The thickness of the commissures is, as a rule, proportional to the

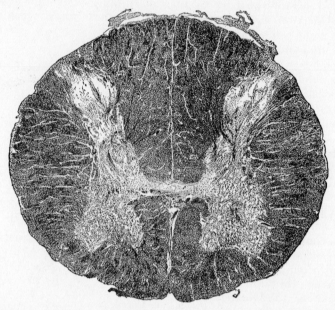

FIG. 27.—Transverse Section Through the Spinal Cord in the Upper Thoracic Region. (From Starr's *Atlas of Nerve Cells*, by permission of the Columbia University Press.) The section was stained with the "Weigert stain," which leaves the gray matter light, while darkening the white matter. The dorsal columns and horns are above in the figure, the ventral columns and horns below. Magnified 10 diameters.

size of the corresponding nerve-roots; their form, as they pass into the lateral parts of the cord, varies in different sections of its length.

§ 8. Transverse sections of the spinal cord show us that, as its external appearance would indicate, the substance of which it is composed is arranged in two symmetrical halves, almost, but not quite, separated by the median fissures. This substance, like that of all the nervous centres, consists of both white and gray nervous matter. The former is external and composes the columns of the cord; while the latter is internal and is surrounded by the white. The relative amount of the two kinds of nervous matter varies in the different parts of the cord. At its beginning from the *filum terminale* scarcely any white matter appears; the amount of such

matter, however, increases from below upward, and is largest in the cervical part of the
cord. The amount of gray matter is greatest
in the upper and lower enlargements of the
cord.

The gray columns on either side of the
cord, together with the commissures which
unite them, form a figure somewhat like a
large Roman H, with diverging sides; but
the lateral masses of these crescent-shaped
bodies are narrower in the thoracic (or dorsal)
region, and broader in the cervical and lumbar enlargements. Sometimes the figure is
rather like that of a pair of butterflies' wings.
The two limbs of each side of the figure into
which the gray columns are thus formed are
called Horns; (a) the *ventral horn* is rounded,
(b) the *dorsal* long and narrow (compare
Fig. 27).

§ 9. The gray matter of the cord contains
nerve-cells and their dendrites, and short
lengths of axons which pass from the white
columns into the gray to terminate there in a
tuft of fine branches; collaterals of axons
(compare p. 42) similarly enter the gray
matter and split up into fine branches; in
addition, the gray matter contains neuroglia.
From cells in the ventral horns of gray matter
issue axons which make their way through the
white matter to the surface of the cord, and
pass outside, to form the ventral roots (compare p. 42). These are the fibres which then
pass to muscles and other effectors; and,
therefore, the cells from which they arise are
called motor nerve-cells. Accordingly, the
ventral horn is largely motor in function. The
dorsal horns, on the contrary, do not contain
the cells of origin for the fibres in the dorsal
or sensory roots; but these fibres, as has already been stated (p. 42), arise from cells in
the ganglia situated on the dorsal roots (the
spinal ganglia) and grow into the cord by
the dorsal roots. Since the cells of the sensory root fibres lie outside the cord, while

FIG. 28. — Transverse Sections of the Cord at Dif-
ferent Levels. (Erb.) The
ventral side of the cord
lies above in each cross-
section. The shaded areas
are the pyramidal or cor-
tico-spinal tracts, which
have degenerated in this
individual because of in-
jury to the motor area of
the left hemisphere. The
shaded area in the lateral
column is the "crossed"
pyramidal tract, and that
in the ventral column the
"direct" pyramidal.

those of the motor root fibres lie in the ventral horns, it is natural that the latter should be thicker than the dorsal horns. The thickness of the ventral horns, however, varies greatly in differen' levels of the cord (see Fig. 28).

While in the cervical and lumbar enlargements of the cord, from which issue the nerves to the extremities, the ventral horns are large, in the mid-thoracic region, the nerves from which supply the less mobile trunk, the motor fibres are relatively few, and the ventral horns are correspondingly slender. More careful study of the shape of the ventral horns in the enlargements shows that they increase by the addition of gray matter at their sides; and the evidence is that these lateral portions of the ventral horns are the seat of the cells whose fibres supply the muscles of the extremities. The cells of origin of the fibres which pass to the sympathetic, seem to lie in the dorsal part of the ventral horn. Thus a certain amount of localization of function can be made out in the ventral horn of the cord.

Well-defined groups of cells appear elsewhere in the gray matter of the cord. For example, one column of large cells at the base of the dorsal horn ("Clarke's column") gives rise to fibres which pass up to the cerebellum.

The spinal cord shows no clear division into segments, such as appear, for instance, in the ganglion chain of the earthworm (p. 22); and the spinal "centres," or groups of nerve-cells which control particular muscles, do not exist as compact nuclei, but rather as slender columns of cells, within the ventral horn, extending for a distance of two or three vertebræ up and down the cord. The fibres destined for a particular muscle issue from the cord by two or three adjacent ventral roots; and each root carries fibres destined for several muscles. The spinal centres of neighboring muscles overlap.

The spinal ganglia, which supply the sensory fibres for the skin and other tissues, are clearly segmental; and the fibres from each ganglion have a definite field of distribution. But the distributions of adjacent ganglia overlap in the skin, so that destruction of a single ganglion or dorsal root does not entirely abolish sensation in any cutaneous area.

The White Substance of the spinal cord, besides connective tissue and lymph- and blood-vessels, is composed of nerve-fibres of comparatively large or of medium size. The essential constituent of these fibres is the axon, the diameter of which is generally one-third or one-fourth of their breadth. When fully developed, they are rarely or never without a medullary sheath, but probably have no neurilemma. Their diameter is not constant; the thickest fibres

($\frac{1}{1200}$ to $\frac{1}{2000}$ of an inch) are found in the outer portions of the ventral columns, where their size is tolerably uniform. In the lateral columns the nerve-fibres vary greatly in size, the finer ones lying inward near the gray matter. In the dorsal columns they increase in thickness as they approach the posterior gray commissure. In the upper thoracic, and through the whole of the cervical, region, there is found a wedge-shaped bundle of fine fibres that is separated off from the dorsal columns toward the middle line of the cord by a strong septum; this is called *fasciculus gracilis,* or "column of Goll."

§ 10. Some idea of the complexity of the cord may perhaps be gained from the counts of fibres which have been made by several authors. In so small an animal as the frog, Hardesty[1] found, in general agreement with the earlier work of Birge, that the total number of fibres in all the

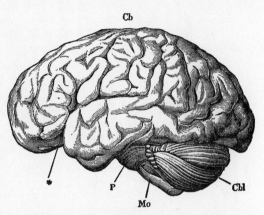

FIG. 29.—View of the Brain in Profile. $\frac{1}{2}$. (Henle.) *Cb,* cerebrum ; *Cbl,* cerebellum; *Mo,* medulla oblongata; *P,* pons Varolii ; *, fissure of Sylvius.

dorsal and ventral spinal roots combined would be some such number as 20,000 to 30,000. The number varied with the size of the frog, increasing with the body-weight. The fibres of the dorsal roots were more numerous than those of the ventral roots; in one specimen there were 8,572 dorsal and 6,211 ventral in the roots of one side. In man, Ingbert[2] determined the number of fibres in the dorsal roots entering one side of the cord; the total count was about 650,000. The ventral roots must contain at least half as many more, so that the total number of root fibres entering or leaving the human cord cannot be less than two million.

§ 11. The same elements of nerve-fibres and nerve-cells, in conjunction with connective tissue and neuroglia, and enveloped in the three enclosing membranes (dura mater, arachnoid, and pia mater)

[1] Irving Hardesty, "The Number and Arrangement of the Fibres Forming the Spinal Nerves of the Frog," *Journal of Comparative Neurology,* IX, 64–112, 1899.

[2] Chas. Ingbert, "An Enumeration of the Medullated Nerve Fibres in the Dorsal Roots of the Spinal Nerves of Man," *Journal of Comparative Neurology,* XIII, 53–120, 1903.

already described, are combined with an increased variety and complexity of arrangement to form those intercranial central organs with which the upper end of the spinal cord is continuous.   Uniformity of elementary parts, together with the greatest intricacy of

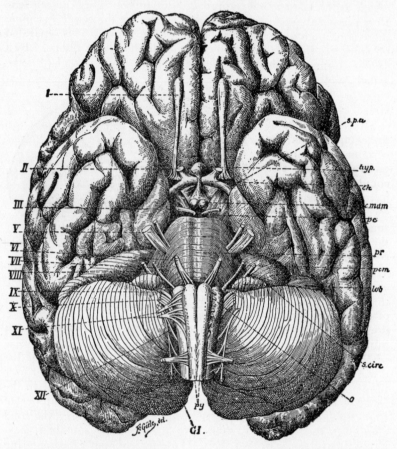

FIG. 30.—Under Surface of the Brain.   (Van Gehuchten.)   The Roman numerals at the left margin of the figure indicate the 12 cranial nerves; *hyp*, hypophysis; *ch*, optic chiasm; *c. mam*, mammillary body; *pc*, peduncle of the cerebrum; *pr*, pons; *o*, olive; *py*, pyramids; *CI*, first spinal nerve.

arrangement, prevails, above all other regions of the body, in the structure of the brain.   The significance of the elements and elementary parts can, therefore, only be understood when they are considered in the localities and relations to other parts which are assigned them by this so intricate arrangement.

§ 12. The Encephalon, or Brain, in the most extended sense of the word, includes all that portion of the central nervous system which is contained within the cavity of the skull. Its division into five principal parts, and the subdivisions of some of these, have been mentioned in the chapter on the development of the individual nervous system (see p. 48). On removing the entire human brain from the skull, and viewing it from above, one sees only the cerebral hemispheres, which have grown back and covered the other parts. A view from the side shows the cerebellum lying beneath

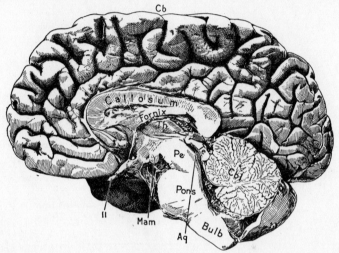

Fig. 31.—Mesial Section of the Brain. ½. (After a photograph by Retzius.) *Cb*, the mesial surface of the right cerebral hemisphere; *Cbl*, the middle lobe of the cerebellum in section; *Te*, roof of the mid-brain; *Pe*, peduncle of the cerebrum; *v4*, fourth ventricle; *Aq*, aqueduct; *Th*, thalamus; *Mam*, mammillary body; *II*, optic nerve.

the back part of the cerebrum, and the bulb lying beneath the cerebellum (compare Fig. 29); the transverse bundles of the pons can also be seen. From the under side can be seen, in addition, the peduncles or crura of the cerebrum, which form the ventral part of the mid-brain; the mammillary bodies and the hypophysis, which are parts of the inter-brain; and also the cranial nerves. In the bulb can be distinguished on this surface, two central hillocks called the "pyramids"; and two somewhat similar at the sides, called the "olives" (see Fig. 30). If a section is made in the median plane, separating the cerebrum into its hemispheres, and dividing the rest of the brain into right and left halves, the cerebrum, cerebellum, and brain stem are easily distinguished; and the pons is known by the swelling on the ventral side made by its transverse fibres. Next forward of the pons and cerebellum lies the mid-brain; the dorsal part of this, close to the cerebellum, consists of the quadrigemina, four rounded eminences, of which two, the right anterior and posterior, show in the section. The broad cavity showing in this section beneath the cerebellum is the fourth ventricle, and the slender prolongation of this under the quadrigemina is the "aqueduct." Forward of this the cavity swells into the third ventricle, the walls of which constitute the inter-brain. To the inter-brain belong the pineal gland above and the hypophysis and mammillary body beneath. The main portion of the inter-brain,

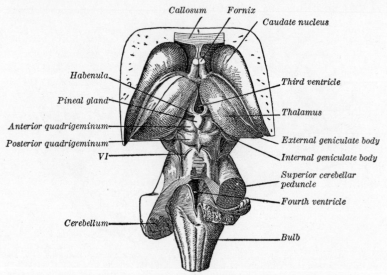

FIG. 32.—Dorsal Surface of the Brain-Stem. (Sobotta and McMurrich.)

the thalamus, lies to the side of the third ventricle, and its inner surface can be seen in the figure. Of the cerebrum, the median surface of the frontal, parietal, and occipital lobes, and of the tip of the temporal lobe, is shown; and the callosum and the fornix are seen in section (compare Fig. 31).

To obtain a view of the dorsal surface of the brain-stem, it is necessary to trim away the cerebellum and most of the cerebrum. We then see the bulb swelling out from the cord; and the fourth ventricle beginning below in an acute angle. The quadrigemina are fully exposed; slightly further forward is the pineal gland; and, to its side, the habenula. The large masses to the front and side of the quadrigemina are the thalami (one on each side); and still further in the same direction is seen the caudate nucleus, a part of the striatum. Appended to the thalamus are two small eminences, called the geniculata, median and lateral, which are of interest as portions respectively of the auditory and visual apparatus (see Fig. 32).

§ 13. It is important again to note in this connection the nerves which belong with each part of the brain, and which issue from the brain-stem. A list of the twelve pairs of cranial nerves has already been given (see p. 55). To emphasize their relations to the brain more clearly, we note that the first or olfactory nerve enters the olfactory bulb, the end-station or terminal nucleus of this nerve; and that fibres passing back from this through the olfactory tracts

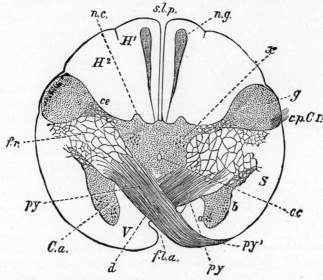

Fig. 33.—Section of the Bulb at the Decussation of the Pyramids. 6/1. (Schwalbe.) *f.l.a.*, ventral fissure; *s.l.p.*, dorsal fissure; *py*, *py'*, bundles of pyramidal fibres, crossing at *d*; *V*, ventral column; *S*, lateral column; *C.a*, ventral horn with groups of ganglion cells, *a* and *b*; *cc*, central canal; *f.r.*, reticular formation; *ce* and *g*, dorsal horns; H¹ and H², dorsal columns; *n.c.* and *n.g.*, their nuclei; *x*, central gray matter.

serve to connect this sense-organ with other parts of the system. The second, or optic, pair of nerves are seen to enter the inter-brain. The third and fourth nerves, both motor to the eye, issue from the mid-brain. The fifth or trigeminal, the great sensory nerve of the face, including also a motor root to the muscles of mastication, issues from the pons. The remaining seven are connected with the bulb; the sixth, seventh, and eighth with its forward end, the others further back.

§ 14. The brain-stem may properly be considered as a continuation of the cord. As compared with the cord, it is in the first place thicker, owing (1) to the large body of nerves which it receives; (2) to the passage through it of all the fibres which connect the cerebrum and cerebellum with the cord; and (3) to the appearance of special groups of cells within it.   In shape, the difference of the brain stem from the cord is largely due to the circumstance that the

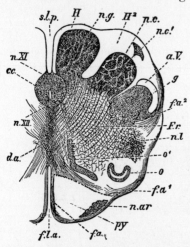

FIG. 34.—Section of the Bulb at the Level of the Sensory Decussation. (Schwalbe.) *s.l.p.*, dorsal, and *f.l.a.*, ventral fissures; *cc.*, central canal, surrounded by *n. XI* and *n. XII*, the nuclei of the 11th and 12th nerves; *H* and *H²*, the dorsal columns, with *n.g.* and *n.c.* (also *n.c.¹*),their nuclei; *a.V.*, spinal root of the fifth nerve, the fibres of which terminate successively in the adjoining gray matter, *g*, which may be regarded as a continuation of the dorsal horn of the cord; *F.r.*, the "reticular formation," containing fibres which issue from the nuclei of the dorsal columns and of the fifth nerve, and which cross the middle line in the sensory decussation, *d.a.*; *f.a.*, *f.a.¹*, *f.a².*, arciform fibres, passing toward the cerebellum; *n.l.*, *o¹*, *o*, *n.ar.*, different nuclei of gray matter, of which *o* is the lower end of the olivary nucleus; *py*, pyramid.

central cavity of the neural tube sometimes opens out into ventricles, and at all times lies near the dorsal side.   Passing upward from the cord, we find the central canal, in the lower region of the bulb, first verging toward the dorsal surface, and then opening out into the fourth ventricle. The dorsal wall here becomes a wide membrane, overlying the ventricle, and itself overlain by the cerebellum. The fourth ventricle continues upward through the pons, narrows in the midbrain to the aqueduct, which broadens again in the inter-brain to the third ventricle. This last is continuous through a narrow opening with the "lateral ventricle" of each hemisphere.

§ 15. A series of sections across the brain-stem will give some idea of its internal structure (compare Fig. 33).

If we make our first section through the bulb, shortly above the imaginary line which separates it from the spinal cord, we find an arrangement of parts much like that of the cord.   The ventral, lateral, and dorsal columns of white matter can be identified; also the ventral and dorsal horns of gray matter.   The most striking feature of this section is the appearance of large numbers of fibres, crossing from the ventral column of each side to the lateral column of the other.   This is the crossing or "decussation of the pyramids"; here motor fibres from the left hemisphere cross to the right side of the cord, and *vice versa*, so that the left hemisphere of the brain controls the right half of the body.   This section shows another peculiarity, as compared with the cord; there is a small mass of gray matter in the midst of the dorsal column.

A little higher up the bulb, as the next section shows, the dorsal columns are chiefly filled with gray matter, and their white matter has nearly disappeared; for the fibres which have ascended the cord in the dorsal columns end here, in this gray matter, and their places are taken by new fibres arising from this gray matter. These new fibres, instead of continuing upward in the dorsal region, promptly

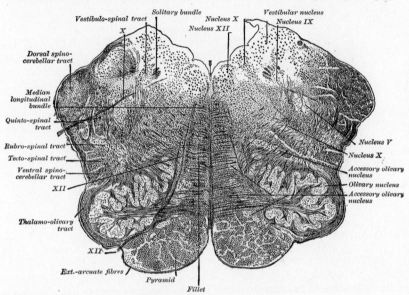

FIG. 35.—Section of the Bulb Through the Olive. (Magnified 4 diameters.) (Rauber-Kopsch, *Lehrbuch der Anatomie.*)

cross to the other half of the medulla, and pass upward near the middle line. The gray matter in the dorsal columns is named the "nuclei of the dorsal columns"; the crossing of the sensory fibres is the "sensory decussation," and the bundle of these fibres which runs up near the middle line, and which can be traced to the thalamus, is the "fillet," or "bulbo-thalamic tract." This is one of the chief sensory pathways toward the cerebral cortex.

§ 16. A section near the upper limit of the bulb shows that the central canal has now opened out into the fourth ventricle. On the floor of the ventricle are seen the nuclei of the local nerves. Near the nucleus of the tenth or vagus nerve is a spot which is essential for life, for if it is punctured, breathing ceases. This is the "respiratory centre." The most striking feature of the bulb at this level is the olivary nucleus showing in section as a wavy line (see Fig. 35). Of the numerous crossing fibres which appear in this section, some are from the olives, and some belong to the sensory decussation, which is not yet complete. At the side is seen the inferior peduncle of the cerebellum, not as yet quite separate from the bulb; a little higher up the separation is complete.

At the upper limit of the bulb, where it passes over into the pons, there enters the eighth nerve (see Fig. 36), its two branches, the

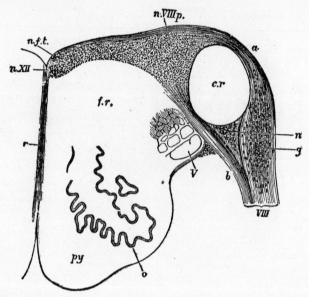

FIG. 36.—Section of the Bulb at the Entrance of the Eighth Nerve. (Schwalbe.) Note particularly the division of the eighth nerve, *VIII*, into *a*, its cochlear portion, and *b*, its vestibular portion. The portion left clear in the drawing is to be understood as filled largely with decussating fibres. *Py*, pyramid; *o*, olive; *V*, fibres from the fifth nerve; *c.r.*, inferior peduncle of the cerebellum.

cochlear and the vestibular, separating as they enter, and having entirely different central terminations. At this level are large masses of gray matter connected with these two nerves. The central continuation of the cochlear nerve is called the "lateral fillet."

§ 17. A section through the pons, at the level of entrance of the fifth nerve (compare Fig. 37), shows the peculiar arrangement which gives the name of "bridge" to this part of the brain-stem. Numerous transverse fibres extend across the middle line, and appear, indeed, to run from one side of the cerebellum to the other; but this appearance is illusory, as these fibres all originate from cells in the pons itself; they cross from one side to the other, and enter the cerebellum, forming its middle peduncle. Interwoven with these transverse pontine fibres are the longitudinal fibres of the pyramids. Small collections of nerve-cells (the "pontine nuclei") lie imbedded in the meshes of this network of fibres, and give origin to the pontine fibres. Above this bridge-like portion of the pons is another re-

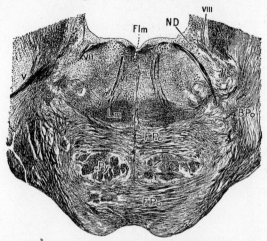

Fig. 37.—Cross Section of the Pons at the Level of the Fifth Nerve. (Marburg.) *V* (at the left) is the fifth nerve; parts of the sixth, seventh, and eighth nerves also are indicated by Roman numerals; *FPo.*, bundles of pontine fibres, which pass to *BPo*, the middle cerebellar peduncle.   The cerebellum is cut away, but is to be thought of as lying to each side and on top, above the fourth ventricle which shows at the top of the figure.   *Py* is the pyramidal tract; *Lm*, the fillet; *Flm*, close beneath the ventricle, is the median longitudinal bundle; *ND* is the nucleus of Deiters; *Crst*, a remnant of the inferior cerebellar peduncle; *Vs*, the descending bundle of fibres from the fifth nerve, which has been shown in sections lower down.   The "hood" includes everything between the ventricle and the uppermost pontine fibres.

sembling the bulb, the bundles of which are indeed continued upward here. This dorsal part of the pons is called the "hood" or *tegmentum;* and the ventral part is called the foot.

§ 18. A section somewhat farther forward cuts the mid-brain at the level of the posterior quadrigemina (compare Fig. 38). The fillets, medial and lateral, are visible above the foot; and the lateral fillet is seen to have moved dorsally, its fibres passing to the posterior quadrigeminum, which is a centre for hearing. The abundant decussating fibres above the fillet are from the superior peduncles of the cerebellum. The third ventricle has now narrowed to the aqueduct, which is surrounded by gray matter, containing the nuclei of the third and fourth nerves, which are motor to the eye muscles.

§ 19. A section through the anterior quadrigemina (Fig. 39) may strike also the hind part of the inter-brain, which overlaps the mid-

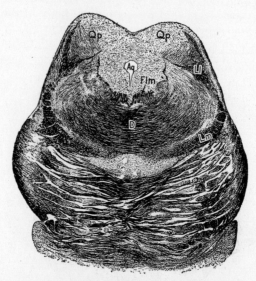

FIG. 38.—Cross-section of the Mid-Brain at the Level of the Posterior Quadrigemina. (Marburg.) In place of the fourth ventricle we have here the narrow Aqueduct, *Aq.* Above this, on each side, lie the posterior quadrigemina, *Qp.* The aqueduct is immediately surrounded by gray matter, below which is *Flm*, the median longitudinal bundle. Below this is a large mass of decussating fibres, *D*, from the superior cerebellar peduncles; below and to the side of this is the fillet, *Lm*; and above this, near the quadrigeminum, the lateral fillet, *Ll.* So much for the tegmentum; the foot still shows the interweaving of pontine and pyramidal fibres.

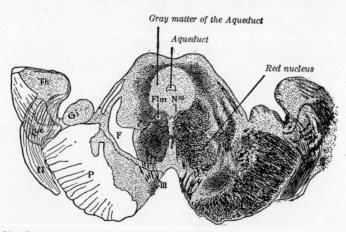

FIG. 39.—Section Through the Anterior Quadrigemina. Magnified about 1¾ diameters. (Dejerine.) *II, III*, the second and third nerves; *Th*, thalamus; *Ge* and *Gi*, the external and internal geniculate bodies; *P*, peduncle of the cerebrum, containing the pyramidal tracts; *F*, fillet; *Flm*, median longitudinal bundle; *N*iii, nucleus of the third nerve.

brain. In the mid-brain can still be recognized the foot and the hood, but the foot has bifurcated into the peduncles of the right and left cerebral hemispheres. The tegmentum contains the red nucleus, in which terminate most of those fibres from the cerebellum, that were seen decussating in the preceding section. At the

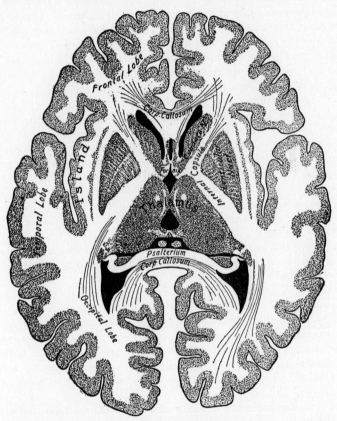

FIG. 40.—Horizontal Section Through the Brain. (Edinger.) $\frac{2}{3}$. White matter shows white, gray matter gray, and ventricular spaces black.

side appear the median and lateral geniculate bodies. The cut-off stump of the second or optic nerve is seen entering the lateral geniculate body.

§ 20. The relations of the inter-brain can perhaps be better seen in a section (see Fig. 97, p. 223), which is made vertically through the cerebrum, and further to the front than the preceding section; but which includes the thalamus, because of that overlapping of some of the end-brain and inter-brain of which mention has already been made (see p. 51).

Of the pallium, the temporal lobe is seen below, and the frontal lobe above, separated by the fissure of Sylvius, which spreads out at its bottom into the "Island." Passing inward from the island, we encounter first a strip of white matter, then a strip of gray (the "claustrum"), next the lenticular nucleus, showing three parts; after that, the white matter of the internal capsule, and finally the thalamus toward the centre and the caudate nucleus above. The caudate and lenticular nuclei are parts of the striatum, and were separated, in the early development of the brain (p. 53), by fibres growing through from the thalamus and from the cortex.

§ 21. A *horizontal* section through the cerebrum gives another view of these same structures. The full extent of the internal capsule is better seen here than in the vertical section. It will be noted that the lateral ventricles, the caudate nucleus, and the callosum are each cut twice in the section. This results from the curved growth of the cerebrum about a fixed point (compare p. 51), which gives to each of these structures an arched shape. The arch of the callosum can be seen in Fig. 31, which also shows another arched band, the fornix, lying beneath the callosum. The fornix appears in section in Fig. 40. It consists of fibres which arise in the temporal lobe, and which arch forward over the thalamus, and then descend to the mammillary body in the base of the inter-brain. It belongs to the archipallium, and some of its fibres decussate, forming the "psalterium," which is the commissure of the archipallium, as the callosum is the commissure of the neopallium.

§ 22. The cerebellum consists of a middle lobe called the vermis, and two lateral hemispheres. As in the cerebrum, the greater part of the gray matter lies outside, in a cortex, whose surface is folded into numerous fissures. Other nuclei lie in the base of the vermis. The cerebellum is attached to the brain-stem by three pairs of peduncles (see Fig. 41).

The inferior peduncle consists of afferent fibres from the spinal cord, from the nuclei of the sensory cranial nerves, and from the olive. The superior contains a bundle of fibres from the cord, but is largely composed of fibres which originate in the cerebellum and pass forward to the mid-brain and thalamus. The middle peduncle consists of the pontine fibres, which arise from the pontine nuclei, and are connected with fibres descending from the cerebrum. This is the path of communication from the cerebrum to the cerebellum. The pontine fibres, then, are afferent to the cerebellum; they pass to the cortex of the cerebellar hemispheres; whereas the rest of the afferent fibres go to the vermis. The development of the cerebellar hemisphere varies with that of the cerebrum, being largest in man.

(Further study of the inner structure of the cortices and other nuclei of the brain is deferred to a chapter on the nerve-cell and its connections; and, in case of the cerebral cortex, to a special chapter on that cortex.)

§ 23. As can readily be imagined from the large number of tracts and nuclei which have been mentioned even in the above hasty review, the internal structure of the brain presents a bewildering complexity of collections of nerve-cells and of bundles of fibres

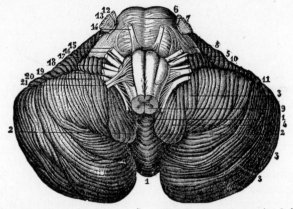

Fig. 41.—Lower Surface of Cerebellum. ⅔. (After Sappey.) 1, vermis; 3, hemisphere. The pons, bulb, and various pairs of nerves are also seen, thus: 12, 13, the fifth nerve; 14, the abducens; 15, the facial; 16, the "intermediate"; 17, the auditory; 18, the glosso-pharyngeal; 19, the vagus; 20, the accessory; 21, the hypoglossal.

coursing in various directions. In attempting to unravel this complexity, the most important task is that of tracing fibres from the cells which give them off to the cells which receive them. If we knew the fibres which connect the various "centres" or collections of cells, we should have taken a long step toward discovering the functions of the centres thus connected.

Many ingenious methods for tracing the nerve-tracts have been employed, the chief of which are the embryological and the pathological or degeneration method. The principle of the former—the myelinization of different tracts at different times in the individual's development—has already been mentioned in the chapter on embryology (see p. 58). The principle of the pathological method is the general fact that any part of a living cell, when cut off from the cell nucleus, dies. Thus, a nerve-fibre separated from its cell of origin speedily begins to degenerate, and is then stained by several reagents (especially by osmic acid) to a different degree from normal nerve-fibres (compare Fig. 42). If, therefore, a bundle of fibres has been severed by disease or injury, or by the knife of an experimenter, the fibres of this bundle degenerate, and can thus be traced in their course amidst other fibres. This method has proved remarkably serviceable. Many other methods have been employed. Von Bechterew mentions[1] no fewer than eleven, of which we may cite the comparative study of different vertebrates, especially of lower forms with simpler fibre systems; and the physiological method which deals with a living animal by exciting to activity some limited region—a

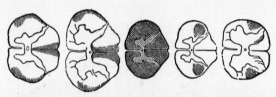

FIG. 42.—Degeneration of Tracts after Injury to the Cord. (Strümpell.) Five sections of the cord are arranged in order, the uppermost being at the left. The middle section, lying close to an injury which has completely severed the cord, shows degeneration in every part. The amount of degeneration decreases gradually in the sections further from the injury. The upper sections show "ascending" degeneration in the dorsal and the outside of the lateral columns. The lower sections show descending degeneration in a certain part of the lateral column.

sense-organ, a tract of fibres, or a portion of gray matter—and then observing either the *locus* and character of the end-effect, or the electrical change which accompanies the conduction of the nervous impulse in the nerve-fibres.

The object of such studies is attained when we know: (1) the origin of a tract, i. e., the group of nerve-cells from which the fibres proceed; (2) the course of the tract to (3) its termination in some other group of nerve-cells; and (4) the connections of the tract with other tracts at its origin and termination.   The fact is also to be considered that nerve-fibres often send out collateral branches at some part of their course, and thus a tract may have more than one terminus.   It is part of our object to discover the function subserved by each tract.   If the connections of the tract were thoroughly known, this alone might be a sufficient indication of its function; but in the present state of knowledge, the physiological method is often the only one which gives a knowledge of the function; and in many cases even this fails us.

§ 24. A system of naming the nerve-tracts, now coming into favor, consists in the use of compound terms, in which the origin and terminus of the tract are indicated.   For example, the "cortico-spinal tract" arises in the cortex and terminates in the cord; it is

[1] *Die Leitungsbahnen im Gehirn und Rückenmark*, 1899, pp. 2–9.

what we have previously called the pyramidal tract. A list of the analytical names of the tracts will convey some notion of the progress thus far made in the unravelling of the white matter; but it should be added that very many fibres still remain to be traced.[1]

§ 25. The most interesting of these tracts to the student of mental life are probably those which convey sensory impulses to the cerebral cortex and those which convey motor impulses away from the cortex; and these may now be examined with some care.

The sensory pathway from the trunk and limbs enters the cord by the dorsal roots. On reaching the cord, the sensory fibres turn in different directions. Some pass directly to the ventral horn of the gray matter, where they form connections with the motor cells, and so influence the motor fibres and provide a direct reflex pathway back to the muscles. Others of the sensory fibres turn up the dorsal columns; and some of them continue in these columns up through the cord to the bulb, where they terminate in the nuclei of the dorsal columns. The cells in these nuclei send out axons which continue the sensory pathway toward the cerebrum, by first crossing to the other side of the bulb, and then proceeding upward in the

---

[1] In understanding this list it should be remembered that the names of the different nerve-tracts are designed to combine the place of origin and the place of termination; and that tracts having the same origin are grouped together. Those which have hitherto been fairly well made out are the following:

Radiculo-bulbar.
Spino-cerebellar; Spino-olivary; Spino-tectal; Spino-thalamic.
Cervico-lumbar.
Nucleo-cerebellar.
Bulbo-tectal; Bulbo-thalamic; Bulbo-mammillary.
Acustico-tectal; Acustico-thalamic.
Vestibulo-spinal.
Nono-spinal (or "solitary bundle").
Quinto-spinal; Quinto-thalamic.
Retino - thalamic and Retino - tectal (optic).
Olfacto-cortical (or ammonic); Olfacto-habenular; Olfacto-mammillary.
Olivo-cerebellar.
Ponti-cerebellar.
Rubro-spinal; Rubro-thalamic.
Cerebello-rubral; Cerebello-thalamic.

Tecto-bulbar; Tecto-spinal, lateral and medial.
Thalamo-spinal; Thalamo-olivary; Thalamo-habenular; Thalamo-parietal.
Thalamo-temporal; Thalamo-occipital.
Habenulo-peduncular.
Mammillo - thalamic; Mammillo - tegmental.
Striato-peduncular; Striato-thalamic.
Fronto - spinal (cortico - spinal), direct and crossed; Fronto-bulbar; Fronto-pontine.
Occipito - temporo - pontine; Occipito-thalamic.
Cortico-tectal; Cortico-habenular.
Ammono-mammillary.
Fronto-thalamic.
Temporo - frontal; Temporo - parietal; Temporo-occipital.

To these should be added the median longitudinal bundle and the numerous commissures.

This list will probably need some revision from future discoveries; and it will certainly require numerous additions. But, as it now stands, it is a striking monument to the industry of neurologists.

"fillet" to the thalamus, where they terminate; but the path is further continued by fibres arising from the cells of the thalamus and passing up through the internal capsule to the cortex. Three sets of fibres, placed end to end, are therefore required to convey sensory impulses from the limbs and trunks to the cortex; three tracts are linked to form this sensory pathway—tracts which may be named the radiculo-bulbar, the bulbo-thalamic, and the thalamo-cortical. This is the most clearly traced of the sensory pathways from the limbs and trunk; but apparently it is not the pathway for the sense of touch, for interruption of this pathway by injury does not abolish conscious sensations of touch, temperature, and pain. Injury to the dorsal columns interferes with the "muscle-sense," whereas the cutaneous senses are affected by injury to the lateral columns of the cord.

Now some of the sensory fibres, on entering the cord, terminate in the dorsal horn of gray matter; and cells located there send out fibres which, after crossing to the other side of the cord, ascend in the lateral columns, and can be traced up to the thalamus. This spino-thalamic tract is apparently employed by the cutaneous senses, though it appears rather too slender to constitute the sole path from the skin to the brain.

Some of the dorsal root fibres pass to that part of the gray matter of the cord which is called Clarke's column, and here connect with the cells which give rise to a tract to the cerebellum. Still other connections are formed in the spinal cord between the incoming sensory fibres and various tracts running to different parts of the brain. Probably, however, these tracts, as well as the cerebellar, are not concerned in conscious sensation.

Cutaneous sensation from the face is provided for by the fifth pair of cranial nerves. From the terminal nuclei of these nerves, in the pons and bulb, arise fibres which pass to the thalamus— the quinto-thalamic tract—and end there, as do the sensory tracts from the cord.

The sense of taste is served by fibres of the seventh and ninth pairs of nerves; these fibres end in a common terminal nucleus, but the further course of the gustatory pathway toward the cortex can not yet be stated.

The fibres from the cochlear branch of the eighth nerve, the nerve of hearing, end in nuclei close to the entrance of the nerve. The secondary fibres, issuing from here, cross the middle line of the bulb and end in another mass of gray matter, called the superior olive. From these, tertiary fibres arise which conduct the auditory impressions forward to the mid-brain and thalamus—more precisely, to that part of the mid-brain known as the posterior quadrigeminal body, and to that part or appendage of the thalamus known as the internal geniculate body.

§ 26. The central connections of the second or optic nerve—the nerve of sight—are particularly worth noting. The right and left optic nerves, as they pass backward, approach each other, meet, and appear to cross in much the shape of an X or of the Greek letter

FIELD OF VIEW

Left   *Right*

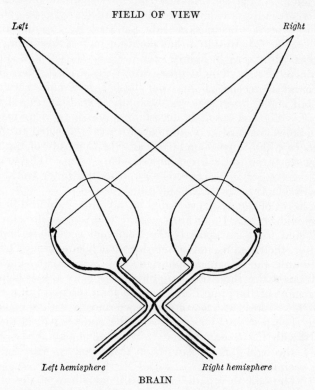

Left hemisphere   *Right hemisphere*

BRAIN

Fig. 43.—Diagram of the Semi-Decussation of Optic Fibres in the Chiasm.

X, from which resemblance the crossing is called the "optic *chiasm*." The nerves which lead back from the crossing and into the brain are called the "optic tracts." Just how much crossing of fibres occurs in the chiasm depends on the species of animal, and on the position of the eyes in the head. Those animals which have eyes on the sides of their heads, and directed to right and left so as to give almost totally different fields of view, show at the chiasm a nearly complete crossing of fibres. In such animals, therefore, the right eye is connected with the left half of the brain, and the left eye with the right half of the brain. This crossed relation holds for the other sense-organs. But in animals whose eyes are placed somewhat forward, with fields of view more or less overlapping, the decussation at the chiasm is less complete; and in animals such as man, whose eyes are directed straight forward and have almost identical fields of view, the crossing becomes a *semi-decussation* (see Fig. 43). The nerve-fibres from the nasal half of each retina cross, whereas those from the temporal half do not cross, but bend into the optic tract of the same side, and pass back to the same side of the brain. The result is that the right half of the brain receives the fibres from the right half of each eye, and the left half similarly. Now since the rays of light cross within the eyeball, the right half of each retina receives light from the left side, and therefore the right half of the brain receives the impressions that come from the left side. The net result is accordingly the same in animals with eyes directed forward as in animals with eyes directed to the side: in each case the impressions originating at one side of the middle line are conveyed to the opposite half of the brain. The brain has, therefore, the same crossed relation with the outer world in the case of vision as in the case of all other receptors.

The fibres of the optic tracts end in the inter-brain and in the adjoining mid-brain. In the former, the end-stations are the "pulvinar" and more particularly the "external geniculate body"; in the latter, their ending is the anterior quadrigeminum. The quadrigeminum is the principal ending in fishes, reptiles, and birds. But in mammals the inter-brain endings, especially the geniculatum, receive most of the optic fibres; and in man the mid-brain receives only a few fibres, which are concerned mostly with the pupillary reflex. The principal connections of the optic nerve, in man, are, directly with the thalamus and external geniculate body, and indirectly, through fibres arising from these bodies, with the cortex of the occipital lobe.

§ 27. The olfactory path begins with the fibres of the olfactory nerve, which terminate in the olfactory bulb. A secondary and then a tertiary tract leads to the cortex of the "archipallium," in the pyriform lobe and the hippocampus.

The previous survey of the sensory pathways shows that, with the exception of the olfactory and possibly of the gustatory, all of these pathways lead to the inter-brain. The thalamus, with its accessory bodies, is an intermediate station in the sensory paths toward the cortex. It is curious that the thalamus should intervene in this manner, and no well-grounded explanation presents itself. Why should not the sensory fibres run right up to the cortex, without interruptions, first in the terminal nuclei and then in the thalamus? In general, we can see that where a fibre ends by splitting into fine branches which are mingled with the fine branches of other fibres, opportunities are afforded for something analogous to the switching that goes on at a railway junction. Sensory impulses from various receptors may here be collected; and those from any one receptor may be widely distributed. The terminal nuclei, quite surely, provide for the distribution of sensory impulses to the motor nerves, to the cerebellum and to the thalamus. The thalamus, since it possesses many short fibres connecting its own parts, is probably something more than a mere way-station. Apparently, the sensory impulses from different receptors come together here and join in such a way that the impulses which pass from here to the cortex are already organized or synthesized to a certain extent. For example, the adult man possesses a really remarkable power of locating visual objects in reference to the body, when the position of the head differs greatly; and although a given visual appearance of the object means quite different locations in space according to the position in which the head happens to be at the moment. There must clearly be some means of bringing together (or "synthesizing") the visual impulses with those other sensory impulses which indicate the position of the head. The conjecture that this means is furnished by the thalamus serves, at least, to direct attention to the kind of work which is apparently done in the switching stations along the route of sensory impulses to the cortex.

§ 28. The most interesting motor pathway, from the psychologist's point of view, is that which leads from the "motor area" of the cortex, and which may be called the pyramidal, or the corticospinal; or, taking more precise account of its origin, the frontospinal. This is the longest of all the tracts, and is visible in every cross section of the cord or brain-stem. After passing down through the white matter underlying the cortex, its fibres come together into a compact bundle in the internal capsule (where they are frequently injured by hemorrhage, in apoplexy), then emerge upon the ventral surface of the mid-brain. They retain this ventral position down through the pons and bulb; but in the lowest part of the bulb each pyramidal tract (the right and the left) splits into two, the smaller of which continues down the ventral column of the cord, while the larger part passes over to the opposite side of the cord and descends in the lateral column. Those fibres which do not cross in the bulb do so, one by one, at different levels of the cord. The cortico-spinal fibres terminate in the gray matter of the cord, and the motor pathway is continued by axons from the motor cells of the cord, which pass out by the ventral roots, and finally reach the muscles.

§ 29. Though the connections of the cerebrum with the sense-organs and muscles—together with the paths of association within the cerebrum itself, to which we shall return in another chapter—constitute the most interesting system of nervous connections, yet a false impression would be created if these only were described; for not all the nuclei and fibre-bundles which exist in the brain and cord are directly subservient to the cerebrum. We may recognize the existence of several systems of tracts and nuclei which are more or less independent in their growth and function, though connected at various points. We may, therefore, recognize the following systems of centres and connections: the fundamental, the mesencephalic, the cerebellar, the archipallial, and the neopallial. A brief description of each follows.

§ 30. (1) The fundamental system consists of the sensory and motor nerves, with the cells of origin of the motor fibres and the groups of cells, called terminal nuclei, into which the sensory fibres lead and in which they terminate. In addition, the fundamental system includes the central fibres which directly connect the motor and sensory nuclei. In the cord, this system includes the gray matter and the ground bundles; in the brain-stem, it includes the motor and terminal nuclei of the cranial nerves, and many short connecting fibres. An important part of the fibre connections is represented by the "median longitudinal bundle" of the brain-stem, a continuation of the ground bundles of the cord. It extends the length of the brain-stem, and consists mostly of short fibres connecting neighboring nuclei; it affords direct connection, for example, between the nuclei of the several motor nerves of the eye, and so contributes to the co-ordination of the eye muscles.

The fundamental system is the oldest in the race, and the earliest to develop in the individual. In accordance with a principle set forth in the chapter on embryology (see p. 57), the structures belonging to this system lie close to the cavity of the neural tube; in the bulb, they lie close beneath the ventricles, and in the mid-brain, close about the aqueduct. They are overlain by the more voluminous structures of the later-developing systems.

The function of the fundamental system is to provide for local reflexes, and also, through its connecting fibres, for reflexes that are more wide-spread. Since it includes the origins of the motor nerves, it has direct control of the muscles; and other systems probably act first on it, and only through it on the muscles.

§ 31. (2) The mesencephalic or, more precisely, the "tectal" system[1] is apparently the dominant system in fishes, amphibia,

---

[1] From "tectum," the "roof" of the mid-brain, comprising the corpora quadrigemina.

reptiles, and birds; but in mammals and especially in man, its importance has decreased. Its nuclei are those of the quadrigemina; its incoming fibres are partly from the optic nerve, and partly from the terminal nuclei of the cochlear nerve; it also receives slender tracts from the cord. Its outgoing fibres lead to the nuclei of the motor nerves of the eye, and also, by slender tracts, to the bulb and cord.

§ 32. (3) The cerebellar system is, in man, very extensive. To its gray matter must be reckoned the cortex of the cerebellum, the nuclei which lie imbedded in the base of the cerebellum, and four other nuclei, which lie outside the cerebellum, but near it in the brain-stem, and closely connected with it. These are the olivary nucleus, the nucleus of Deiters, the pontine nuclei, and the red nucleus of the mid-brain. The olivary and pontine nuclei send numerous fibres into the cerebellum; the red nucleus receives many fibres from the cerebellum; and the nucleus of Deiters both sends and receives. The cerebellum also receives many fibres directly from the terminal nuclei of the sensory nerves; the "direct cerebellar" tract from the cord is an example, and there are other bundles from the cranial nerves. The connection of the vestibular nerve with the cerebellum seems especially close. To the cerebellar system should also be reckoned those tracts which lead into the olives (from the cord below, and from the thalamus above), and into the pontine nuclei (from the cerebral cortex). This connection between the cerebrum and the cerebellum, by way of the pontine nuclei, may be reckoned either with the cerebral or with the cerebellar system, and is interesting as showing a broad path of communication between the two great organs. The path conducts, apparently, from the cerebrum to the cerebellum.

All the tracts of the cerebellar system, thus far mentioned, lead toward the cerebellum. The principal outgoing tract passes out of the cerebellum by the superior peduncle into the mid-brain, where its fibres terminate mostly in the red nucleus. From this nucleus arise several tracts, one of which passes down into the cord, and must afford a means by which the influence of the cerebellum is exerted on the cord and so on the muscles. From Deiters' nucleus, also, a tract passes down into the cord. This account of the cerebellar system, though still far from exhaustive, is enough to awaken respect for this organ and its probable importance.

§ 33. (4) The "archipallial" system, closely related in function to the sense of smell, includes in its gray matter certain portions of the cortex ("pyriform lobe," "hippocampus"), and certain nuclei in the inter-brain ("mammillary body," "habenula"). Its fibre-bundles include the olfactory tracts, the "fornix" (connecting the archipallial cortex with the inter-brain), and several other tracts.

§ 34. (5) The neopallial system includes much the greatest part of the human cortex, and so the greatest part of all the gray matter of the nervous system. Besides this, it includes other nuclei, the chief of which lie in the inter-brain. Most of the thalamus belongs here, and also the external and internal geniculate bodies. The interposition of these nuclei in the path of sensory impulses to the cortex has already been discussed. The tracts of the neopallial system include the various sensory tracts which lead into the inter-brain, the fibres leading from the inter-brain to the cortex, the outgoing fibres from the cortex (cortico-spinal, cortico-bulbar, cortico-pontine, cortico-thalamic, etc.), and, most numerous of all, the fibres joining one part of the cortex with another.

§ 35. Regarding the relations of these several systems, in some instances (as from the neopallium to the cerebellum) broad paths of communication are anatomically visible; in other cases, such connections have yet to be discovered. Since all systems make use of the same muscles, they must all converge upon them, and therefore, as was said before, on the fundamental system which alone has a direct connection with the muscles. In this sense, the fundamental system might be called the centre of the whole mechanism. On the other hand it is clear that, in intelligent human behavior, the neopallial is the dominant system. Such a survey as has preceded serves to correct the tendency to formulate a too simple and diagrammatic scheme of the inner relations of the nervous system. To regard the whole system as a connected mechanism is eminently proper, but it is distinctly a biological mechanism, and its plan shows the marks of growth and adaptation, and *of possible effects from use and from learning*, being quite different from such a design as is drawn up by an engineer for a machine or an electric system.

The previous description makes the significant fact quite clear that the white matter of the brain and cord, instead of being, as it appears, a homogeneous mass, is a vast and intricate network of fibres and bundles of fibres, which have the office of forming mechanical connections between definite parts of the gray matter. These connections are manifold, but are not indiscriminate. Apparently, there is no one centre to which all paths lead; all parts of the nervous mechanism are interconnected, but some much more directly than others. In this way, both long and short paths, both converging and radiating paths, between both the nearer and the more remote parts, seem to be characteristic features of the entire system.

CHAPTER IV

ELEMENTS OF THE NERVOUS STRUCTURE

§ 1. In considering the nervous systems of invertebrates, and the embryology of the human system, we have already acquired some knowledge of the elementary structures of which the nerves and nerve-centres are composed. In the development of the nervous system, the germinal cells lining the cavity of the neural tube generate daughter cells, the earlier of which become neuroglia cells, and the later form the nerve-cells. From the latter the so-called axons are branches, which often run to great distances; some of them pass out of the neural tube, and others come from the cells of the spinal ganglia, to contribute to the formation of the nerves. Besides the axons, the cells in the brain and cord give out other branches, which are shorter and less cylindrical. Because they often branch like the limbs of a tree, they are called "dendrites." Nerve-cells, axons, and dendrites, along with neuroglia cells, are, therefore, the best-known elements of the nervous system.

The different kinds of branches which the nerve-cells give out were first fully described by Deiters.[1] He based his work on that of R. Wagner[2] and Remak.[3] The term "dendrites" was suggested by His. In general, as has already been indicated, the dendrites are relatively thick and short, and have a knotted appearance. That these knots, or knobs, are not the result of treatment, but are the natural characteristic of these elements, would seem to be proved by the facts that all kinds of stainings show them, and that their distribution is characteristic of different kinds of cells. And since they are more marked in the embryo, they may be looked upon as points of growth. The axons are more uniform in calibre, smoother; and their diameter differs in some correspondence to their lengths. In some cells of the so-called "Golgi type," the branches of the axon soon end in a fine network. In certain cases where a branch leads off from the main axon, before the latter emerges from the gray

[1] *Untersuchungen über Gehirn u. Rückenmark d. Menschen u. d. Säugetiere*, pp. 55 ff. (Braunschweig, 1865).

[2] *Handwörterb.*, III, i, pp. 377 ff.

[3] "Ueber multipolar Ganglienzellen," in the *Berichte über d. Verhandl. d. Kgl. preuss. Academie*, pp. 29 ff. (Berlin, 1854).

97

matter, it may be regarded as of importance enough to be called a "paraxon." Sometimes, also, the axon divides into two branches, each with its own medullary sheath. In the spinal cord, some axons even have three branches.

In general, the axon is developed before the dendrites appear. The first dendrite usually appears just opposite the axon and travels

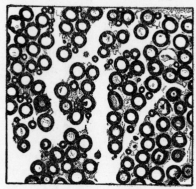

toward the centre. The axon itself starts from the neuroblast and, "guided by some mysterious power," grows through the embryonic body to its appropriate muscle. This, and similar facts, have led some observers to affirm that "all nerve-fibres of the body are extraordinarily long outgrowths from either central or peripheral ganglion cells." Every nerve-fibre is thus "to be recognized as being, from beginning to end, a product or, more correctly, a part, of a single nerve cell."[1]

Fig. 44.—Part of the Cross Section of a Nerve. (Schäfer). The myelin sheath is stained black while the axon remains white.

§ 2. The peripheral nerves, and the white matter of the centres, contain no nerve-cells or dendrites; and the nerves contain no neuroglia. A cross section of a nerve (see Fig. 44) shows great numbers of nerve-fibres, which then appear as little circles. Teasing of a nerve divides

[1] Lenhossék, *Der feinere Bau des Nervensystems* (Berlin, 1895), p. 89. There are few more obscure and uncertain problems than that proposed by the question: "What controls the direction of the fibres in their outward growth?" But this problem may be considered as only a special case of the general biological problem as to the causes which control the direction of all growths in living bodies. And biology is not yet able satisfactorily to solve this problem, even when, as is highly probable, influences from a variety of controlling forces must be admitted to share in the result. In the special case of the nerve-fibre, some have held that the growth of its protoplasmic node as it moves forward through the tissues, taking up nutrition from the surroundings, has its direction controlled by the mechanical ease of passing through certain tissues rather than others (so His: "Die Entwickelung d. ersten Nervenbahnen beim menschlichen Embryo," *Archiv f. Anat. u. Phys., Anat. Abt.*, 1887, pp. 376 ff.; and "Die Entwickelung d. Nervensystems bei Wirbelthieren," *Abhandlungen d. math-phys. Klasse d. kgl. sächs. Ges. d. Wiss.*, Bd. XVIII, 189). Others account for the phenomenon as due to the chemical attractions of secretions given off from the muscles (so Cajal). Still others consider that the cells are all the time functioning, and this primitive functioning accounts for their growth; and also, perhaps, that their growth is dependent on electrical stimuli. All these explanations, however interesting and helpful they may be, leave the matter still an unexplained mystery, of a character similar to that of all the performances of living tissues.

it into fibres which run along parallel to each other. They are bound together by sheets of connective tissue, which give the necessary tensile strength to the nerve. The whole nerve is enclosed by connective tissue (called the *epineurium*), and within it can be distinguished larger and smaller bundles of fibres—each bundle being enclosed by connective tissue (the *perineurium*); while more delicate sheets of the same tissue penetrate the bundles between the individual fibres (the *endoneurium*). The branching of a nerve often consists simply in the separation of one of its bundles from the rest; in the same way the minuter subdivision of the branches consists of the separation of the fibres from one another. The fibres, however, maintain their individuality throughout the peripheral nerve and its branches. Only at the very end of the fibre, in the receptor or effector organ, does the single nerve-fibre split up into fine branches.

§ 3. The nerve-fibre is thus the element or unit of which the nerve is essentially composed. The fibre itself consists of the axon, surrounded by one or more sheaths (compare Fig. 45). Most of the axons in the peripheral nerves have two sheaths, the "primitive sheath" on the outside, and the "medullary" or "myelin sheath," inside of the primitive sheath and next to the axon. The primitive sheath is a thin membrane, while the medullary sheath is often comparatively thick, and is composed of a white, fatlike substance called "myelin." A considerable proportion of the fibres in the peripheral nerves do not possess a myelin sheath, and are called non-medullated fibres; in general, the fibres originating in the sympathetic ganglia belong to this class. On the other hand, the fibres in the white matter of the brain and cord possess the myelin sheath but not the primitive sheath, and there is a short length of the axon, just after it emerges from its cell, which is not provided with either of the sheaths. It seems clear, accordingly, that the axon is the most essential part of the nerve-fibre, since it is the only part which is present in all fibres and in all parts of the nervous system.

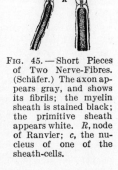

Fig. 45.—Short Pieces of Two Nerve-Fibres. (Schäfer.) The axon appears gray, and shows its fibrils; the myelin sheath is stained black; the primitive sheath appears white. *R*, node of Ranvier; *c*, the nucleus of one of the sheath-cells.

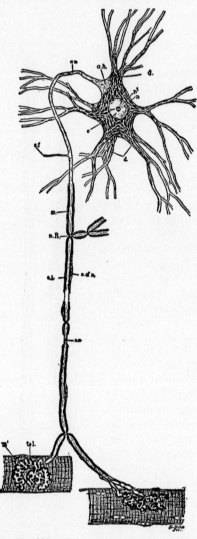

F‍IG. 46.—Motor Cell of the Ventral Horn of the Cord, with Scheme of the Course of its Axon. (Barker.)   *n*, the nucleus, with *n¹*, nucleolus; *d*, dendrites, only the stumps of which are shown; *a.h.*, hillock from which the axon arises; at *m*, the axon becomes invested with the myelin sheath; *n.R.*, a node, with branching of the axon; *m¹*, a muscle, in which the axon terminates in *tel.*, the motor end-plate.

A nerve-fibre has the general form of a thread or long narrow cylinder. It is not, however, a perfect cylinder, but shows at short intervals slight constrictions or "nodes." The space between two nodes may be called a segment; it is primarily a segment of the primitive sheath, corresponding to one cell of the sheath-forming substance. The myelin sheath is also interrupted at each node, and thus appears in segments. The axon, however, is continuous through the node, though it is narrowed at this point.

The inner structure of the axon is so minute that even the higher powers of the microscope afford barely enough magnification to enable the histologist to see it.

§ 4. The size of the different nerve-fibres in the human body varies greatly, according to their kind, position, and, perhaps, function. As a rule the non-medullated fibres are smaller than the medullated, the former being from $\frac{1}{6000}$ to $\frac{1}{8000}$ of an inch in diameter, and the latter (in the trunk and branches of the nerve) from $\frac{1}{1500}$ to $\frac{1}{8000}$ of an inch. But this rule is not always followed. In the white matter of the cord the medullated fibres range in size from $\frac{1}{1200}$ to $\frac{1}{2000}$ of an inch, in parts of the anterior columns, and about $\frac{1}{7000}$ of an inch in those regions of the lateral and posterior columns which are nearest the gray matter of the cord. In the gray matter of the cord and brain the fibres are much finer—being from $\frac{1}{7000}$ to $\frac{1}{14000}$ of an inch in diameter, or even of an almost immeasurable fineness; they are finest of all in the superficial layers of the brain and in the nerves of special sense. In some instances the axis-cylinder may be not more than $\frac{1}{100000}$ of an inch in diameter.

The number of fibres which enter into the composition of individual nerves also varies greatly. In the common motor nerve of the tongue it has been estimated at about five thousand, in that of the eyes at fifteen thousand, in the optic nerve at one hundred thousand at least.

Success in analysis of the nerve depends, in large measure, on the discovery of stains which color some portions more deeply than others, and so bring out their differences. The most important fact regarding the inner structure of the axon is that it consists of plasma in which run very minute fibrils. These fibrils extend lengthwise of the axon, and are continuous for long distances; it is inferred by many authorities that they are the conducting part of the axon. In short, just as a moderate magnification of a nerve shows it to be a bundle of nerve-fibres, so higher magnification applied to the single fibre seems to show that it too is but a bundle, and that the real unit of the nerve is the minute fibril. It should be mentioned, however, that, in our lack of exact knowledge of the physical or chemical process which is conducted along the nerve we cannot make an inference, with any assurance, from the structure of the axon to the function of its separate parts.

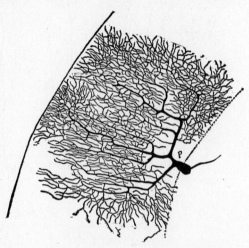

FIG. 47.—Purkinje Cell.   (Starr, Strong and Leaming.)

§ 5. The white matter of the brain and cord is made up much as are the nerves, except that the sheets of connective tissue are absent, and also the primitive sheath of the fibre. The nervous substance is protected by the enveloping bone and membranes, and strengthened by the fibres of the neuroglia which pass between the nerve-fibres.

The gray matter contains neuroglia, nerve-cells and their dendrites, the terminations of axons which enter from the adjoining white matter, and blood-vessels, which are present also, though in less abundance, in the white matter and in the nerves. That this list exhausts the contents of the gray matter is regarded by some authorities as improbable, in view of the small bulk of the nerve-

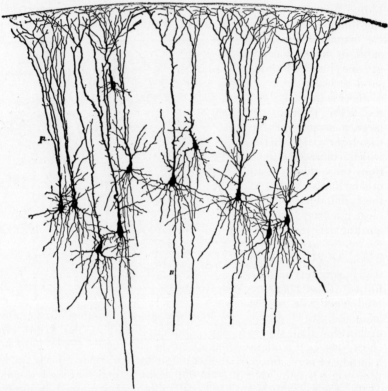

FIG. 48.—Pyramidal Cells from the Cerebral Cortex.   (Kölliker.) *n*, axon; *p*, apical dendrite.

cells. Donaldson[1] estimates that the nerve-cells occupy but 1.3 per cent. of the bulk of the gray matter; while the dendrites, as he believes, cannot occupy more than half the space of the cells. This estimate seems to leave much space unaccounted for. Nissl[2] has advanced similar indirect evidence in favor of yet unknown components of the gray matter. It should be said, however, that the

[1] *Journal of Comparative Neurology*, 1899, IX, 141.
[2] *Die Neuronenlehre und ihre Anhänger*, 1903, p. 75.

best stains, such as that of Cajal, show the gray matter to be very largely filled with fine fibres, which appear to be the branches of dendrites and of axons.[1]

§ 6. The true nerve-cells vary in size as much as in shape; the limits may, perhaps, be given as from about $\frac{1}{250}$ to $\frac{1}{3500}$ of an inch. The general shape of a nerve-cell is chiefly dependent on the dendrites and the manner or place of their leaving the cell-body. The accompanying figures (Nos. 46, 47, 48, 49) show several different forms. The cells of the ventral horn of the spinal cord—which through their axons directly control the muscles—send out dendrites in every direction, and are accordingly called "multipolar." The Purkinje cell from the cerebellar cortex sends out one dendritic stem, which branches into a beautiful tree, though this branching is

[1] Progress in tracing the branches of the nerve-cells within the gray matter has depended largely on the invention of methods of staining gray matter in ways which bring out one or another of its features. For showing the external form of the cells and their branches, a method which has done remarkable service is the silver method of Golgi, according to which pieces of gray matter that have first been soaked in potassium bichromate are treated with nitrate of silver, with the result that a deposit of dark silver chromate is precipitated on some of the cells. The peculiarity of this method is that comparatively few cells are thus blackened, but these few are blackened throughout, even to their fine branches; in this manner an individual cell, which would otherwise be lost in its intricate interlacing with other cells, is made to stand out clearly. The *internal* structure of the cell is not, however, brought out by the Golgi method, which simply encrusts the surface with a black deposit. Other methods have been found which permit of study of the internal structure. The method of Nissl consists in first staining densely with a basic dye such as methylene blue, and then dissolving out some of the dye with alcohol; this leaves some parts of the cell still deeply stained. Apáthy and Bethe have also introduced methods for selectively staining the fibrils within the cells.

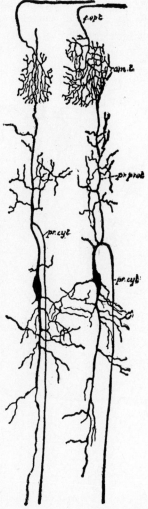

FIG. 49.—Cells of the Mid-brain (Optic Lobe of Chick). (Van Gehuchten.) *pr. cyl.*, the axon, which here emerges from a dendrite; *f. opt*, axon entering from a distance, and connecting with the dendrite.

peculiar in that it is confined to one plane. The pyramidal cells of the cerebral cortex send out one long dendritic stalk toward the surface of the cortex, and other stalks to the sides. Many small cells have only a small development of dendrites. The cells of the spinal ganglia, and of the similar ganglia of the sensory cranial nerves, have no dendrites (see Fig. 15, p. 44).

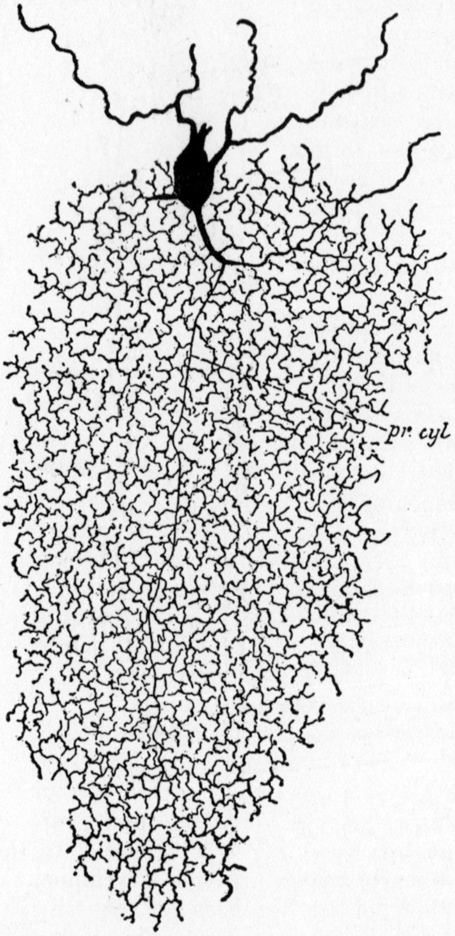

The nerve-cell is usually, at first, a round or somewhat angular body without branches. From this a band of tissue issues, like a sort of *pseudo-podium*, and then breaks up into branches, thus forming the dendrites. Some cells in the brain (as the Purkinje and pyramidal cells) develop dendrites after birth. Most central cells have only one axon (monaxion); but in the external layer of the cerebrum polyaxion cells are said to be found. Bipolar cells are found in abundance in the dorsal root ganglia; and the peripheral sympathetic cells are polyaxion. Wholly anaxion cells are rare; but are said to be found in the olfactory bulb, the ear, and the papillæ of some animals. No special function, either sensory or motor, has been proved to be assignable to any of these different shapes.

FIG. 50.—Cell with Short and Much Branched Axon. (Van Gehuchten.) *pr. cyl.*, the axon.

Dendrites never extend far from their cell-body, but bifurcate repeatedly in the immediate neighborhood of the cell. In both these respects they differ from the typical axon, which is long, narrow, cylindrical, and in general branches but little. Where it does divide, the branch comes off at right angles to the trunk of the axon, and is called a collateral. The axon is peculiar also in that it passes into the white matter, and acquires a myelin sheath. It often extends, in the white matter and in the peripheral nerves, to a length of several feet. But there is another type of axon (compare Fig. 50), which is short, and branches abundantly near the cell-body; it can still be distinguished from the dendrites by its uniform slenderness, and by the rectangular character of its branching.

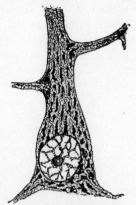

FIG. 51.—A Nerve-Cell, Stained by the Nissl Method, and Highly Magnified. (Ewing.) The blue of the stain is here represented by black.

§ 7. The inner structure of the cell-body shows a nucleus with a minute nucleolus within the nucleus. When the Nissl stain is employed (compare Fig. 51), there are seen many large granules, often of spindle shape, with spaces between them. These "Nissl bodies" are present in the dendrites as well as in the cell-body, but are absent from the axon and from the conical projection of the cell from which the axon arises. It is not easy to make sure that such appearances as these represent structures which exist in the living cell; for the chemical treatment through which the cell must pass in order to show details may cause coagulations and other changes of the substances within the cell. What is certain is that the cells contain a particular substance which has an affinity for basic dyes; and that the same sort of nerve-cell always gives the same sort of picture when it is treated by the Nissl method, if it has come from an animal in normal condition. But there are many conditions, more or less abnormal, which cause the cells to present quite a different picture after staining. Thus poisoning with lead, mercury, arsenic, alcohol, strychnine, and many other poisons, asphyxia, or excessive activity and fatigue, causes a diffusion of the stainable substance throughout the cell-body— a condition known as *chromatolysis* (see Fig. 52). Further action of the poison may cause a complete disappearance of the stainable substance. The results suggest, but do not fully prove, that this substance is of the nature of stored food or fuel, which the cell utilizes in its activity, and uses up in excessive activity.

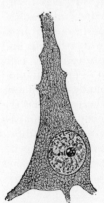

FIG. 52.—Chromatolysis. (Ewing.) To be compared with Fig. 51.

§ 8. Methods of staining nerve-cells have also been introduced[1] which show numerous *fibrils* in the cell-body and dendrites, as well as in the axon (see Fig. 53). Small bundles of fibrils from each dendrite enter and pass through the cell-body into other dendrites or into the axon. Fibrils thus pass from each branch of the cell into nearly or quite every other branch. In the cells of the vertebrate brain and cord, the fibrils seem to maintain their individuality through the cell, not anastomosing with each other.[2]

In the spinal ganglion cells, however, the fibrils unite with each other into a network or latticework; and the same is true of the cells in the nerve-centres of invertebrates, as demonstrated by Apáthy.

Occasionally a deposit of pigment is found in nerve-cells; the amount of it increases with the age of the individual. The significance of the pigment is otherwise unknown.

§ 9. The arrangement of cells, dendrites, and terminations of axons in the gray matter is of no less importance than the structure of the single cell. In general, it may be said that the interweaving of branches from different cells is very dense and intricate. The number of cells is great, even in a small ganglion or nucleus; the number of axons entering and terminating is also great; and the relations of the axons to the cells near which they terminate is not by any means easy to make out. It is fairly certain that axons, on entering a mass of gray matter, come into definite functional relations with the cells located there, or with their dendrites; but the exact mode of connection is often obscure. In certain localities, however, the relations are clear as to certain facts.

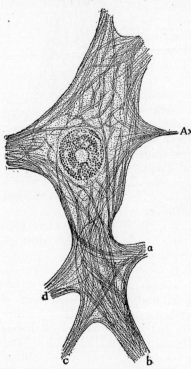

FIG. 53.—Nerve-Cell Stained for Fibrils. (Bethe.) *a, b, c, d*, the stumps of several dendrites; *Ax*, stump of the axon.

§ 10. The connections of the fibres of the olfactory nerve, for example, are specially clear. These fibres arise from sensory cells

[1] By Bethe, Bielchowsky, Cajal.   [2] Bethe, op. cit., pp. 56–60.

in the mucous membrane of the nose, and, passing through the bone into the brain cavity, enter the olfactory bulb, where each axon breaks up into a little bush of branches. Interlacing with these are the branches of a dendrite which belongs to a cell of the olfactory bulb. This dendrite, extending outward from its cell-body, meets the axon coming in from the nose, and the two break up

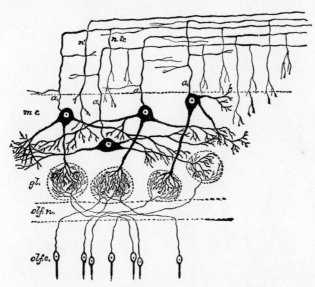

Fig. 54.—Diagram to Show the Connection of Axons and Dendrites in the Olfactory Bulb. (Schäfer, from *Quain's Anatomy*, by permission of Longmans, Green & Co.) *olf.c.*, olfactory cells in the nasal mucous membrane; *olf.n.*, the olfactory nerve, consisting of axons from the cells just mentioned; *gl.*, "glomeruli," in which the terminal branches of these axons are interwoven with dendrites of cells of the olfactory bulb; *m.c.*, these cells; *a*, their axons, passing further into the brain.

together into a mass of interlacing branches (see Fig. 54). On the other side, the axon of the cell in the olfactory bulb runs back to other parts of the brain.

Now it is certain that the line of communication must, in this case, lead from the nose to the brain. It enters the brain by the fibres of the olfactory nerve; it must therefore pass from these fibres to the structures into which they enter into relation; and these structures are the dendrites of the cells of the olfactory bulb. The case thus shows communication from the axon of one cell to the dendrites of another, and from these dendrites to their cell-body and its axon. The dendrites must, therefore, be the receptive part of the cell, i. e., the part which receives the nervous influences or impulses from other more peripheral parts of the nervous system.   What is certain in this case, is probable enough in many other parts of the gray matter, in which sensory axons terminate; for example, in the case of the optic path.   There are always dendrites present which may be the recipients of the sensory impulses.   Moreover, there are no anatomical peculiarities of any part of the gray matter which would discredit the general conception of the dendrites as receptive organs; or which would make

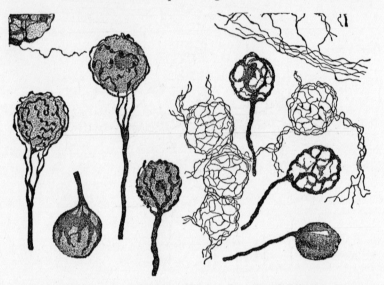

FIG. 55.—Baskets of Axon-branches Around Nerve-cells.   (Veratti, Edinger.)   The spherical bodies are nerve-cells, the branches of which do not show in the figure; but the cell-bodies are seen to be closely enveloped by "baskets" of fibres which result from the splitting up of axons from other, distant cells.

more probable any other function for them.   That they have this receptive function may, therefore, be taken as a highly probable and generally accepted view.

There are, however, indications that impulses are sometimes received directly at the surface of the cell-body, as well as through the dendrites.   In certain cases the terminal branchings of an axon are closely applied to the body of another cell.   The cells of the "trapezium," a portion of the bulb and pons which is closely connected with the auditory nerve, show examples of this (compare Fig. 55).   Here the structure strongly suggests that the axon influences the cell-body directly.

§ 11. The cerebellum affords interesting examples of various forms of communication between one cell and another.   The cortex of this organ contains several varieties of nerve-cells, such as the Purkinje cells, with their richly branched dendrites, granule cells, "basket cells," and cells with short and much branched axons. Of all these, the Purkinje cells are those which send axons away from the cortex of the cerebellum; apparently, therefore, the influence of the cerebellum on the other parts of the nervous system is exerted through these axons of the Purkinje cells. Accordingly, the different nerve impulses which may be present in the cerebellar cortex must be concentrated on the Purkinje cells.

There are fibres entering this cortex from other parts of the nervous system, and some of these, called "climbing fibres," grow up the dendrites of the cells of Purkinje, like a vine up a tree; other incoming fibres, however, do not come into direct relation with the Purkinje cells at all, but end in peculiar, mossy terminations in the neighborhood of the little granule cells. The axons of these latter cells then

Fig. 56.—Fibre-baskets Around Purkinje Cells. (Cajal.)

pass upward to the level of the Purkinje dendrites, and extend in great numbers through, or between, the branches of these dendrites. The "basket cells" lie in the same region as the Purkinje dendrites; but their axons divide into several branches each of which splits up into a basket-like arrangement of fine branches around the cell-body of a cell of Purkinje. Thus one basket cell appears "to hold the reins on" several cells of Purkinje. The cells with much branched axons seem to spread influences, similarly, over many granule cells. We certainly are far from a full comprehension of these intricate relations of cells; though the main fact that the cells of Purkinje are subject to a combination of influences from other cells is clear; and it is also highly probable that both the dendrites and the cell-body of the Purkinje cell are receptive of influences from the axons of other cells (see Figs. 56 and 57).

§ 12. If the dendrites are receptive in function, the terminations of the axon must be transmissive; i. e., they must pass on the nerve-impulse to the dendrites and cell-bodies of other cells. There is much evidence to favor this view, and little opposed to it.   The nerve-cell may therefore be said to be "polarized"; since one end of it is capable of taking up stimuli, and the other is capable of giving

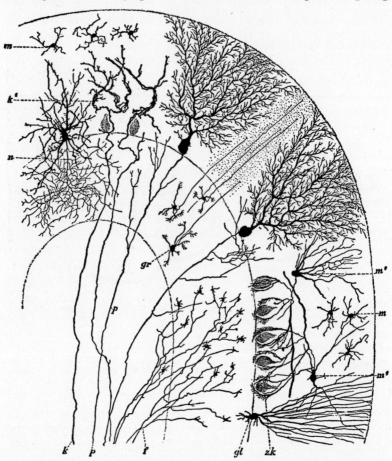

Fig. 57. — Diagram of the Cells of the Cerebellar Cortex.   (Kölliker.)   *gl*, neuroglia cell; *gr*, granule cell; *p*, axon of a Purkinje cell; *f*, "moss-fibre"; *k*, climbing fibre, and *k¹*, its termination; *m*, small nerve-cell; *n*, cell with short and much branched axon; *m¹*, basket cell, the axon of which branches at *zk*, about the body of a Purkinje cell.

off stimuli.   In case of the sensory fibres which have no dendrites —such as those of the dorsal roots of the cord, whose cells lie in the spinal ganglia—the peripheral termination of the axon in the sense-organ becomes the functional equivalent of the dendrites; i. e., it is the receptive part.   In the usual type of cell in the centres, the impulse seems to enter at the dendrites, to pass thence to the cell-body and thence into the axon, and out at the terminal arborizations of the axon and its collaterals.

The axon, therefore, usually conducts toward its own branched ends. Experiment proves, indeed, that the axon is inherently capable of conducting in either direction. But experiment also seems to prove that conduction from an axon to the dendrites of another cell can occur only in this one, and not in the reverse, direction. Thus, in the spinal cord, an impulse passing in by the

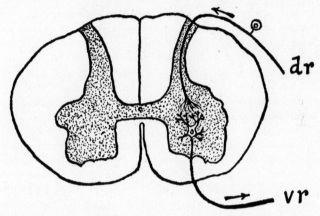

FIG. 58.—Diagram of a Synapse in the Cord.   dr, fibre of the dorsal root, passing into the ventral horn, and connecting, at the synapse, with a motor cell from which arises the fibre of the ventral root, vr. Stimulating dr arouses vr to activity, but stimulation of vr does not arouse dr.

fibres of the dorsal roots is transmitted over to the motor fibres of the ventral roots; but an impulse artificially generated in these motor fibres, and conducted back into the cord, does not make its appearance in the dorsal roots. Now we have already seen (p. 89) that the connection between the dorsal and the ventral fibres lies in the gray matter of the ventral horn; it appears, therefore, to be a connection between the terminations of the incoming sensory axons and the dendrites of the large cells of the ventral horn. If this appearance is correct, the above experimental result may be restated in the following terms: *Nerve-impulses are conducted from the terminations of the sensory axons to the dendrites of the motor cells, but will not pass in the reverse direction.* Thus the connection between axonic terminations and dendrites acts as a sort of valve, allowing nerve-impulses to pass in only one direction.

The above-mentioned and similar facts—such as that conduction is slower in the gray matter than along the axons of the nerves, and more liable to interruption by the action of drugs, etc.—have led physiologists to the conception of a certain looseness of connection within the gray matter, or lack of such complete continuity as obtains between the parts of the axon. They have accordingly given a special name to the connection between the terminations of an axon and the dendrites of another cell. This name, *synapse* (compare Fig. 58), signifies a "fitting" together, as distinguished from a "growing" together. In this way, axon and dendrites are conceived of as dovetailed together;—perhaps very snugly, but without such complete continuity as obtains between an axon and its cell-body, or between the cell-body and its dendrites. A cell-body, with the axon and dendrites especially belonging to it, is thus thought of as a continuous whole, within which conduction is easy and can occur in any direction; whereas a certain degree of discontinuity or separation is conceived to exist between one cell and another. When regarded in this way, each cell with its branches is called a *neurone;* and the doctrine that some degree of discontinuity exists between the neurones is called the *neurone theory.*

§ 13. The history of the neurone theory is interesting and suggestive as to the difficulties and the nature of the conclusions in this entire field of inquiry. The first clearly defined theory regarding the connections existing within the gray matter was that of Gerlach, who, in 1870, concluded from the knowledge then in hand that the dendrites and other branches of the nerve-cells united with one another into a dense and continuous network throughout the gray matter. This "nerve-net" conception held the field for about twenty years. Meanwhile the use of the Golgi method of staining, especially in the hands of the Spanish investigator, S. Ramón y Cajal, gave pictures of individual cells with numerous branches, but with no indication of anastomoses between cells, or of a continuous network of branches. On the contrary, each cell, with its branches, appeared separate from every other cell. This anatomical, or histological, result was quite in accord with the embryological observations of His,—namely (see above, p. 41), that the gray matter starts as a collection of separate cells, out of which the branches grow. Summing up the anatomical and embryological evidence, Waldeyer, in 1891, formulated the theory that nerve-cells, however much they might branch, remained, as they had begun, separate units which he named "neurones." The rapidity with which this new conception won its way among all classes of students is notable in scientific history. To the physiologists it was welcome as affording an explanation of the slow conduction and valve-like action of the connections within the gray substance of the nervous system. To the pathologist, it was also welcome as affording an explanation of the peculiar fact that de-

generation of nervous tissue resulting from injury extends only to
the terminations of the axons injured; and does not spread freely
over to other cells. Even the psychologist found the neurone theory
useful, since learning and association could now be understood as
dependent on the formation of new synapses; while sleep and unconsciousness might very well be due to slight influences obstruct-
ing the synapse. Many other mental facts received help from this
theory, in respect of their psycho-physical interpretation. From
about 1891, accordingly, the neurone theory attained great vogue
and came into well-nigh universal acceptation.

There was always, however, a minority of able neurologists who
did not fully accept the neurone theory, and who were stimulated
by it to look more carefully for direct connections between the cells
of the gray matter. Protoplasmic 'bridges were found to exist in
the nervous systems of very low orders of invertebrates (compare
p. 18); but in the higher invertebrates and in vertebrates, such
bridges were not found; and all now admit that they do not exist.
The centre of discussion was, accordingly, shifted with the new discoveries regarding the inner structure of the nerve-cell and its
branches (see p. 106). Since the fibrils, from their appearance,
are probably the real conductors of nerve-impulses, continuity
between two cells might be established if simply the fibrils, rather
than larger protoplasmic branches such as the dendrites, could be
traced as emerging from one cell and entering into another cell.
In some invertebrates, a passage of fibrils from cell to cell was announced by Apáthy; but this alleged discovery has not been confirmed by some of the competent authorities who have followed
Apáthy's methods.

In the exceedingly intricate gray matter of vertebrates, the task
of tracing such minute structures as the nerve-fibrils from one cell to
another would at best be extremely difficult; and for this reason,
no strong disproof can be based on failure to trace them. In point
of fact, however, the evidence for such passage of fibrils from one
cell to another in the gray matter is, up to the present, slight and
dubious. There is, indeed, an appearance observed on, or near,
the surface of many cell-bodies, which has been called, from its
discoverer, the "Golgi net," and which consists of fine fibrils; and
some observers, as Bethe,[1] have found some evidence of fibrils
issuing from within the cell and joining the Golgi net. On the
other hand, this net has seemed to be in continuity with axons approaching the cell from elsewhere. These observations seem to
show a possible path of fibrillar connection between the nerve-cells.

[1] *Allgemeine Anatomie und Physiologie des Nervensystems*, pp. 65–78 (Leipzig,
1903).

The full meaning of the fibrillar theory may be summed up in this: that the fibrils are the real units of the nervous system. The cells, which are the units according to the neurone theory, are to the fibrillar theory merely the medium in which the fibrils grow and by which they are nourished. The fibrils issue freely from the cells and perhaps form a fibril network in the spaces between them. This network, according to the theory, would therefore be the essential structure of the gray matter; it would contain the connections between incoming and outgoing axons. Fibrils would enter the network from axons coming into the gray matter; and fibrils from the network would enter the dendrites and cell-bodies, and then pass—at least some of them—into the axons of these cell-bodies and so away to other parts.

As between the neurone theory and the fibrillar theory, it is impossible at present to decide with certainty; but there is no doubt that the neurone theory still commands the support of the majority of authorities; and that it serves, for the present, the useful purpose of summing up a large proportion of the known facts that have a bearing on the connections within the gray matter of the nervous system.

§ 14. It has already been said (p. 40) that a considerable part of the central nervous system consists of a substance which is characteristically different from either of the definitely recognized nerve elements, and to which the name of "neuroglia" has been given. This name was originally designed to embody the opinion that it acted as a kind of "nerve-cement" (nerven-kitt); and neuroglia has frequently been classified with the connective tissue. But as long ago as 1880, Henle said of this substance: "It is at all events to be distinguished from connective tissue on account of its chemical properties."[1] Microscopic examination shows that the neuroglia is by no means a homogeneous mass, but is composed of innumerable minute cells which differ in their physical characteristics from the typical nerve-cells. The cell-body is small;[2] the branches are, in general, of tolerably uniform size, and at the very edge the fibres end in minute balls or knobs. The method of the branching of the neuroglia cells, when any branching occurs, enables the observer to differentiate them from the dendrites of the true nerve-cell. Thus their appearance has caused some of them to be called "spider cells" (see Fig. 59).

Neuroglia cells differ both in size and in distribution, in the different parts of the central nervous system. They are most numerous

---

[1] *Anatomie d. Menschen*, text, p. 306.
[2] Some of these cells are, indeed, exceedingly minute, being scarcely more than $\frac{1}{8000}$ or $\frac{1}{5000}$ of an inch in diameter.

where there are fewest nervous elements—as though their office were
to fill in the interstices, and to constitute the background or soil for
holding the nerve-cells and nerve-fibres. They sometimes arrange
themselves in regular order, as, for example, around the central
commissural region of the cord. The distribution of their branches
is fairly uniform in the middle of the cord, but changes at the edge,
where the massing of the fibres constitutes the outer wall of the cord
and the posterior fissure.

As respects their origin, these spider cells seem to be ectodermal
and not connective tissue cells. They therefore arise from the same

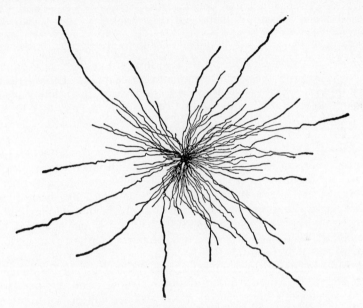

FIG. 59.—A Spider Cell from the Spinal Cord. (V. Lenhossék.)

embryological elements as the nerve-cells. This, however, does
not prove that they are, functionally considered, true nerve-cells;
for cells from the same source may have altogether different functions in their developed form. In general, the *supporting cells* of
the nervous substance are older, ontogenetically, than the true
nervous elements. They begin in primitive cells, which are arranged radially around the cord centre. But these primitive cells
gradually undergo modifications of shape, before their place appears to be taken by the spider cells. On the other hand, some of
the spider cells seem to come directly from the ectodermal cells, without passing through the intermediate cell period.

It thus appears that we cannot as yet be perfectly certain as to what is the whole functional relation of the neuroglia to the acknowledged elements of the nervous system. And, indeed, although we now know much more than when these words were written, it still remains true, as Eckhard[1] said years ago: "If we start the inquiry, what formal elements of the brain and cord take part in the activities of these organs, and in what way they do take part, we are able to give to it only a very unsatisfactory answer."[2]

[1] Hermann, *Handbuch d. Physiologie*, II, ii, p. 15.

[2] The modern view of the nature of neuroglia was first hinted at by Kölliker (*Handb. d. Gewebelehre*, 4th Aufl., 1862, pp. 304 ff.); it was worked out more fully by Golgi in contributions to the histology of the central nervous system, published in the *Rivista clinica di Bologna*, during 1871–1872. Further important contributions to our knowledge were made by F. Boll ("Die Histologie u. Histiogenese d. nervösen Centralorgane," *Archiv. f. Psychiatrie u. Nervenkrankh.*, Bd. IV, p. 1); by H. Gieke ("Die Stützsubstanz d. Centralsystems," *Archiv. f. mikr. Anatomie*, Bd. XXV, pp. 441 ff., and Bd. XXVI, pp. 129 ff.); and by W. Vigual ("Sur le dévelloppement des éléments de la moëlle des mammifères," *Archives de Physiol. normale et pathol.*, I, 1884, pp. 230 ff.). The conclusions of these investigators, which were at first rather vague, have subsequently been on the whole confirmed by His, Cajal, and other later workers.

CHAPTER V

CHEMISTRY OF THE NERVOUS SYSTEM

§ 1. It is conceivable that, in the progress of the sciences concerned, the action of the nervous substance should be brought into such relations with its chemistry and physics, that nervous functions might be stated very largely in terms of physical and chemical processes. At present so engaging a prospect seems indefinitely remote; partly because of our meagre knowledge of the chemistry of the nervous tissues, and partly because of insufficient knowledge regarding the intimate functions of the nervous elements. Much the same thing is true, indeed, of the muscles and the glands: the known functions of these organs, too, cannot as yet be explained in terms of physics and chemistry. In regard to nervous tissue, we know fairly well the chemical elements which enter into its composition; and we know some of the compounds which exist there. In general, the same chemical elements are represented in nervous as in other tissues, though in somewhat different proportions. Also, the same general classes of compounds occur in nervous and in other tissues. In respect neither of their elements nor of their compounds, therefore, do the different tissues present such striking differences as might be expected from their various functions.

§ 2. The general chemistry of the brain and nerves is still in an undeveloped condition. Apparently, a great number of somewhat similar compounds exist in the brain, the isolation and analysis of which is attended with great difficulty. These difficulties are not due simply to the complex constitution of most of the substances with which we have to deal. They are also very largely due to the fact that these substances are products of life; and living tissue cannot be at the same time kept in normal condition and subjected to the handling necessary for chemical analysis. As soon as it is no longer alive, or at any rate long before any chemical analysis can be completed, the constitution of such tissue is changed. However carefully the chemical elements, the constituents, which enter into the nervous substance may be preserved, their *constitution*, their chemical arrangement and behavior, cannot be preserved. It is impossible—for example—for the chemist even to determine the specific gravity of uncoagulated blood, "except by operating with extreme expedition and at temperatures below 0° C."

The specific gravity of the white matter is somewhat greater than that of the gray. Danilewski found the specific gravity of the gray matter in the human brain to vary from 1.029 to 1.039; that of the white matter from 1.039 to 1.043.[1] Other authors have assigned slightly lower values for both. This difference in the weight of the white and the gray matter is chiefly due to difference in the relative amounts of water and of solids which they respectively contain. Determinations by several authors[2] agree in assigning about 86 per cent. of water and 14 per cent. of solids to the gray matter (cerebral cortex); whereas the white matter shows only from 70 to 71 per cent. of water. The water-content of the peripheral nerves is still less, ranging from 40 to 70 per cent.

§ 3. The chemical elements chiefly present in the brain, as in all living cells and tissues, are carbon, hydrogen, oxygen, nitrogen and phosphorus, chlorine, sodium, and potassium.

Of chemical compounds, the brain, like all living cells, contains water, salts (such as sodium chloride and potassium phosphate), proteids, and lipoids.

The proteids are highly complex organic compounds of carbon, hydrogen, oxygen, and nitrogen; they form a large proportion of the substance of all living cells, whether animal or vegetable, and appear to play a very important part in the life of the cells. They have, indeed, been regarded as the essentially living parts of the cells; but it is probable that the role of the salts held in solution, and of the lipoids, is no less essential to life.

Of the solids contained in the nervous centres, more than one-half in the gray, and about one-third in the white, consist of these proteid substances. Four such bodies are now generally recognized; of which the most abundant is a nucleo-proteid containing phosphorus, which is soluble in water; it is believed to come in large measure from the nuclei of the cells, and is analogous to the nucleo-proteids derived from all other cellular tissues. Two other proteids found in the brain substance are globulins, differing in their solubilities and in the temperatures at which they coagulate (47° C. and 70° C. respectively); they are also quite similar to the globulins derived from all other cellular tissues, such as muscle, liver, and kidney.[3] It will be noticed that all these three proteids have been found to be soluble and coagulable at varying temperatures.

[1] *Med. Centralbl.*, xviii, p. 241.

[2] Cited by S. Fränkel, in his "Gehirn-Chemie," in Asher and Spiro's *Ergebnisse der Physiologie*, 1909, VIII, p. 217. This work has been followed largely in the statements made in the following pages with regard to the chemistry of the nervous substance of the brain.

[3] Bernhardt; also Halliburton, *Journal of Physiology*, 1893, XV, 90; *Chemistry of Muscle and Nerve*, 1904, p. 61.

Besides these three soluble proteids, the brain yields a small proportion of an insoluble proteid, called neurokeratin,[1] which is similar in its properties to the keratin that forms so large a proportion of the hair, horn, nails, and other like appendages of the skin. This substance is found both in the medullated nerves and in the central organs—according to Kühne in both gray and white matter, but according to W. Koch[2] only in the white. As the researches of Kühne and his pupils showed some years ago, neurokeratin occurs also in the retina. It contains carbon, hydrogen, nitrogen, and sulphur, besides inorganic constituents.

§ 4. It is the lipoids which are likely to be of most interest in their relation to the physiology and psycho-physics of the brain. Indeed, the brain is chiefly characterized, chemically considered, by its exceptionally large content of these substances. It is the white matter, however, rather than the gray, which is peculiarly rich in them; and this is the same thing as saying that the white matter is chemically more specialized than is the gray; while the latter seems to differ but little from the substance of other living cells. Since the myelin sheath of the nerve-fibres is the distinguishing feature of the white nervous matter, it appears probable that the lipoids are constituents of the myelin sheath; this, indeed, may be regarded as certain; and it is likely also that a large share of the lipoid content of gray matter is due to the fine myelinated fibres which penetrate it. In a word, the chemistry of the brain, so far as it presents anything peculiar, appears for the most part to be the chemistry of the myelin sheath. And the chemistry of the myelin sheath is for the most part the study of its "lipoids."

§ 5. The term "lipoid" means, etymologically, a "fat-like body"; it covers a considerable number of organic compounds which are not exactly fat, but which resemble fat in some of its physical and chemical properties. To understand the use of the term, it is necessary to consider briefly the chemistry of living cells in general.

As we have already seen (p. 14), one of the most essential properties of a living cell is its power of taking in and letting out dissolved substances through its surface; while, nevertheless, not allowing the passage of such substances to be perfectly free. This we have called "the selective," or "preferential," power of the living cell. Such a product could not live without exchange of substances with the medium in which it lives; but, at the same time, it could not live if the diffusion of these substances were perfectly free, for then it would soon differ in no respect from its surrounding medium.

---

[1] Ewald and Kühne, *Verhandlungen der nat.-hist.-med. Vereins*, N. F. I, 357 (Heidelberg, 1877).

[2] *Zeitschrift für physiologische Chemie*, 1902, XXXVI, p. 134.

The individuality of the cell depends on its power of resisting free osmosis through its surface. Its surface is not freely permeable, but "semi-permeable." In many cells, accordingly, the outer surface consists of a more or less definite membrane, and the necessary "semi-permeability" is very likely a property of this membrane. Certain chemical agents dissolve or otherwise alter the membrane; among these are the cell-narcotics, ether, chloroform, benzol, and others. From this it is inferred that substances which are dissolved out of the cell by the application of ether, etc., have special importance in the membrane of the living cell, and probably have much to do with the resistance offered by the cell to free osmosis.[1]

Now since substances extracted by ether, etc., include, besides the true fats, the class of bodies called lipoids, the definition of the term ("lipoid") may be given in terms of this property of being extracted by ether and other cell-narcotics; or, more biologically but less definitely, in terms of the probable function of these bodies in the cell membrane. This function may be shared by the fats proper.

§ 6. The brain contains a large amount of substances which can be extracted by ether, etc., but which are not fats. It is probable, as was said before, that these substances come chiefly from the myelin sheath, which may perhaps be regarded as a highly developed cell membrane. Thudicum,[2] whose work on the chemistry of the brain is very elaborate and fundamental, recognizes three well-defined classes of brain lipoids, besides others less well understood. The compounds of the first class contain both nitrogen and phosphorus; those of the second contain nitrogen but no phosphorus; and those of the third class contain neither of these elements, but only carbon, hydrogen, and oxygen. He is further able to subdivide these classes, and to point out several members existing within some of the groups; but inasmuch as most of these substances are as yet imperfectly defined, and as great difference of opinion regarding some of them exists among chemical authorities, it will not be worth our while to give a full list of them here; we may confine our attention to a few of the best-established.

§ 7. Cholesterin is the best established of all the brain lipoids; it belongs to the third of the classes just mentioned, containing neither phosphorus nor nitrogen. Its composition corresponds

[1] See Ivar Bang, "Biochemie der Zell-lipoide," in Asher and Spiro's *Ergebnisse der Physiologie*, 1907, VIII, 1 and 2 Abth., pp. 134 ff.

[2] "Researches on the Chemical Constitution of the Brain," in Reports of the Medical Officer of the Privy Council and Local Government Board, 1874; and *Die chemische Konstitution des Gehirns des Menschen und der Tiere* (Tübingen, 1901).

closely to the formula $C_{27}H_{44}O$, which may also be written, as a slight indication of its structure, $C_{27}H_{43}OH$. It belongs to the alcohols, being the hydroxide of a hypothetical hydrocarbon, $C_{27}H_{44}$, which has not yet been prepared. It is a "monatomic" alcohol, having one OH group by which it combines with acids, as with the fatty acids, and thus forms compounds which are probably present in the brain. Cholesterin is also widely present in other tissues, and indeed in all tissues, both animal and vegetable; but is especially abundant in nervous tissue. Cholesterin is a solid at body temperature, its melting-point being 147° C. Its specific gravity is 1.046. It is insoluble in water, though a mixture of it and other lipoids is soluble. It is soluble in hot alcohol, in ether, chloroform, etc., and crystallizes out of these solutions in the form of fine needles (out of ether) or of rhombic tables (out of alcohol). It is electrically a non-conductor.

To the class of lipoids which contain nitrogen but no phosphorus are to be reckoned a considerable number of substances, such as cerebrin, cerebron, phrenosin, and kerasin. Some of these differ but little among themselves, according to the analyses, and may even be identical, if allowance be made for accidental impurities.[1]

§ 8. Most interest, however, attaches itself to the class of *phosphorized* lipoids. The fact that the brain is rich in phosphorus has long been deemed significant, and at one time the rather crude dictum, "No thought without phosphorus," attained considerable vogue. But on the one hand, there are many other elements which are essential to the brain's activity; and, on the other hand, phosphorus is present in all living cells. Phosphorus as a chemical element of the nervous substance has, therefore, no monopoly; and the statement, "No life without phosphorus," would more adequately represent the facts of the case. The phosphorus of the brain is for the most part contained in its lipoids, that is to say, in the myelin sheaths of its nerve fibres; and, instead of hoping to discover some direct connection between phosphorus and consciousness, we should, if we desire to follow a scientific and promising course of investigation, seek first for the part played by phosphorus-containing lipoids in the myelin sheath.

While a large share of the lipoid substances which have been extracted from the brain do, without doubt, contain phosphorus, and while a considerable number of different compounds, belonging to this class, have been obtained, analyzed, and named by chemists, the difficulties of satisfactory determination are here so great that

[1] See Posner and Gies, *Journal of Biological Chemistry*, I, 59; and S. Fränkel, in Asher and Spiro's *Ergebnisse der Physiologie*, 1909, VIII, 249.

there is no one of these bodies which has been generally accepted as a *preformed* constituent of the brain. There is no doubt concerning some of the decomposition products of these lipoids, and none, therefore, regarding some essential facts of their structure; but the agreement ceases when the exact composition and formula of the brain constituents is in question. Controversy between authorities has been especially bitter in this field, and the substances around which the controversy has principally centered are these two: lecithin and protagon.

§ 9. Lecithin is a well-recognized and fairly well-understood substance; but its occurrence preformed in the living brain is not established beyond dispute. It occurs abundantly in the yolk of eggs, and is known also to occur in muscle tissue; it probably also occurs quite widely in cells of different kinds. The formulæ assigned for it by different authors differ somewhat, possibly because there is more than one lecithin. Thudicum's formula for brain lecithin is $C_{43}H_{84}NPO_9$. It is described as a phosphorized fat, and its relation to the ordinary fats may be roughly expressed by saying that, whereas these consist of glycerin combined with fatty acids, lecithin contains, in addition, phosphoric acid and the alkaloid cholin.[1]

Lecithin is an unstable compound, easily breaking up into simpler compounds, while on the other hand it apparently enters into still more complex compounds with proteids and with cholesterin. Physically, lecithin is a yellowish-white, waxy, hygroscopic solid, which in thin layers shines with a silky lustre. It is soluble in alcohol, ether, etc., but in water it swells to a sort of paste, much like starch. Electrically it is a non-conductor; and bound up with this is its property of resisting free osmosis through any membrane into which it enters. It may also be called a highly sensitive substance, since its physical condition, while in solution, is readily changed (as by the action of ions).[2] All of these properties are interesting and suggestive of the probable importance of lecithin in the life of the cells. As was stated above, the existence of lecithin preformed in the brain is not completely made out; but if it does not occur there, then other similar substances, such as Thudicum's kephalin, or else more complex compounds into which lecithin and kephalin enter,

---

[1] The complex structure of lecithin is more precisely stated by saying that glycerin contains three hydroxyl groups; by one of which it takes up phosphoric acid, and by the others, two molecules of fatty acid; meanwhile, the phosphoric acid also combines with the base, cholin, which has itself a rather complex structure, as expressed by its analytic name, trimethyl-oxyethyl-ammonium hydroxide.

[2] W. Koch, "The Lecithans," *Decennial Publications of the University of Chicago*, 1902, vol. X; *American Journal of Physiology*, 1904, XI, 303.

must exist in the brain. In other words, the phosphorus of the brain is partly contained in compounds presenting the general characteristics which have been described as those of lecithin.

§ 10. Protagon was discovered, as a new proximate principle that can be separated from the brain, in 1864, by Dr. Oscar Liebreich; his discovery was announced in a paper [1] published in 1865. This investigator gave to this substance the name which it still bears, as in his opinion the first to be definitely ascertained among the specific constituents of the brain ($\pi\rho\omega\tau\alpha\gamma\delta\varsigma$, leading the van). He assigned to it the formula $C_{116}H_{241}N_4O_{22}P$. More recent work has changed this formula to some extent—especially in assigning five atoms of N to each one of P, and in adding a small proportion of sulphur to the molecule.

The process by which he obtained it from the brain may be thus briefly described (the description will serve to illustrate in general the processes of physiological chemistry): Perfectly fresh ox's brains are freed from the blood and membranes, and are then digested for about a day in eighty-five per cent. alcohol; from this fluid, when filtered, a quantity of white flocculent precipitate is obtained, and the cholesterin and other bodies soluble in ether are dissolved out; from the substance left undissolved, when dried and reduced to powder and digested for many hours with alcohol, and then filtered and cooled, microscopic crystals separate themselves, arranged for the most part in rosettes. The substance thus crystallized is protagon. Repetition of the alternate processes of solution and crystallization is resorted to for purifying the protagon.

§ 11. The history of the protagon problem is interesting and curious in several ways, even apart from the importance which has been assigned this substance as the most characteristic chemical substance of the brain, and the one which would therefore have especially to be considered in any attempt to correlate the composition of the brain with its functions. A substance apparently identical with Liebreich's protagon had been obtained by several previous observers (1834–1850), with whose work Liebreich was unacquainted. The consensus of expert opinion on the chemical unity of the substance has swung back and forth several times in the last half century. At first, on Liebreich's discovery, it was accepted, and lecithin was regarded as probably non-existent in the fresh brain; then the work of Diaconow (1868) and of Thudicum (1874) discredited protagon, by tending to show that it was a mixture of no constant composition; and for years the belief in its unity was relegated to the limbo of exploded views. Next, Gamgee (1879) re-

[1] "Ueber die chemische Beschaffenheit der Gehirnsubstanz," *Annalen der Chemie und Pharmacie*, CXXXIV, pp. 29–44.

suscitated it, and it enjoyed for two decades general acceptance. Beginning about 1900, results supporting Thudicum have been obtained by several writers, who do not hesitate to say that the chemical unity of protagon has been fully disproved. Gies and his collaborators[1] have shown that if the method employed for purifying protagon is repeated time after time, instead of approximating to a constant composition, the protagon changes at each repetition of the process. They infer that pure protagon, if it exists, has never been prepared, and that probably it does not exist as a definite compound. Their results have been confirmed and accepted by other observers.[2]

On the other hand, Cramer has found it possible to prepare from the brain, by an entirely different method, a substance which has the same quantitative composition as Liebreich's protagon. This constancy of composition under different methods of preparation, taken in connection with the crystalline form of the substance, leads authorities such as Hammersten[3] and Halliburton[4] to conclude that its chemical identity has not been disproved. The former of these two authorities regards protagon as a crystalline substance which is extremely difficult to separate from other substances that are in part its decomposition products. But Fränkel's position[5] is alone tenable; for he regards the whole state of the subject as at present thoroughly unsatisfactory. To illustrate and enforce this truth may be regarded as the principal justification for the attention which we have ourselves bestowed upon so-called protagon.

§ 12. The specific chemistry of the histological elements of the nervous system, or of the various parts of such elements, is yet more meagre and doubtful than its general chemistry. The differences between the composition of gray and of white matter indicate that the nerve-cell body is rich in proteids, whereas the myelin sheath consists very largely of lipoids. The internal structure of the cells and axons, as revealed by selective stains, is an indication of chemical differences between the parts differentiated by the stains; but the interpretation of the reactions on staining is by no means easy, and little can at present be said regarding the chemistry of parts of the cells.

§ 13. It need scarcely be said, in conclusion, that we have little knowledge respecting the relation which exists between the chemical constitution and chemical processes of the nervous system, on the one hand, and, on the other, the phenomena of so-called mind.

[1] See Posner and Gies, *Journal of Biological Chemistry*, 1905, vol. I, p. 98.
[2] Rosenheim and Tebb, 1907, *Journal of Physiology*, XXXVI, pp. 1 ff.
[3] *Lehrbuch der physiologischen Chemie*, 1907, p. 483.
[4] *Biochemistry of Muscle and Nerve*, 1904, p. 65.   [5] Op. cit., p. 251.

Nevertheless, certain important general relations may be pointed out between the chemical nature of the nervous mechanism and its psycho-physical functions. The extremely high organization and chemically sensitive constitution of this mechanism are beyond doubt related to all its distinctive activities. Like every other natural material structure, the nervous system is obviously adapted to its peculiar kind of work. Chemically considered, it appears as composed of a number of extremely complex and highly unstable compounds. It therefore holds in its chemical constitution a large amount of disposable energy; this energy it yields readily when the equilibrium of its molecules is in any way disturbed. Within certain limits, it explodes with increasing surrender of its disposable energy as the number and intensity of the demands upon it are increased—very much as would a gun which should be arranged so as to go off with greater energy as the pressure of the finger on its trigger is repeated or increased.

It is probable that the substance of the nerves is the seat of a chemical synthesis, as the result of which still more complex bodies are constructed from the already complex alimentary material furnished by the blood; such bodies have a high value as combustibles, and thus, as has been said, possess a significant amount of disposable energy. The relation of a supply of oxygen to the nerve-centres is also important to notice. The nerve-fibres require comparatively a small amount of oxygen. It may be conjectured that in their case, as in the case of muscle-fibre, intra-molecular oxygen is of some use in preparing explosive materials. But at present we must be satisfied with conjecture on this point. On the contrary, the vascular nature of the central organs creates a presumption that the chemical processes which have their seat in them require an abundance of oxygen. Experience confirms this presumption. The respiratory centre in the medulla oblongata is chiefly controlled in its action by the amount of oxygen which reaches it in the blood. The phenomena of consciousness vanish when the supply of oxygenated blood is cut off from the brain.

Although we are still in the dark as to the precise significance of the visual purple, the phenomena which the study of it has brought to light are suggestive of unseen chemical processes that are set up in the retina, and so serve as stimulus for the fibrils of the optic nerve. In general we know that certain sensations are dependent upon the chemical constitution and activity of the various end-organs of sense.

Further researches can scarcely fail to enlarge our knowledge of those facts of relation which exist between the chemical constitution and changes of the nervous mechanism and the phenomena of psychical life. Perhaps the more particular statements of fact may ultimately be gathered into those more general statements of fact, more or less verifiable by experiment, which we consider sufficient to constitute scientifically verifiable *laws*. But *why* certain chemical constituents, when combined and changed in definite fashion, should be specifically connected with certain conscious experiences, will probably always remain a quite unanswerable inquiry.

CHAPTER VI

THE NERVES AS CONDUCTORS

§ 1. In that threefold economy of organs which characterizes the developed nervous mechanism, the office of propagating the neural process between the central organs and the end-organs has been assigned to the nerves. The power to originate this process under the action of external stimuli, although experiment shows that it belongs to the nerves, is not exercised by them while in their normal place within the mechanism. It is the office of the end-organs to transmute the physical molecular processes, which are their stimuli, into the physiological and neural process, and hand it over, as it were, to these conducting cords. But the office of the nerves as conductors is, of course, not like that of a tube which conducts along its channel some kind of fluid, nor is it like that of the wire or bell-metal which is thrown into vibration throughout. It is a molecular commotion which, when started at any point in the nerves, moves in both directions from point to point along its course. The intimate connection between the two functions of excitation and conduction becomes, then, at once apparent. Indeed, *excitation* may be considered as the setting-up of the process of conduction; *conduction* as the uninterrupted continuance, or propagation from point to point, successively, of the process of excitation. Each minute subdivision of the nerve, then, must be regarded as constituting, in some sort, a source or centre of stimulation with respect to its neighboring subdivisions. If the nerve-commotion is to move along the nerve N, between two distant portions of its structure, a and z, then a must act upon its neighbor b as a stimulus, b upon c, and so on successively until y is found stimulating z, and the process of progressive excitation or conduction is complete.

§ 2. It follows from what has just been said that, in considering the nerves as conductors, the conditions and laws of the origination of that process of excitation which they conduct must be taken into account. It is neither necessary nor convenient, however, to carry throughout a distinction between the two functions—the excitability and the conductivity—of the nerves; it is better to regard them as one process, looked at from somewhat different points of view.

127

Clearly, if the "nerve impulse" is to be propagated, it must first be aroused at some point in the nerve; and under normal conditions, by the action on it of other organs. In the case of sensory nerve-fibres, the stimulus is furnished by the action of modified receptive cells; as, for example, the optic nerve is normally excited by the rods and cones, which themselves have been aroused by the action of light. In the case of motor nerve-fibres, the normal source of their activity lies in the spinal cord or brain-stem; here they are aroused by the action on them of other nerve-fibres—such action occurring at the synapse, where the fine terminations of an axon come into relation with the dendrites of another cell and so, indirectly, with the axon of that cell.

§ 3. In studying the physiology of the nerves, it is often necessary to separate them from their normal connections in the body, and arouse them by artificial means. At first sight, this artificiality in the experimental procedure would seem to vitiate the results; but control experiments show that the nerve impulse behaves in the same way—so far as can be observed—whether it is aroused in the natural or in an artificial manner. Apparently a nerve-impulse is a *nerve* impulse, however aroused. The objection that the experiments are made on the nerves of animals, from which an inference to human nerves may be doubtful, is also met by the statement that a nerve is a nerve, from whatever species of animal. Such observations as have been possible on human nerves show no difference between them and the nerves of other mammals; and there are only minor differences between the latter and the nerves of the frog, which have most often been used in experiments. While this is true of the medullated nerves, unmedullated nerves form, in many respects, a separate class.

In experimenting with a nerve, some sort of indicator is needed to show when it is active; for an active nerve does not differ visibly from an inactive one. For a motor nerve, a good indicator is afforded by the attached muscle, which contracts when the nerve impulse reaches it, and so indicates the activity of the nerve. For a sensory nerve a reflex movement or a sensation (in the human subject) may be used as the indicator. Since, however, reflexes and sensations involve the complex and variable activity of nerve centres, the physiologist prefers the motor nerves, and makes a large share of his experiments on what he calls a "nerve-muscle preparation."

This preparation consists of a muscle freshly taken from the living animal with its attached nerve dissected out; for example, the gastrocnemius muscle of the frog with the attached sciatic nerve. Such a preparation may be kept alive for some time in a moist chamber. By the simple contrivance of connecting the end of the muscle with a lever, arming the lever with some means of making a mark—either pen, or bristle, or needle—and bringing its point thus armed to bear on a rapidly travelling surface (plain paper, or smoked paper or glass), the time and amount of the contractions of the muscle may be recorded. The most refined means for noting the exact instant when the stimulus is applied, and also the state of the effects produced at every succeeding instant of their duration, are of first importance. The nerve may be stimulated with different kinds, degrees, and directions of the electrical current (or with other forms of stimuli) at any points preferred in its stretch, and under a great variety of conditions with respect to temperature, moisture, mechanical pressure or stricture, integrity and vitality of its structure, etc.; and the effects of such stimulations upon the contractions of the muscle may be noted and compared as they have been recorded. Means for testing the most delicate and rapid changes in the electrical or thermometric conditions of the nerve may be applied to it at any point of its stretch. Variations and refinements of experiments essentially the same may be almost indefinitely multiplied; the experiments may be repeated, and verified or corrected, by the same observer or by others. Inasmuch as the preparation is both muscle *and* nerve, an acquaintance with the behavior of the muscle, and with the laws of its contraction, is necessary in order that it may be known how much of the complex phenomena is to be ascribed to the functional activity of muscle, how much to that of nerve. But into a statement of the general laws of contractile tissues, and of the nature and explanation of the behavior of muscle when irritated, we cannot enter in great detail.[1]

Being thus provided with a fresh nerve and a muscle to serve as indicator of the nerve's activity, the physiologist is able to observe and draw inferences with regard to the excitability and conductivity of the nerve.

§ 4. As respects its excitability, the nerve is found to be easily aroused by stimuli applied directly to it at any point. Pinch the nerve, and the muscle instantly contracts; drop a light weight on the nerve, and again the muscle contracts. These are examples of "mechanical stimuli," which are thus proved to be capable of arousing the nerve to activity. A variety of chemical substances also excite the nerve; acids are especially effective, bases less so;

[1] For a description of the method and results of experimenting with the nerve-muscle preparation, more accessible to the general reader than the books to which reference will chiefly be made, see Howell's *Text-book of Physiology*, chap. I, p. 5.

of salts, some, like sodium chloride, act as stimuli, while others, such as most of the salts of the heavy metals, kill the nerve without exciting it.   The same effect follows use of too strong a solution of any of these chemical agents.   Sudden heating of the nerve acts as a stimulus.   Electric shocks, especially in the form of induced currents, are highly effective.   These four classes of agents —mechanical, chemical, thermal, and electrical—are called "general stimuli," because they are capable of arousing, not only nerves, but a great variety of forms of living matter, including the muscles and glands of the higher animals and the less specialized protoplasm of protozoa.

§ 5. The effectiveness of any of these stimuli depends in part on its *suddenness*. Slow changes of temperature, for example, do not excite the nerve; and very gradually increasing pressure may crush the nerve without exciting it.   The electric current, too, must have a degree of suddenness in its changes, if it is to act as a stimulus to nerve.

In regard to this last point, Du Bois-Reymond, one of the pioneers in "electrophysiology," announced in 1845[1] the discovery of two closely related laws of the electrical excitation of nerve.   The first law is that the mere passage of a current through the nerve does not arouse it; only *changes* in the electric current act as stimuli; but these changes may consist either in increasing the current or in decreasing it.   This law is the expression of a fact which is easily verified on the nerve-muscle preparation.   When the current from a battery is passed through a nerve, the muscle gives a twitch at the starting of the current, and then, usually, remains at rest during the passage of the current, only to twitch again at the stopping of the current.   Or, if the current is not entirely stopped, but is suddenly cut down in strength, still the muscle twitches, as it does also if the current is suddenly increased.   The second law of Du Bois-Reymond is that the exciting effect of any change of current is greater, the more sudden the change.   If the current is gradually increased by a certain amount, the muscle does not twitch, whereas if the same amount of increase is effected quickly, the muscle twitches.

The validity of the first of these laws has not been much affected by later investigations, at least so far as concerns the nerves.   Certain other tissues are excited by the passage of a steady current, but the nerve is usually not excited in such a way as to arouse the muscle which is attached to it.   The nerve is not, however, by any means in its normal quiescent state during the passage of a current, but is

[1] In a paper communicated to the Physiological Society in Berlin; see also his *Untersuchungen über thierische Electricität*, I, 258.

in quite an unusual condition as concerns its excitability and conductivity. This fact will be brought out later in the chapter.

The second law of Du Bois-Reymond needs qualification in the light of further experience. With the introduction of very rapidly oscillating currents ("Tesla" or "d'Arsonval currents"), it has been found that this effectiveness as stimuli by no means increases indefinitely with the rapidity of the oscillations. Oscillations up to 1,000,000 per second will indeed excite the nerve, but only if the current is very intense.[1] Beyond a certain point, the effectiveness of the oscillations decreases as their rate increases. It seems probable, therefore, that in order to have the greatest exciting effect on the nerve, the change of current must have a certain high speed, on either side of which its effectiveness decreases. Nerves would be in this respect like other irritable tissues, some of which are best stimulated by rather slow changes in the current, while others are best excited by more rapid changes. Each kind of tissue is best excited by a certain speed of change of the current; but the nerve has the distinction of being that tissue which is adapted to the most rapid change.

§ 6. Another similar distinction of the nerve is its very short "refractory period." An organ which is excited by a stimulus is apt to be inexcitable by another stimulus which follows immediately; it is said to be *refractory* during a certain period after commencing its response to the first stimulus. The length of this refractory period differs in different organs. In the heart, in which the phenomenon is most striking, the refractoriness lasts undiminished until the full strength of the muscular contraction is reached (or about 0.4 second), after which it gradually passes away. In the spinal cord and brain, the refractory period of some groups of nerve-cells may be as long, or even longer, than that of the heart. On the contrary, skeletal muscle has a much shorter period, not exceeding .01 second; while nerve-fibres have a refractory period of not over .002 second.[2] The nerve is, then, in all respects a quick-acting organ: it is best excited by a sudden stimulus; its response is prompt and brief, and it is very soon ready for a fresh stimulus.

§ 7. In still another and very important respect the nerve is distinguished for its quick action; and that is the speed of its conduction. In measuring the speed of conduction in a motor nerve, the nerve-muscle preparation is again employed. The determination of the rate of transmission in nerves was an achievement of

[1] Einthoven. Cited by Biedermann, *Ergebnisse der Physiologie*, 1903, II, part 2, 114.
[2] See Gotch and Burch, *Journal of Physiol.*, 1899, XXIII, p. xxii.

Helmholtz,[1] and it was the more noteworthy because it followed close on the prediction by Johannes Müller,[2] another eminent physiologist, that the speed of nerve-conduction would never be determined, because, as he was led to suppose, its speed was comparable with the speed of light. The method of Helmholtz was, however, simple enough. He measured the time elapsing between the moment of stimulation and the beginning of the muscular contraction, when the stimulus was applied as near the muscle as possible; and he then compared this with the corresponding time, when the stimulus was applied as far from the muscle as possible. The difference in time and the length of nerve between the two points of stimulation enabled him to calculate the speed of transmission between the same two points. Helmholtz's work has often been repeated and confirmed; and in this way, the rate of transmission in frog's nerve is known to be approximately 28 metres per second. In the human subject, similar experiments, in which a motor nerve is stimulated through the skin, at two distant points, have led to slightly higher values, or about 33 metres per second. For a convenient approximation, in English measures, we may take 100 feet per second as the rate in the motor nerve. In sensory nerves, the rate is much harder to measure, because the nerve leads into the centre, and the activity of the centre, which consumes a considerable and variable time, intervenes before any movement, reflex or voluntary, can be made to indicate that the nerve-impulse has arrived.[3] When stimulation is confined to single "touch spots," and spots of equal sensitivity are chosen, fairly precise results have been obtained,[4] indicating a speed of about 30–33 metres per second in the sensory nerves of the arms and legs.

This speed of about 100 feet per second is certainly modest in comparison with the speed of light. Yet, in this respect, as well as in the others mentioned in preceding paragraphs, nerves occupy a place of distinction among living tissues. This is specially true of medullated nerves. The non-medullated nerves have a much slower rate of transmission, which varies greatly in different animals. Mammalian unmedullated nerve conducts at about the speed of 8 metres per second; in the lobster, figures have been obtained ranging from 8 to 12 metres; but in some other invertebrates, speeds as low as a centimetre or even a millimetre per second have been observed. In human "striped " muscle, the rate of transmission of activity is 10–13 metres per second; in the cold-blooded

---

[1] *Archiv f. Anat. u. Physiol.*, 1850, pp. 276–364.
[2] See his *Handbuch der Physiologie*, I, pp. 581 f. (Coblenz, 1844).
[3] Cf. Dolley and Cattell, *Psychological Review*, 1894, I, 159.
[4] Kiesow, *Zeitschr. f. Psychol.*, 1903, XXXIII, 444.

frog, the speed is less than one half of this; and in the "unstriped" muscles of the stomach and other internal organs it is much slower still.[1]

§ 8. The conductivity of a nerve is altered by the physical and chemical agents applied to it. For example, cooling a nerve slows its rate of conduction, and warming it, within narrower limits, hastens the conduction. The anæsthetics, alcohol, ether, and chloroform, when applied in the form of vapor to a length of nerve enclosed in a small gas-tight chamber, lower the conductivity, and may entirely abolish it. The passage of an electric current through a length of nerve also interferes with its conductivity, as will be more fully explained later.

It is a curious fact that some of these agents act differently on the conductivity and on the excitability of the nerve. Thus, alcohol vapor, though lowering the conductivity, may even, at a certain stage in its action, raise the excitability of the portion of nerve to which it is applied, so that weaker stimuli will take effect there than in the portions under normal conditions. Carbon dioxide gas has the opposite effect: if applied to a short length of nerve, it lowers or abolishes the excitability of that portion without, for a time, interfering with the conduction through it of nerve impulses generated elsewhere. Cold, also, though lowering the speed and effectiveness of conduction, may even raise the excitability to certain classes of stimuli; especially, to those which consist of relatively *slow* changes. Cold, that is to say, makes the nerve a slower-acting mechanism, and so adapts it to take up slower changes in the agents which are applied to it.

It appears from these results that the excitability of a nerve is to some degree independent of its conductivity, and a separation of the two functions is indicated. Perhaps a better generalization of the results would be to say that the taking up of stimuli artificially applied to the surface of the nerve is subject to different conditions from those which determine its normal activity in taking up stimuli from adjoining parts of itself.[2]

§ 9. Another important fact regarding the conductivity of nerve-fibres is that they conduct in both directions. Under the normal conditions of stimulation a nerve-fibre has occasion to conduct only in one direction. Sensory fibres receive stimulation only from the receptive cells with which their peripheral ends are in connection; and they conduct only toward the nervous centres. Motor nerves,

---

[1] The figures are from several authorities; some of them have been brought together by Biedermann, *Ergebnisse der Physiologie*, 1903, II, part 2, 147, and by Gotch in *Schäfer's Textbook of Physiology*, 1900, II, p. 482.

[2] For these results, and a discussion of them, see Gotch, op. cit., pp. 484 ff.

in normal conditions, receive stimuli only at their central ends in the cord or brain stem; and they conduct only outward to the muscles. But when, in experimental work, a nerve-fibre is excited somewhere along its course, and not at its natural end, it is found to conduct in both directions; this it does, apparently, as perfectly in one direction as in the other. The evidence for these statements is not quite so easy to obtain as would at first appear, because most nerves are composed partly of sensory and partly of motor fibres, which, normally, conduct in opposite directions. The dorsal roots of the spinal nerves are, indeed, composed almost or quite entirely of sensory fibres, and the ventral roots of motor fibres. But in attempting to use these roots for experimental purposes, the difficulty arises of finding some sure indicator. If the fibres in the sensory root did conduct outward to the sense-organ, they could produce no movement or other change in that organ to show their outward conduction. And if the motor roots did, when excited, conduct inward to the cord, there is nothing to show this; because these fibres end in synapses in the gray matter of the cord, and no conduction occurs across these synapses, except in the outward direction.[1]

There is, however, an indicator in the wave of electrical change, which attends the impulse in its passage along a nerve, and which can be detected by a galvanometer. When this electrical "current of action" is used as an indicator, excitation of a sensory root is found to cause an outward-travelling impulse, and excitation of a motor nerve is found to cause an inward-travelling impulse which betrays itself by an electrical change in the motor roots.

Additional evidence of double conduction in nerves is afforded by experiments in which the muscle is utilized as the indicator. When, as happens in certain muscles, the motor axons split on approaching the muscle, one branch of each axon going to one part of the muscle, and the other branch to another part, it may be possible to cut the muscle in two without injuring the nerve, and then to excite one branch of the nerve and obtain contraction of both parts of the muscle. The excitation has been conveyed by the branched axons, which have conducted up along one branch to the point of bifurcation, and then down along the other branch. The motor axons have, therefore, conducted in both directions. To make this result convincing, the nerve must be severed from the spinal cord; otherwise the farther part of the muscle might be excited by reflex action—the upward conduction being afforded by sensory axons, which are sure to be interspersed with the motor fibres in the nerve. But sensory axons can transmit their excita-

---

[1] In regard to the irreversibility of conduction at the synapse, we have spoken in a preceding chapter.

tion to motor axons only through the nerve-centres, and severing the nerve from the cord destroys this possibility. When these conditions are complied with, the positive result of the experiment, combined with the positive result obtained on using the current of action as an indicator, leaves no room for doubting *the double conductivity of nerve-fibres.*

§ 10. What is it that is conducted along the nerve with the speed of 100 feet per second, but which is blocked by a cold stretch in the nerve, and by ether? Any satisfactory answer to this question is extraordinarily difficult. There is no visible motion of the nerve; no pull or push is exerted through it; no "animal spirits" circulate rapidly through it, to constitute the nerve-impulse. What is conducted must, therefore, be of a much more subtle nature.

By analogy with other living tissues, the activity of a nerve is readily thought of as a chemical process. It might be likened, in a measure, to the setting-off of a train of gunpowder or of a fuse, in which the oxidation of one part acts to ignite the next. The simile would halt, since the fuse is burnt out in its activity, while the nerve remains in good condition and ready for further activity. A comparison with other living tissues, such as the muscle, is more appropriate. The muscle, after one contraction, remains in good condition, and yet oxidation has gone on in the muscle; explosive material has been consumed; in a word, catabolism has occurred in the active tissue. Since living cells are subject to the law of the conservation of energy, and cannot perform work without the utilization of stored energy, the conclusion seems unavoidable that there must be catabolism also in an active nerve.

If the activity of the nerve is like other chemical and catabolic processes, it should give rise to the waste products of catabolism, even as the active muscle gives rise to carbon dioxide, lactic acid, etc. With this in view physiologists have looked for the carbon dioxide produced by nerve action, but the most delicate tests have been unable to detect any. They have looked for the acid reaction which should betray catabolism, but have got no clear evidence of the production of acid products. They have looked for the heat which is evolved in all known instances of oxidation, and have applied instruments capable of detecting a rise in temperature of $\frac{1}{5000}$ of a degree centigrade, but have not been able to detect the slightest production of heat. These negative results impress different physiologists differently. Some conclude that the activity of the nerve is, after all, not a chemical process, or at least not a process involving catabolism. Others are still confident that there is catabolism there, only that it is too slight for our present means of detection.

§ 11. There is another line of evidence which is of special in-terest. A universal result of catabolic activity in any organ is, apparently, *fatigue*. The using-up of the store of available energy weakens a muscle or gland; and the accumulation of the waste products of activity also depresses the activity of the organ.[1] If, therefore, nerve action is catabolic, the nerve should be fatigued by any long-continued activity.

In examining the question of fatigue in nerves, great pains must be taken to find a suitable indicator. We cannot simply take the nerve-muscle preparation, and, after repeatedly exciting the nerve, look for evidence of its fatigue in a weakening of the muscular contractions; for the muscle is itself subject to fatigue, and its fatigue is quite sufficient to mask the fatigue of the nerve. To use the muscle as an indicator, it must itself be protected from excitation, while the nerve is continually excited. This result has been reached in several different ways. Bowditch[2] used the drug *curare*, which blocks the passage of excitation from the motor nerve to its muscle, without paralyzing either the nerve or the muscle. He kept the animal alive by artificial respiration for four or five hours, exciting the nerve many times a second during all this time, at the end of which, as the effect of the drug began to pass off, the muscle began to contract. Thus the nerve had not been exhausted by several hours of continued activity—many times as much as would have reduced the muscle to an extreme condition of exhaustion. The same experiment has recently been repeated with an improvement, which consists in giving an antidote to the curare, which acts with great promptness. In this way the block between the active nerve and the protected muscle can be instantly removed, and it is then found that four to ten hours of continued activity have left the nerve still with unimpaired powers of functioning.[3] The non-medullated nerves of mammals seem to have the same absence of fatigue:[4] it has been claimed, however, that the olfactory nerve of the pike, a non-medullated nerve, gives signs of fatigue as tested by the "current of action."[5] The action current has also been used in medullated nerves as an indicator, and has been found not to weaken in the course of long-continued excitation of the nerve at the rate of many shocks per second.[6]

[1] A fuller discussion of the phenomena of fatigue will be given later on.
[2] *Journal of Physiology*, 1885, VI, 133.
[3] This form of the classic experiment is due to Durig, and the antidote is the salicylate of physostigmin. See *Zentralblatt f. Physiol.*, 1902, XV, 751.
[4] Brodie and Halliburton, *Journal of Physiology*, 1902, XXVIII, 181.
[5] Sowton, *Proceedings of the Royal Society of London*, 1900, LXVI, 379; Garten, *Pflüger's Archiv f. d. gesammte Physiol.*, 1899, LXXVII.
[6] Edes, *Journal of Physiology*, 1892, XIII, 431.

The evidence, therefore, all goes to demonstrate the practical indefatigability of nerve-fibres. It may be, of course, that this remarkable trait is after all only relative; that, in truth, the catabolism of the nerve is excessively slight, and it therefore recovers with extraordinary promptness from the effects of each phase of activity, just as the heart beats at a moderate rate for many hours without fatigue, recovering from the effects of each beat in the pause that intervenes before the next. And this is the view of Biedermann,[1] who also brings forward some evidence, not wholly convincing, that a perfectly continuous electric stimulation, as distinguished from a rapid series of brief shocks, produces fatigue of nerve.

There are one or two facts of a different order which bear on the same problem. The blood supply of the nerves is very slight; and their need of oxygen is also very slight. It has been shown,[2] indeed, that several hours' confinement in an atmosphere perfectly free from oxygen destroys the excitability of a nerve, and that there is prompt recovery as soon as oxygen is admitted; and this is taken to mean that the nerve consumes oxygen and therefore undergoes catabolism; but some doubt still remains as to whether it is the *activity* of the nerve which demands oxygen, since even an inactive nerve gets out of condition in the absence of oxygen.

Another line of evidence in favor of assuming catabolism in the active nerve is adduced by Waller.[3] The action current of a nerve is increased by activity of the nerve, as induced by exciting it with a rapid series of induction shocks. If, then, the character of the activity of the nerve is changed by its own action, this is *prima facie* evidence that the nerve has itself changed; and the change is probably chemical. Now the same increase in the action current is caused by exposing the nerve to a very slight dose of carbon dioxide; and Waller is therefore inclined to infer that the increased action current after activity is due to the production within the nerve of very small amounts of this gas. The evidence, however, is at best indirect.

§ 12. In the absence of mechanical, thermal, or chemical manifestations of the nerve-impulse, we should be wholly at a loss regarding its physical nature, were it not for the fact that there is an electrical manifestation, in the "current of action," to which reference has already several times been made. If a nerve is excited by any means at one point, and if the poles of a galvanometer or capillary electrometer are laid on a distant part of the nerve, every excitation of the nerve is followed by a swing of the galvanometer

---

[1] In *Ergebnisse der Physiologie*, 1903, II, part 2, 131 f.

[2] A. v. Bayer, *Zeitschrift f. allgem. Physiologie*, 1902, II, 169.

[3] *Philosophical Transactions of the Royal Society of London*, 1896.

needle, or by a movement of the mercury in the electrometer—thus indicating the existence of an electric current in the nerve itself. The rate at which this electrical disturbance travels along the nerve is the same as the speed of the nerve-impulse. Such a current of action is, indeed, not peculiar to the nerve; it occurs in muscles, glands, the retina, and apparently in all active living tissues. In most of these other cases, there are other manifestations of activity, and the current of action is usually regarded as a mere by-product. But since the nerve shows no other manifestation, the suggestion has been made by several physiologists that there is no other process; but that the nerve-impulse is *essentially* an electrical disturbance moving along the nerve.

Without committing ourselves to this view of the nerve-impulse further than to recognize it as a respectable hypothesis with a considerable number of facts in its favor, we may employ it to give point to our further consideration of the electrical phenomena of the nerve in action. The study of these phenomena has engaged the attention of many able investigators and has proved a fruitful field. To present the subject fully, we should need to enter much more deeply into the science of electricity and the closely related science of physical chemistry than can be expected within the limits of a brief discussion. A rough sketch is all that can be here attempted.

§ 13. The facts bearing on this subject may be conveniently grouped under two heads: (1) the effects of the electrical current *on the nerve;* and (2) the electrical phenomena developed *by the nerve* itself. To the latter class belongs the current of action.

Let us suppose that we have at our disposal, for examining its effects on the nerve, a current from a zinc-copper battery, and let us follow the common usage, and speak of the copper pole as positive and the zinc as negative, and of the current as "flowing," outside of the battery, along any conductor which is provided, in the direction from copper to zinc. For applying the current to the nerve, we shall need to employ "non-polarizable electrodes." On connecting the positive or copper pole with one point of the nerve, and the negative pole with another point, the current may be conceived of as entering the nerve at the positive pole, or anode, and leaving at the negative pole or cathode. A key is provided in the circuit, which enables us to start and stop the passage of the current, at will. As has already been stated, the nerve is excited by the starting or stopping of the current, but not, ordinarily, by its steady flow. The excitation is found to occur at the cathode when the current is started, and at the anode when the current is stopped. In other words, the nerve-impulse starts at the cathode when the circuit is closed and at the anode when the circuit is broken. Further, it was shown by Pflüger[1] that the regions of the anode and of the cathode are each in a condition of altered excitability during the passage of the current. There is an increase of excitability at and near the cathode, and a decrease at and near the anode. On the stopping of the current, a back swing occurs, making the anode for a time over-excitable and the cathode under-excitable. The changes in excitability are greatest at the poles and decrease gradually as we move into the extrapolar regions and into the region between the poles; in the latter region there is an indifference point where the cathodic effect merges into the opposite anodic. On increasing the strength of the current, the extent of the nerve affected increases, and, between the poles, the anodic depression encroaches more and more on the cathodic exaltation. This depressing effect also occurs when the current is prolonged; the depression then finally invades even the region of the cathode. The lowering of excitability at the anode during the passage of the current is attended by a lowering of the conductivity of the nerve for nervous impulses; the conductivity is so far lost at the anode during the passage of strong currents as to form a complete block to the passage of the impulses generated elsewhere. These changes in the nerve during the passage of an electric current are grouped under the name "electrotonus"; and the anodic depression is sometimes known as *anelectrotonus,* while the cathodic exaltation is called *catelectrotonus.*

§ 14. Electrotonus may then be defined as an altered excitability and conductivity of the nerve produced by the passage of a current through some part of its extent. But there are also certain purely electrical results from the passage of the current, in the form of additional currents which appear in the nerve, or on its surface; and these are called the electrotonic currents. Such currents appear in the extrapolar region, and their direction is the same as that of the current that is led into the nerve. They cannot, therefore, be mere leakages of the exciting current; they are new currents generated in the nerve by the action of this external current.

§ 15. These electrotonic currents have formed the starting-point for an interesting line of experiments, the object of which is to determine whether the phenomena of nerve action can be imitated in a physical model. Since the model may be regarded as an artificial nerve, just as an arrangement of tubes and syringes gives a working model of the circulatory system, it is hoped in this way to throw some light on the physical structure of the nerve. Such an instrument of investigation is called a "core model" (see Fig. 60),

[1] *Untersuchungen über Electrotonus,* Berlin, 1859.

or a "core conductor." It consists of a central core of good electrical conductivity, surrounded by a sheath of lower conductivity.
It may be constructed of various materials; that of Hermann[1] consisted of a platinum wire (the core) stretched the length of a glass
tube filled with a solution of some salt. The glass tube was employed simply for the purpose of holding the "sheath" of solution in
place, and was provided with small side tubes through which the
exciting current could be led in, and the electrotonic currents (if any)
led out to a galvanometer. Hermann found, in fact, that currents

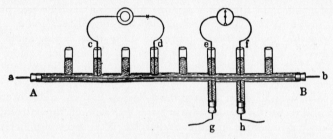

FIG. 60.—Hermann's Core Model. *AB*, glass tube; *ab*, platinum wire;
c, d, e, f, g, h, side tubes.

equivalent to those of electrotonus were produced in the extrapolar
regions of the core model as in the nerve; he, accordingly, concluded that the physical structure of a nerve resembles that of the
core conductor, and that the electrotonic currents were purely
physical phenomena.

The same line of investigation has been carried further by Boruttau,[2] who has found that, not only the electrotonic currents, but
all the electrical phenomena occurring in the nerve from the action
of a current on it can be imitated in the core model. In this way,
even the current of action can be imitated; and as this is closely
associated, in a genuine nerve, with the transmission of the nerve
impulse, Boruttau advances the view that the core conductor, like
the nerve, can really be "excited"; and that the activity of a nerve
is imitated, in all essential respects, by the action of the core conductor. According to this view, the nerve owes its functional power
to its physical structure, which makes of it an electrical conductor
of a certain type—namely, a so-called "core conductor." Nerve
action would, then, not be a catabolic affair, but a physical rather
than a chemical action, consisting in the propagation of a certain
electrical state. The electrical state may be generated in the nerve

[1] *Handbuch der Physiologie*, vol. II, i, 174.
[2] In several articles in *Pflüger's Archiv für die gesammte Physiologie*, from
1894 on.

by various sorts of stimuli, as was mentioned in a preceding page. In the core model also, the electric wave can be initiated by a mechanical "stimulus" as well as by an electrical; and this fact rather strengthens the analogy between the nerve and the core conductor. The rate of propagation of the electric wave, in a core conductor, varies according to the materials of which it is constructed; but it may be as low as 100 metres per second, and thus it is not incomparable with the speed of transmission in nerve. The fact that electricity travels along a wire between the poles of a battery or dynamo at an infinitely faster rate is therefore no disproof, as was formerly held, of the view that the nerve impulse is essentially electrical.

The actual microscopic structure of a nerve-fibre affords some reason for believing that it may act as a core conductor. There is the axon, containing its fibrils; and, if the fibrils are better electrical conductors than the protoplasm which surrounds them, the axon corresponds in structure to that of the core model. Or, again, and less hypothetically, if the axon as a whole is a better conductor than the myelin sheath, then the axon represents the core, and the myelin sheath the less conductive envelope.

§ 16. A further set of facts bearing on the theory of the nerve has not yet been touched upon. When a nerve is cut, and the cut end connected with one pole of a galvanometer, while the other pole is connected with the uninjured convex surface of the nerve, a current flows through the galvanometer from the convex surface to the cut end. The cut end is negative with respect to the convex surface. This current was discovered by Du Bois-Reymond, who named it the "current of rest," thus distinguishing it from the "current of action," and indicating also his view that the current so demonstrated existed in the resting and uninjured nerve. Hermann showed good reason for doubting this interpretation, and for believing that the negative potential of the cut end was a consequence of the injury done it in cutting. A controversy waged for years regarding this matter, one of the most bitter controversies in the history of science; but the evidence adduced by Hermann gradually won the assent of physiologists, and the name "current of injury" was substituted for Du Bois-Reymond's "current of rest." Hermann's conception was that chemical changes occurred in the injured and therefore dying part of the nerve, and that these changes were the cause of its negative potential. The phenomenon is not peculiar to the nerve, but appears in all dying tissues. Hermann brought this negativity of dying tissues into relation with the negativity displayed by active tissues toward tissues when resting. The negative potential of active tissue is revealed by the current of action; for the active portion of a nerve becomes negative to the resting portion. Hermann's views, which may be said to be the views now generally accepted, are summed up in the statements that dying tissue is electro-negative with respect to living; and acting tissue is also electro-negative with respect to resting tissue.

§ 17. In spite of the wide-spread acceptance of Hermann's views, very strong evidence has recently been presented in favor of a radically different conception of the current of rest, a conception which has something in common with that of Du Bois-Reymond, but which is based on discoveries in physical chemistry which have been made since his time.

The considerations on which this new conception is based are the following:[1] We have in the nerve-fibre a core containing a solution of salts (the axon), surrounded by the myelin and primitive sheaths, which are known to be electrically poor conductors; while outside of these sheaths is also a solution of salts, the lymph which bathes the nerve as it bathes the outside of all the cells of the body. The sheaths, therefore, like the bounding membrane of all living cells, interpose resistance to the free diffusion of salts between the solutions that are within and those without. If, now, the internal and external solutions were different in strength or in concentration, we should have here the making of a "concentration cell"; and, further, if the separating membrane were ruptured at any point, so that diffusion occurred between the external and internal solutions, the diffusion would be attended by electric currents. It is then only necessary to suppose that the internal solution is more concentrated than the external, and the former would be negative with respect to the latter: thus we should have the exact conditions necessary to give rise to the current of rest or of injury, as this current is actually observed.

Macdonald[2] has given definite evidence in favor of this theory by showing that the current due to injury of a nerve is increased by weakening the external solution, and diminished or even reversed by making the external solution sufficiently concentrated. The results come out as they would on the supposition that the nerve, in case of the current of injury, acts as a concentration cell, with the more concentrated solution normally inside the sheaths. Such a current can be imitated by a core model constructed of two solutions of different concentration separated by a membrane (Boruttau). The evidence of these experiments is therefore favorable

[1] See J. S. Macdonald, "The Injury Current of Nerve," in reports of the Thompson Yates Laboratories, Liverpool, 1902, III, 213–347; *Proceedings of the Royal Society of London*, 1900, LXVII, 310.

[2] Op. cit., pp. 273, 288.

to the conception of the nerve as a core conductor of the construction already described. The non-conducting character of the
myelin sheath is indicated by direct observation.[1]

§ 18. According to this view, which is thought to explain the
electrical phenomena as well as the absence of signs of catabolism
in the active nerve, the nerve-impulse is a special sort of electrical
wave propagated from point to point along the nerve-fibre, and capable of exciting a muscle-fibre where the terminations of the axon
come into close contact with the muscular substance. The objection to this theory which is derived from the fact that a dead
nerve will not conduct, may be met by maintaining that a physical
structure which is capable of transmitting the electrical wave depends upon the life of the fibre.

While, then, certain competent authorities still oppose this theory
and it would be out of place in a book like this to take sides in a
controversial matter, it must be admitted that it accounts for more
of the very puzzling phenomena than do any other of the present
theories of conduction in the nerves. It may, then, properly serve as
a hypothesis about which to gather the principal facts of the physiology of nerves. At any rate, the only rival view, at the moment,
seems to be a chemical theory, which must either controvert the
doctrine of the conservation of energy, or else admit such an amaz-
ing ability for promptness and completeness of metabolism as it
is difficult to imagine. To suppose the nerve-fibre capable of instantaneously recombining, without any detectable loss of energy,
the elements which have been separated by the work done through
hours of continuous functioning, is to convert it into a wonderful
kind of laboratory. But it can scarcely be denied that nature may
impart such a capacity to such a kind of living tissue. In a word,
then, the physico-chemical theory of the process in which consists
the impulse passing along an excited nerve, is still in need of prolonged and careful investigation.[2] But whatever, more precisely,

[1] Göthlin, *Upsala Läkareforenings Förhandlingar*, 1902, VIII, 156 ff.

[2] It seems to us that there is no incompatibility between the two theories
which have been presented in this chapter and which are customarily looked
upon as rival ways of explaining the phenomena. On the contrary, both the
classes of phenomena to be explained, and also the theories that are set forth
in their explanation, are supplementary and necessary to be combined in
order to account for all the facts. It will have been noticed that in the model
core conductor, as in the nerve itself, one of the materials used in its construction is a saline solution. If this were not so, the phenomena could not
be obtained. But saline solutions are electrolytic conductors; and electrolysis is the chemical change which is analogous to catabolism in living tissues.
It is perfectly possible, however, to construct an electrolytic conductor which,
on passing a weak current through it, and yet a current far within the limits
of detection by a galvanometer, will give no detectable evidence of any chemi-

this impulse is found to be, there is no doubt that *conduction is the fundamental function of nervous tissue;* and all its other functions are secondary and derived.

cal or thermal change along its course—*except at the poles.* Even here, the chemical changes may be so small that it would take thousands of years for it to disengage from one pole, and transfer to the other, a single cubic centimetre of copper; but all the while chemical changes, too small to be detected, would be taking place along the entire stretch of the conducting medium.

Still further, it is not proper to speak of what does take place in an electrolytic conductor as the passage of a *mere* wave of electricity. It is doubtful whether there can be any such "mere wave" in any material structure.

Now, we know that catabolism does take place in the muscle-fibre; and there is sufficient evidence to show that it also takes place in the nerve-cells of the central organs. These are the terminals, between which the nerve-fibres are conductors. *The analogy, we repeat, seems to suggest a combination of both theories.*

CHAPTER VII

REFLEX FUNCTIONS OF THE NERVOUS SYSTEM

§ 1. When a stimulus acting on a sense-organ arouses to activity a muscle, *by the medium* of a sensory nerve, a nervous centre, and a motor nerve, the entire transaction is said to be reflex; and its path is called a "reflex arc." In the case of the lower forms of animal life we have already seen how the simplest reactions of an organism which depend on nervous action are of the reflex type. The reflex is, therefore, the unit or element of nervous function. (Compare Fig. 61).

§ 2. In the case of the higher animals, or of man, there are many prompt reactions to stimuli which, because they involve either volition, or previous learning, or both, are not usually classed as reflexes. In reading aloud, for example, the reaction conforms to the neurological type of a reflex; since a stimulus to the eye arouses promptly a response of the vocal muscles; but the reaction has been learned. A true reflex should be not learned, but innate. A good example of the true reflex is afforded by the contraction of the pupil in response to bright light entering the eye. This is not an acquired reaction, nor is it dependent on the will. Of some of these true reflexes we are wholly unconscious; in the case of others, such as flushing, shivering, starting, the secretion of saliva, we are aware of their occurrence, but have no voluntary control over them; in the case of still others, such as coughing, sneezing, winking, we have some degree of control, and yet there can be no doubt that they were never learned by the individual. There are yet other reactions, of which a good example is afforded by the turning of the eyes toward any "attractive" object, which appear at a very early age in the infant, and without any evidence that they are learned; but which are very closely interwoven with our conscious life, and which are controllable, to a large extent, by the adult animal. There is thus a graded series of reactions to stimuli, which are alike in being native to the individual, but which vary in their relations to consciousness. The most satisfactory basis for classifying reflexes would seem, then, to be found in the history of the reaction in the individual— according as it is innate or has to be learned.

145

Another graded series of reflexes can be arranged on the basis of their complexity. The pupillary reflex, for example, is about as simple and strictly local as any; only one or two muscles are called into action. Much the same is true of winking and of rotations of the eyes. Coughing, by comparison, is highly complicated; in this reflex, a strong inspiration is followed by forced expiration, at first against the closed glottis, which then is suddenly opened, allowing the air to escape with a rush. Some reflexes call into action only one of the limbs, whereas others involve all four limbs, the

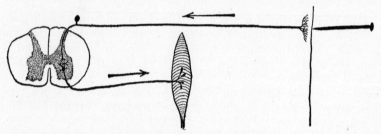

FIG. 61.—Diagram of a Reflex Arc.

trunk, and perhaps the head besides. Since it is impossible to draw any sharp line between the most simple and the more complex, the degree of complexity cannot be used as the basis for separating reflexes from other reactions.

§ 3. *Instinct*, also, is a word which cannot be sharply distinguished from the type of reactions called *reflex*. Both have in common the notion of innate, as distinguished from learned, reaction. "Instinct," however, is seldom applied to such simple reactions as that of the pupil to light; it is most frequently applied to complex series of reactions, like those of birds in nest-building, or of frogs in hibernating. It is also probable that such typical instincts are attended by much of consciousness, and even of desire. But, as we have seen, neither in terms of the attendant consciousness nor in terms of complexity, is it anywhere possible to draw a sharp line; and instinct and reflex may best be regarded as synonymous terms, definable as innate reactions to stimuli.

The conception of a "simple reflex," or better, perhaps, of an "isolated reflex," should also be considered in this connection. The point here is not that the movement evoked shall be as limited and free from complexity as possible, but that it shall run its course uncomplicated with other reactions that may be occurring at the same time. In any complex nervous mechanism, there is much going on simultaneously; many receptors are undergoing stimulation, and many effectors are acting at once. A quite simple reflex would, therefore, be one which went through without interfering with other reactions, or being interfered with by them. This requires that a certain reflex centre, starting from a condition of rest, shall be acted on by one group of sensory fibres, and shall discharge into a group of motor fibres, the centre meanwhile remaining unaffected by influences from any other parts of the system. But such simplicity is seldom, if ever, realized. Every centre is continually subjected to some degree of excitation or other influence, from the periphery; and the centres are so richly connected by fibres with one another, that mutual influences are probably always in operation. Hence Sherrington[1] has called the "simple reflex" a convenient but artificial abstraction, and has emphasized the fact that "the nervous system functions as a whole"; while Dewey[2] directs attention to the psychological errors which result from treating this abstraction as an actuality and building a psychology on it.

In distinguishing purely reflex from learned and from voluntary reactions, we need to notice that many, or perhaps all, reactions of the higher class are based on reflexes, and include reflex elements. It is within the power of an adult to direct his eyes on an object at will; but in so doing he makes use of the same movement which appears reflexly in the infant. A similar combination of volitional, habitual, and instinctive factors is seen in speaking, chewing, or walking. Reflex elements are therefore more common in human action than would at first appear; and a knowledge of the reflexes is important in the psychology of human behavior, as well as in understanding the inner mechanism of the nervous system.

§ 4. The reflex, it has been stated above, is the unit of nervous function. There is, indeed, another possible unit—another sort of functioning of the nerve-centres, which is known by the name of *automatic action*. In this, the centre discharges into its motor nerves, without itself receiving any stimulus, either from a sense-organ or from any other part of the nerve-centres. Such activity is supposed to originate within the centre. Its cause may be sought either in the inner metabolism of the centre; or in stimuli acting directly on the centre, as for example from the chemical action of the blood. In these cases, the centre itself would seem to play the part of a receptor. For a time, the concept of "automatic" action seemed to fall into discredit; since it was found that certain reactions which had been considered such were really reflex. For example, the convulsions which result from strychnine poisoning, and which

---

[1] *The Integrative Action of the Nervous System*, 1906, p. 114.
[2] "The Reflex Arc Concept in Psychology," *Psychological Review*, 1896, III, 357.

were formerly attributed to automatic discharge of the motor cells
of the spinal cord, do not take place, if all the sensory nerves leading to the spinal cord are severed.[1]

One of the most probable instances of automatic action occurs
in the respiratory centre in the bulb. It is certain that venous
blood—i. e., blood poor in oxygen and rich in carbon dioxide—acts
as a stimulant to this centre, raising its irritability and thus increasing respiration. When the blood circulating through the bulb is
abnormally rich in carbon dioxide, the rate of breathing is increased;
and when the blood is poor in carbon dioxide, the rate of breathing is
slackened. These facts have led to the view that the normal stimulus
to respiration is venous blood, and especially the carbon dioxide in
such blood, which, by circulating through the medulla, directly
excites the respiratory centre. More precisely, the centre is conceived as automatic, at least so far as concerns inspiration; expiration, in quiet breathing, is mere passive relaxation; and the cause
of the relaxation has been traced to sensory impulses reaching the
centre through the tenth or vagus nerve. The fibres concerned in
expiration come from the lungs, and are excited by the distension
of the lungs which occurs in inspiration. The effect of these sensory impulses, themselves resulting from inspiration, is to "inhibit"
the centre, and check inspiration, thus giving rise to passive expiration. According to this view, inspiration would be an automatic movement, but expiration a reflex. But even inspiration
can be shown to be sometimes the result of sensory stimuli, originating in the lungs or elsewhere; so that the possibility remains
that inspiration may be, in part at least, a reflex function.[2]

§ 5. Very recently, a strong support to the theory of automatic
functions has come from the discoveries of physiological chemistry.
It is found that certain chemical compounds, called "hormones"—
especially those formed by the internally secreting glands, and some
which can even be made synthetically—when introduced into the
blood, have the power to select definite tissues in the animal organism, and produce directly in them specific reactions of a type necessary (some of them, absolutely) to the maintenance of the physiological system. If this is true of other than the nerve tissues, it

[1] H. E. Hering, in *Archiv für experimentelle Pathologie und Pharmakologie*,
1896, XXXVIII, 276.

[2] For a fuller discussion of this question, the reader may be referred to the
text-books of physiology, and to the authorities, especially to Rosenthal (*Die
Athembewegungen*, 1865), who supported the automatic conception by isolating
the bulb—though not quite completely—from the sensory nerves, and finding
that a slow and imperfect respiration persisted in spite of this operation; and
to Head (*Journal of Physiology*, 1889, X, 1–70, 279–290), whose work went
far toward making the reflex conception seem probable.

would seem remarkable that the capacity for such special automatic reactions should be denied to the tissues of the central nervous system. All our theory of the specialized functions of this system, especially in its higher forms of development and of activity, seems, therefore, to favor the opinion that it is, among all the organic structures, pre-eminently *automatic*. It is, therefore, highly probable that the reflex and the automatic forms of its functioning are most frequently, if not uniformly, combined in ever-varying proportions.

§ 6. From these preliminary considerations, we may turn, first, to a brief survey of the reflexes observed in mammals, and, after that, to a discussion of the laws of reflex action in general.

In beginning a survey or inventory of reflexes, attention should first be given to a class of actions which may be even simpler than reflexes. An example is the beating of the heart. Since the heart is supplied with nerves, the early assumption was that the heart-beat is a reflex. Later, it was discovered that all of these nerves could be cut, or the heart taken entirely out of the body, without destroying the power of the heart to beat. An excised heart, if supplied with suitable blood, will continue to beat, of itself, for hours. Since the walls of the heart contain nerve-fibres and ganglia of nerve-cells, the next view adopted was that the reflex was strictly local, the ganglia acting as reflex centres. Another theory was proposed by Gaskell and by Engelmann.[1] According to this theory, the contractions of the heart muscle are essentially independent of any nervous influence; or, in other words, the heart muscle is automatic, depending only on chemical or other stimuli acting directly on the muscle itself. This view was supported by the observation that pieces of the heart muscle, so cut as to contain no nerve-cells, showed the rhythmical beat. The evidence is perhaps less convincing now than formerly, since the advance of histological study has shown the existence of minute nerve ganglia in parts of the muscle which were formerly thought to be free from them. There is, however, no inherent improbability in the view that the heart muscle has the power of reacting directly—and rhythmically—to chemical stimuli affecting it; and it is said that the heart commences to beat, in the embryo, before the growth of nervous tissue into it. Essentially the same things may be said in regard to the movements of other internal organs, such as the stomach and intestines, ureter, etc. This view would accord, too, with the facts mentioned in the preceding article.

[1] Gaskell, *Philosophical Transactions*, 1882, p. 993; Engelmann, *Pflüger's Archiv für die gesammte Physiologie*, 1882, XXIX, 425; and many other papers by each of these authors.

§ 7. The appearance of the chain of *sympathetic ganglia* is such as to suggest that it is a series of connected reflex centres, much like the ganglionic chain of a worm. It was long accepted, as a matter of course, that this appearance furnished a correct view of the functions of the entire sympathetic system. The fibres of this system are ultimately distributed to the heart, stomach, intestines, and other internal organs; and to the walls of the blood-vessels, the iris of the eye, the sweat-glands, and the cutaneous muscles which erect the hairs. Associated with the sympathetic fibres in the control of these organs are other nerve-fibres which issue from the brain and cord, but which do not pass to the sympathetic chain, though they do make connections with other more scattered ganglia. This whole system of nerves has been named the "autonomic system."[1] It is characteristic of the organs supplied by the fibres of this system that they have a large measure of local automatism, as was noted above in the case of the heart. Yet they are all also subject to reflex effects. The problem is, therefore, to determine the reflex centres concerned. Are they located in the sympathetic ganglia themselves? Goltz and Ewald,[2] in some remarkable experiments in which they removed the spinal cord—leaving the upper part, or that necessary for breathing—from dogs, which were kept alive for a long period after the operation, found indeed that the actions of many of these organs—for example, the evacuation of the bladder and rectum, and the bearing and nursing of young— were retained. But they found also that the action of these organs was no longer influenced by stimuli acting on distant parts of the body. In short, there was evidence of the automatic action of these organs, but not of reflex action on them exerted through the sympathetic ganglia. More minute experiments[3] have shown that it is impossible to secure long-distance reflexes through the medium of the sympathetic chain. For such reflexes, the connections of the sympathetic with the cord are essential. It is evident, accordingly, that the older conception of the sympathetic as a relatively independent reflex centre, charged with the co-ordination of the more "vegetative" functions of the organism, must be abandoned. The centre for such co-ordination is to be sought in the central nervous system, of which the sympathetic is but an adjunct. It is even doubtful whether limited local reflexes occur by way of the sympathetic ganglia. The latter are, more probably, not reflex

[1] See the article by Langley in *Schäfer's Textbook of Physiology*, 1900, vol. II, pp. 616–696.
[2] *Pflüger's Archiv für die gesammte Physiologie*, 1896, LXIII, 362.
[3] See Langley, op. cit.

centres at all, but simply relay stations in the path of the outgoing fibres to the organs mentioned.[1]

§ 8. In contrast to the musculature of the internal organs, what is called the skeletal or "voluntary" musculature does not have local automatism and is not controlled by the fibres of the sympathetic system. Its nerve supply comes directly from the cord and brain-stem, on which it is dependent for all normal stimuli to activity. If severed from the central nervous system, the skeletal musculature becomes incapable of functioning, and even degenerates and atrophies, thus losing entirely the characteristics peculiar to it. The muscles of the limbs are therefore dependent on spinal reflex action for their very existence. They are not, however, dependent in the same way on the brain; but only on the ventral horn of the cord, from which the motor nerve-fibres for these muscles issue.

For an exact study of the reflexes of this order, it is necessary to exclude the action of the brain on the muscles; and for studying the reflex powers of any particular portion of the brain-stem or cord, it is necessary to isolate this portion from the rest of the central system. Physiologists who investigate the laws of reflex action begin, therefore, by making a reflex or, usually, a spinal prepara-

---

[1] The nervous system, by the connections which it establishes between different parts of the body, is the supreme factor in the co-ordination or integration that is necessary if the body is to maintain life and efficiency. But not all co-ordination is effected through the nervous system. The chemical integration of the body is very largely accomplished by transmission of chemical substances from one organ to another, through the circulation (see p. 148). Thus, the fuel taken in at a meal is, to a large extent, stored in the liver, and doled out into the blood as muscular activity makes demand for it. The mechanism by which the demands of the muscles are transmitted to the liver is supplied by the circulation. An active muscle draws fuel from the blood, thus lowering the proportion of sugar in the circulation; and when the blood circulating through the liver has less than a certain proportion of sugar, the liver gives out enough to bring back the proportion to the normal. There are many "internal secretions," produced by certain organs, as the adrenal bodies, the pancreas, and the pituitary body, which pass, by the circulation, to other organs, and affect their activity. One of the best examples of chemical co-ordination is that discovered by Bayliss and Starling (*Journal of Physiology*, 1902, XXVIII, 325. See also Starling, *Recent Advances in the Physiology of Digestion*, 1906), through which the secretion of the pancreas is excited. The hydrochloric acid which forms part of the gastric juice, when it passes with the partly digested food from the stomach into the intestine, excites cells in the wall of the intestine to secrete into the blood a substance, called secretin, which, being carried by the blood to the pancreas, excites that gland to pour its secretion into the intestine. Thus a reaction which formerly was taken to be a nervous reflex is seen to be of quite a different nature. It is probable that this sort of chemical action of one organ on another is of great importance in the processes of growth and metabolism.

tion. For this purpose, the brain need not actually be destroyed; but it must be disconnected from the part of the cord to be examined. Since the cord and brain-stem afford the only path of nervous connection between the brain and the cord, or between the brain and the muscles, a transection of the brain-stem or cord, at any level, isolates the part below the cut from the brain, and makes of the part thus severed from the brain a "reflex preparation." Several varieties of such preparations have been employed. The "spinal frog" is constituted by simply decapitating the animal. Since the frog, like other cold-blooded animals, can maintain life without breathing, such a spinal preparation can be kept alive for days and even for months.[1] In mammals, however, decapitation is promptly fatal, unless artificial respiration be provided; the animal must also be kept warm and much loss of blood prevented, in order to secure the best results. With these precautions, a decapitated cat can be kept alive for several hours, and forms one of the most useful of preparations for the study of reflex action.[2]

Another very useful preparation is the "decerebrate" animal, which differs from the spinal animal in that the transection is made through, or just above, the mid-brain—thus leaving the cerebellum, pons, bulb, and cord in continuity, but excluding the action of the cerebrum, thalamus, and (usually) part of the mid-brain. Goltz successfully performed decerebration of a dog, by removing the cerebrum in three operations, allowing the animal to recover, as far as possible, from each operation before resorting to the next. In this way he kept one animal alive for 18 months.[3]

Sherrington has found that, if care is taken to prevent loss of blood and of bodily heat, a decerebrate dog or cat can be easily prepared and kept alive for several hours, during which time it shows many reflex phenomena.[4]

§ 9. The different separate parts of the cord can be isolated by similar methods. In the frog, for example, a transection of the cord in the middle of the back, secures a reflex preparation consisting principally of the hind-limbs and their nerves, together with the part of the cord which receives these nerves. Similarly, two cuts across the frog's cord, just above and just below the exit of the brachial nerves, isolate a fore-limb preparation; and both of these fractions of the animal show reflex activity. In mammals, it is common to sever the cord below the exit of the phrenic nerve, a pro-

---

[1] See especially the work of Schrader, *Pflüger's Archiv für die gesammte Physiologie*, 1887, XLI, 82, and 1888, XLIV, 175.

[2] Sherrington, *Journal of Physiology*, 1909, XXXVIII, 375.

[3] Goltz, *Pflüger's Archiv für die gesammte Physiologie*, 1892, LI, 570.

[4] Sherrington, *Proceedings of the Royal Society*, 1896, LX, 411.

cedure which allows respiration to persist and the animal to be kept alive for months, while at the same time isolating the lower two-thirds of the cord as a reflex preparation. Such "spinal dogs" show a variety of reflexes. A second transection can be made at some distance below the first; the animal then, while remaining a unit so far as concerns digestion and circulation, is divided into three, so far as concerns the nervous system. The "fore-dog" includes the head and the fore limbs, and retains brain action; the "mid-dog" consists of the trunk (or a large part of it) with its nerves and the central portion of the cord; while the "hind-dog" consists of the hind-limbs, tail, and pelvic region, with its nerves and the lower portion of the cord. In the case of such a preparation, the "hind-dog" shows many reflexes; the "mid-dog"—in accordance with the small variety of trunk movements—shows comparatively few reflexes; while the "fore-dog," retaining as it does the brain intact, is a "normal" as opposed to a "reflex" animal, and behaves about as dogs usually do, except that it receives no sensations from the middle and rear portions of its body, and has no control over the movements of those parts.[1]

In the human subject, accidents to the spine sometimes sever the cord, leaving the lower portion isolated from the brain, as in the animal preparations; and hemorrhage more frequently interrupts the motor pathway from the cerebrum to the brain-stem, leaving a condition of the cord which corresponds, in some respects, to that of the decerebrate animal. The discoveries with regard to the reflex functions of the nervous system have, however, been chiefly obtained from the animal preparations.

§ 10. One of the most striking results of experiment is the fact that reflexes are elicited from very short lengths of the cord, provided the sensory and motor nerves attached to the part in question are intact. In the frog, for example, the "flexion reflex" of the hind leg, which occurs when one foot is gently pinched, consists of a drawing-up of the whole leg, with flexion at hip, knee, and ankle. This is obviously a highly co-ordinated movement, since it brings several muscles into play; it has also the character of "purposiveness" or utility, being in fact a protective reflex. Another example obtained from the frog preparation is the so-called "clasp reflex" which involves both of the fore-limbs. This reflex is obtained from a fore-limb preparation of the male frog, by touching the skin of the chest, and consists of a clasping action. In the normal frog, this action is elicited only by the presence of the female frog at the breeding season; but in the reflex preparation it can be

[1] Goltz and Ewald, *Pflüger's Archiv für die gesammte Physiologie*, 1896, LXIII, 362.

elicited by so indifferent a stimulus as a mere touch by the finger. Like the "flexion reflex," it is clearly co-ordinated and "purposive." The characteristic of purposiveness is in fact true of reflexes in general.

The best interpretation of all such reflexes assumes that, the sensory and motor nerves to a part being intact, and likewise the central connections between them, the reflex is to be expected as a matter of course.   The results show that the necessary connection between the sensory and motor nerves to a given part is established at, or very near, their place of entrance into the cord.   Such a connection is what would be anticipated from the minute anatomy of the sensory and motor fibres of the cord (see p. 89); since some branches of the sensory fibres bend immediately into the ventral horn of the gray matter, from which, in turn, issue motor fibres that pass directly out of the cord into the motor roots.   These short reflex pathways may be called local arcs, and their reflexes local reflexes.   The most local of all reflex arcs are those which start in a given muscle and lead back to the same muscle.   The receptors concerned in such cases are sense-organs situated in the muscle and its tendon, and excited by movements, active or passive, of the muscle itself; they may be called *proprioceptors*.   This is to say that movements and tensions within a muscle act *reflexly* on the muscle itself, causing it, according to the exact nature of the stimulus, to contract, or to relax, or to maintain the degree of contraction which it already has.[1]   Similar reflexes are important in maintaining posture against the action of gravity; and also in giving steadiness and persistence to muscular action in general.

§ 11. Among other local reflexes may be mentioned the "wiping" reflex of the frog, which is excited by placing a bit of paper moistened in weak acid on the skin of the flank; the leg of the same side is then brought up and brushed across the place stimulated; and this action is repeated a number of times.   If the leg of the same side is held, and the stimulus continued, the leg of the other side is brought up and across, to perform the wiping movement.   In the spinal dog may be mentioned the "stepping" or "marking-time" reflex, which is aroused by supporting the animal under the arms and letting the hind legs hang down.   In this case, the weight of the legs seems to constitute the stimulus; and the reaction is an alternate raising and lowering of the two hind legs as in normal walking.   The "extensor thrust" (Sherrington) is a brief but strong pushing down of the foot when pressure is exerted upward on the sole.

[1] Sherrington, "On Plastic Tonus and Proprioceptive Reflexes," *Quarterly Journal of Experimental Physiology*, 1909, II, 108; and *Integrative Action of the Nervous System*, 1906, pp. 129 ff.

Other reflex arcs pass from receptors in one hind leg to muscles in the other, or from the tail to the hind legs. There are also vaso-motor and visceral reflexes, obtainable from the "hind-dog"; some of them, such as micturition and defecation, are accompanied by suitable movements or postures of the limbs.

From a "mid-dog" preparation can be obtained such reflexes as shivering, curving of the trunk toward the side stimulated, and shaking of the trunk. From an isolated fore-limb preparation can be obtained reflexes similar to those of the hind-limbs. In case of the monkey, even more varied and detailed reflexes can be obtained. In man, reflexes are obtained which are on the whole similar in character to those seen in the lower animals; but the reflex activity of severed portions of the cord is usually comparatively small in man; perhaps, in part, because of the greater roughness and severity of the accidental, as compared with the experimental severing of the cord; but more probably, because of the greater importance, in man's case, of the dependence of the cord on the brain and the receptors of the head.

§ 12. If longer portions of the cord, or if the whole cord, be left in continuity, there are added to the local reflexes others involving longer arcs, and the co-ordination of more muscles. Thus, if the cord is transected at about the level of the shoulders, the "scratch reflex" of the hind leg can be aroused by tickling or pricking the skin as far forward as nearly to the fore-limbs. If the whole cord is left in continuity, pinching the *pinna* of the ear may evoke a combination of movements of the ear, neck, all four limbs, trunk, and tail. These larger movements are, like the simpler local reflexes, co-ordinated; they often have either a protective or a locomotor character. The movements of the four limbs are frequently combined as in the trotting common to quadrupeds. Such locomotor movements are not very efficient, however, when the cord is isolated from the brain; one important difference is that balance is not maintained. In the decerebrate animal some of this deficiency is supplied; and a decerebrate frog can jump and swim in almost a normal manner. The decerebrate dog or cat, soon after the operation, usually does little more than crawl; but the animal which Goltz kept alive came to walk normally. The contribution of the brain-stem to the function of locomotion is in large measure to be explained by reference to the vestibular branch of the eighth nerve, with its receptors in the inner ear, and its central connections in the pons and bulb. These receptors are located in the vestibule and semi-circular canals; they are excited by movements and positions of the head, and their reflexes consist of compensatory or corrective movements and postures, and also result in maintaining the *tonus* of

many muscles.   Such reflexes are essential for the maintenance of
the erect posture and for well-directed locomotion.

§ 13. The cerebellum is closely related to the reflex functions
just mentioned.[1]   It is located, as an outgrowth of the brain-stem,
near the level of the eighth nerve, and receives many fibres from its
vestibular branch.   The disturbances which result from injuries
to the cerebellum resemble those which result from injury to this
nerve or to its receptors.   The cerebellum seems, therefore, to be
fundamentally an expansion of the local centre of the vestibular
branch of the eighth nerve.   But it receives also numerous fibres
from other sense-organs, especially, as appears probable, from those
situated in and about the muscles, and belonging to that proprioceptive system which was mentioned a few paragraphs back in
connection with local reflexes (see p. 154).   We there took note of
the action reflexly exerted on a muscle by stimuli arising in the muscle itself from its own contractions and from pulls and pushes exerted on it.   Such local reflexes were found to be important in
efficient muscular action.   But it is likely that these same stimuli
act on the cerebellum through the cerebellar tracts (compare p. 95);
and this portion of the brain thus becomes an organ where are
gathered together sensory impulses from all the muscles of the body.
In this way, the cerebellum receives information, as it were, regarding the condition of every muscle; in it is formed a sort of representation, or reproduction, detailed and yet comprehensive—though, as
far as known, unattended with consciousness—of the dynamic condition of the entire musculature.   To this is added the very important function, provided for by the receptors in the inner ear,
which responds to the position and movements of the head in space.
Thus the posture, movements, muscular tensions, and external
strains exerted on the body at every moment, act on the cerebellum,
and through it, reflexly, react on the muscles.

We need to recall, further, that in mammals the cerebellum receives a large mass of fibres which apparently bring impulses from
the cerebrum.   The exact function of this connection is altogether
unknown; but it is reasonable enough to suppose that, if the cerebellum is to preside over the dynamic condition of the muscles, it
should receive advance information from the cerebrum regarding
what movements are next to be made; and in the higher mammals,
it is the cerebrum which very largely determines the nature of the
postures assumed and the general course of bodily movements.

In accordance with this rather vague conception of the function

[1] See Luciani, *Il cerveletto*, 1891; Sherrington, in *Schäfer's Textbook of
Physiology*, 1900, vol. II, pp. 903–910; and *Integrative Action of the Nervous
System*, 1906, p. 347.

of the cerebellum, we find that the results of injury to it are seen principally in defects of balancing power or of co-ordinated movement. The muscles that maintain the posture of the animal, in which this organ has been injured, do not maintain their "tone," or mild steady state of contraction, so well as do the muscles of a normal animal. The movements are also lacking in force and are affected with a tendency to tremor. There is uncertainty in maintaining equilibrium against gravity, and in keeping to a straight line in locomotion. If the injury to the cerebellum is one-sided, the symptoms are even more striking; because there is a lack of symmetry or balance between the movements of the two sides of the body: "forced movements" occur, such as an uncontrollable turning, or rolling, to one side (the "circus movement"). It is indeed remarkable to what an extent the early symptoms of cerebellar injury disappear with time. Sometimes, in the case of man, very extensive destructions of cerebellar substance, if they come on gradually, betray themselves scarcely at all to ordinary observation. It should be said, however, that such cases have not yet been studied with the minuteness which the subject demands. Part of the difficulty of the study, and part of the vagueness to our minds of the resulting conception of the reflex functions of the cerebellum, may be due to the fact that the matters over which this organ presides are not customarily dependent on conscious control, and so do not arouse our attention.

§ 14. The completeness with which locomotion occurs in decerebrate animals makes it probable that the cerebrum is not fundamentally concerned in this form of co-ordination. That locomotion is reflex, in the sense of not needing to be learned, is clear in the case of those animals which walk, run, crawl, swim, or fly, at birth or on emerging from the egg. In animals which pass through a period of helpless infancy, the case is not so clear; but it was proved by Spalding[1] that birds, at the proper age, fly perfectly, even when they have been prevented from seeing old birds fly and from exercising their own wings. In the human infant, walking seems, from such observations as have been collected,[2] to occur at the proper age without training or unsuccessful efforts.

§ 15. The bulb, or medulla, from its being the place of entry of the vagus nerve, is the local reflex centre for the receptors, supplied by that nerve, and located in the lungs, heart, stomach, etc. (compare p. 148). It contains the chief centres for respiration, for regulating the rate and force of the heart-beat, for controlling the diameter of the blood-vessels and so the distribution of the blood, for swallow-

[1] *Nature*, 1875, XII, 507.
[2] See Woodworth, *Le Mouvement*, 1903, p. 315.

ing and for regulating the movements of the stomach. These, and other related functions, are not fundamentally interfered with by severing the brain-stem close above the bulb. Other visceral reflexes, as previously mentioned, have centres in the cord, especially in its lower portion, where also are the centres of the fundamental sexual functions, these also being reflex.

It appears, accordingly, that visceral and locomotor reactions are fundamentally reflex; and to these should be added the protective reactions aroused by "painful" or injurious stimuli; of the latter class of reflexes, the flexion and scratch reflexes are examples; and so also is the pupillary reflex, whose centre is in the mid-brain. With the protective reflexes may perhaps be classed cries of pain and anger, and some movements of facial expression, which appear in the decerebrate mammal. All in all, it would seem that the fundamental co-ordinations of movement are, generally speaking, of a reflex nature. It is as provided with such materials that the processes of learning movements and of gaining voluntary control take their start.

§ 16. As to the influence of the cerebrum on the reflex activity of the lower centres, it was formerly held[1] that reflexes to present stimuli are more regularly and easily elicited, but that anything like spontaneous movement is absent, in the decerebrate animal. This statement of the case is, however, too simple to cover all the facts. It is indeed true that many reflexes are more certainly evoked in a spinal or a decerebrate animal than in a normal animal; among such are especially the protective reflexes. But in the higher mammals, separation from the brain seems on the whole to depress the reflex activity. Much depends, too, on the level at which the transection occurs. If special care is taken not to injure the mid-brain, thalami, and optic nerves, removal of the cerebrum is followed by much less of apparent loss of "spontaneity."[2] The difference in such cases must, therefore, be largely due to the retention of the connections with the organ for vision, and so of visual stimuli. Cutting off so important a class of stimuli necessarily reduces the animal's activity. It is unavoidable, in all removals of the cerebrum, that the olfactory lobe, and the central connections of the sense of smell, should be destroyed; the loss of this class of stimuli, also, lowers the activity of the animal—particularly in the case of those animals which depend greatly on the sense of smell. In mammals, most of the central connections of sight and hearing, as well as of smell, run through the cerebrum; loss of the hemispheres therefore renders

[1] See Ferrier, *Functions of the Brain*, 1886, p. 109.
[2] Schrader, *Pflüger's Archiv für die gesammte Physiologie*, 1887, XLI, 75; and 1888, XLIV, 175.

the mammal practically blind and deaf.   Accordingly, the loss of
all these senses needs to be considered, whenever the behavior of
a decerebrate mammal is examined.   There is no doubt that loss
of the cerebrum means loss of learned movements; and it also involves the loss of both the inhibitory and the tonic influences which
are exerted normally by the cerebrum on spinal and brain-stem reflexes.

Regarding the general characteristics of the reflex functions of the
nervous system, much may be gleaned from the incomplete inventory
of reflexes which has been given in the preceding paragraphs.
Much, however, still demands more special and detailed consideration.   Probably the greatest authority on reflex action in general
is Sherrington; and in what follows reliance will be placed chiefly
on his numerous special studies, and especially on his philosophical
presentation of the whole matter in his book with the title "Integrative Action of the Nervous System."[1]

§ 17.   Returning to the conception of the reflex arc, we see that
the particular muscular movement which is to follow any stimulus
is dependent on the nervous paths that lead from the receptor which
has been stimulated.   Since a most general characteristic of reflexes is to bring into play a considerable amount of musculature
in response to the excitation of even a very small group of receptors,
it follows that the reflex arc must undergo more or less of branching,
so as to distribute the excitation sufficiently widely.   Such distribution (compare Fig. 62) is provided for, to a limited extent, by the
branching of motor nerve-fibres, each of which may innervate several muscle-fibres.   But the required distribution is much more the
result of the branching which takes place within the nervous centres themselves.   As has already been shown (see p. 47), the sensory fibres, when they enter the cord, branch widely, by means of
collaterals; and it is highly probable that central neurones, or what
von Monakow has called "interpolated cells,"[2] intervene between
the sensory and the motor cells, and act as still further distributing
agents.   Such central cells are shown by histology to exist in abundance, and part of their function is, probably, the distribution of
impulses.   The character of any reflex is dependent, then, first of
all, on a large amount of branching in the pathway which extends
from any given receptor to many effector units.   How wide this
distribution can become, is seen most clearly when the stimulus
is very intense; for then the reflex may even spread over a large
share of the muscles of the entire body.   In certain abnormal conditions of the nerve-centres, such as, especially, the condition brought

[1] New York, 1906.
[2] *Ergebnisse der Physiologie*, 1902, I, part ii, 563.

about by strychnine poisoning, a stimulus to any receptor calls into action almost the whole musculature; and this result shows that, potentially at least, paths exist from each receptor to every effector unit.

But the distribution of nervous impulses over large areas of the musculature is by no means at random; for, in normal conditions

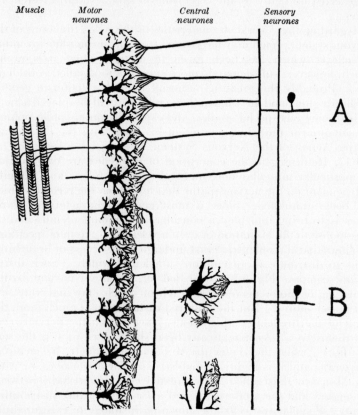

Muscle *Motor neurones* *Central neurones* *Sensory neurones*

A

B

FIG. 62.—The Distribution of Sensory Impulses in the Cord. In *A*, the distribution is accomplished by the branching of the sensory axon; in *B*, by the branching of an interpolated central axon.

of the nervous centres, the reflex is not a general convulsion, but a co-ordinated movement. The distribution, in other words, is highly *selective:* the excitation is carried to muscles which work in harmony; while other muscles, which would work against those employed, are passed over in the distribution of excitation. The distribution is different, also, according as it comes from one particular receptor or from some other: one receptor calls into play a certain combination of muscles; another receptor, a very different combination.

§ 18. Distribution of excitation, by means of branching pathways, is therefore a primary characteristic of reflex action. Another equally salient feature of this class of nervous functions is almost the reverse of this. There is a *convergence* of pathways, so that the same effector organ can be excited from any one of many receptors. This is made evident, first of all, by the fact that the same reflex can be excited from any one of many different points. The scratch reflex, for example, can be evoked by suitable stimulation applied anywhere within a large area of the skin of the back and sides. The flexion reflex of a limb can be evoked by a stimulus applied almost anywhere on the same limb. The pupillary reflex can be aroused by a beam of light falling anywhere on the retina. In general, the "receptive field" of a reflex is often wide; and from anywhere within this field the same muscles are thrown into action, though not always to the same degree, or in the same proportion. It is made obvious, from such facts as these, that the paths from the numerous receptors within any receptive field must converge upon the same muscles. And, plainly, such convergence does not occur within the sensory or the motor nerves themselves; for the fibres in these nerves run their courses parallel and independent, with no chance for communication from one to another. The convergence must, therefore, occur within the nervous centres; and it seems to be provided for, in part, by the spreading dendrites, which are capable of receiving excitation from many axons, and which converge upon their own cell-body and axon. It is probable, also, that central or interpolated cells have a share in the convergence of excitation, as well as in its distribution.

The convergence of reflex paths from all parts of the receptive field of a single reflex is only one case of convergence; and it is the simplest case. But the same muscle may be employed in different reflexes. For example, the muscles which bend and which extend the knee are active in the scratch reflex, and also in the stepping reflex. The receptive field for the latter lies within the muscles themselves, far distant from the receptive field of the scratch reflex. Moreover, though the two reflexes employ the same muscles, they employ them differently; the action of the knee muscles is differently combined with the action of other muscles, and besides, the rhythm of the scratch reflex is faster than that of the stepping reflex. Since the same muscles act differently in different reflexes, the difference cannot be attributed to the muscles themselves; they are merely obedient to the different excitations which they receive. Nor can the difference lie in the peculiarities of the receptors, as can be proved by suitable experiments.[1] Such differences, on the contrary, must be located in the nerve-centres; and the converging paths that lead within the centres toward the motor cells governing a given muscle must, therefore, not simply converge, but discharge their impulses with differing force and rhythm. Among the central cells of the cord there must apparently be, not only collectors of sensory impulses, but different collectors for the several reflexes which employ the same muscle; and these different collectors must have differing rates of discharge, etc. The collectors themselves have also differing distributions to the motor cells of the cord.

If these inferences make the connections within the cord seem highly complicated, we must remember that the complexity of connections revealed by histology is as ample as could be desired by the physiologist.

§ 19. There is a yet further complication to be noted. The effect exerted reflexly on a muscle is not always that of arousing it to activity; it may be the exact opposite, that of suppressing whatever activity is going on in a muscle. This process of checking activity is called *inhibition*, and the process of inhibition seems to be scarcely less important than that of excitation, in securing harmonious action by the muscles. It is seldom, indeed, that a stimulus to a sense-organ finds the system in a completely resting condition; almost always, some action is already going on within the system. In particular, the muscles which maintain the posture of the animal are usually in activity; such are, especially, the extensor muscles of the limbs and neck, and the muscle which supports the jaw against gravity.

Now, whatever movement is called for by any stimulus is pretty sure to require the temporary abandonment of the existing posture; and if the muscles which maintain this posture were left in their active state, they would hinder the quick and powerful execution of the newly required reflex movement. It is found, as a matter of fact, that the contraction existing in such muscles is inhibited by the reflex action of the new stimulus, simultaneously with the excitation of the muscles which execute the reflex movement.[2] This has been demonstrated by Sherrington in the case of the extensor muscles of the knee, which lose their tonic contraction simultaneously with any reflex action of the flexors of the knee; he has also demon-

---

[1] Sherrington (op. cit., pp. 55–61) finds that the rhythm of the scratch reflex is not interfered with by simultaneously or alternately exciting two points on the dog's back, and argues that, if the rhythm were determined in the receptors, the rhythmic impulses sent in from one point of stimulation would combine with those sent in from the other point, and produce a rhythm of twice the frequency, or at least change the rhythm, as it fails to do.

[2] Sherrington, op. cit., 83–101.

strated the same phenomena in the muscles of the eye and in other pairs of antagonistic muscles. When one muscle of a pair of antagonists is excited reflexly, the opposing muscle is simultaneously deprived of whatever contraction it may have.[1] There are no doubt exceptions, of a sort, to this rule, since in voluntary action it is possible to fix any joint in a rigid position by contracting at the same time the antagonistic muscles that act on the joint. But in *movements*, the inhibition of antagonists seems to be a very general principle.

Inhibition is a frequent phenomenon in some of the internal organs. The movements of the stomach and intestines, which, as noted above (p. 149), go on without the action of the central nervous system, can yet be checked by outgoing impulses from the nervous centres. The muscles of the arteries, similarly, are made to relax by the action of the "vaso-dilator" nerves. But the most interesting case is that of the heart. The vagus nerve, which sends a branch to the heart, acts to check the heart-beat. When this nerve is stimulated, the heart-beat is slowed down or even stopped for a time. Since this result is obtained by stimulating the outgoing nerve to the heart, it is obvious that the inhibition operates within the heart itself; and strong evidence has been offered to show that it operates within the heart muscle. But such inhibition as we are here considering—namely, the inhibition of the skeletal muscles— does not operate within those muscles; for no good evidence exists that there are any specifically inhibitory fibres running to the muscles, as there are running to the heart by the vagus. The inhibition of the skeletal muscles operates within the spinal cord. The postural activity of these muscles is itself of a reflex nature, being maintained through reflex centres; and the inhibition works on those centres, stopping them from sending out excitatory impulses to the muscles.

When inhibition as well as excitation is taken into account, the breadth of a reflex action, or the extent of its distribution, is seen to be twice as great as at first appears. For the influence extends not only to the muscles which become active, but also to those muscles which are inhibited. A small group of sensory fibres may thus exert a wide influence on the motor cells of the cord; but they may excite some of these cells and others they may inhibit or depress.

§ 20. It is not easy to form a complete conception of the mechanism of inhibition,[2] but there is one significant fact about it which

---

[1] In the case of movements which amount to changes of posture, the inhibited muscle often loses only a *part* of its contraction (Sherrington, *Quarterly Journal of Experimental Physiology*, 1909, II, pp. 109 ff.).

[2] See, however, pp. 289 ff.

is of no small assistance to this end. *Inhibition itself is not merely an interruption of activity;* for it has an after-effect which is the opposite of depression. When a muscle has undergone inhibition, it becomes at once readier for a new phase of activity. It is more easily aroused than it was before, and it is likely to show more force in its next contraction. That is, the phase of inhibition is followed by a rebound to greater activity;[1] and the rebound, like the inhibition, is primarily a central, and not a muscular affair. This after-effect of inhibition is probably important in the numerous alternating movements which occur in locomotion, breathing, chewing, pounding, etc.; the muscles (or their controlling nerve-cells) which are inhibited in one phase of the movement are thereby made ready for the succeeding, opposite phase.

§ 21. Closely related to inhibition is the phenomenon of the "refractory period," already mentioned (p. 131) in the case of nerve-fibres. Immediately after acting, or starting to act, any excitable organ loses its excitability and becomes refractory or unresponsive for a brief period. The duration of the refractory period differs in different organs; it is shortest in the case of nerve-fibres, where it does not exceed .002 sec. It is much longer than this in some of the reflexes, but varies greatly from one reflex to another. The "extensor thrust," for example, has a long refractory period, which may reach a full second; this means that repeating the stimulus within a second after a thrust has been evoked does not evoke a second thrust. More concretely stated and illustrated: If a gentle upward pressure is exerted on the "pads" of a spinal-dog's hind foot, the leg responds by a vigorous downward thrust (as if in jumping). Now, though this thrust lasts for only a fifth of a second, yet repeating the upward pressure on the pads does not evoke another thrust, unless an interval of a full second is allowed to elapse between the two stimuli. The duration of the refractory period in this, as in other reflexes, is, however, somewhat variable.

The length of the refractory period in the winking reflex is about the same as that in the extensor thrust; and in the swallowing reflex it is half a second or longer. In the "stepping reflex" it is about two-fifths of a second, and in the "scratch reflex," about one-fifth. In other movements, which are not obviously rhythmical, and which show a prolonged contraction of the muscles (such as the flexion reflex), it is found, on careful examination, that the apparently steady contraction of the muscle includes a series of waves, following one another at the rate of eight to twelve per second. These waves represent discharges from the cord, which are, in effect,

[1] Sherrington, op. cit., p. 206.

fused into the steady prolonged contraction. The refractory phase, in such cases, varies from an eighth to a twelfth of a second; as we know by the fact that the waves are not increased in frequency by stimulating the receptor at a faster rate, as, for example, by electric shocks at an interval of from twenty to fifty per second.

§ 22. Like those other peculiarities of reflex action that have already been mentioned, the refractory phase is not a peripheral phenomenon, the cause of which resides either in the muscles or in the receptors. That it does not reside in the muscles is evident from the fact that the same muscle shows refractory periods of different duration according to the reflex combinations into which it enters. The extensor muscle of the knee, for example, takes part in both the scratch reflex and the extensor thrust; but in the first reflex, its refractory period is only a fifth of a second, while in the extensor thrust this period lasts for a full second. That the refractory phase cannot be attributed to the receptors is evident from the fact that a reflex evoked by stimulating one receptor is refractory, for the usual time, to stimuli applied to any other receptor which normally evokes the same reflex. Accordingly, the refractory period must be considered as pre-eminently a central phenomenon; and it probably belongs to those central or interpolated neurones which have been referred to in previous paragraphs, as taking an important part in the reflex functions of the nervous system. Different central mechanisms have refractory periods of different duration; and the duration is in each case adapted to secure the final purpose, or greatest utility, of the particular reflex. The general utility of a refractory phase is clearest in the case of rhythmical or alternating movements, such as scratching, walking, etc. The stimulus is here continuous; but a single prolonged contraction of the muscles would not be an efficient response. The refractory phase, on the contrary, secures a *rhythmical response to a continuous stimulus*.

§ 23. It seems obvious, accordingly, that the "impulses" which pass along the fibres in the nerve-centres are, very often at least, *diphasic*. An excitatory phase is followed at once by an inhibitory phase. In other cases the inhibitory phase precedes, and is followed by a phase of rebound to a condition of heightened excitability. In general, the duration of the phases varies in different reflexes—i. e., in different fibres or neurones, or at different synapses.

We have, therefore, not exhausted our knowledge of reflex action, and of the central mechanisms which control it, until we have taken note of all the facts regarding the time, extent, and intensity of the different reactions.

§ 24. As to the time, the rhythmic character of reflex action has already been sufficiently considered. The duration of the reflex contraction depends to some extent on the duration of the stimulus; but such dependence is far less close in the case of reflex action than when a muscle is directly excited by an artificial stimulus, or when it is excited by stimulating artificially its motor nerve. In these cases of direct stimulation, the response lasts as long as the stimulus, and stops when the stimulus stops—or nearly so—subject of course to modification by fatigue. But in reflex action, the movement in response has in many cases a fixed duration that is more or less independent of the duration of the stimulus. This is true, for example, of the winking reflex and of the extensor thrust. In the scratch reflex, also, the alternating movement of the leg is likely to stop during the continuation of the stimulus. On the other hand, if the stimulus is brief, but sufficiently intense, the scratching considerably outlasts it. Other reflexes, too, outlast a brief stimulus; and, in general, the duration of this "after-discharge"[1] is greater for a strong stimulus than for a weak.

Between the beginning of the stimulus and the beginning of the muscular response there is always an interval, which is called the latent time of the reflex, or, more briefly, the *reflex time*. This is analogous, on the one hand, to the "reaction time" of voluntary movements, and, on the other, to the "latent time" of muscular contraction. When a muscle is directly excited by an artificial stimulus, a brief interval elapses between the stimulus and the commencement of visible movement in the muscle. This latent time usually appears as about .01 sec. It is probable that each receptor, likewise, has a latent period, i. e., an interval between the application of the stimulus and the starting of the nerve impulse along the sensory nerve. The latent time is probably different for the different kinds of receptors; but, in general, it is fully as brief as that given above for the muscle. The total reflex time includes the latent periods of both receptors and muscles; in addition, it includes the time consumed in nerve transmission to and from the centres; and, finally, it includes whatever time is consumed within the gray matter of the centres. It is, therefore, a highly composite affair; but its most interesting and important factor, as bearing upon our knowledge of the reflex functions of the nervous system, concerns the problem of how much of this time is lost, or absorbed, in the nerve-centres. This problem may be approximately solved, in the following way: If we take the speed of nerve conduction to be 30 metres per second, and assume the receptor and muscular latent periods to be each .01 second, then, knowing the length of

[1] Sherrington, *Integrative Action of the Nervous System*, p. 26 ff.

nerve traversed in the reflex arc, we can subtract the time consumed in the nerves, and in the receptors and muscles, and have left the so-called "reduced reflex time."[1] Some of the uncertainties of this reduction can be avoided by stimulating the sensory nerve close to the spinal cord. The shortest reduced reflex times seem to amount to about .01 second.

We have already seen, however, that the reflex time is far from constant. It varies, first, with the intensity of the stimulus, becoming shorter with increasing stimulus. Thus, the latent time for the flexion reflex of the dog may rise to .20 second with weak stimuli, and sink to .02 second with strong stimuli; and the time for the scratch reflex varies, similarly, between .14 and .50 second.[2] These figures show that the reflex time varies, not only with the intensity of the stimulus, but also with the character of the particular reflex. The flexion reflex is about the quickest of all;—and here the final purpose of protecting the organism applies; for this reflex needs to be prompt, since its normal stimulus is a harmful agent from which the muscular reaction must snatch the limb away. The scratch reflex is much less prompt. The winking reflex is also relatively slow, giving times of about .05 of a second. These differences can not be due to the muscles; and not entirely, at least, to the receptors; they must be attributed, principally, to differences in the character of the different central neurones and of the central connections involved.[3]

§ 25. The intensity, or muscular force of a reflex varies in about the same ways as the latent time. In many reflexes, the response increases in force with increasing intensity of the stimulus. But

[1] Exner, *Pflüger's Archiv für die gesammte Physiologie*, 1874, VIII, 526.

[2] Sherrington, op. cit., p. 21.

[3] The "knee jerk," or kick of the lower leg aroused by a blow on the patellar tendon just below the knee-cap, has a very brief latent time—as short, in some measurements, as .02 second. This extreme shortness leads to a doubt whether this movement is properly a reflex at all; though it is often called the "patellar reflex" and is regarded as a true reflex by many authorities. The difficulty with this view is that the length of nerve which must be traversed, from the knee to the spinal cord, and back to the quadriceps muscle of the thigh, which performs the movement, is so great that, at the accepted rate of nerve transmission, a time of .03 would be consumed in the nerve; and, of course, some time must also be allowed for the latent period of the muscle and of the receptors. These times add up to considerably more than the total latent time of the knee jerk; and this fact has led to the conclusion that this jerk is a direct response of the muscle to the mechanical stimulus. On the contrary, it is found that the knee jerk cannot be got unless the sensory and motor nerves of the muscle are both intact; it is dependent on the existence of reflex "tone" in the muscle; therefore, whether it is itself a reflex or not, it serves admirably as a test of the reflex condition of the muscle, and so of the condition of the cord.

there are exceptions to this rule, in which the reflex shows about the same force whatever the intensity of the stimulus, provided only that the latter is strong enough to arouse any reflex at all. The extensor thrust, for example, is found by Sherrington to show this peculiarity.

The reflex movement in response to stimulation also differs in strength according to the receptor stimulated. Within the receptive field of a reflex, some points yield a stronger effect than others. To give an example: the pupillary reflex is stronger, i. e., the pupil is more narrowed, when a beam of light falls on the centre of the retina than when it falls toward the side of the retina. A comparison of different reflexes shows that there is little general correspondence between the energy of the stimulus and that of the response. Some reflexes show a powerful response to a weak stimulus, while others give a comparatively feeble response to a strong stimulus. A clear example of the former class is seen in the violent reaction which is made to a tickling stimulus; in this case, slight brushing of the skin evokes a much stronger reaction than does a firm pressure. Or, again, a feeble force exerted on a point of the skin, so as to prick it, gives a strong reaction; while a much greater force exerted on a large area of the skin results in a comparatively feeble reaction. The same muscle, too, may contract strongly in one reflex and much less strongly in another. From such phenomena as these it is safe to conclude that the central mechanisms of the different reflexes differ in the intensity with which they excite the motor cells of the cord and brain-stem.

§ 26. The extent of the reflex movement, or the amount of the musculature which it brings into play, differs greatly in different reflexes; since some of them, as, for example, winking or the contraction of the pupil of the eye, involve only a small mass of muscle, whereas others, as locomotion, bring into play a large share of the whole musculature. In other words, the pathways of some reflex arcs are much branched and widely distributory—the pathways of others much less so. But to speak of this difference tells only half the story. The distribution is not fixed in extent for each reflex, but, as we have seen, increases with the strength of the stimulus. Even in case of the pupillary reflex, any considerable increase of the intensity of the light entering the eye causes an extension of this reflex beyond the little muscle of the iris, to which it may be confined when the light is of ordinary intensities. A very intense light even causes the eyelids to close, the head to be turned away, the hand to be brought up before the eyes, or a general movement of flight to be begun. Other similar examples can be obtained from the spinal or the decerebrate animal. Pinching the *pinna* of a spinal-cat's ear will, if the stimulus is weak, arouse nothing more than a twitch of the *pinna*. If the stimulus is increased, the head may be turned to the other side, and the fore limb of the same side brought forward toward the ear. Still stronger stimulation arouses movements of all four limbs. Again, pinching gently the forefoot of a decerebrate cat evokes only the flexion reflex in that limb; but a firmer or more persistent pinch causes the head to turn toward the point stimulated, and, perhaps, the jaw to snap; locomotion may also be evoked in this way, and strong stimuli may bring out a snarl or whine. Sometimes, as the stimulus is increased, the original local response is abruptly abandoned, and another reaction of a different, more efficient nature is substituted. But, in many cases, the original local reflex is maintained, and other movements are added to it.

The wider distribution of the response with increasing stimulus is often called by such names as "irradiation" or "spread" of reflexes. Neither of these names, however, is entirely suitable, since both seem to present a picture of a general diffusion of the same effect. The fact is, on the contrary, that the effect is far from being diffused indiscriminately to neighboring regions of the cord, or of the body. It is indeed true that the reflex often spreads to neighboring regions—as from the pinna to the neck—before it reaches more distant members. *But it always spreads only to muscles which give a harmonious total result.* Or, more precisely, the stimulus is "selective," and *excites* only muscles which combine harmoniously; when it spreads to their antagonists, also, its effect is to serve the same purpose of the organism by inhibiting them. Still more precise would probably be the statement that the reflex, in spreading beyond its local area, excites the central mechanisms of *other reflexes*, which belong more intimately to other stimuli occurring in their own locality, but which are allied to the reflex which in the given case is primary. Other reflexes, however, which are antagonistic to the primary reflex of the moment, are not excited in this spread. This "alliance" is, beyond all doubt, pre-eminently a central and not a peripheral phenomenon; it must be an "alliance" amongst the central mechanisms of different reflexes; and it therefore depends on the particular distribution of the neurones in the centres.

These facts, regarding the distribution, convergence, time, and intensity relations of reflex action, show the extreme nicety with which the reflexes are, in general, adapted to their several uses. When taken neurologically, they convey some conception of the complex, co-operative workings of the spinal cord and the other reflex centres.

§ 27. It remains to take due account of the fact stated near the beginning of this chapter;—the fact, namely, that the "simple" or isolated reflex, which has virtually been the theme of the last few pages, is an abstraction. This appears true for the following reasons: first, that more than one reflex, and indeed several reflexes, are simultaneously in progress, interacting as a rule with each other; and, second, that any new stimulus breaks in upon a condition which is not one of rest and neutrality, but upon an existing condition of reflex activity already established. We have, therefore, always to consider how the reflex effect of a given stimulus is modified by the action of other stimuli, both simultaneous and preceding.

Light has been thrown on this rather complicated problem by the studies of physiologists, among whom Exner[1] and Sherrington[2] deserve special mention. The two notions of "facilitation" and "inhibition," first clearly formulated by Exner, seem to give the key to the true explanation of the phenomena. Exner used the German word, *Bahnung*, which cannot easily be rendered into English. Its meaning is, however, that one stimulation of any part of the nervous mechanism may prepare a path, or break open a way, and so increase the effect of other and subsequent stimulations. The same meaning is fairly well expressed by saying that one stimulus "facilitates" the action of another. "Reinforcement" is a fact closely related to facilitation; and "inhibition" is the opposite of facilitation. The application of these conceptions to reflex action will now be illustrated by a few examples.

Suppose that two stimuli act simultaneously on a spinal animal, and we observe carefully their combined effect. The simplest case is that in which both stimuli are of the same nature, and applied within the receptive field of the same reflex. In this case, each of them, taken by itself, would tend to evoke a merely local response; and this response would spread if the stimulus were made more intense. But taken together, they *facilitate* or *reinforce* each other's effect. If then each of them, taken alone, is just too weak to arouse any reflex whatever, the two acting simultaneously, or nearly so, will call out the customary, normal reflex. And if each of them, taken alone, is of such an intensity as only to evoke a feeble or moderate response, the two acting together reinforce each other's effect, so that the response becomes relatively strong. This phenomenon can be easily obtained in the case of the scratch reflex. Feeble irritation of two points of the spinal-dog's back may evoke the scratching, though neither of the two irritations does so by itself; and the strength of the scratching movement evoked by moderate irritation at one point

[1] *Pflüger's Archiv für die gesammte Physiologie*, 1882, XXVIII, 487.
[2] *Integrative Action of the Nervous System*, pp. 114–234.

is increased by moderately irritating another point. The nearer together the two points are on the skin, the more powerfully do they act in this co-operative way.

The more interesting cases of facilitation are those in which the two points of stimulation do not lie in the same receptive field; and, therefore, do not tend to call out the same local reflex. It was noticed above that a reflex, in spreading, takes up local reflexes from other parts and, as it were, incorporates them into itself. For example, pinching either hind leg causes, as its local response, a pulling-up of the same leg; but if this reflex spreads, it results in a similar movement in the opposite fore limb. This movement of the fore limb is the local flexion reflex to pinching the forefoot; and it can, accordingly, be more readily aroused in this latter way than by stimulating the hind limb. Now if both of these

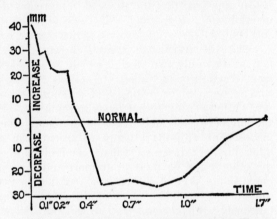

Fig. 63.—Reinforcement of the Knee Jerk Giving Way to Inhibition. (Bowditch and Warren.) Distances along the horizontal line represent the time elapsing between the clenching of the fist and the tap on the tendon which evoked the jerk. Distances above the "normal" line represent the amount by which clenching the fist increased the movement of the foot, and distances below the line represent the amount of decrease. The increase gives way to decrease at about 0.4 sec.

points—for example, the left forefoot and the right hindfoot—are stimulated at the same time, but so feebly that neither stimulus, taken alone, would arouse the movement of the fore limb, this limb may, nevertheless, be made to move through the combined effect of the two stimuli. In general, distant stimuli may facilitate each other's action. The impulses started at two widely separated receptors may converge upon the same central cells, and so produce movement of the same muscles. Even an auditory stimulus may facilitate a reflex in the hind limb. In man, the knee jerk is strengthened by a sudden noise or other stimulus which has the effect of startling the subject of experiment.[1]

Mental states may exert a similar reinforcement on various reflex functions of the nervous system; and artificial stimuli applied

[1] See Lombard, *American Journal of Physiology*, 188", I, 1.

to the cortex of the brain may facilitate the reflex effect of stimulation to the skin.

§ 28. This facilitating effect is, however, customarily one of brief duration; and it probably is subject to the diphasic law which was noted above (compare p. 165 and see Fig. 63). That is to say, the reinforcement soon gives way to its opposite, inhibition, which latter then fades away more gradually. In some experiments on the knee jerk, when reinforced by a vigorous voluntary clenching of the fist, it appeared that the phase of reinforcement yielded to the phase of inhibition, after about half a second, and that no effect of any sort could be discovered after a period much exceeding two seconds.[1]

§ 29. Not every two stimuli, however, facilitate each other's action; but only two stimuli which, when taken singly, lead to the same reaction or to "allied" reactions. If the two stimuli, singly, lead to opposed or inconsistent reactions, the one does not facilitate the other, but rather tends to inhibit it. For example, the execution of the scratch reflex with one hindleg of the animal is inconsistent with the attempt to execute the same reflex with the other hindleg; because, when one limb is engaged in scratching, the other must be used to support and brace the body. Accordingly, if the skin of the back is irritated in two spots at the same time, one on each side of the mid-line, two stimuli are acting simultaneously, which would tend to call out inconsistent results. One of these stimulations must inhibit the other.

But it is important to inquire into the exact character of such cases of inhibition. The law of the results obtained from applying two stimulations simultaneously does not follow the parallelogram of forces, nor any sort of algebraic addition; neither does it give an average or compromise of the two reflexes. The actual result is that either one leg or the other scratches; that is to say, one stimulus gains the right of way, and the other is excluded. By nicely balancing the stimuli, it may be possible to obtain a mutual inhibition of both reflexes, and it is often possible to delay the onset of either; but, finally, one or the other is pretty sure to break through. In a normal state of the nervous centres, it is probable that the muscles are never simultaneously excited for antagonistic reflexes; and this is true, although the sensory stimuli for both are acting at the same time. However mixed the stimuli at any moment—and they are often much mixed—the reaction itself is never a mixture of opposing movements, but is always a harmonious whole, consisting of allied reflexes, with their antagonists shut out. Nothing could be more essential to well-directed and efficient reaction than this principle. And no more conclusive proof can be demanded of the

[1] Bowditch and Warren, *Journal of Physiology*, 1890, XI, 25.

selective and purposeful character of the functions of the nervous mechanism—at least so far as its normal reflex activities are concerned.

The suppression of any given reflex by an opposing reflex is not, however, the end of the matter. Inhibition, we saw (p. 164), is followed by a rebound effect; and a reflex which has been inhibited is, the next moment, specially sensitive to a new stimulus. The scratch reflex, in the experiment mentioned in the last paragraph, begins on one side; but, if the stimuli continue to act, one on each side of the animal, the scratching may shift from one leg to the other. Each of the opposed reflexes has its turn. This is true, at least, when the stimuli are about evenly balanced. And, in general, a reflex which has just been inhibited is for some time afterward much more readily excited.

§ 30. The situation in the spinal cord and other reflex centres at any time is accordingly one of competition between different stimuli for the control of the muscles. Some of the stimuli are allied, in the sense that their action on the muscles would be the same; but other stimuli are antagonistic. There are not simply two parties, since the same muscle may be used in several different ways by as many different reflexes. The scratch reflex of one leg is not only inconsistent with that of the other leg; but it is also incompatible with the flexion reflex in either leg, with the extensor thrust, and with the tonic postural reflex which would maintain the standing position. However keen and many-sided the competition for the control of a muscle may be, the control goes, at any moment, to one reflex; and this same reflex and its allies have control of all the muscles, either to excite them or to inhibit their action. "All the muscles" makes the preceding statement pretty strong; it is doubtless true in the case of intense stimuli and widely spreading reflex effects; but in the case of weak stimuli, some reflexes may be so neutral to others that each may go on without interfering with the other.

In the competition of reflexes, certain kinds usually have more or less advantage over others. As a rule, protective reflexes have the advantage over all others. Postural reflexes, on the other hand, are usually the most at a disadvantage, and are liable to be thrust aside by almost any stimulus which calls for a movement.

The fatality and predictability of reflex action have sometimes been overstated. In the case of protective reflexes, which have the right of way over anything else in the cord, prediction is easy; but in the case of many others, prediction is by no means sure, because of the diversity of the stimuli which are likely to be acting at the same time. In general, reflex action is much less predictable than the response of a muscle to direct excitation; and the reflexes obtained from abbreviated nervous centres, such as the "mid-dog" and "hind-dog" mentioned earlier in the chapter, are more predictable than those obtained from an entire and uninjured spinal cord. The rule seems to be that the greater the number of influences to which any organ is exposed, the greater will be the variability of its action, and the less of regularity and fatality will appear in its responses to stimuli.

§ 31. Many of the characteristics of reflex action—such as distribution and convergence, facilitation and inhibition—are to be regarded as *fundamental properties of the action of nerve-centres*, and as applicable to the brain, in all probability, as well as to the cord. There are psychological facts (to be brought forward later) which are closely analogous to these facts of reflex action; and the analogy is of great importance in any attempt to comprehend the action of the brain in its relation to these psychological phenomena. The cord offers a simpler field for the unravelling of nervous function, and the results obtained are also of great importance in a physiological psychology.

CHAPTER VIII

END-ORGANS, OR RECEPTORS, OF THE NERVOUS SYSTEM

§ 1. In order to understand the end-organs, or receptors, it is necessary to refer again to the place which they hold in the threefold arrangement of the nervous mechanism. In the general division of labor, the function of certain cells situated at the surface of the body becomes that of receiving the action of the stimuli, of modifying this action, and thus of setting up in the conducting nerves the neural process which is propagated to the central organs. It is obvious, then, that the structure and grouping of such superficial cells must bear some definite relation both to the external stimulus and also to the nerve-fibres which convey inward the nervous impulse occasioned by it. The end-organs of sense may then all be described as special adaptations of the superficial cells to different kinds of stimuli. Even undifferentiated living matter is chiefly sensitive to certain stimuli, such as mechanical jar, heat, chemical agents, and electricity. But in the process of differentiation, certain cells become further specialized in the direction of their sensitivity, so that very slight stimuli of a particular sort are capable of arousing them. This increase of sensitivity is "specific" in the sense that each receptor is thus made highly sensitive to one kind of physical agent; whereas it loses rather than gains in its receptiveness toward other agents. The eye, for example—or more precisely the retina—combines with its very delicate sensitivity to ether vibrations of certain frequencies relative insensitivity to mechanical jar and even to other vibrations of the low frequency which affect the sense of temperature.

It is such specialization of receptors that gives precision and detail to the deliverances of the senses. If the eye were as sensitive to sound as it is to light, we should see so much that we should get little definite information regarding surrounding objects. That is, there could be no "apperceptive" vision. The particular agent to which a receptor is adapted is called its "adequate stimulus."

§ 2. In the end-organs of the special senses the fibrils of the sensory nerves, as a rule, terminate in cellular structures which have the *morphological significance of metamorphosed epithelial cells.* The end-organs of smell show this characteristic development

175

most clearly. These end-organs are, in general, made up of cells which, posteriorly, pass into nerve-threads that are gathered together into the sensory nerve of the special sense; and which, anteriorly, pass into conical or fusiform processes. The simplest type of an end-organ may then be described as follows: A hair-like process extending outward, and connected by a sensitive cell with a nervous filament extending inward. Such processes are probably extremely sensitive to external stimuli; and perhaps peculiarly so to the chemical changes which, at least in the case of three of the special senses (smell, taste, and sight), appear to be their immediate excitants.

All the end-organs of sense may be regarded as modifications of the type described above. Only a small part, however, of what are ordinarily called "the organs of the special senses" (e. g., the nose, the mouth, the ear, the eye, the skin) belongs, strictly speaking, to the nervous system. By far the greater part consists of mechanical contrivances, designed to prepare the external stimuli and conduct to the true nervous apparatus the impulses they occasion. These non-nervous mechanical contrivances, however, modify the nature of the stimulus in so important a manner as to merit some brief description in our consideration of the *nervous* mechanism.

§ 3. Besides the end-organs of sense, histology points out another kind of terminal apparatus. The efferent nerves, in order that they may stimulate the muscles, must have some special form of attachment to them. Special contrivances for connecting the motor nerves and the muscles are actually discoverable. We distinguish, then, two classes of end-organs: first, End-organs of Sense, and, second, End-organs of Motion.

§ 4. Among the end-organs of sense, those of Smell have been least successfully investigated. That portion of the mucous membrane of the nose which clothes the upper region of the nasal cavity and is marked by a brown-yellow color—the region of the expansion of the olfactory nerve—is called *"regio olfactoria"; it contains the end-organs of smell. Here Ecker and Eckhardt (in 1855) discovered two different kinds of cells; one is called *"epithelial,"* or *"supporting,"* the other *"olfactory."* The epithelial cells are the larger, have an oval nucleus of considerable size, and extend through the whole epithelial layer. The olfactory cells are spindle-shaped, with a large, round nucleus, and very long, fine processes. The external process reaches to the free surface of the mucous membrane, and is elongated into a stiff hair or hairs; at least in many cases, although Schultze considers that in man the olfactory cells have no cilia. The olfactory cells are surrounded by the epithelial cells (see Fig. 64).

Most physiologists follow Schultze in holding that the two kinds of cells are distinct both in form and in function, and that only the "olfactory" cells are connected with the end-fibrils of the nerve of smell, the others serving the purpose of supporting the olfactory cells. The internal or proximal process of the olfactory cell is a nerve-fibre, which passes back through the cribriform or sieve-like plate of the ethmoid bone into the brain cavity; and these fibres from the numerous olfactory cells are made up into small bundles which, taken together, are called the olfactory nerve. Arrived within the brain cavity, the fibres penetrate the olfactory bulb, and there end, forming synapses with other fibres which conduct further back into the brain (compare p. 107).

§ 5. The contrivance for applying the stimulus to the end-organs of smell is very simple; in general it is only necessary that a current of air, in which the stimulating particles float, shall be drawn through the nasal passages over the mucous membrane of the *regio olfactoria*. Even ammonia and camphor, when placed under the nostrils, have no smell so long as the breath is held or drawn through the mouth. In quiet inspiration much the greater part of the current of air is conducted to the pharynx directly, and comparatively little reaches the ridge situated above the nasal dam at the back of the nose, where the end-organs of smell are placed. In full inspiration, and still more when short and deep draughts are drawn through the nasal passages, a considerable amount of the air is forced over the sensory parts. By snuffing we

Fig. 64.—Olfactory Cells and Epithelial Cells from the Mucous Membrane of the Nose. $^{500}/_1$. (After Schultze.)

increase the amount of air drawn into the region by first creating a partial vacuum in its cavity, and also by creating eddies in the air current, which carry the odoriferous substance out of the main stream and into the olfactory recess. In expiration the breathing passage is so located as to carry nearly all the air past the sensory parts without striking them. For this reason smelling is almost exclusively confined to inspiration; it has been disputed whether the current of expiration can be smelled at all. But Debrou showed that the odor of orange blossoms, when water tinctured with them has been drunk, can be detected in the expired air. The current which passes through the anterior part of the nasal passages seems to be the more important. This is probably the reason why the loss of the nose is so frequently attended with loss of the sense of smell.

§ 6. The end-organs of taste, called gustatory bulbs or flasks, or more commonly taste-buds, lie, for the most part, on the upper surface and edges of the tongue; though some occur on the soft palate, and even on the epiglottis and in the larynx. More precisely, they are situated in the papillæ or projections which give a rough surface to the tongue. The roughness is, however, chiefly due to the filiform papillæ, which do not contain taste-buds; the latter being found in the circumvallate papillæ (Fig. 65) at the back of the tongue, and in the fungiform, scattered over its upper surface. The circumvallate, few in number but large in size, are circular and surrounded by a trench, in the walls of which are embedded the taste-buds. The fungiform papillæ are comparatively small structures; the taste-buds lie in their tops and sides.

Fig. 65.—Transverse Section through a Papilla Circumvallata of a Calf. Showing the arrangement and distribution of the gustatory bulbs. $\frac{25}{1}$. (Engelmann).

The extent of distribution of the taste-buds, and of the sense of taste, on the upper surface of the tongue varies somewhat in different individuals, and considerably as between children and adults. In young children all of the upper surface of the tongue has taste-buds, but in adults the front third is free from them, except at the edges; and there is no sense of taste in this part of the tongue.

§ 7. Taste-buds resemble minute bulbs (less than one-tenth of a millimetre in length) growing in the mucous membrane. In shape they are flask-like, narrowing to a neck and opening to the surface by a little pore (see Fig. 65). They are composed of cells which are arranged like the leaves of a bud in closely compressed rows around the axis. As in the olfactory end-organ, there are here two sorts of cells (Figs. 66 and 67), the supporting and the gustatory. The latter, also called taste-cells, are slender with a central enlargement containing the nucleus, and two processes. One process extends toward the mouth or pore of the taste-bud, and terminates in a short hair-like projection, which enters into the pore. The other process extends away from the pore, and is often branched.

Sensory nerve-fibres penetrate the taste-bud, and branch among and around the taste-cells. These fibres are derived from three of the cranial nerves. The glosso-pharyngeal supplies the rear of the tongue, and the lingual branch of the trigeminus the front of the tongue; while the vagus supplies the few taste-buds in the pharynx and larynx. The course of the fibres from the front of the tongue is curiously intricate and apparently varies in different individuals. From the lingual nerve they pass to the chorda tympani, which crosses the cavity of the middle ear; in some cases they enter the medulla by way of the intermediate nerve.

§ 8. An interesting example of the far-reaching results of that more discriminating and thorough analysis in which modern science delights, is afforded by the case of the so-called Sense of Touch. It was formerly customary to lump together all forms of sensation caused by irritating any area of skin, and to classify them all as one of the five senses with which the human animal was endowed.

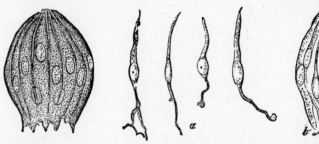

FIG. 66.—Isolated Gustatory Bulb, from the Lateral Gustatory Organ of the Rabbit. $\frac{600}{1}$. (Engelmann.)

FIG. 67.—a, Isolated Gustatory Cells, from the Lateral Organ of the Rabbit; b, an Investing and Two Gustatory Cells, isolated but still in connection. $\frac{600}{1}$. (Engelmann.)

It is now recognized, however, that the conscious states which result from applying different stimuli to the superficial area of the body resemble one another scarcely more closely than do sight and hearing, and no more closely than do smell and taste.

In considering the sensory end-organs in the skin, we must therefore anticipate what will be said in the chapter on qualities of sensation regarding the division of the old "sense of touch" into several senses, namely, those for contact, for temperature, whether warm or cold, and for pain. The problem which psychology proposes to physiology is, accordingly, that of discovering, if possible, the minute structures in the skin which serve as receptors for these different forms of sensation. It may be said at once, however, that this is possible only to a limited extent from present knowledge.

§ 9. The short hairs on hairy surfaces, which comprise ninety-five per cent. of the area of the skin, are to be regarded as specific organs of the tactile sense. About the root of the hair is coiled the termination of a sensory nerve-fibre. The nerve-ending is thus excited by touching the hair, or by touching the skin on the "windward" side of the hair.

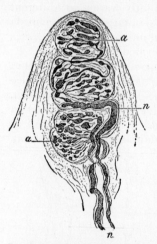

FIG. 68.—Corpuscle of Touch
from the Palm of the Human
Forefinger. (Ranvier.) *n*, sensory axon; *a*, its branching
termination within the corpuscle.

On hairless surfaces there occurs in great numbers a form of nerve-ending which apparently takes the place of the hair-receptor. This form is called the "touch-corpuscle" (see Fig. 68). These corpuscles occur in some of the papillæ of the skin of the palm and sole. They are composed of a capsule of connective tissue and a core of cells among which winds the branched termination of a nerve-fibre.

These two forms of end-organ may with probability be assigned to the sense of touch proper; but it is not certain that none of the other forms of nerve-ending met with in the skin are connected with this sense.

"End-bulbs" of various shapes also occur in the skin, some cylindrical, some nearly spherical. Their structure is much like that of the touch-corpuscles: a capsule encloses a core, into which penetrates a sensory nerve-fibre. The nerve-fibre loses its sheaths, and coils and ramifies as a naked axon in the interior of the bulb (see Fig. 69).

The most highly developed in structure of the cutaneous end-organs are the Pacinian corpuscles (compare Fig. 70). They are larger than the other forms, and their capsule is composed of concentric plates of connective tissue like the layers of an onion. Each Pacinian corpuscle is entered at one end by a nerve-fibre, which loses its myelin sheath in the interior of the corpuscle, and, passing along the axis, terminates near the other end. The Pacinian corpuscles lie just beneath the skin, or deeper in; and also in other situations, as in the muscles, in the neighborhood of tendons, ligaments, and bones, and in the mesentery.

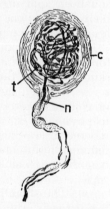

Fig. 69. — End-Bulb from the Human Conjunctiva. (Dogiel.) *n*, axon; *t*, its branching termination within *c*, the capsule.

There is still another mode of nerve-ending on the skin, quite different from the forms already described, in that the nerve-fibre branches freely among the cells of the skin, being unprovided with a capsule (Fig. 71). This form may be called a "free nerve-ending."

§ 10. As to the specific function of the end-bulbs, Pacinian corpuscles, and free nerve-ends, there is nothing of a conclusive nature to bring forward. The distribution of the various forms over the skin is unequal, and, since the distribution of the four cutaneous senses is also unequal, attempts have been made[1] to determine the function of the end-organs by correlating their distribution with that of the senses. Thus, spherical end-bulbs occur in the conjunctiva of the eye, which, to many observers, lacks tac= tile sensation, though possessing that of temperature and especially that of cold; this form of end-organ may very well, then, be the receptor for cold. On account of the longer reaction-time to warmth than to cold, and of the less sharp localization of the "warmth-spots," it is believed that the end-organs for this sense probably lie in the deeper layers of the skin, and this fact leads to the supposition that a cylindrical form of end-bulb, which occurs deep in the skin, may be the warmth-receptor.

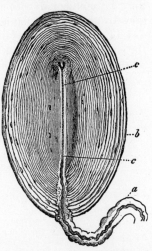

The pain sense is perhaps served by the free nerve-ends. A fact supporting this view is the absence of other sense qualities from the cornea, the nerve-ends in which are of the free-branching type. The Pacinian corpuscles, from their location, must serve a subcutaneous form of sensibility—perhaps what is known as "deep sensibility" to pressure.

Fig. 70.—Corpuscle of Pacini (or Vater) from the Mesentery of the Cat. (After Frey.) *a*, axon with its sheaths; *b*, system of tunics constituting the capsule of the corpuscle; *c*, axial canal, in which the nerve-fibre ends.

Sensory endings of complicated structure are found in muscles and their tendons, and are of interest in connection with the "muscle sense." The "muscle spindle" (Fig. 72) occurs embedded in the substance of the muscle, and is composed of several modified muscle fibres bound together by a capsule of connective tissue, and supplied by one or more sensory nerve-fibres, which, losing their myelin sheath, break up into fine branches that coil around the muscle-fibres within the spindle. That these are sense-organs has

---

[1] Especially by von Frey, *Beiträge zur Sinnesphysiologie der Haut*, in *Berichte d. k. sächs. Gesellsch. d. Wissensch. zu Leipzig, math.-phys. Klasse*, 1894, 1895, 1897; see also later discussions by Sherrington, in Schäfer's *Textbook of Physiology*, 1900, II, 920 ff., and by Thunberg in Nagel's *Handbuch der Physiologie*, 1905, III, 654.

been proved by showing that the nerve-fibres which enter them do not degenerate after section of the ventral spinal roots supplying the muscle in question;[1] these nerve-fibres, therefore, come from the dorsal roots and are sensory. Tendon spindles occur in the part of a tendon near to its muscle, and are of very similar structure to the muscle spindles. Other simpler sensory end-organs—Pacinian corpuscles and end-bulbs—are found in muscles, tendons, the capsules of joints, the periosteum and interior of bones; and these all may be connected with that complex of sensory apparatus which goes by the inexact name of "muscle-sense."

§ 11. With the exception perhaps of the ear, the eye is by far the most elaborate and complicated of the end-organs of sense. This is true of those portions of it which are designed merely to

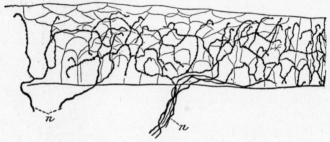

Fig. 71.—Free Branching Sensory Axons from the Larynx. (Retzius.) *n*, axons.

bring the external stimulus to bear upon the nervous structure, as well as of this structure itself. Considering it as a whole, we may say that the peripheral organ of sensations of light and color is an optical instrument constructed on the plan of a water camera obscura, with a self-adjusting lens, and a concave, sensitive, nervous membrane, as a screen on which the image is formed.

§ 12. The eyeball consists of three *coats* or tunics enclosing three translucent refracting media. Since, however, the front part of the outer one of these coats is itself translucent and refracting, the number of refracting media in the eye is really four. (1) The first or external coat consists of two parts: (*a*) the Sclerotic or posterior five-sixths part ("white of the eye"), which is a firm, fibrous membrane formed of connective tissue intermingled with elastic fibres; and (*b*) the Cornea, or translucent anterior one-sixth part, which is circular and convex in form, and covered with con-

[1] Sherrington, *Journal of Physiology*, 1894, XVII, 211 ff. Sensory endings are found also in the mucous membrane and quite widely distributed through the viscera.

junctival epithelium. The cornea rises and bulges in the middle like a watch-glass. (2) The second coat, or tunic of the eye, also consists of two parts: these are (a) the Choroid coat, which comprises much its larger portion, is of a dark brown color, due to its pigment cells (except in the case of albinos), and is abundantly provided with nerves and blood-vessels; and (b) the Iris, a circular, flattened, disk-shaped diaphragm in front of the lens (the colored part of the visible eyeball), bathed with aqueous humor, and having in its centre a circular aperture called the "pupil" of the eye. The anterior border (*corpus ciliare*) around the iris consists of the ciliary muscle and the ciliary processes. (3) The Retina is the third or inner coat of the eye. It is a delicate membrane of exquisite transparency and almost perfect optical homogeneity; it has a highly complex structure, consisting of nine or ten layers, the truly nervous portions of which contain nerve-fibres, nerve-cells, and special end-organs, together with supporting tissue and blood-vessels. The inner surface of the retina is moulded on the vitreous body, and it extends from the entrance of the optic nerve nearly as far forward as the ciliary processes.

§ 13. The eyeball has four translucent *refracting media*. The first of these—enumerating inward from the outside front—is (1) the Cornea, already spoken of as the anterior one-sixth of the outer coat of the eye.

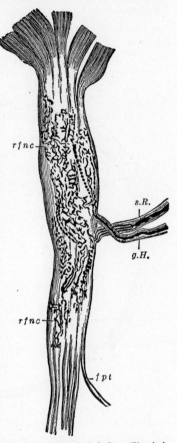

Fig. 72.—A Muscle Spindle. (Ciaccio.)

(2) The Aqueous Humor fills the space between the cornea and the lens, and is divided by the iris into two chambers, of which the front one is much the larger. It is limpid and watery; it holds in solution the salts of the blood-serum, with traces of organic substances. (3) The Crystalline Lens is situated between the iris and the vitreous body. It is a transparent biconvex lens, with its antero-posterior diameter about one-third less than the transverse diameter. It consists of a capsule

and enclosed body. It is of "buttery consistency," composed, like an onion, of a number of easily separable layers. Each layer consists of fibres, which within the layer are, as a rule, radial. Between the entire ciliary part of the retina and the corresponding part of the vitreous humor is interposed a structureless membranous body,

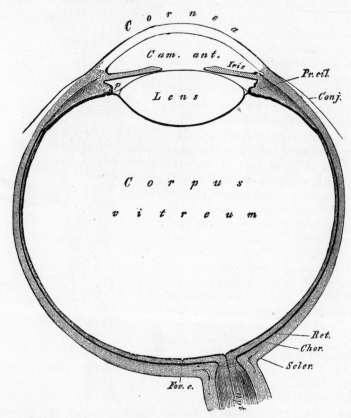

FIG. 73.—Horizontal Section through the Left Eye. ⁴⁄₁. (Schematic, from Gegenbaur.)

to which the edge of the lens is attached, and which radiates outward and maintains the lens in tension. It is called the *suspensory ligament* (or *Zonula of Zinn*), and its office is very important in the accommodating of the eye to different distances. (4) The Vitreous Humor consists of a number of firm sheets or layers (lamellæ), between which fluid is contained, built into a body that is, optically considered, transparent and homogeneous. It occupies most of the space enclosed by the tunics of the eye.   It is thought to be a gelatinous form of connective tissue, and is composed mostly of water with salts in solution, of proteids and mucin, fats and extractive matters—especially urea.   Its peculiar structure is of little significance for the physiology of the eye.

§ 14. Of the *appendages* or accessory parts of the eye—such as the eyebrows, the eyelids, lachrymal apparatus, muscles of the eyeball—only the mechanism by which the eye is moved in its

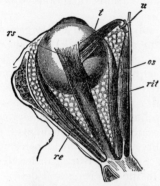
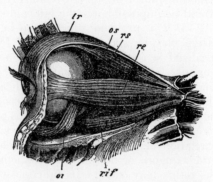

FIG. 74.—Muscles of the Left Human Eye, seen from above. *rs*, rectus superior; *re*, rectus externus; and *rit*, rectus internus; *os*, superior oblique, with its tendon, *t*, which runs through the membranous pulley, *u*, at the inner wall of the cavity of the eyeball.

FIG. 75.—Muscles of the Left Human Eye, seen from the outside. *lr*, levator of the upper eyelid, which covers the rectus superior, *rs*, *re*, *os*, as in the preceding figure; *rif*, rectus inferior; *oi*, inferior oblique.

orbit has any special significance for physiological psychology. The building-up of a world of visible objects, and even the formation of a so-called "field of vision," is dependent upon the great mobility of the eye.   The eyeball is moved in its bony socket, where it is embedded in a mass of fat as in a socket-joint, by six muscles, which are attached to it somewhat like the bridle to the horse's head.   Four of these muscles spring from the bony wall near the point where the optic nerve enters, extend through the length of the socket, and pass directly to the eyeball, where they are attached to it, one above, one below, one on the outer, and one on the inner side (the *recti internus* and *externus, superior* and *inferior*).   In moving both eyes up or down, the same muscles in both contract simultaneously; in moving the eyes to the right, the outer muscle of the right eye and the inner of the left contract simultaneously (and *vice versa*); in turning both eyes inward to converge them upon a near object, the two inner muscles contract together.

The other two of the six muscles of the eye are called *oblique*. Of these one is superior and internal; it does not pass directly forward from its place of origin, at the posterior aperture through which the optic nerve enters to the eye, but first runs through a ring, then turns around, and is attached obliquely to the upper surface of the eyeball. The other oblique muscle begins at the inner wall in the socket, passes under the eyeball, and is attached to it opposite to the superior oblique muscle. The two oblique muscles combine with the four recti to move the eyes in various directions which would be impossible for the latter alone.

§ 15. The problem which is to be solved by the end-organ of vision may be stated in a general form as follows: A mosaic of localized sensations must be so constructed that changes in the quantity, quality, local relation, and sequence of these sensations shall be quickly interpreted as indicative of the color, shade, size, shape, locality, and motion of external visible objects. The most important part of the solution of this problem falls upon the nervous structure of the retina. It is itself a mosaic of nervous elements, the excitation of which may vary in quality, quantity, local coloring, and sequence of the different elements excited. But in order that the retina may exercise its function with the precision and delicacy of detail for which its structure fits it, the rays of light reflected from a single point of the surface of the visible object must excite a single one, or at most a small and definite group, of the retinal nervous elements. The sensations thus occasioned can then undergo a systematic arrangement by the mind. It is the work of the translucent refracting media of the eye to apply the stimulus to retinal elements exactly discriminated, and in an order corresponding to the object; that is to say, the cornea, the humors of the eye, and the lens must form an *image* on the retina.

§ 16. Light entering the eye passes successively through the cornea, the aqueous humor, the lens, and the vitreous humor. At each of the surfaces between these media the light suffers refraction. Since the surfaces at which the refraction occurs are approximately spherical, and the centres of the spherical surfaces all lie in one straight line—the so-called "optic axis"—the eye is, optically considered, a centred system. An important result of this arrangement is that it avoids distortion in the image. For example, the pencils of rays issuing from the various points of any plane perpendicular to the axis will be finally focussed in points which lie in a plane having the same direction; and the image formed of these latter points will, therefore, be in approximately true proportion to the seen object.

To determine the refractive power of the eye, we need to know (1) the index of refraction of each of the media through which the light passes, (2) the radius of curvature of each of the surfaces at which refraction occurs, and (3) the distance apart of these surfaces.

The indices of refraction which have been worked out by various ingenious methods are in round numbers the following: for aqueous and vitreous humors, 1.34, or very nearly the same as for water; for the cornea, 1.38; for the lens, increasing from 1.39 in the outer layers to 1.41 at the centre. Since the curvature of the layers of the lens becomes sharper from the outside inward, the refractive power of the lens is increased; taken as a whole, it is equivalent to a lens of the same size and shape with an index of about 1.44. But since the cornea is thin and differs but little, in its index of refraction, from the adjacent aqueous humor, it may be considered as a part of the latter. The only surfaces at which incoming rays are effectively bent are, therefore, the outer surface of the cornea, and the front and rear surfaces of the lens. The radii of these surfaces are as follows: of the cornea, about 8 millimetres; front of lens, about 10 millimetres; back of lens, about 6 millimetres. It should be understood, however, that these measurements differ considerably in different individuals.

The distance from the corneal surface to the front of the lens is about 3.6 millimetres, and the thickness of the lens about the same. The data are thus provided for calculating the strength of the eye as an optical instrument, and the calculation gives it a strength of about 67 diopters. Its power is such that parallel rays—rays from a distant object—entering the eye are brought to a focus at a distance of about 20 millimetres behind the cornea— a distance which in the normal eye corresponds to the actual location of the retina.[1] If, however, the axis of the eye, from the cornea to the retina, is too long for the refractive power, the image of distant objects is formed in front of the retina, and only near objects can be clearly seen (near-sightedness or myopia); whereas if the axis of the eyeball is too short, the image of distant objects will be formed behind the retina, and the refractive power of the eye must be increased to permit of clear vision (hypermetropia). If, as is common, the surface of the cornea is not truly spherical, the rays of light are brought to a line rather than a point on the retina (astigmatism).

§ 17. The preceding remarks apply to what is called the "resting eye." The eye, when its internal mechanism is at rest, is focussed on distance, and does not form clear images of near objects.

[1] These measurements and calculations are from several investigators, and are here cited after Schenck, in Nagel's *Handbuch der Physiologie*, 1905, III, 38 ff.

To obtain clear vision for near objects, the optical power of the eye must be increased. The process by which this is accomplished is called "accommodation." The mechanism of accommodation differs in different orders of animals;[1] in amphibia and reptiles the lens is moved forward as in the camera. In mammals this is not the case, but the power of the eye is increased by increasing the convexity of the lens; its front surface bulges forward, becoming more curved, while its rear surface remains in position.

There are several methods of experiment which demonstrate that in accommodation for near distances the front of the lens becomes more strongly arched. When accommodation is taking place, the pupil may be seen not only to contract, but also to draw its edge forward. Helmholtz calculated the amount of this forward movement for two cases at about $\frac{1}{70}$ and $\frac{1}{59}$ of an inch, respectively. Moreover, by an ingenious contrivance the image reflected from the anterior surface of the lens may be watched as it becomes smaller and more distinct on adjustment for near distances, thus showing that the surface from which it is reflected has increased its curvature.

It is obvious that the mechanism for adjusting the eye must be under the brain's control, since adjustment is voluntary; and that it must consist of muscles which lie within the eyeball. The accepted hypothesis concerning the nature and action of this mechanism was first proposed by Helmholtz. This investigator assumes that the lens, when the eye is at rest, does not have the form which corresponds to a condition of equilibrium in its own elastic power. If it were not held in by its surroundings, it would be more arched than it is both before and behind. But it is kept flattened by the radial tension of the *suspensory ligament;* when this tension is withdrawn the lens becomes curved by the action of its own elasticity. The withdrawal of the tension is accomplished by the action of the ciliary muscle, the fibres of which have their point of fixation at the edge of the cornea, and run from here in the direction of a meridian toward the equator of the eye. When the ciliary muscle contracts, the free ends of its fibres are drawn toward its fixed ends on the edge of the cornea; the radial tension of the suspensory ligament is thus relaxed, and the lens is allowed to assume its natural form under the equipoise of its own elastic forces (Fig. 76).

The iris of the eye corresponds to the diaphragm of the camera. It contains two sets of contractile fibres, one circular, the effect of which is to diminish the size of the pupil; the other radial and enlarging the pupil. Contraction of the pupil occurs under two conditions: When bright light (or, more exactly, light brighter than that

[1] Beer, *Wiener klin. Wochenschrift,* 1898, XI, 942.

to which the retina is at the time adapted) enters the eye; and when the eye is accommodated for a near object.   In both cases the effect of narrowing the pupil is to increase the clearness of vision.   A sudden bright light has a dazzling effect, and this is lessened by diminishing the quantity of light entering the eye.   The divergent rays from a near object are not so well focussed as are the more nearly parallel rays, on account of spherical aberration; but this bad effect is diminished by cutting off the more oblique rays which enter through the periphery of the cornea and lens.

The nerves which supply the muscles of the eye are the third, fourth, and sixth of the cranial nerves, and the sympathetic.   Of these, the third or oculomotor is the largest; in it are contained the fibres which supply the ciliary muscle, and those which supply the circular muscle of the iris. The fibres which supply the radial muscle of the iris are from the sympathetic, and arise from a centre in the cervical cord. The fibres of the oculo-

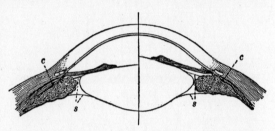

Fig. 76.—The Change of the Lens in Accommodation. (Helmholtz.) The left half of the figure shows the lens focussed on a distant object, the right half on a very near object. c, the ciliary muscle; s, the suspensory ligament.

motor nerve originate in the mid-brain, in the floor of the third ventricle.   Convergence, accommodation, and constriction of the pupil can all and severally be excited by stimulating special portions of this region.   The pupillary reflex to light has as its sensory nerve the optic; the fibres concerned are those which pass to the anterior quadrigemina, whence, apparently, other fibres pass to the nucleus of the oculomotor nerve and so excite the motor fibres to the iris.

§ 18. Given the formation of the image upon the retina, it is further required in order to vision that this physical process shall be changed into a physiological process.   We now examine briefly the mechanism by which such a change is accomplished.   The retina, or inner tunic of the eye, contains the nervous elements by whose action the system of refracted rays is changed into a mosaic of nerve commotions.   But light does not act as a stimulus to the nervous substance, either fibres or cells, unless it have an intensity which is nearly deadly to that substance.   Since we are able to see the feeblest rays of the moon as reflected from white paper, the nervous excitation which is the condition of vision cannot be produced by the direct action of light on the nerve-fibres or nerve-cells of the eye. A photo-chemical substance and process, as well as a special end-apparatus, seems therefore to be necessarily involved in the problem which is given to the retina to solve.

§ 19. The nervous and other elements of the retina are arranged

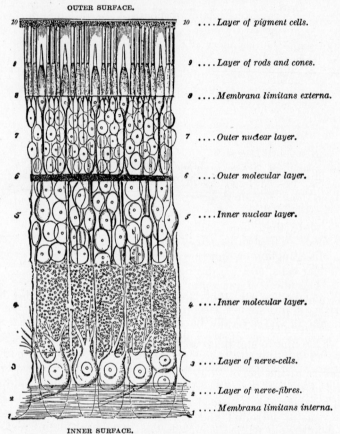

OUTER SURFACE.

10 .... *Layer of pigment cells.*

9 .... *Layer of rods and cones.*

9 .... *Membrana limitans externa.*

7 .... *Outer nuclear layer.*

6 .... *Outer molecular layer.*

5 .... *Inner nuclear layer.*

4 .... *Inner molecular layer.*

3 .... *Layer of nerve-cells.*

2 .... *Layer of nerve-fibres.*

.... *Membrana limitans interna.*

INNER SURFACE.

Fig. 77.—Diagrammatic Section of the Human Retina.   (Schultze.)

(see Figs. 77 and 78) in the following ten layers, counting from within outward and backward: (1) the *membrana limitans interna*, which is the retinal border toward the vitreous body; (2) the *layer of optic nerve-fibres* distributed from the papilla where this nerve breaks in through the tunics of the eye; (3) the *ganglion cell-layer*; (4) the *inner molecular layer*; (5) the *inner nuclear layer*; (6) the *outer molecular layer*; (7) the *outer nuclear layer*; (8) the *membrana limi-*

tans externa; (9) the bacillary layer, or *layer of rods and cones;* (10) the *pigment-epithelium layer.* The membranes (Nos. (1) and (8)) are not really uninterrupted layers, but an extremely fine network.

By no means all the retinal substance is nervous. Indeed, the numerous radial fibres (*fibres of Muller*) which seem to penetrate its entire thickness are now held to be in great part elements of the support-ing tissue; moreover, the whole connective substance is a kind of sponge-like tissue, in the gaps of which the true nervous ele-ments lie embedded. The gaps thus filled are especially large in the second, third, fifth, and seventh layers.

The principal *nervous* elements of the retina can be arranged in three parallel sets, and may, therefore, be spoken of as lying in three layers, each of which in-cludes more than one of the layers just mentioned. These three sets of nerve-cells are (1) the ganglion or optic nerve-cells, (2) the bipolar cells, and (3) the rod and cone cells. The fibres of the optic nerve arise in the main from the ganglion cells; they are, indeed, the axons of these cells, and have no medullary sheaths in their course over the retina to the point of exit of the nerve. They converge from all parts of the retina to the nerve, thus forming the second of the ten layers mentioned above. Their arrangement is special at the yellow spot, so as to surround and not cover it. The dendrites of the ganglion cells branch in the fourth layer, the "molecular" ap-pearance of which, in cross section, is due to the cut ends of numerous fine dendritic branches. This molecular layer may also be called a synapse layer, since it contains the synapses between the ganglion cells and the bipolar cells. The cell-bodies of the latter lie in the fifth or inner nuclear layer; their short axons branch and terminate among the dendrites of the ganglion cells.

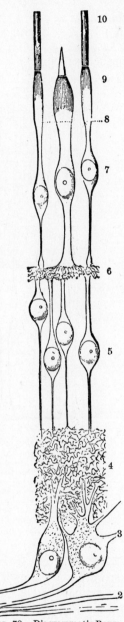

Fig. 78.—Diagrammatic Repre-sentation of the Connections of the Nerve-fibres in the Retina. (Schultze.) The numbers have the same ref-erence as in Fig. 77.

The dendrites of the bipolar cells extend toward the layer of rods and cones, branching in the outer molecular layer, which is, again, a synapse layer between the bipolar cells and the rods and cones. The cell-bodies of the rod-and-cone-cells lie in the outer nuclear layer; their axons run inward to form synapses with the dendrites

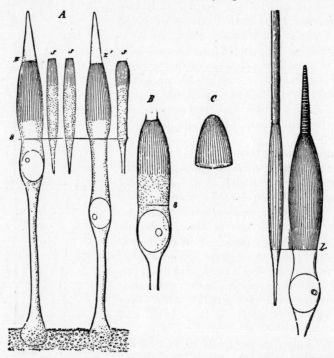

FIG. 79.—Rods and Cones of the Human Retina. (Schultze.) *A*, showing inner segments of the rods, *s s s*, and of the cones, *z z'*; the latter in connection with the cone-nuclei and fibres as far as the outer molecular layer. $\frac{800}{1}$. *B*, inner segment of a cone with a cone-nucleus. $\frac{1200}{1}$. *C*, isolated interior portion of a cone.

FIG. 80.—Rod and Cone from the Human Retina, preserved in perosmic acid, showing the fine fibres of the surface and the different lengths of the internal segment. $\frac{1000}{1}$. (Schultze.) The outer segment of the cone is broken into disks which are still adherent.

of the bipolar cells, while what correspond to their dendrites are the specialized branches called rods and cones. These branches are the real receptors of the retina; it is they which are sensitive to light; and the nerve impulses set up in them by the action of light pass from them to the bipolar cells; from the bipolar to the ganglion cells, and so, by the axons of the latter cells to the optic nerve and its terminations in the brain (compare p. 91).

The researches of Cajal and other recent histologists have un-earthed a wealth of further facts regarding the internal structure of the retina, to only a few of which brief reference can now be made. It is found that some of the fibres of the optic nerve orig-inate within the brain, and terminate in the retina; these probably conduct outward from the brain, but their exact function is not clearly made out. There are also cells in the retina which do not conduct in the direction of the rod-and-cone-bipolar-ganglion cells, but spread out horizontally, as if to associate cells of the same layer. Among the bipolar cells, two classes are recognized, linked respec-tively to the rods and to the cones. Several rods are linked to the same bipolar cell; whereas it appears that each cone may have an individual bipolar cell connected with it.

§ 20. To this description of the minute nervous elements of the retina, a brief notice of some of the more distinctively physical characteristics of certain of its parts may now be added. As its very name suggests: The layer of rods and cones (No. 9) consists of a multitude of elongated bodies arranged side by side, like rows of palisades, with their largest extension in the radial direction. These bodies are of two kinds—one cylindrical, and called "rods of the retina," the other rather flask-shaped, and called "cones of the retina" (compare Figs. 79 and 80). The rods extend the entire thickness of the layer, and are about $\frac{1}{350}$ inch in length, but the cones are shorter; the rods are about $\frac{1}{14000}$ inch in diameter, the smallest cones of the central depression $\frac{1}{10000}$ inch. Each rod or cone is composed of an inner and an outer segment or limb; the latter is highly refractile, the former only feebly so. The inner limbs ap-pear under the microscope like a mass of protoplasm.

In general, the rods are more numerous than the cones. The distribution of the two elements is different for different parts of the retina. In the yellow spot only cones appear, but these are of more slender form, and of increased length, so that not less than one million are supposed to be set in a square $\frac{1}{10}$ inch; while not far from this spot each cone is surrounded by a crown-shaped border of rods. Toward the ora serrata the cones become continually rarer. In close connection with the rods and cones stand the cells of the pigment-epithelium. These cells form a regular mosaic of flat, six-sided cells, which send out pigmented processes between the outer limbs of the rods and cones (see Figs. 81 and 82).

§ 21. Two minute portions of the inner surface of the retina re-quire to be distinguished from the rest of its area: the yellow spot (macula lutea) and the "blind spot" (papilla optica). The yellow spot is of oval shape, about $\frac{1}{12}$ of an inch in its long diameter, and has in the centre a depression called the fovea centralis. It is the place of clearest vision, and the physiological centre of the eye. About ⅙ of an inch inside the eye, or 15,° from the middle of the yellow spot, is the middle of the papilla, or place where the optic nerve breaks into the retina (compare Fig. 83).

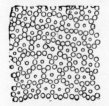
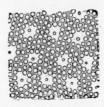

The *blind spot*, or portion of the retina which can be experimentally shown to be inoperative in vision, has been proved by Helmholtz to correspond in both size and shape to that covered by this papilla. Its diameter is about $\frac{1}{12}$ or $\frac{1}{15}$ of an inch, varying considerably for different eyes. It is wanting in all the nervous elements, except, of course, the nerve-fibres.

FIGS. 81 and 82.—Superficial Aspect of the Arrangement of the Rods and Cones in the Retina. $\frac{500}{1}$. (Schultze.) The former is from the region of the macula lutea; the latter from the peripheral region.

§ 22. In answer to the question, What elements of the retina are directly affected by the light? both anatomy and physiology refer to the layer of rods and cones. This layer alone possesses that mosaic nervous structure which appears to correspond to the demands made upon the end-apparatus of vision. It can be demonstrated that the waves of light pass through the structure of the retina, and that the nervous process must begin in the back part of this structure. Indeed, it is possible, by an experiment (devised by Purkinje), to perceive with one's own retina the figure formed by the shadow of the blood-vessels expanded upon its front part.

§ 23. Certain changes which occur in the retina under the stimulus of light are of interest from their possible bearing on the mode of this organ's action. Electrical currents can be detected, both when the eye is kept in the dark and

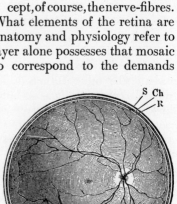

FIG. 83.—Equatorial Section of the Right Eye, showing the Papilla of the optic nerve, the Blood-vessels radiating from it, and the Macula lutea. $\frac{2}{1}$. (Henle.) *S*, sclerotic; *Ch*, choroid; and *R*, retina.

when it is suddenly exposed to light; these currents are analogous, in a general way, to the currents which appear in nerves and in muscles; they show certain peculiarities, but not much use can as yet be made of them for an explanation of the function of the retina.

Of the chemical changes in the retina, the most striking is connected with the famous visual purple. When an eye has been kept for some minutes in the dark, the outer limbs of the rods become tinged with purple or rose-color. This color is quickly bleached by exposure to light, and reappears again in the dark. The bleaching effect of different parts of the spectrum is of very different strength, being greatest for a yellowish green. Along with the changes in the visual purple go movements of the cones and of the pigment cells of the tenth layer. The reaction to light consists in a shortening of the cones by drawing back toward the *membrana limitans externa;* and, on the part of the pigment cells, by a pushing forward of their processes between the rods. When exposed to the dark, the processes of the pigment cells are withdrawn, and the cones extend backward.

It has long appeared probable that the first effect of light on the retina must be of a chemical character, and therefore the discovery of the visual purple, and of its reaction to light, was hailed as opening the way to a more complete understanding of retinal function.[1] It soon appeared, however, that the visual purple was not essential to sight. Kühne showed that a frog, with the purple bleached by exposure to light, still saw. It is now clear that the changes produced by light in the visual purple are not the photo-chemical processes which were looked for as the intermediary between light and nervous activity. At the same time, it is not impossible to see a relation between the visual purple and retinal function. One of the most remarkable facts in the physiology of the retina is its power of adaptation to different degrees of illumination. Every one is familiar with the fact, that on passing from light to dark the eye seems at first nearly blind, but soon becomes "used to the dark," or dark-adapted. Also, in passing from dark to light, the first effect is that of being dazzled; but soon the eye grows used to the light, or light-adapted. Adaptation to the dark goes on rapidly within the first ten minutes after passing into the dark, and thereafter more slowly for half an hour or more. Adaptation to the light occurs much more swiftly. These times of adaptation correspond rather closely with the times for bleaching and regeneration of the visual purple. It is probable, from this and other correspondences, that the changes in the color of the rods have something to do with the processes of adaptation to light and dark.

The fact that the centre of clear vision, corresponding to the fovea, is blind in dim light, and does not become adapted to it, combined with the fact that the fovea contains only cones, in connection with

[1] The important names in connection with this discovery are those of Boll and Kühne.

other similar facts, has led to the view that the cones are insensitive to very faint light, and have less power of dark-adaptation than the rods. The further fact that clear vision, and vision for colors, diminish from the fovea toward the periphery of the retina—along with the diminution of cones—has led to the view that color vision, and distinctness of vision, are properties of the cones. There is thus some evidence of a difference in function between the rods and the cones.[1]

In very dim light, all colored objects appear gray, and the relative brightness of different colors is much different from what it is under good illumination. Thus, a red and a green which appear equally bright in good light are seen in very dim light as if the green were much brighter than the red (the Purkinje phenomenon). The point of greatest brightness in the spectrum, which is in the yellow under good illumination, moves into the green in very dim light. These changes do not occur in central or foveal vision.

§ 24. In a word—to repeat our summary: The human eye is a camera, which—if one were advertising it—might be described as "a wonderfully compact little instrument, capable of being focussed on any distance from five inches upward, provided with the only original iris diaphragm, and having the special feature of a self-renewing plate, which automatically alters its sensitivity to suit the illumination, and also gives colored photographs. The camera cannot, however, be guaranteed, as some specimens are defective, and even the best are liable to be injured by hard usage; none will be replaced, though some of the defects can be partially corrected."

§ 25. The end-organ of hearing is the Ear. But in this case, as in that of the eye, a very large part of the apparatus of sense is significant simply as a contrivance for applying the stimulus to the true end-organ, to the differentiations of epithelial cells and nervous cells connected with the terminal fibrils of the sensory nerve. The entire human ear consists of three parts, or ears: namely, the external ear, the middle ear, or tympanum, and the inner ear, which is also called the "labyrinth," from its complex construction.

I. The External Ear—exclusive of the cartilaginous plate which is extended from the side of the head—consists of (a) the concha, a deep hollow, and (b) the external meatus, or passage leading from the bottom of this hollow to the drum of the ear. The concha is probably of only slight service in sharpening and defining our perceptions of sound. Its position, however, favors the reception of sound-waves which come from in front rather than behind; it may,

[1] The principal champion of this "duplex theory" of vision is von Kries. See his papers in *Zeitschrift f. Psychol.*, IX, 82; XII, 1; XIII, 242; and his article in Nagel's *Handbuch der Physiologie*, 1905, III, 184.

therefore, be of some service in enabling us to determine more readily and accurately the direction from which the sound-waves come.

The most patent office of the external meatus is the protection of the ear-drum; the passage is so curved that the drum cannot be reached from the outside in a straight line. Helmholtz called attention to the fact that certain tones of a high pitch resound strongly in the ear when the meatus is of normal length, but cease so to resound when its length is increased artificially. The meatus

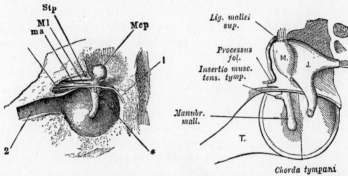

FIG. 84.—Drum of the Right Ear with the Hammer, seen from the inside. ⅔. (Henle.) 1, chorda tympani; 2, Eustachian tube; *, tendon of the tensor tympani muscle cut off close to its insertion; *ma*, anterior ligament of the malleus; *Mcp*, its head; and *Ml*, its long process. *Stp*, Spina tympanica posterior.

FIG. 85.—Side Wall of the Cavity of the Tympanum, with the Hammer (*M*) and the Anvil (*J*). The former shows the connection of its handle with the drum. *T*, Eustachian tube. ¾. (Gegenbaur.)

probably, therefore, modifies certain tones by its own resonant action—strengthening the high ones, and deadening the low, in some degree.

Simple experiments—such as placing a resounding body in contact with the teeth—prove that the surrounding cranial bones conduct sound to the ear. Various paths for this conduction, both direct by way of the cranial and petrous bones to the inner ear, and indirect by way of the ear-drum and bones of the middle ear to the fenestra ovalis, are theoretically possible. But the amount of conduction to be assigned to each is difficult of precise determination.

§ 26. II. The Middle Ear, or Tympanum (Figs. 84 and 85), is a chamber irregularly cuboidal in form, and situated in the temporal bone, between the bottom of the meatus and the inner ear. Its outer wall is (*a*) the *membrana tympani*, which consists of three layers—an external tegumentary, an internal mucous, and the intermediate *membrana propria*, composed of unyielding fibres arranged both radially and circularly. In the inner wall, which separates the tympanum from the labyrinth, are two openings or windows— the *fenestra ovalis*, which corresponds to the vestibule of the labyrinth, and the *fenestra rotunda*, which corresponds to the tympanic passage in the cochlea. Near its anterior part the tympanum opens into (*b*) the *Eustachian tube*, a canal which communicates with the nasal compartment of the pharynx.

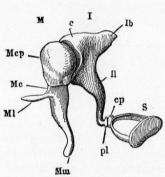

FIG. 86.—Bones of the Ear, as seen in their connection from in front. $\frac{4}{1}$. (Henle.) *I*, Incus (anvil), of which *Ib* is the short, and *Il* the long, process; *c*, its body, and *pl*, the process for articulation with the stapes (*processus orbicularis*). *M*, Malleus (hammer), of which *Mc* is the neck, *Mcp* the head, *Ml* the long process, and *Mm* the manubrium; *S*, stapes (stirrup), with its capitulum, *cp*.

(*c*) The auditory bones are three in number, called *Malleus, Incus*, and *Stapes*, and arranged so as to form an irregular chain stretched across the cavity from the outer to the inner wall of the tympanum (see Fig. 86). The malleus has a head, separated by a constricted neck from an elongated handle; its handle is connected with the centre of the membrana tympani; its head articulates with the incus. The incus has a body and two processes. On the front surface of the body is a saddle-shaped hollow, in which the head of the malleus fits; the short process is bound by a ligament to the posterior wall of the tympanum; the long process ends in a rounded projection (*os orbiculare*) through which it articulates with the stapes. The stapes, or stirrup-shaped bone, has a head and neck, a base and two crura. The head articulates with the incus; from the constricted neck the two crura curve inward to the base, which is attached to the fenestra ovalis. These bones are moved on each other at their joints by (*d*) two small muscles—the *tensor tympani* and the *stapedius*. The first of these is inserted into the malleus, near the root, and serves to tighten the tympanic membrane by drawing the handle of the malleus inward; the stapedius is inserted into the neck of the stapes, and draws the stapes from the fenestra ovalis, thus diminishing the pressure of the chain of bones and lessening the tension of the tympanic membrane; it therefore acts as the antagonist of the tensor tympani.

§ 27. The general office of the tympanum may be described as that of transmitting the acoustic waves to the inner ear, while at the same time modifying their character. Some modification is necessary in order that these waves may occasion such vibrations in the elements of the inner ear as shall be adapted for the excitation of its end-organs. The acoustic motion of the molecules of air, in the form in which it reaches the ear-drum, has a large amplitude, but a small degree of intensity. This motion must be changed into one of smaller amplitude and greater intensity; and it must be transmitted, with as little loss as possible, to the fluids of the labyrinth. The transmitting vibrating media must also have the power of answering to the different tones of any pitch perceptible by the ear. The description of the manner in which this apparatus of membrane and bones solves so complicated a mechanical problem belongs to the physics of anatomy; it has been worked out with great detail by Helmholtz and others, although certain questions still remain unsolved. We can here only indicate one or two particulars.

A flat membrane, evenly stretched, whose mass is small in proportion to the size of its superficies, is easily thrown into vibration by the impact of acoustic waves upon one of its sides. Such a membrane responds readily to tones which approach its own fundamental tone; but if divergent tones are sounded the membrane is unaffected. A motion which consists of a series of harmonious partial tones cannot then be repeated by such a membrane in the form in which the air brings it. If, then, the membrane of the tympanum were not so arranged and connected as to have no preponderating tone of its own, it could not be the medium of our hearing a great variety of tones. The property of taking up the vibrations of a large scale of tones is secured for the tympanum by its funnel-shaped form and by its being loaded. It is contracted inward into a depression of the right shape by means of the handle of the hammer; it is therefore unequally and only slightly stretched, and has no fundamental tone. It is also loaded with the auditory bones, which deprive it of every trace of such a tone and act as dampers to prevent long-continued vibrating. Moreover, since the apex of its funnel bulges inward, the force of the vibrations from all sides is concentrated in vibrations of greater intensity in the centre, where it is spent in setting the chain of ear-bones in motion.

The acoustic vibrations of the auditory bones, which are occasioned by the movements of the ear-drum, are not longitudinal, but transverse; they do not, however, resemble the vibrations of a stretched cord or a fixed pin. They do not vibrate by reason of their elasticity, but like very light small levers—vibrating as a system, with a simultaneous motion around a common axis. Direct observation of these bones in motion shows that their sympathetic vibrations vary greatly for tones of different pitch and similar intensity, from a scarcely observable motion to a surprisingly great elongation.

The effect of the muscles of the tympanum upon the transmission of tones of different pitch is not quite clearly demonstrated. In general, the stretching of the tensor muscle, within the limits which have thus far been investigated, seems to weaken the higher much less than the lower tones. But the tension of the drum under the influence of this muscle does not indicate the slightest change on passing from low to high tones. The tensor tympani can, therefore, scarcely be regarded as the mechanism which has complete control of accommodation to pitch. On the other hand, its reflex contractions are most easily excited by tones of high pitch. The resulting favoring of high tones, and corresponding dampening of simultaneously sounding low tones, would seem thus to be of assistance in picking out a high tone from a mixture of sounds of differing pitch. The stretching of the tendon of the stapedius muscle has no observable influence on the acoustic vibrations of the tympanum.

§ 28. The Eustachian Tube, when in its normal position, is neither closely shut nor wide open. Its office is to effect a renewal of the air in the tympanum, to maintain the equilibrium of atmospheric pressure on both sides of the tympanic membrane, and to convey away the fluids which collect in the tympanic cavity. If it remained open, so as to permit the acoustic waves of the air from the mouth to enter, our own voices would be heard as a roaring sound, and the passage of air inward and outward during respiration would affect the position and tension of the tympanic membrane. That it is opened, however, on swallowing, Valsalva proved two centuries ago. For if we keep the nose and mouth closed and then swallow, with the cheeks blown violently out, a feeling of pressure is felt in the ears and the hearing is weakened. These effects are due to the forcing of the air through the Eustachian tube into the tympanic cavity. The tube is thus of indirect service in respect to the physiological functions of the middle ear.

§ 29. III. The Internal Ear, or Labyrinth, is the complex organ in which the terminal fibrils of the auditory nerve are distributed and the end-organs of hearing situated. The so-called "bony labyrinth" is a series of cavities channelled out of the petrous bone. It consists of three parts—the Vestibule, the Semicircular Canals, and the Cochlea. In each osseous part a membranous part is suspended, corresponding to it in shape, but filling only a small portion of the bony cavity which contains it. It is in the labyrinth that the acoustic waves transmitted by the tympanum are analyzed and changed from a physical molecular process to a nerve-commotion, by the special end-apparatus of hearing (see Fig. 87).

(A) The Vestibule is the central cavity of the internal ear; it is the part of the labyrinth which appears first in animals and is most constant.   The membranous vestibule is composed of two sac-like dilatations—the upper and larger of which is named *utriculus*, the lower *sacculus*.   In the outer wall of the vestibule is the fenestra ovalis; its anterior wall communicates with the *scala vestibuli* of the cochlea, and at its posterior wall the fine orifices of (B) the Semicircular Canals open into the utriculus.   These canals are three in number, are bent so as to form nearly two-thirds of a circle, and are about an inch in length and $\frac{1}{20}$ of an inch in diameter.   They are called the *superior*, the *posterior* or vertical, and the *external* or horizontal canals.   The contiguous ends of the superior and pos-

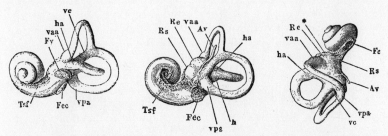

FIG. 87.—No. 1, Cast of the Osseous Labyrinth of the Left Ear, from below; No. 2, of the Right Ear, from the inside; No. 3, of the Left Ear, from above.   (Henle.)   *Av*, aqueduct of vestibule;   *Fc*, fossa of the cochlea;   *Fec*, its fenestra (*rotunda*);   *Fv*, fenestra of the vestibule (*ovalis*);   *ha*, external ampulla;   *h*, external semicircular canal; *Tsf*, *tractus spiralis foraminosus;* *vaa*, ampulla of the superior semicircular canal; *vc*, posterior semicircular canal;   and *vpa*, its ampulla.

terior canals blend together and have a common orifice into the vestibule.   They all have a regular relative position. their planes being nearly at right angles to each other.   Near the vestibule they dilate to about twice their average diameter and form the so-called *ampullæ*.   Both the osseous vestibule and the osseous canals contain a fluid (the *perilymph*) in which the membranous vestibule and canals are suspended; the membranous labyrinth is also distended with a similar fluid (the *endolymph*).

(C) The Cochlea is by far the most complex part of the labyrinth, and, according to present evidence, the only part directly concerned with auditory sensations and perceptions (compare Figs. 88, 89, and 90).   It is about $\frac{1}{4}$ of an inch long, and is shaped like the shell of a common snail.   It, too, consists of a membranous sac embedded in an osseous cavity.   The whole passage of the cochlea is imperfectly divided into two canals by a partition-wall of bone, which is wound $2\frac{1}{2}$ times around an axis (the *modiolus*), from the base to the apex, somewhat like a spiral stair-case.   It is called the osseous *lamina spiralis*.   Of the two canals or passages thus formed, the one which faces the base of the cochlea is called the *scala tympani;* since it has its origin in the circular aperture (fenestra rotunda) which leads to the tympanic cavity. The other, which faces toward the apex, opens into the vestibule, and is called the *scala vestibuli*. At the apex of the cochlea these two scalæ communicate with each other through a small hole (*helicotrema*). The division of the membranous cochlea is completed by a membrane (the *basilar membrane*, or membranous spiral lamina), which bridges the interval between the free edge of the osseous spiral lamina and the outer wall of the pas-

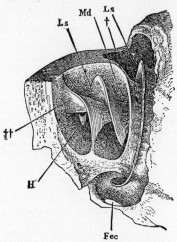

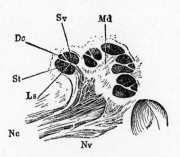

FIG. 88.—Osseous Cochlea of the Right Ear, exposed from in front. ⁴⁄₁. (Henle.) †, section of the division-wall of the cochlea; ††, upper end of the same. *Fec*, fenestra; *H*, hamulus; *Md*, modiolus; *Ls*, lamina spiralis.

FIG. 89.—Cross Section through the Acoustic Nerve and the Cochlea. ³⁄₁. (Henle.) *Nc*, nerve of the cochlea; *Nv*, nerve of the vestibule; *St*, scala tympani; *Sv*, scala vestibuli; and between them the ductus cochlearis, *Dc*. *Ls* and *Md*, as in preceding figure.

sage; it is attached to this wall by the spiral ligament. Another membrane (the *membrane of Reissner*) arises from a spiral crest (limbus, or *crista spiralis*) attached to the free edge of the osseous lamina, and extends to the spiral ligament, so as to form a small aqueduct between it and the basilar membrane (the *scala intermedia*, or *ductus cochlearis*, or canal of the cochlea). It is in the vestibule, in the ampullæ of the canals, and in the scala intermedia that the nervous end-organs of hearing are to be found.

§ 30. The auditory nerve, on approaching the labyrinth, divides into a vestibular and a cochlear branch (compare Fig. 89). As stated in another chapter (see p. 82), these two parts of the eighth nerve separate also at their entrance to the medulla and pass to different portions of the central organs. They serve two senses, the end-organs of both of which are located in the inner ear.   The vestibular branch or nerve enters the vestibule, and divides into five branches, one for the utriculus, one for the sacculus, and one for each of the three ampullæ.   In each of these dilatations the membranous wall forms a thickened projection, which is called the *crista* in the ampulla and the *macula* in the utricle and saccule.   The characteristic feature of each of these is the presence of epithelial cells provided with tufts of fine hairs.   The hairs, instead of projecting directly into the endolymph, are embedded (as discovered by Retzius) in a soft gelatinous or mucous-like mass. In the ampullæ this mass is dome-shaped, and the hairs are of considerable (microscopic) length.   In the utricle and saccule, the hairs are shorter, and the soft mass in which they are embedded is flatter, but is principally remarkable for containing little particles of carbonate of lime (limestone), which are called the *otoliths*, or "ear-stones."   The base of the

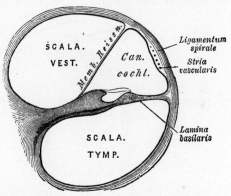

Fig. 90.—Section through one of the Coils of the Cochlea. $\frac{20}{1}$.   (Schematic, from Gegenbaur.)

hair-cells, in the ampullæ, utricle, and saccule, are embraced by the terminal ramifications of the fibres of the vestibular nerve; there is no doubt, accordingly, that the hair-cells are sensory cells (compare Fig. 91).

§ 31.   The terminal nerve-apparatus which constitutes the special end-organ of hearing is noteworthy for its exceedingly complicated structure and striking appearance.   The cochlear branch of the auditory nerve pierces the axis of the cochlea and gives off laterals which enter the canals of the osseous spiral membrane. Here they radiate to the membranous spiral lamina, and are connected with a ganglion which contains the cell-bodies of the fibres of the cochlear nerve.   Beyond this ganglion, they form a plexiform expansion, from which the delicate fibrils—losing their medullary sheath and becoming extremely fine axis-cylinders—pass through a gap in the edge of the lamina into the organ of Corti, where they terminate around the base of certain hair-cells, soon to be described (compare Fig. 92).

It is the so-called "organ of Corti," however, in which the ingenuity of the natural processes engaged in constructing the mechanisms of the human body would seem to have reached the ultimatum of endeavor to create an elaborate and effective, but mystifying, structure for the conversion of physical stimuli into nervous impulses. A study of the accompanying figures, together with the following description of some of its more obvious features, will suffice the purposes of our treatise.

It will be noticed that the organ of Corti is a wonderful arrangement of cells, some of which are elongated and curved, and are gathered into two groups that may be designated, respectively, as an inner and an outer. Since the cells of the inner group pro-

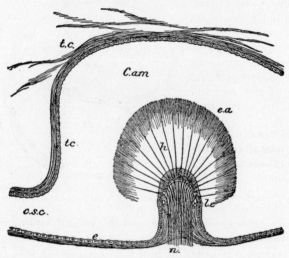

Fig. 91.—Nerve Endings in an Ampulla. (Retzius.) *n*, sensory axons; *h*, hair-cells.

ject forward and outward, while those of the outer group incline forward and inward, the two form a sort of bow which arches over an exceedingly minute channel (the *canal of Corti*) between them and the membrane on which they both rest. This membrane itself is composed of fibres arranged in a transverse direction, and in such manner that a single rod-like cell rests upon one or two of these fibres.

Internal, and almost parallel to the inner one of the groups just described, is a row of columnar cells with short and stiff hair-like processes (*inner hair-cells*). External and almost parallel to the outer group are four or five rows of hair-cells (*outer hair-cells*) which are attached to the basilar membrane, while their other extremity projects as a brush of hairs through the reticular membrane (*membrane of Kölliker*). This latter membrane is a very delicate framework, perforated with holes, through which the hairs of the outer hair-cells project, and which extends from the inner rods to the external row of hair-cells. It acts as a support for the ends of these cells. The interval between the outer hair-cells and the spiral ligament is occupied by cells of a columnar form (the *supporting cells of Hensen*). The organ of Corti is covered over and separated from the endolymph of the ductus cochlearis by the so-called *membrana tectoria*.

§ 32. The problem before the labyrinth of the ear is in part the same as that solved by the tympanum, namely, the problem of conveying the acoustic waves to the true end-apparatus of hearing.

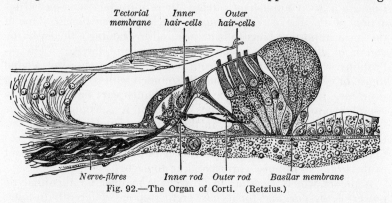

Fig. 92.—The Organ of Corti. (Retzius.)

The repeated shocks of the stirrup at the fenestra ovalis—and perhaps, in far less degree, the pulsations of air at the fenestra rotunda—produce waves in the fluid of the labyrinth. Any molecular oscillations of this fluid, thus occasioned, cannot, however, act directly as the appropriate stimulus of the sensations of sound. Since the dimensions of the whole mass thrown into vibration are so small in comparison with the length of the acoustic waves that the extension of the shock from the stirrup would be practically instantaneous throughout, and since the surrounding walls may be regarded as absolutely immovable by any such impact, the labyrinth-water would act as an incompressible fluid. It would, therefore, be unsuitable for the transmission of various kinds of acoustic waves. But different parts of the labyrinth are capable of yielding to the waves in the fluid caused by the repeated shocks of the stirrup. This is especially true of the membrane of the fenestra rotunda which is left free to bulge out into the tympanic cavity. Waves started by impact at the fenestra ovalis would pass into the scala vestibuli of the cochlea; and from there—it is probable—through the membrane of Reissner, the fluid in the cochlear *duc-*

tus, and the basilar membrane, into the air of the middle ear. In their passage through the basilar membrane, they would, of course, cause it to vibrate and so excite the sensory hair-cells which rest on this membrane.

§ 33. We may be fairly certain that the process by which vibrations excite the end-organ of hearing is as just described— namely, in brief, that vibrations of the fluid in the cochlea excite the hairs of the hair-cells. But a more difficult problem is that of explaining the great variety of responses which the ear makes to different stimuli, and which we know by means of the many distinguishable noises, tones, and tone-combinations. Since we distinguish a great number of pitches, there must be some special reaction of the ear corresponding to each of these tones. One of the most important facts to bear in mind in framing a theory of the action of the cochlea is the analytic power of the ear. The vibrations which reach the ear from the air, when a chord of several tones, or even when a single tone, is sounded with its accompanying overtones, are highly complex; but a "trained ear" can analyze the complex into the separate tones of which it is composed. The "training" occurs, no doubt, in the brain and not in the ear; but the brain could not distinguish the components unless the ear had first broken up the complex vibration into its elements, and sent to the brain an impulse corresponding to each.

A theory which accounts in an elegant manner for this analytic power of the ear, and for its power to respond differently to tones of differing pitch, is the resonance or sympathetic vibration theory of Helmholtz.[1] What is meant by "sympathetic" vibration is illustrated when a piano string, for instance, which is tuned to vibrate at a certain rate, takes up vibrations of this rate from the air, and is itself set in vibration by them. If the dampers are lifted from the strings of a piano, and a particular tone be sung into it, it answers with the same tone; if two or more tones are simultaneously sung into it, it answers with the same combination of tones, the strings tuned to these tones having been set into sympathetic vibration. Helmholtz conceived that the transverse fibres of the basilar membrane might be likened to the strings of a piano, and since they are of different length, might be tuned to tones of different pitch, and vibrate sympathetically, each to its own vibration rate. The vibration of any fibre of the basilar membrane would naturally excite the hair-cells in its immediate neighborhood; different hair-cells would thus be set in vibration for different pitches, and different combinations of them for different combinations of

---

[1] See his *Sensations of Tone*, 1895, pp. 145 ff.

tones; and thus the sense for pitch and the analytic power of the organ would find their explanation.

The theory of sympathetic vibration has been worked out with great thoroughness to cover the various peculiarities of auditory sensation, and in general has been found to be adequate. It is not, however, altogether free from internal difficulties, the chief of which lies in the extreme minuteness and small range in length of the fibres which are supposed to be tuned to the various audible pitches. The longest of them is but half a millimetre in length, and it is difficult to conceive that a fibre of such length, even though loaded with its segment of the organ of Corti, and even though suspended, not in air, but in a liquid, could be tuned so low as the lowest string of the piano. Moreover, though the number of fibres in the basilar membrane—about 24,000—is adequate for the range of audible pitch and the number of discriminable pitches which a trained ear can detect, the difference in length of these fibres is only about as one to twelve, much less than would be required for tuning to the range of audible pitch—unless, indeed, we can conceive of these fibres as being under different tension or differently loaded. M. Meyer [1] has called attention to a physiological difficulty in the way of accepting the suggestion that the fibres are under different tension: when a living tissue is subjected to a continued tension, it yields or accommodates itself, so that the tension is relieved; and there is no evidence that this rule is broken in the case of the basilar membrane. Hardesty,[2] on minute anatomical examination, finds that the basilar membrane contains, not only the radial fibres which the Helmholtz theory likens to the strings of a harp, but also numerous other fibres running athwart these and binding them so tightly together that it seems a physical impossibility that they could vibrate singly or in small groups, as required by the theory.

Such difficulties have caused dissatisfaction, in the minds of many students of acoustics, with the Helmholtz theory, and several other theories have been put forward, but the working of them out in detail, to explain, as well as the Helmholtz theory does, the various facts of hearing, has not yet been accomplished. The most prominent of the opposing theories is that of Ewald.[3] By experimenting with a little model of the basilar membrane, he finds that even so minute a membrane as this is set into vibration of a fixed form, giving a fixed vibration figure, by the action of vibrations of any given rate; and that the figure varies with the rate; and, further,

[1] *University of Missouri Studies*, 1907, II, 1.
[2] *American Journal of Anatomy.* 1908, VIII, 109.
[3] *Pflüger's Archiv f. d. gesammte Physiologie*, 1899, LXXVI, 147, and 1903, XCIII, 485.

that the combined action of two vibration rates is such as to induce in the membrane a compound vibration-figure, in which, however, the component figures are not obliterated. As applied to the
cochlea, these facts would indicate that vibrations of any given
rate, acting on the basilar membrane, would cause it to vibrate in
certain places—not simply in one place as according to the Helmholtz theory—and that therefore corresponding parts of the sensory
apparatus would be excited by each vibration rate. Apparently a
combination of nerve-fibres, from different parts of the cochlea,
would be excited by even a single tone; and thus the nervous result
would be less simple and easy to conceive than according to the
sympathetic vibration theory. But Ewald has made it probable
that the basilar membrane does vibrate in the manner supposed by
his theory.

With regard to these and all similar physiological theories, however, it must be remembered that we are not in search of a nervous
apparatus which can be listened to by the brain, or by the soul in
the brain, as we listen, so to say, to the tones produced by the
vibrations of the strings of a piano. What we are seeking, the
rather, is some sufficient account for a series of more or less
complex nervous changes which can be adequately correlated
with the varieties of elements into which we can analyze our sense
experience.

§ 34. From the fact that the utricle, saccule, and semicircular
canals are parts of the inner ear, it was natural to suppose for them
an auditory function; and they have often been regarded as connected
with the reception of noises and with the perception of the direction
from which sound comes.   There is, however, no positive evidence
of an auditory function for these structures, while there is positive
evidence of a function of another sort.   Experimental knowledge
of this, their true function, began with Flourens, who applied, about
1825, the method of extirpation to the canals of pigeons, and found
the result to consist in certain disturbances of movement. Since
then numerous results of the same tenor have accumulated, and the
technique of stimulating and extirpating these minute structures
has been perfected, till, in the hands of Ewald,[1] very delicate operations with precise results have been achieved.

The position of the canals should first be noted. As has already
been said, the three canals of one labyrinth lie in three planes
nearly at right angles to each other; and the planes of the canals of
the two labyrinths are related to each other, so that the two hori-

---

[1] *Physiologische Untersuchungen über das Endorgan des Nervus Octavus*
(Wiesbaden, 1892).   See also Kreidl, in Asher and Spiro's *Ergebnisse der Physiologie*, 1905, V, 572, and Nagel, *Handbuch der Physiologie*, 1905, III, 778.

zontal canals are parallel, and the superior of either side is parallel with the posterior of the other side. The planes of the canals are not, however, the three primary planes of the head, but lie at angles of about 45° to these (compare Fig. 93).

The three planes at right angles remind one of the planes of reference in co-ordinate geometry; and this peculiarity of arrangement has suggested to some authors the theory that the canals are concerned with the perception of the direction of sound; and to one author the still vaguer theory that they furnish sensations of three-dimensional space.[1] To understand the real function of the canals, it is necessary first to have in mind the class of reflexes which are called *compensatory movements*. If a frog is placed on a board, and the board is so tilted as to lower the frog's head, he responds by raising his head; and similarly, he lowers his head if the board is so tilted as to raise it, and turns his head to the right if the board is so rotated as to turn it to the left, etc. These reactions "compensate for," or correct, the movement impressed on him.

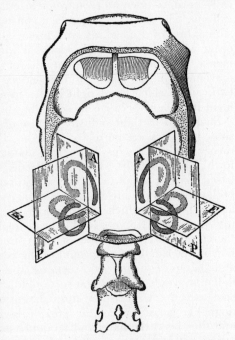

Fig. 93.—The Position of the Semicircular Canals in the Head. (Ewald.)

Similar movements are found through a wide range of animals, including fishes, birds, and mammals. Along with compensatory movements of the head go compensatory rotations of the eyes, and movements of the body as a whole. These reflexes are of great importance in maintaining the position and equilibrium of the body, and in keeping it to a straight line in locomotion. Now one marked result of the extirpation of the semicircular canals is the loss of compensatory movements; and another closely related result is the loss of the "tonus" of many of the muscles, and the consequent inefficiency

[1] **Von Cyon**, *Pflüger's Archiv f. d. gesammte Physiologie*, 1900, LXIX, 211.

of many movements. Locomotion becomes uncertain, and, if the destruction of the canals is unilateral or otherwise partial, "forced movements," such as running in a circle, or rolling to one side, appear. These forced movements can be explained as the result of the loss of some of the compensatory movements, along with retention of the rest. Thus, if every incipient movement to the right calls up a compensatory movement, while movements to the left call up none, the result must be a constant turning to the left. On stimulation of a canal, as with a current of electricity, movements occur which are apparently identical with the compensatory movements. Stimulation of the ampulla of any single canal arouses a movement in the plane of that canal. Stimulation, at once, of two canals which lie at right angles to each other arouses a movement in a plane between those of the stimulated canals.

Such facts as these indicate the use of the canals, but do not also show how they are normally excited. The now generally accepted theory of these organs dates from about 1873–75, when it was put forth independently by Mach, Breuer, and Crum Brown. It is based partly on physical considerations. Each canal opens at both ends into the utricle, and may be considered as a circular pipe, at one point of which (the ampulla) a sensory end-organ projects into the pipe. Rotation of the head in the plane of any canal must therefore cause, by inertia of the contained endolymph, a back-flow in the canal. On account of the very small calibre of the pipe, and the consequent friction against the wall, the back-flow of endolymph would certainly be very slight, but inertia must have some such effect. A back-flow through the ampulla would act on the dome-like mass in which the hairs of the sensory cells are embedded, and thus bend the hairs and no doubt excite the cells. Even a rotation not in the exact plane of a canal would cause some back-flow, unless the rotation were in a plane at right angles to that of the canal; and the more nearly the plane of rotation approached that of the canal the greater would be the effect within that canal. Given, therefore, three canals at right angles to one another, and no rotation of the head can occur without exciting currents in at least one canal; and no two rotations, in different directions, can excite exactly the same direction and proportion of back-flow in the three canals. Thus this physical theory explains the facts made evident by compensatory movements: first, that the canals are somehow stimulated by head rotations, and second, that they are differently stimulated by rotations in different directions.

More direct evidence is at hand in support of the theory; for Ewald has been able to produce artificial currents of the endolymph in a canal, and the canal is thereby excited, as is shown by the occurrence of a reflex movement. Moreover, this movement is in the same direction as the current in the canal; and this is as it should be to agree with the theory; for both the back-flow and the compensatory movement are opposed to the impressed rotation, and therefore act in the same direction, one with the other.

§ 35. Regarding the utricle and saccule, physical considerations again suggest a similar theory (Breuer). Since the gelatinous mass in which the hairs of the sensory cells are here embedded is weighted with the otoliths, it would tend to sag downwards, and would pull differently on the hairs according to the position of the head with reference to gravity. Probably we have here a sense-organ for indicating the position of the head; this would explain certain *compensatory positions*, which disappear on destruction of the labyrinth. Not only gravity, but any rectilinear acceleration would be expected to act on the otoliths; and there is some evidence that this is the case.

§ 36. It should be noted that it is acceleration and retardation, or change in movement rather than movement as such, which would be expected to excite the canals. The inertia current would gradually cease, as the fluid became carried along by friction with the walls of the canal, till finally the fluid would move with the head. If then the rotation of the head should cease, inertia would tend to cause a continued movement of the fluid, and the effect would be the same as if rotation were begun, from rest, in the opposite direction. This is what actually happens in dizziness, and the facts of dizziness lend further support to the theory. Many deaf persons—those, probably, whose disease extends to the semicircular canals—are not made dizzy by rotation.[1] The swimming sensation of the head which accompanies dizziness is probably to be ascribed to the semicircular canals, and the somewhat similar sensations which occur on starting up or down in an elevator are probably connected with the utricle and saccule. With milder stimulation of these organs, the sensations are not obtrusive, but the power of perceiving changes in the speed or direction of rotation is very keen.

We apparently possess, then, in the labyrinth, the end-organ of a sense for the positions and movements of the head, which provides for perceptions of rotation, etc., and which reflexly excites compensatory movements and muscular tonus. The nerve of this sense is the vestibular branch of the eighth. As the central connections of this nerve with the cerebellum are close, and as the results of extirpating the labyrinth resemble those of injuring the cerebellum (compare p. 156), it is probable that the reflex functions connected

[1] James, *American Journal of Otology*, 1882, IV, 239.

with this sense-organ have their centre, in large measure, in the cerebellum.

§ 37. A brief description of the End-Organs of Motion, or motor end-plates, will suffice for our purposes. In general, the terminations of the efferent nerves are connected either with electrical organs (as, for example, in the torpedo), or with secretory glands, or with the muscular fibre. We consider only the last of these three cases.

After an efferent nerve has entered the substance of the so-called voluntary or striated muscle, it subdivides among the individual muscular fibres, separating these fibres from each other. Such nerve-twigs usually lose their medullary sheath, and their axis-cylinder splits up into fibrils, whose exact mode of termination has been much debated. It appears now to be demonstrated (by Kühne, Margo, Rouget, and others) that the axis-cylinder itself pierces the sarcolemma or sheath of the muscular fibre; that the neurilemma becomes continuous with the sarcolemma; and that the fibrils, into which the axis-cylinder divides, form a flat, branching mass within certain peculiar, disk-shaped bodies situated inside the sarcolemma, and called "*motor end-plates.*" In the non-striated (or non-voluntary) muscles, the nerves divide and subdivide to form more and more minute plexuses of nerve-fibres, which are distributed in the connective tissue that separates the muscular fibres from each other, and finally applied to the surfaces of the muscular fibres. The exact manner of this application is of no particular interest to psychology, even when approached from the physiological point of view.

CHAPTER IX

THE CEREBRAL HEMISPHERES AND THEIR FUNCTIONS

§ 1. Ordinary observation recognizes the fact that the phenomena of consciousness are more or less definitely correlated with the condition of the bodily organs. Certain alterations in our mental states, on account of the injury of any of its masses, as well as a constant dependence of those states upon the way some of the masses stand related to each other and to the outside world, impress the fact upon our daily experience. It is by no means so obvious that the *nervous* substance has any particular relation to the thoughts and feelings of the mind. For the functions of the nervous system are not exercised in giving information as to itself, its own condition and changes. By aid of these functions, however, we have presented in consciousness a more or less clear picture of the condition and changes of the superficial parts of the body. In the same way a knowledge is gained of the successive states of tension belonging to the muscles in movement, and even—though rather obscurely—of the place and condition of the internal organs. But as long as they are healthy and excited with only a moderate intensity of their stimuli, the nerves do not even reveal their own existence; and when they are injured or unduly excited, the notice they furnish of the fact comes in the form of painful feeling which we have learned to localize, not in the nervous substance itself, but in the adjacent parts of muscle and skin. Attention may be called, however, to the peripheral nerves by the accident or the dissecting-knife which exposes them to sight. But in the case of the central nervous organs, and especially in the case of the brain, there is little in ordinary experience which leads to a suspicion of their significance or even of their existence.

It is not very strange, then, that no general recognition of the supreme importance of the brain, in relation to the phenomena of consciousness, is to be found in early history. It is true that Plutarch[1] and Theophrastus[2] inform us of the opinion of the physician Alcmæon, who is said to have been a younger contemporary of Pythagoras, and who regarded the brain as the common meeting-place of the senses. The same view is also ascribed to the

[1] *De Placitis Philosophorum*, IV, 17, 1.   [2] *De Sensu*, § 25 f.

celebrated Hippocrates. Later on Plato accepted it. But Aristotle,[1] the greatest of all thinkers in antiquity, the son of a physician, especially educated in physical science, and well acquainted for the time in the dissection of animals, regarded the brain as a lump of cold substance, quite unfit to be the seat and organ of the *sensus communis.* This important office he ascribed rather to the heart. The brain he considered to be chiefly useful as the source of fluid for lubricating the eyes, etc.

§ 2. The opinion of Exner,[2] however, who supposes that feeling in no way immediately informs us that we think with the head, still less with the brain or the cortex of the cerebrum, seems somewhat extreme. For we certainly localize in the head certain phenomena of consciousness that are inextricably interwoven with the processes of thought. The act of attention, for example, results in feelings which indicate that the muscles of the eye are being innervated; or in the more indefinite and diffused sense of strain produced by contracting the skin of the forehead and adjacent parts of the face. The special sensations of hearing, smelling, and tasting, which impress so strongly our conscious life, are frequently referred to the head. The same thing is true of many of the sensations of sight—particularly of such as appear when the eyes are closed, in the form of after-images, or spectra, or indefinite and changing color-spots, seated in the upper front part of the face. Moreover, that inchoate and sometimes half-articulated language, with which we support our trains of thought, even when we are not conscious of resorting to the expedient of "talking to ourselves," is felt to be going on within the head. When one has been engaged for some time in intense thought, or in eager and concentrated observation, one is suddenly made aware of more or less painful feelings which are somewhat indefinitely ascribed to the same cerebral region. Men commonly lean the head upon the hand in supporting meditation; or rub it vigorously to awaken the powers of memory and reasoning; or stroke it to relieve the disagreeable sensations which follow severe mental excitement. *Head*ache, of more or less intensity, thus becomes associated with active exercise of the intellect. The head is wearied with thought; and not only so, but also with intense physical exercise. The discomfort which bodily strain produces in the hinder regions of the head are an indication, although of only a very general kind, that processes have gone on in that locality which are of great importance to the succeeding states of consciousness. All this apparent

---

[1] See *De Partibus Animalium*, 652, b. 5; (II, 7); 656, b. 22 (II, 10); *De Juvent.*, 467, b. 28; and *De Anima*, III, 1 and 2.

[2] See Hermann's *Handb. d. Physiol.*, II, ii, p. 192.

testimony of immediate feeling is, doubtless, somewhat exaggerated
in an age so distinctively "nervous" as our own; but it cannot well
be doubted that a certain amount of testimony from immediate
feeling as to the important relation which exists between the state
of mind and the contents of the cranial cavity, belongs to all human
experience.

However uncertain the witness of immediate feeling upon the
point in question may be, very little observation of others is needed
to amplify and confirm its witness.   We are not infrequently led to
notice how quickly and profoundly the states of consciousness are
changed by injuries to the brain. The effect of a blow upon the
head in suspending consciousness is decisive of this question.   It
is but a step from this conclusion to a recognition of the truth that
the physiological significance of the contents of the cranial cavity
consists in their affording a field upon which all the impressions of
sense can meet together, and so furnish the basis and material of
comparative thought.   Indeed, it was this line of inquiry which
probably led certain ancient anatomists, like Herophilus and Galen,
to locate the soul, or psychical principle, in the brain.[1]

§ 3. A great multitude of physical considerations, advanced by
modern science, place beyond doubt the supreme importance of
the brain in its influence upon the phenomena of consciousness.
The free circulation of arterial blood, with its supply of oxygen,
is a necessary condition for the fulfilment of the functions of all
the central organs; but this necessity is especially marked in the case
of the brain.   The stoppage of one of the great arteries leading to
this organ, either by compression in the neck, or by embolism at
some point along its course, at once produces profound disturbances and even complete cessation of consciousness.

Certain other arguments of a similar nature, which have been advanced from time to time, have either been rendered doubtful or
quite discredited by recent investigations.   Such are the claims
made by Lombard and Schiff that a rise of temperature either in
the entire cerebral area or in particular circumscribed regions of
the cortex, results from all kinds of psychical activities.   Indeed,
the amount of such variation (less than $\frac{1}{100}$° C.) would seem to fall
below the limits of accurate observation.   So, too, the claim of
Byasson and others to measure with any reasonable approach to
accuracy the amount of thought accomplished, by the increase of
waste in the cerebral tissues, and by the resulting quantity of sul-
phates and phosphates excreted, may be said to have involved orig-

[1] In the subsequent discussions, such terms as "seat," "localize," "localization," " resides in," and similar terms, must be understood only as involving a convenient figure of speech.

inally far too many uncertain factors; and besides, it is not confirmed by more recent work. For the present, then, all such arguments for the special connection of the cerebral hemispheres with the phenomena of consciousness must be left in abeyance.[1]

§ 4. In the case of man, the cerebral hemispheres are, apparently, the only portions of the nervous system, between the size, condition, and molecular activity of which and the phenomena of consciousness there is a direct correlation. If, then, we are to speak of mental activities as "localized" at all, the locality must be in the cortex of the cerebrum. The position that, in the case of man, the spinal cord and all the intercranial organs below the cerebral hemispheres, are incapable of acting as *the immediate physical basis* of mental states, is confirmed even by those experiments upon other animals, which seem at first sight to discredit it. The hypothesis that consciousness has a seat in the spinal cord of the frog; that, in fact, we may properly speak of the decapitated animal as having a soul—has been urged by eminent physiologists (Pflüger, for example). That the cord alone is capable of various purposeful activities, such as serve, under certain circumstances, as signs of a psychical experience, may be demonstrated by experiment. But unless one is prepared to maintain that *all* purposeful activity, as resulting from excited nervous substance, must be correlated with phenomena of conscious sensation and volition, one can scarcely assume with confidence that such phenomena accompany the movements of the decapitated frog.

§ 5. The evidence from comparative anatomy in favor of regarding the cerebrum as, in some peculiar manner, the "seat" of mental life has been so fully set forth in preceding chapters (pp. 33, 61), that it needs here but a brief note. In general, the size of the cerebrum bears a fairly close relation, as between different orders of vertebrates, with the apparent intelligence of the animal. The size of the cerebrum is indeed correlated also with the size of the animal; and there are some apparent exceptions, in which animals, such as the ruminants, though possessing large hemispheres do not give the impression of special intelligence. It must be admitted, however, that comparative psychology has not yet progressed to such a stage that we can definitely assign the grade of intelligence of each of these animals; and our casual observations may have deceived us in regard to them. In a general way, it certainly seems that the intelligence of animals is correlated with the size of their cerebra, and not, on the other hand, to the same degree with the size of any other part of the nervous system. The power of learn-

---

[1] This paragraph is in correction of the views expressed in the earlier edition of this work. See *Elements of Physiological Psychology*, p. 242.

ing also seems to depend on the development of the cerebrum. It cannot, indeed, be said that nothing can be learned without developing this particular part of the brain; for even a fish can learn to some extent; and the behavior of invertebrate animals has been found to be modifiable.[1] It would be rash to assert that absolutely no plasticity, no modifiability by experience, is retained by the spinal cord; and it would be impossible to demonstrate in logical form that no dim and rudimentary consciousness resides in the cord; but comparative anatomy leaves no serious doubt that the highly developed consciousness of man, and his great power of learning by experience, are associated with the functions of his cerebral hemispheres.

§ 6. Reference should also be made to our previous discussion (compare p. 158) of the functions destroyed and spared, in animals, by removal of the cerebrum. We found that the functions remaining after such an operation are the vegetative, locomotor, and protective reflexes—along with some of the simpler expressive movements—comprising, all in all, the elementary movements of the members, but involving a few of the most essential combinations of such movements. What was destroyed by the operation was, most clearly, the learned reactions, together with the power of new learning, and the "anticipatory reactions," or reactions of only indirect utility. From these facts, the conclusion seemed justified that the cerebrum is the organ for learned reactions and for reactions to the wider environment, that is, for the reactions made possible by the existence of the "distance receptors." Now it is especially with reference to this "wider environment," as revealed by these receptors, that learned reactions have their chief importance in securing physical well-being and mental development.

§ 7. Perhaps the most conclusive evidence that the cerebral hemispheres are the seat of consciousness and of the intellectual operations, as well as, chiefly, of learned movements and reactions, is afforded by the results of *partial* injuries to the brain. When the injury is total or general, as in the case of a blow on the head, an objector might possibly reply that breaking of the neck, or piercing the heart, also promptly abolishes consciousness and all mental function. The argument, in this bald form, cannot be taken seriously at the present day; yet it has this much of force, that the loss of consciousness following brain shock is, in strict logic, evidence only that the brain is necessary to consciousness—even as the heart is. That is to say, as a vital organ, it is part of the bodily mechanism with which consciousness is associated. It might still be true that the whole nervous system—cerebrum, cerebellum, brain-stem, cord and nerves—are the seat and organ of the mental

[1] See Jennings, *Behavior of the Lower Organisms* (New York, 1906).

life. But *partial* injuries, which do not abolish all consciousness, but simply make impossible some of its phenomena, cannot be considered in the same light. Life persists; the organ destroyed is not vital; and yet some functions of the mental life are rendered impossible.

To introspection, it certainly seems as if the consciousness of the hand, for example, had its seat in the hand itself; and as if the skilled movements which the hand learns are learned by the hand itself; and common forms of speech agree with this naïve view. This seeming consciousness may even be projected into the tool which the hand is using. But if the nerves going to the hand are severed, at any point between the hand and the spinal cord, stimuli affecting the hand are no longer perceived, and no power of skilled or even of reflex movement is retained. The hand has become as though non-existent for consciousness. Yet the power to think of the hand has not been lost; nor the power to will movements of the hand, which are, however, no longer carried out. In cases of amputation of the hand, stimulation of the stump—and, thus, of the remnants of the nerves which formerly ran to the hand—often arouses sensations located in the hand as if it were still there. Such observations show that the consciousness of the hand resides not in the hand, but somewhere in the central nervous system.

The same argument can be carried further by noting the results of injuries to the cord. If the cord has suffered such an injury that the lower part of it is severed from the upper, the whole lower part of the body is cut off from consciousness and all mental influences, just as the hand was in the preceding case. The consciousness of the legs does not then reside in their reflex centres in the cord, but somewhere higher up, in the brain. In the same way, injuries may occur to the brain-stem, which, without severing it entirely—for this would be a mortal injury, and would therefore destroy the value of the observation from our present point of view —may yet interrupt the sensory or motor tracts connecting the cerebral cortex with the cord; and in such cases, the same general result, as regards consciousness and learned movements, is to be noted. The power to think of the parts of the body concerned is retained, and the power to will movements; but the execution of the movements is impossible, and sensations of the members no longer arise in consciousness. It seems possible, in this way, to push back the seat of consciousness from the periphery to the cerebral cortex, and to conclude that the latter is the essential seat of consciousness.

The argument is further strengthened by observing the effect of partial injuries to the cortex itself. Injuries to certain portions of it—as will be set forth in more detail in the next chapter—cause a loss of certain of the more elementary functions of normal life. A person may lose, as the result of such injury, the sense of sight, or that of hearing, or the sensations from any part of the periphery. The hand and its nerves, it may be, as well as the cord, brain-stem, and cerebellum, are uninjured, but the destruction of a small part of the cortex has destroyed all sensation of the hand. Indeed, the person thus afflicted seems unable even to imagine the sensation as localized in his hand, in any very realistic way. As far as consciousness is concerned, therefore, he has suffered a more severe loss than would have been suffered if the injury had affected simply the nerves of the hand. So again, destruction of certain portions of the cortex deprives a person of visual sensations, and sometimes of visual images as well. Much the same sort of evidence is available in regard to other than strictly sensory functions. Learned movements, memories of any particular sort, mental operations in general, may be thrown out of power to function, even though the injury is not wide-spread or severe enough to abolish all consciousness.

§ 8. Having been convinced by this evidence that the cerebral hemispheres are, in some special sense, the seat and organ of mental functions, the psychologist next appeals to anatomy and to physiology for an answer to these questions: (1) What plan is followed in the apportionment of the various mental functions over the whole extent of the cortex? and (2) What is the precise character of the functions of this organ in its relations to the phenomena of consciousness? Both problems—that of the "localization of cerebral functions," and that of the intimate physiology of the cortex—are fraught with such difficulty that the answers given are still very fragmentary and often tentative. The results of investigation, however, are well worthy the serious attention of the psychologist.

§ 9. The cerebral hemispheres consist, as has been stated in an earlier chapter (see pp. 50 f.), of the olfactory lobes, the corpora striata, and the pallium. It is the latter with which we are now concerned. The pallium itself can be divided, on the basis of comparative anatomy (compare pp. 31 f.) into the archipallium and the neopallium; of these the former is older in the animal series, and is concerned especially with the sense of smell and with the "snout sense." In mammals the archipallium is eclipsed in size by the neopallium, which, by expanding laterally, forward and backward, leaves the archipallium in a central location and for the most part conceals it. It cannot be seen on the upper, lower, or lateral surfaces of the brain, and only a little of it is visible on the mesial surface of a hemisphere. It includes the fornix and the dentate gyre, but it is best seen, as the "horn of Ammon," in a section through the brain (see Figs. 9 and 97).

§ 10. The cortex is divided, for convenience of reference, into lobes. The great Sylvian fissure makes a clear division between the frontal lobe above it, and the temporal lobe beneath. The fissure of Rolando, or central fissure (compare Fig. 94), constitutes the

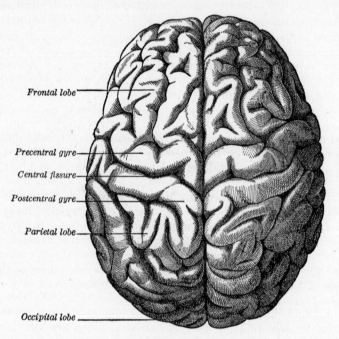

Frontal lobe

Precentral gyre

Central fissure

Postcentral gyre

Parietal lobe

Occipital lobe

FIG. 94.—The Upper Surface of the Cerebral Hemispheres. (Sobotta-McMurrich.)

boundary between the frontal and the parietal lobes. The parietal lobe is separated from the temporal by the posterior portion of the fissure of Sylvius. The rearmost portion of the cortex is designated as the occipital lobe. A partial boundary between the occipital and parietal lobes is afforded by the parieto-occipital fissure. There is no clear boundary between the occipital and the temporal lobes. In fact, the whole division into lobes is somewhat artificial. There is no break in the cortex between one lobe and the next; for the cortex extends down the sides of the boundary fissures, and continuously around the bottom of the fissures into the adjoining lobes. Within the Sylvian fissure, the cortex expands into a considerable area, cut up by smaller fissures: and this concealed part of the cortex is known as the "island of Reil," or, more briefly, as the Island.

Besides the fissures which have been chosen as the grand boundaries between the lobes, many other fissures—in the superficial manner above indicated—divide the lobes into smaller parts known as convolutions or gyres. Some of these smaller fissures are inconstant, when one individual brain is compared with another; but certain of the more important are fairly constant, and so form ap-

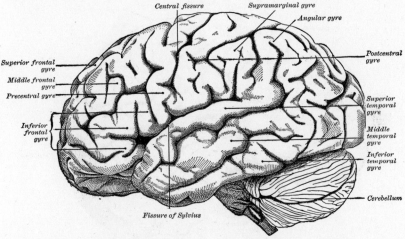

FIG. 95.—Lateral Surface of the Left Cerebral Hemisphere. (Edinger.)

propriate landmarks on the surfaces of the cortex. Those of most interest are the following: In the "central region" (see Fig. 95), or that immediately adjacent to the central fissure, we may distinguish two gyres, one on each side of the central fissure, and extending along it; they are separated from the rest of the frontal and parietal lobes, respectively, by the precentral and postcentral fissures. These gyres are named the precentral and the postcentral. To the front of the precentral fissure lies the great extent of the frontal lobe, which is partially divided into superior, middle, and inferior gyres by two horizontal fissures, called the superior and the inferior frontal. In the temporal lobe, also, there is a series of horizontal fissures, which divide the lobe into the superior, middle, and inferior temporal gyres. The subdivision of the parietal and occipital lobes is not quite so simply made. The intraparietal fissure separates the superior parietal gyre from the rest of the lobe; below this, two parts are easily distinguished—namely, the supramarginal gyre, which curves around the end of the fissure of Sylvius, and the angular gyre, which curves around the end of the superior temporal fissure. On the lateral surface of the occipital lobe the divisions are not specially clear or constant; but superior, middle, and inferior gyres are customarily recognized.

On the mesial surface (Fig. 96), a prominent fissure is the cingulate, extending parallel to the callosum, and separating the limbic lobe from the frontal and parietal. The central fissure often shows itself on the mesial surface; and the gyre which curves

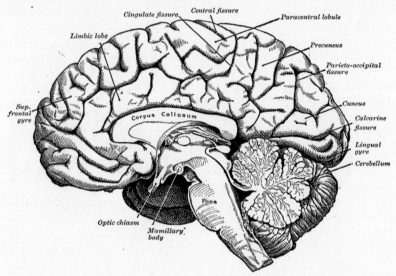

FIG. 96.—Mesial Surface of the Right Cerebral Hemisphere. (Edinger.)

around its end is called the paracentral lobule. The parieto-occipital fissure is strongly marked on this surface, and forms a clear division between the parietal and occipital lobes. Within the occipital lobe, there appears on the mesial surface a prominent fissure, called the calcarine, which is of great importance in discussions of localization. The calcarine fissure joins the parieto-occipital, and the triangular gyre which lies between them is called the cuneus, while the gyre which lies immediately beneath the calcarine fissure is the lingual; beneath this, again, is the fusiform.

These, then, are the chief landmarks on the surface of the brain, which are of use in our studies for the localization of cerebral functions.

§ 11. A section through the cerebral hemispheres (Fig. 97) shows the gray matter, or cortex, on the surface, and extending to and around the bottom of the various fissures; but beneath the cortex appears a large mass of white matter. This white matter is composed of medullated (or myelinated) nerve-fibres, which are of varied origin. Some, as was stated in considering the development of the brain (see p. 53), grow into the cerebrum from the interbrain, and pass to various regions of the cortex. Others originate in the cortex, and grow down, converging into the internal capsule, whence they pass to the peduncle and so on down to the pons. These two classes of fibres form paths of communication between the cortex and the lower parts of the nervous system; they are known as "projection fibres," in distinction from the "association fibres," which pass from one part of the cortex to another. Much the greatest part of the cerebral mass of white matter, however, is composed of *association* fibres, some of which are short, and connect neighboring gyres, while others are long and connect distant parts of the cortex with each other. Of these long association fibres, several distinct bundles can be distinguished: a massive bundle of fibres running between the temporal and occipital lobes; a bundle running between the temporal and frontal lobes; another between the temporal and parietal lobes; one between the frontal and occipital lobes; and one extending from one end to the other of the curved limbic lobe. Not all the fibres in a bundle, however, extend the whole length of its course, but some enter or leave at various points (compare Fig. 98).

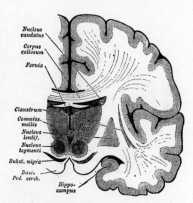

FIG. 97.—Frontal Section through the Cerebral Hemispheres. (Gegenbaur.) A portion of the archipallium is seen at the part marked "Hippocampus."

Though projection fibres have been traced to or from nearly all parts of the cortex, they are by far most numerous in certain definite portions of the cortex; such are, especially, the central region, on both sides of the central fissure; the calcarine region; and the superior temporal gyre. This fact in itself suggests, at least, a certain amount of localization of function; since the regions directly connected by fibres with lower parts of the system would probably be the regions most directly connected with the senses and with movement. This suggestion is borne out, as we shall see, by the results of other methods of localization.

As was stated in considering the development of the brain (see pp. 58 f.), different bundles of fibres become myelinated at different times. At birth the only myelinated fibres passing to the cortex of the human infant go to the central zone; but soon other regions receive myelinated fibres. Flechsig, on the basis of extended studies of the date of myelinization of different regions, is able to divide the cortex into areas (Fig. 99), some of which show myelinated fibres early, others late, and others at intermediate dates. He believes that the map of the cortex so obtained is also to be regarded as a map of the distribution of functions; and in particular he supposes that the regions whose fibres receive their myelin sheath early are the centres of the lower functions of sensation

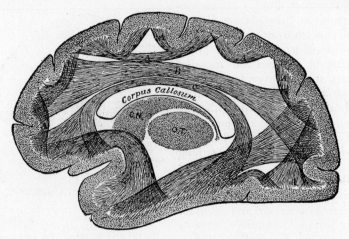

FIG. 98.—Association Fibres of the Cerebrum. (Starr's *Atlas of Nerve Cells*, by permission of the Columbia University Press.)

and movement, while the late-myelinating regions are the seat of the highest intellectual functions. As far as concerns the early-myelinating areas, this theory is confirmed by the results of other methods of study; as far as concerns the localization of the intellectual functions, the theory should be entertained with considerable reserve. There is no improbability, however, in the view that areas distinguished on the basis of their differing dates of myelinization should also have different functions.

§ 12. Microscopic examination of the cortex reveals a wealth of nerve-cells, embedded in an intricate net-work of fine fibres. The study of these cells and fibres, and of the differences which they present in different parts of the cortex, has been prosecuted with great vigor and success during recent years. The most logical order for presentation of this subject would demand at once some account of the results of these histological studies. But they will mean more to the reader if he is first made acquainted with the results of other work in the localization of functions in the cortex. It will, therefore, be better to abandon the strict logical order of presentation for a historical order. The physiological and pathological results have, in fact, preceded the histological, and have served as the chief impetus to the minute examination of all parts of the cortex—with a view to determine whether regions which have special functions are also characterized by a specialized structure.

To superficial examination, indeed, the cerebrum appears to be a fairly homogeneous mass, of soft consistency—an appearance which

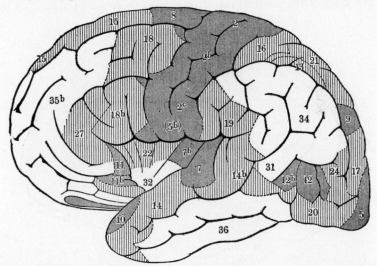

Fig. 99.—Division of the Cortex on the Basis of Date of Myelinization. (Flechsig.) The frontal lobe lies to the left. The numbers indicate the approximate order of myelinization. The early-myelinating areas are heavily shaded, the intermediate areas lightly shaded, and the late-myelinating areas left clear.

easily gave rise to the notion that it functions as a whole, much as a gland functions. Such an epigram as "The brain secretes thought, as the liver secretes bile," has even at times gained currency. But when the microscope, aided by differential stains, revealed the inner structure of this mass, and when it was seen to consist, like the nerves, of multitudes of fibres running in various directions in the white matter, and entering and leaving the gray, the glandular simile lost its force, and the opinion that each fibre or set of fibres—like each nerve—had something specific to do, became almost a matter of compulsion.

§ 13. We begin, then, our search for more definite knowledge as to the localization of cerebral functions with strong presumptions in its favor. The cerebral cortex is itself a very complex organ, or system of organs. Its different regions are marked by comparatively slight, and yet not insignificant, differences of structure; they stand in different local relations and nervous connections with one another and with the ganglia lying below. This outlying rind of gray nervous matter is, of course, not a homogeneous mass. It is made up of innumerable nervous elements combined in various ways and multiform connections. It may be regarded, then, as a complex of organs.

Most of our definite knowledge concerning the functions of the other parts of the nervous mechanism also creates a presumption in

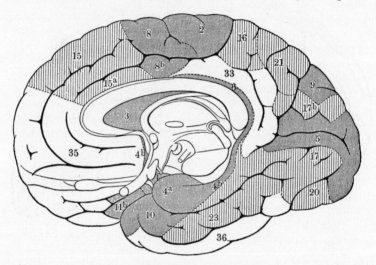

Fig. 99a.—The Same as Fig. 99, Mesial Surface.

favor of some localization of *cerebral* functions. All the different parts of this mechanism are, indeed, constructed by combining variously a few elements of essentially the same structure; all of them likewise are capable of exercising essentially the same neural functions. But each part of this mechanism has also its special functions. Thus we found that the different nerves become classified functionally; some are motor, voluntary or involuntary, some inhibitory, some secretory, some sensory, etc. Hints of a certain kind of classification may be discovered for the smaller ganglia or collections of nerve-cells. In making transverse sections of the cord, different regions with different functions appear. Considered longitudinally, the cord is capable of being more or less definitely divided into several so-called centres, with specifically different functions. Localized centres, where specific kinds of reflex-motor activity have their particular seats, are fairly crowded together in the medulla oblongata. All the lower parts of the encephalon appear subject, in a measure, to the principle of localization. Shall we, then, stop short in our attempts at differencing the functions of the locally separate parts of the nervous system just at the point where we reach the most complex and extended organ, or rather collection of organs, which this system contains?

§ 14. Notwithstanding the strong presumption in favor of the localization of cerebral function, the beginnings of a successful attempt to establish this theory are comparatively recent. The doctrines of Gall, Spurzheim, and others in the older school of phrenologists, proved so inconclusive as to bring contempt upon subsequent attempts to divide the hemispheres of the brain into different functional areas. Moreover, certain indisputable facts seemed to render impossible the assured beginnings of a theory of cerebral localization. Considerable portions of the human brain, it was found, might be lost without destroying any one sensory or motor function. Moreover, the gray matter of the cerebral hemispheres, it was then thought, could not be directly excited by electricity or by other forms of stimuli. The greatest experimenters in physiology, such as Longet, Magendie, Flourens, Matteucci, Van Deen, Budge, and Schiff, declared against the localizing of cerebral function. In 1842 Longet[1] affirmed that he had experimented upon the cortical substance of dogs, rabbits, and kids, had irritated it mechanically, cauterized it with potash, nitric acid, etc., and had passed galvanic currents through it in different directions, without obtaining any sign whatever of resulting muscular contraction. In the same year Flourens[2] asserted, on the basis of numerous experiments in extirpation, that the lobes of the cerebrum perform their functions with their whole mass; that there is no special seat for any of the cerebral activities; and that even a small remnant of the hemispheres can serve all the uses of their collective functions.

So great was the authority of the distinguished names just mentioned, that their confident opinions gained general credence. The evidence brought forward by Broca and others seemed, however, to show some special connection between a single convolution of the frontal lobe and the complex activities of articulate speech; and the anatomist, Meynert, held the opinion that the structure and connections of the cerebrum show its anterior portion to be in general used for motor, its posterior for sensory, functions. In 1867 Eckhard repeated the significant observation which had been

---

[1] *Anatomie et physiologie du système nerveux*, etc., Paris, 1842, I., pp. 644 f.
[2] *Recherches expérimentales sur les propriétés et les fonctions du système nerveux*, etc., pp. 99 f.

made by Haller and Zinn more than a century before: namely, that, on removing parts of the cortical substance of an animal's brain, convulsive movements occur in its extremities.

It was not until 1870 that the "epoch-making" experiments of Fritsch and Hitzig[1] began the modern era of investigation into this subject. These observers announced the fact that the cerebral cortex of dogs is, at least in certain minute areas of it, excitable by electricity. They pointed out the further fact that, while some parts of the convexity of the cerebrum are capable of motor excitation and others not, the motor parts lie in general to the front, the non-motor to the rear of this convexity. By stimulating with an electrical current the so-called motor parts, co-ordinated contractions of the muscles in the opposite half of the body were obtained. Of such so-called "motor-centres" they indicated, in their first announcement, the following five: One for the muscles of the neck, another for the extension and abduction of the fore limb, another for the bending and rotation of the same limb, another for the hind limb, and lastly one for the face. From such facts they drew the conclusion that the principle announced by Flourens is demonstrably false. We must rather admit, say they, that "certainly several psychical functions, and probably all, are shown to have their point of entrance into matter or of origin from it at circumscribed centres of the cerebral cortex." The same principle was subsequently defended at length by Hitzig, and the number of so-called cerebral centres increased. The most noteworthy facts which these experimenters first made clear and demonstrable have since been verified by many investigators. Among the physiologists who have amplified the results of Fritsch and Hitzig, the following deserve special mention: Ferrier, for his work on the monkey's brain; and, more recently, Sherrington and Grünbaum, for their work on the anthropoid apes, the brains of which are anatomically much closer to the human brain than are those of the lower monkeys. The testimony of human pathology, and the evidence of comparative anatomy and of histology, have also been largely drawn upon either to confirm or to confute the conclusions originally based on experiments with animals. Before considering the conclusions themselves, it is necessary to understand the true nature and extent of the various kinds of evidence.

§ 15. Three great lines of evidence, leading from three great groups of facts, must be considered. These are the evidence from

---

[1] See the article by G. Fritsch and E. Hitzig in the *Archiv f. Anat., Physiol.*, etc., 1870, pp. 300–332; and subsequent articles by Hitzig in the same *Archiv*, 1871, 1873, 1874, 1875, 1876; also his collected works *Physiologische und klinische Untersuchungen über das Gehirn* (Berlin, 1904).

experimentation, the evidence from pathology, and the evidence from histology and comparative anatomy. Each of the three has its peculiar advantages and value; each also its peculiar difficulties and dangers. It is only by regarding the combined testimony of the three that the highest probability at present possible can be attained.

Experimentation with a view to discover the localized functions of the cerebral cortex is of two kinds, stimulation and extirpation. In stimulation experiments, the procedure is as follows: having first, under anæsthesia, removed the bony and membranous coverings of a portion of the brain, a weak current of electricity is applied to a minute portion of the exposed cortex, and a watch is kept for resulting movements in any part of the body. It was this experiment which, in the hands of Flourens and other early observers, gave negative results, and which first succeeded in the hands of Fritsch and Hitzig. The failure of the older experimenters is not difficult to explain; for only a small proportion of the entire cortex, on stimulation by currents of low or moderate strength, responds with any bodily movements whatever. The rest of the cortex is said to be "silent" under stimulation. In this fact lies a limitation of the method; it supplies information only regarding the fraction of the cortex which gives motor responses.

A further difficulty with the method of stimulation is its dependence on the use of the electric current. This is an admirable stimulus in most respects, but it is subject to one or two limitations, which need to be guarded against by the experimenter; and sometimes by those who would accept his results. One difficulty is the "spreading" of the current, which is thus likely to excite parts not immediately in contact with the electrodes, and so deceive the observer. In the most recent work, the method of "unipolar stimulation" —in which one pole of the battery is broad, and applied to a distant part of the body, while the other is a needle point applied to the surface of the brain—has been employed with success in finer localizations. At one time, it was feared that the spreading of the electrical current seriously jeopardized all the results of cortical stimulation; for—it was argued—the movements might be due not to arousal of the cortex, after all, but to the arousal of some deeper-lying structure. A variety of checks have shown, however, that the cortex is actually the part aroused. Perhaps the best worth citing of these checks is the fact that, in the large brain of the chimpanzee, with its thick cortex, and relatively long distances between parts, weak unipolar stimulation easily arouses movements, but only when the stimulus is applied to certain limited regions; and the same movements are obtained with great constancy from the same spots,

Such regular results could hardly be got by diffusion of current to subcortical parts; and, in fact, the same responses cannot be got by stimulation of any remote subcortical parts. On the contrary, the same responses, or nearly the same, can be got by stimulating the white matter immediately below a given region of the cortex as are got from the region itself; but this is to be expected, since any area must, of course, exert its influence through the fibres issuing from it.

Some use has been made of a similar, but reverse use of the method of stimulation;—namely, that of observing the electrical changes in the cortex on stimulation of certain peripheral nerves. Just as a nerve, excited at one end, is traversed by an electric wave, so it has been found by several physiologists (Caton, Danielewski, and others) that on flashing a light into the eye of an animal, electric currents were produced in a certain definite region of the cortex, which—it is then concluded—must be closely connected with the retina. The value of this method is diminished by the fact that the currents seem excessively weak except in certain regions; and that these same regions happen to have their functions fairly well located by other methods.

§ 16. In the method of extirpation, as practised by physiologists, a well-defined area of the cortex is cut out; the animal is allowed to recover from the general effects of the operation, and is watched and tested with a view to determine precisely what loss of function has attended the loss of brain substance. The assumption that the two correspond is antecedently probable; but he would be an unwary experimenter who should, at the present day, assert unqualifiedly that the injured function had its peculiar, not to say its only, seat in the injured part. Indeed, later on the injured animal often shows a partial or nearly complete recovery of the lost functions. This species of restitution is a puzzling side of the results of the method of extirpation; it will be referred to again. Certain other difficulties of this method can be largely avoided by good procedure. For example, the inflammatory after-effects of an operation, which often impaired the value of the early work, can now be avoided by operating with aseptic precautions. The danger of cutting too deep, and so of not simply extirpating the desired area of the cortex, but also of interfering with other areas by incidentally severing their projection and association fibres, cannot be wholly avoided; but examination of the brain after the death of the animal may reveal the truth in this respect.

One difficulty with all the methods of the physiologist is that he deals with animals, and can learn of their mental processes only indirectly and imperfectly. To a limited extent, there exist observations on man which are of the same nature as those of the physiologists on animals. In some surgical operations, it is necessary to remove definite parts of the brain; and in order to locate these parts precisely, the electric current is applied, when the part is in the "motor region." Thus some opportunity is afforded for examining the effects of stimulation and of extirpation in the human subject.

§ 17. The chief source of direct evidence regarding localization in the human brain is pathology. Injuries occur to parts of the brain, by gunshot wounds, or by fractures of the skull necessitating the removal of splinters of bone and with them some of the brain substance. More common are destructive lesions due to tumors, hemorrhages, or local softening from impaired circulation in one or more branches of the cerebral arteries. It will be observed that accident and disease do much the same thing here to the human brain that the physiologist's knife does to the brains of the animals which he is studying. The pathological method is essentially the same as the method of extirpation. It has the advantage of giving results on the human subject, regarding whose mental operations we have much better sources of information than are available in the case of animals. The pathological method has, on the other hand, the disadvantage that the seat and limits of the lesion are not predetermined by the observer. Too much of the brain substance is usually affected to afford a good subject for precise localization of function. Indeed, in many cases a large portion of the entire cortex is more or less affected, either by pressure exerted by a growing tumor, or by general disturbances of the blood supply, or by spreading of the chemical influences of a diseased spot. The result is that few pathological cases afford perfectly clean experimental evidence. Another difficulty is that the individual whose brain is to be injured by these natural causes is not known beforehand; he, therefore, cannot be examined beforehand as to his mental characteristics, as the animal subject can be. For these reasons, and also because of the intricate interweaving of mental functions, the progress of localization in the human brain has been slow; a large accumulation of material, and good judgment in interpreting the material, are still needed in order to reach sound conclusions. In spite of these difficulties, however, it may be said that by using as guides the best-established localizations in animals, the study of human pathology has established the truth, that the fundamental facts of localization are the same in the brains of both the lower animals and of man.

§ 18. In addition to the physiological and the allied pathological methods, there is a group of methods which belong under the science of anatomy in a broad sense of the latter word.

The comparative anatomy of the brain affords some scientific information regarding the functions of its different parts. The best instance of the use of this method for purposes of localization is the case of the archipallium, and its probable connection with the sense of smell and other related functions. This matter has already been sufficiently discussed. The logic of the method, in all such cases, is as follows: When the behavior of a species of animals shows that a certain function is highly developed (or the opposite), peculiar developments of the brain in these species may, with some probability, be regarded as related to this function. This argument is, indeed, similar to that of Gall and the phrenologists; but they endeavored to apply the method in the comparison of human individuals, and in the first instance, they sought to infer the development of the brain from the external appearance of the skull. The latter inference is now known to be very insecure. There seems no antecedent reason to conclude, however, that a comparison of the brains of different human individuals, whose mental peculiarities were well known, might not assist in the localization of mental functions. The method is still in use; but so far its results are not very trustworthy—partly because of insufficient *psychological analysis* of the individuals concerned, and partly because of insufficient *microscopic study* of the brains.

Comparative anatomy is useful in another way, which has already been noticed in our study of the nerve-tracts (compare pp. 31, 88). Brains of simpler construction afford a better opportunity for the tracing of nervous connections than is afforded by the extremely intricate mass of fibres in the white matter of the human brain. It is a valid assumption, that the *connections* of any part of the cortex are of great, and even decisive importance, in assigning the function of that part. If, for example, it is possible—as it is—to trace the fibres of the optic nerve back to certain parts of the interbrain, and other fibres thence to a certain region of the cortex, this fact is the best possible indication that the region of the cortex to which these fibres run is, somehow, specially concerned with the sense of sight. Indeed, the most decisive localization of the sensory functions of the cortex has been, to a large extent, obtained by this method. To take another example: If the fibres of the cortico-spinal or pyramidal tract, the principal motor tract passing from the cerebrum to the cord, can be traced back to a certain area of the cortex, there is good reason for calling this the "motor area." Such tracing of fibres, as previously explained (compare pp. 87 f.), has been accomplished by several methods.

In the case, too, of parts of the cortex which are directly connected with lower ganglia (either sensory or motor), the tracing of fibre-connections has decisive weight. In general, increased knowledge of the connections of other parts of the cortex with its sensory and motor

areas, and with one another, would conduce greatly to an understanding of the functions of all these areas.   If, for example, a certain limited region can be shown to be the origin of the fibres connecting the cortex with the muscles of the tongue, and if some other
area can be shown to be connected with this motor tongue area by
especially numerous fibres, then there is evidence that this second
area, too, is concerned in movements of the tongue.   The probability
arises in this way, that all these areas are concerned with the complex functions of speech.   In other words, a truly neurological conception of the working of the brain, as distinguished from a rough
assignment of this or that gross function or "faculty" to this or that
part of the cortex, would be advanced by nothing so much as by
an unravelling of the paths of the association fibres.   Unfortunately,
such a task is extraordinarily difficult.   Since it is in this respect that
man differs most from the animals, the work must be largely done
on the human brain; it must, therefore, be subject to the difficulties
that attend other work with pathological material.   Still, progress
is being made even here, and at an accelerated rate.

Another method of an anatomical character which has recently
begun to show great promise is the histological mapping of the
cortex.   Some of the results of this method will be referred to, later
on, in their relation to the more successful of the efforts to solve
the problems of the localization of cerebral functions, and of the
more precise nature, in themselves considered, of these functions.

§ 19.   We close this critical survey of the evidence for the localization of cerebral functions, with these observations as to the nature
of the evidence itself and as to the trustworthiness of its results.
The evidence is always extremely complex and often very conflicting; but it is in general cumulative, and in certain cases it is entitled
to be pronounced quite convincing.   It must always be remembered,
however, that the possibility of differentiations and even of idiosyncrasies is as great in the human brain as it is in any of nature's
most complicated products.   On the psychological side, too, we
find ourselves always faced with great, and often insuperable,
difficulties in our attempts to perfect the necessary analyses.   The
most conclusive results are obtained in those cases where, on the
side of the nervous mechanism, we find all the lines followed by
the different methods converging on the same result; and where,
on the side of the mental life and development, we are dealing with
those forms of conscious activity—such as the co-ordination and
control of bodily movements and the experiences of the more simple
and fundamental of the activities of sensation and association—
which are shared by man with the lower animals, and which are,
whether considered from the biological or the psychological point

of view, most essential to his existence and to the capacity for learning to adapt himself to a varied environment.

More precisely: A hundred years of the use of these different methods of investigation, advanced in the most recent times to a high degree of refinement in the hands of many diligent and skilful workmen, have brought about a general agreement and a reasonable certainty as respect the following of the simpler functions: The "motor area" is definitely located; the "visual area" likewise; and the location of the areas for hearing and smell is only a little less definite.

CHAPTER X

THE CEREBRAL HEMISPHERES AND THEIR FUNCTIONS
(CONTINUED)

§ 1. The first functional area to be localized was the motor area. The pioneer work of Fritsch and Hitzig[1] located it in the case of the dog (Fig. 100). Its position is far forward on the surface of the dog's cortex, in the "sigmoid gyre." Here a small area was detected, on stimulating which with a weak current of electricity, the muscles of the neck were thrown into contraction; another similar area was found for extension of the fore limb; another for flexion of the same limb; and another for facial movements. Movements of the back, abdomen, and tail were also obtained, though their precise area was not, at that time, sharply localized. Many later observers have confirmed and refined these results. As it is not our purpose here to give a comparative description of cerebral localization in different animals, we may simply note that motor areas have been located in other carnivora, in rodents, and indeed in various orders of animals. We turn at once to the primates. Ferrier rendered service[2] to the growing science of localization by extending the study to the monkeys—an important extension, because of the similarity of shape and fissuration between the brains of these animals and the human brain; and also because a much more detailed localization was found possible in the primate brain. Ferrier located the motor area in the central region of the monkey's brain, and, indeed, in both of the central gyres, the precentral and the postcentral. In other words, his motor area extended along the

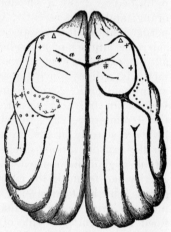

FIG. 100.—Motor Area of the Dog. (Fritsch and Hitzig.) The two hemispheres are drawn from different animals. *a*, the sulcus, around which the sigmoid gyre bends; △, area for muscles of the neck; +, fore limb; *, hind limb, °°°°, facial muscles.

[1] *Archiv f. Anat. und Physiol.*, 1870, pp. 312 f.
[2] *Functions of the Brain* (London, 1876); 2d edition, 1886.

235

central fissure, or fissure of Rolando, and on both sides of it. With-in this area, he distinguished smaller areas for movements of different groups of muscles; movements of the hind limbs were obtained from the upper part of the region, near the middle line, while movements of the fore limbs were obtained about half-way down, and movements of the face at the bottom of the region, near the fissure of Sylvius.

§ 2. Ferrier's results have been abundantly confirmed, with one principal exception, which will be stated directly. We can pass quickly over this work on the lower monkeys and consider the case of the anthropoid apes, whose brain resembles the human brain still more closely. Owing to the difficulty of obtaining animals for experimentation, these highest and most interesting forms were not early examined by physiologists. Beevor and Horsley published in 1890[1] a physiological study of the brain of a single orang; and, more recently, Grünbaum and Sherrington[2] have experimented on all three species of anthropoid apes, including a considerable number of individuals. Their work, done in the light of all the experience of previous investigators, and with improved methods, assigns much the same position to the motor area in the anthropoid brain as that found by Ferrier for the smaller monkeys. Grünbaum and Sherrington, however, employed unipolar stimulation (compare p. 229), by which means the electrical stimulus can be more sharply limited in its application than by older methods; for this reason, among others, they were able to show that the excitable region did not extend to the rear of the central fissure, as Ferrier had found in the monkeys, but was limited to the precentral gyre. This led to renewed examination[3] of the brain of the smaller monkeys, with the result that here, too, the motor area was confined to the anterior side of the central fissure. In this respect, then, the results of Ferrier have received an important correction. The excitable region extends down into the central fissure, and even to its very bottom, but does not reach the free surface of the postcentral gyre. The limits of the motor region, in the forward direction, are less sharp than on the rear. The area is broad at the top, where it extends also over upon the mesial surface of the hemisphere; lower down the precentral gyre, it becomes narrower.

[1] *Philosophical Transactions of the Roy. Soc. of London*, 1890, B. p. 129.

[2] *Proceedings of the Royal Society of London*, 1901, LXIX, 206; and 1903, LXXII, 152; *Transactions of the Pathological Society of London*, 1902, 53, part I, pp. 127–136; Sherrington, *Integrative Action of the Nervous System*, New York, 1906.

[3] See the very extensive investigations of C. and O. Vogt, *Journal f. Psychol. und Neurol.*, 1907, VIII, 277.

These investigators found (compare Figs. 101 and 102) the movements of the different parts of the body represented within the motor region about as Ferrier had said: the hind limbs were excitable from the upper part, near the middle line; the area for the trunk lay below these, opposite the upper of two well-marked curves in the central fissure, which serve as valuable landmarks. Below this same curve is the area for the arms; further below, and opposite

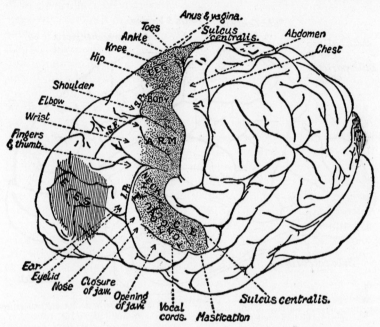

Fig. 101.—Lateral Surface of the Brain of a Chimpanzee. (Grünbaum and Sherrington.) The left hemisphere is shown, with the frontal lobe to the left. The extent of the motor area is indicated by the darkened portion, though it should be understood that a large part of the area lies in the central fissure.

the lower of the two bends of the fissure, is a region for the neck; and below this, again, near the bottom of the fissure, lies the area for the head and face. Still more minute localizations were found to be possible: thus, within the arm area, the sequence, from above downward, is shoulder, elbow, wrist, hand; and in the region corresponding to the lower extremity the sequence is pelvic region, toes, ankle, knee, and hip.

Movements of the eyeballs were not obtained in the anthropoid ape from stimulation of the precentral gyre; there was, however, a considerable area further forward, in the middle and inferior frontal gyres, by excitation of which conjugate movement of both eyes to the other side was obtained.   This agrees with the results of experiments with the monkey.

§ 3. The method of extirpation, applied to the motor area of the anthropoid brain, results in paralysis of the entire opposite side, or of parts of this side.   For example, extirpation of the hand area of the right hemisphere causes an immediate and severe paralysis of the left hand, but without any sign of paralysis in either the face

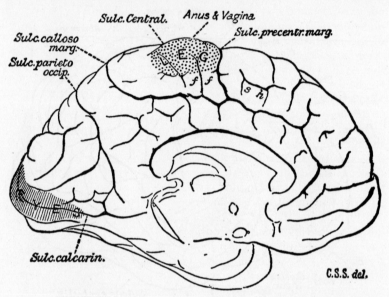

FIG. 102.—Mesial Surface of the Brain of a Chimpanzee.   (Grünbaum and Sherrington.)   The left hemisphere is shown, with the frontal lobe to the right.

or the leg; and extirpation in the leg area causes paralysis of part of the opposite leg. These symptoms are, however, as is usual in such extirpations, recovered from, in large measure, in the course of a few weeks.   All these extirpations are in the precentral gyre; when, on the contrary, part of the postcentral is cut out, no paralysis results.

§ 4. An uncritical transfer from the ape's brain to the human brain, of the localizations obtained in these ways, would not be entirely justified, in spite of the great similarity of the two, both as respects their external form, and also the course of fibre-tracts within them.   But, as previously stated, it sometimes happens that surgeons, in operating on the brain, have occasion to use the electric stimulus for the purpose of orientation.   Previous to these results of Grünbaum and Sherrington, observations of this sort had not definitely contradicted the older localization, which placed the motor area on both sides of the central fissure. But since the problem has been more sharply defined, and their attention more definitely directed, by the recent work on the brains of anthropoid apes, operating surgeons have found that the excitable region in the human cortex also lies in the precentral, and not the postcentral, gyre. The arrangement of special centres within this general region of the human brain is substantially the same as that in the anthropoid brain—namely, the leg at the top, the arm halfway down, and the face at the bottom of the precentral gyre.

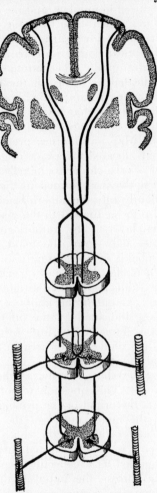

The evidence from paralyses resulting from disease or injury of this region in man is also in general agreement with the same system of localization. The anatomical method lends further support to the same conclusion; for it is after lesion of the precentral gyre that the pyramidal or cortico-spinal tracts degenerate. And since there is no doubt that these tracts are the principal motor path (Fig. 103) of connection between the cortex and the cord, their origin from the precentral gyre is strong evidence that this gyre is the true "motor area." A specially favorable opportunity for examining this question is afforded by cases of the disease known as "amyotrophic lateral sclerosis." This disease produces at the same time a gradual atrophy of the muscles, and also progressive degenera-

Fig. 103.—Diagram of the Motor Pathway from the Cortex.

tion of those portions of the nervous system which are connected with the muscles; namely, of the cells of the ventral horn of the cord, and of the cortico-spinal tract throughout its whole extent. Accordingly the origin of these motor tracts in the cortex ought to be similarly affected; and recent careful examination by several au-

thorities[1] has shown that, in fact, the cortex of the precentral gyre
shows profound pathological changes in cases of this disease. The
"giant cells," which are characteristic of this gyre, are very much
reduced in number, and the other cells are also affected. The large
fibres which issue from the cortex and which pass—many of them
at least—downward to form the pyramidal tracts have largely
disappeared; but no corresponding changes are found in the postcentral gyre. The bottom of the central fissure is, by this method,
indicated as being, in the human brain, the hinder boundary of
the motor region; and although the forward boundary is less sharply
defined, the changes are for the most part confined to the precentral
gyre. Still more convincing is the experimental study by Holmes
and May,[2] who, after severing the pyramidal tract, in different animals, located the exact origin of this tract by aid of the chromatolysis which occurs in cells after their axons have been cut. This
symptom was limited to the precentral gyre (sometimes extending
slightly into the superior and middle frontal gyres), and it seemed
also to be limited to the giant pyramidal cells in the inner pyramidal layer. The authors conclude that "The cortico-spinal fibres
arise only from the giant pyramidal cells . . . and these cells
probably give origin only to cortico-spinal fibres."

§ 5. To these lines of evidence may be added the fact that the
area thus marked out as motor is characterized by a peculiar structure; and that the limits of this structure are nearly the same as
those indicated by the other methods of localization. All in all,
then, there can be little further hesitation in accepting the localization of the motor area in the anthropoid brain, as valid also for
the human brain.

§ 6. What, exactly, is the function of this so-called "motor"
area? This question is not easy to answer. From the fact that
it is the origin of the principal path of conduction from the cortex
to the motor nuclei in the cord and brain-stem, the inference is
clearly valid, that the control of the cortex over the bodily movements is largely exerted through this area. It may, therefore, be
regarded as a collecting centre for impulses from various parts of
the cortex—the impulses thus collected giving rise to discharges
down the cortico-spinal tracts and so to muscular contractions
and relaxations. Since, however, there are no direct fibres from
the motor area, or from any part of the cortex, to the muscles, but
only fibres running to the lower motor nuclei, it would be more proper

---

[1] Among others, see Campbell, *Histological Studies on the Localization of Cerebral Function*, pp. 38 ff. (Cambridge, 1905); Schröder, *Journal für Psychologie und Neurologie*, 1910, XVI, 60–78; Janssens, *ibid.*, 1910, XV, 245–256.

[2] *Brain*, 1909, XXXII, 1.

to speak of the motor area as controlling the lower nuclei, than to speak of it as controlling the muscles. The movements obtained by stimulating the motor area are co-ordinated movements, in much the same way as reflexes are co-ordinated. That is to say: Neither isolated contractions of single muscles, nor general contractions of all the muscles in a limb, are usually obtained on exciting the motor area. The movements are such as, for example, flexions and extensions of the limbs, clenching or opening the fist, pricking up the ear, mastication, turning both eyes to the side, etc. In the higher apes, movements of separate fingers can be obtained; but even these are to be regarded as co-ordinated movements. A clear indication of the co-ordinated nature of these movements is the fact, first discovered by H. E. Hering and Sherrington,[1] that the contraction of a group of muscles, when aroused by excitation of its appropriate cortical area, is attended by relaxation of the antagonistic muscles. This is the same result as appears in reflex action (see p. 162). It is quite likely, then, that the same "central cells" of the cord, which were conceived of as the mechanisms controlling the co-ordination of reflexes, are excited by the fibres of the cortico-spinal tract. In this case, the function of the motor area may be said to be, *the control of spinal co-ordinating mechanisms, in accordance with impulses reaching the motor area from various parts of the cortex.* Accordingly, we can neither regard the motor area as standing in direct relation with the muscles, nor as the original starting-point of cortical influence on the muscles. But it is more properly thought of as an *intermediary* between the cortex in general and the co-ordinating mechanisms of the cord and brainstem (compare p. 94).

§ 7. The foregoing may be taken as a fairly safe and even obvious induction. But there is still considerable difficulty in reaching a satisfactory conception of the precise function of the motor area. The difficulty arises chiefly from the facts of that restitution of function, which so often follows removal or disease of this region, or of parts of it. In connection with the results of extirpating limited portions of the motor area of the anthropoid brain, it was mentioned above that the paralysis of the arm or leg, which is the immediate result, usually disappears in the course of a few weeks. The same result has often been noted in man; for, in certain cases of irritation of small portions of the motor area, resulting in epileptiform convulsions, it has long been found practicable to cure the convulsions by cutting out the irritated portion; and, though this gives rise to temporary paralysis of some group of muscles, the

[1] *Pflüger's Archiv f. d. gesammte Physiol.*, 1897, LXVIII, 222; *Journ. of Physiol.*, 1899, 23 Suppl.

paralysis is recovered from, at least by young persons. When the part destroyed by experiment on the animals, or by disease or accident in man, is more extensive, the recovery of function is less complete. Locomotion is restored, at least to a considerable degree; but in man's case, after extensive destruction of the motor area in both hemispheres, the gait remains insecure and subject to spasm. The more specialized movements are less completely restored. A dog, deprived of the motor region on both sides, is at first pretty completely paralyzed, except for reflexes and such vital movements as breathing. Soon, however, he recovers locomotion; but he is stated (Munk, Monakow) never to recover the use of the forepaw as a hand for holding a bone, etc.

Now since restitution of function is not the result of restitution of the injured parts of the brain by new growth, it is a puzzling phenomenon. It has sometimes been explained as due to the taking up of the function of the destroyed part by other parts ("vicarious function"). Such an explanation seems improbable, since it would call for the growth of new projection fibres, a growth which probably does not occur; and since, moreover, it calls for too much fresh learning of complicated functions. Another explanation is to the effect that other parts of the cortex, besides the part which gives rise on excitation to a given movement, are also connected with that movement, though in a minor degree. They may, therefore, be considered as auxiliary centres, unused to taking full charge of a movement, yet always employed in conjunction with the principal motor centres. After destruction of the principal centre, these auxiliary centres, continuing to act, might in time come to exercise an efficient control. Such auxiliary centres should be looked for in the immediate neighborhood of the principal focus; or in the corresponding area of the other hemisphere. Thus the representation of a given movement in the cortex might be centred at a given point or small area, but still spread somewhat over neighboring areas. There is indeed some evidence, anatomical as well as physiological, that the motor area of the left hemisphere, though principally connected with the right side of the cord and of the body, is connected to a much slighter degree with its own side. It may even be, as Von Monakow is inclined to believe,[1] that there are "motor" spots, scattered generally over the cortex, and connected by projection fibres, perhaps with the thalamus and mid-brain, and so, through the thalamo-spinal, tecto-spinal, and rubro-spinal tracts, with the spinal cord. There do appear to be projection fibres issuing from various parts of the cortex; but hitherto the existence of scattered motor spots has not been demonstrated.

[1] *Ergebnisse der Physiologie*, 1902, I, part 2, p. 611.

Another conception of Von Monakow[1] seems more worthy of attention. It is a mistake, he urges, to consider the functions which are lost immediately after the destruction of a given area of the cortex as exclusively appertaining to that area. The area in question was connected by nerve-fibres with other parts of the cortex and with subcortical centres; and the destruction of the area cuts all these fibres, abolishes their functions, and induces pathological changes in them. It thus interferes with the function of the various parts to which, or from which, they lead. These connected centres are thus left in a subnormal condition; but although they might not discharge their functions at once, they might come in time, since they are not destroyed, to function again in a normal manner, or at least in a manner approaching the normal.

Still another possible explanation of restitution of function following destruction of the motor area holds that the lower centres, in the brain-stem and cord, are responsible for the movements afterward executed. This is likely to be correct to a certain extent— just as the subcortical centres are responsible, in normal conditions, for much of the co-ordination and efficiency of voluntary movements. But it can hardly be held that the cortex has nothing to do with movements after restitution; because the movements occur with some regard to volition and to other mental influences.

Some of the most suggestive and puzzling cases of the restitution of function in a manner to suggest a certain amount of substitution of one cortical area for another, have recently occurred in connection with the surgical practice of nerve-anastomosis. It has been found, for example, that where the facial nerve had been completely severed and all its motor and sensory functions quite destroyed, a partial, and in extremely favorable instances, an almost entire recovery of functions could be obtained by uniting the peripheral end of the injured facial nerve with that portion of the accessory nerve which supplies the trapezius muscle. Now the cerebral areas which control these two nerves are not far distant in space, but in their normal functions are largely different. It would seem, therefore, that such cases must depend for their physiological explanation on the spread of the impulse originating in the cortical areas over their customary limits, when the demand for this is made by abnormal conditions. And on the other hand, there can be no doubt about their emphasizing the *cortical* factors in all cases of recovered functions, since in these cases, imagination and will were shown to be about the most influential forms of excitement, in the interests of a restoration of function.[2]

[1] Op. cit., p. 569, and passim.
[2] See a discussion of some of these cases: Ladd, "A Suggestive Case of Nerve-Anastomosis," *The Popular Science Monthly*, August, 1905.

§ 8. Restitution of function has to be reckoned with in considering the localization of other functions besides the motor, and even to a greater degree; for the localization of the sensory functions is dependent more largely on the method of extirpation and on the corresponding pathological method. The method of excitation is not applicable for purposes of localization in most parts of the cortex, since, with the exception of the motor area and of a few other regions which will be mentioned in due course, the rest of the cortex is "silent" under excitation; i. e., does not give rise to move-

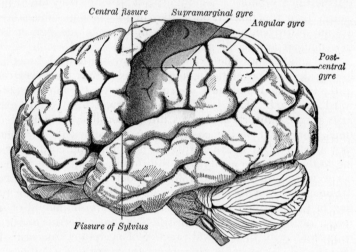

Central fissure   *Supramarginal gyre*

Angular gyre

Post-central gyre

Fissure of Sylvius

Fig. 104.—The Somesthetic Area.

ments. It has only recently been found that the weak electric current can be safely applied to an exposed surface of the human cortex, in surgical cases, without the use of an anæsthetic; pain does not result. It will therefore be possible, in the future, as it has not been in the past, to explore, little by little, as occasion offers, the surface of the brain with the exciting current, in conscious human beings. In this way, direct and convincing testimony can be obtained as to the sensations or ideas, if any, aroused by the excitation of definite cortical areas.

§ 9. Besides the motor area, there have been found areas which are closely related to several of the senses. We pass, then, to the consideration of the "sensory areas" (Fig. 104).

The history of the localization of the so-called "somesthetic area," or area for the sense of "touch"—which, in the older meaning of the term, included the cutaneous senses and the muscular sense—is of interest. It was often observed that injuries to the motor area, in both animals and man, were accompanied by loss of sensation as well as by motor paralysis. If, for example, the injury affected the upper part of the central gyres, on the left side, paralysis, and also, in many cases, loss of sensation in the right leg, would result. This led to the doctrine that the sensory and motor centres are the same; and many authorities preferred to call the cortical area involved sensory rather than motor. But there were, also, many negative cases—i. e., cases in which paralysis occurred without loss of sensation, or in which loss of sensation occurred without paralysis. Such facts as these seemed to disprove the doctrine that the sensory and motor centres are coincident. The discovery that the motor area, instead of occupying both sides of the central fissure, is confined to the frontal side, made necessary a complete revision of all the older observations. It was no longer possible simply to describe an injury as lying in the central gyres, without more minute specification. Critical review of the older cases, and especially the more attentive observation of recent cases, have seemed to show that injury, when strictly confined to the precentral gyre, is not attended by loss of sensation; the precentral gyre, or motor area, can therefore be excluded from the somesthetic area. But destruction of the region immediately behind the central fissure is attended by loss of sensation. Accordingly, the central fissure seems to be the anterior boundary of the somesthetic area; although its posterior limits cannot yet be distinctly assigned. Some authorities[1] are inclined to include within it, in addition to the postcentral gyre, the front part of the superior and inferior parietal; while others[2] would limit it to the postcentral, or even to the anterior part of that gyre. Within this somesthetic area, the representation of the different parts of the body seems to have about the same arrangement as in the adjoining motor area: namely, the leg area at the top; the arm area half-way down; and the head area at the bottom. In this manner the sensory and the motor areas for a given member are brought into close proximity to each other, but on opposite sides of the central fissure.

§ 10. The losses of sensation which attend destruction of the somesthetic area do not affect all varieties of sensation equally. The pain sense is little or not at all affected, except temporarily; the sense of pressure and contact is considerably more diminished; the temperature sense is so much reduced that only extremes of heat and cold are perceived; the muscular sense is almost entirely destroyed; and the perception of form, size, location, etc., by use of the hand is usually abolished. These are the permanent results of extensive

[1] Von Monakow, *Ergebnisse der Physiologie*, 1902, I, part 2, pp. 621–641.

[2] Campbell, *Histological Studies in the Localization of Cerebral Function*, 1905, pp. 97 ff.

destruction involving the postcentral and front part of the parietal regions.[1] This would seem to indicate that the ability to make fine distinctions in sensations and to recognize their "intellectual" qualities is most easily lost.

§ 11. To the pathological and experimental evidence just mentioned may be added the evidence of an anatomical nature in favor of locating the somesthetic area just behind the central fissure. The primary receiving station for the body senses must be that region to which the sensory tracts from the cord and brain-stem lead. In a previous chapter (compare pp. 81, 89 f.), these tracts were traced through the "fillet" to the thalamus; they run to a particular part of the thalamus, namely, the ventral nucleus, where the fibres from the cord and bulb terminate. From this part of the thalamus issue fresh fibres, which pass to the cortex; and these have been traced[2] by the degeneration method to the region behind the central fissure. The myelinization method has led to much the same result.[3] This part, therefore, may with some probability be accepted as the cortical termination of the sensory path from the skin and muscles. On the whole, it seems a highly reasonable conjecture that the function of this somesthetic area is that of receiving sensory impulses, and of distributing them, by association fibres, to neighboring and distant parts of the cortex. Accordingly, if the postcentral gyre, close to the fissure, is the receiving station, the posterior part of this gyre, and the adjoining margin of the parietal convolutions, may be held to be concerned with the combination, "elaboration," perception, interpretation, etc., of somesthetic data.

§ 12. The visual area was first located with some exactness by Munk.[4] He found that removal of portions of the occipital lobe was followed, in dogs and monkeys, by disturbances of vision; and insisted that destructions of other portions of the cortex were not necessarily followed by visual loss. Though this view was for a time subject to much doubt and contradiction, the accumulation of experimental and pathological data, and especially of anatomical facts, has shown that Munk's localization is correct. Ferrier, indeed, located the visual area further forward, in the angular gyre; but this is now agreed to have been an error, due to the fact that the "optic radiation"—i. e., the fibres leading from the external genicu-

---

[1] Von Monakow, op. cit., pp. 629–630.

[2] Von Monakow, op. cit., p. 636.

[3] The myelinization method has not yet excluded the precentral gyre from being part of the receiving station; and the inner structure of the precentral is in some important respects like that of known sensory centres. There is still a chance that some sensory fibres lead directly to the motor area.

[4] *Ueber d. Functionen d. Grosshirnrinde* (Berlin, 1881; 2d ed., 1890).

latum to the occipital lobe, and constituting the continuation of the optic nerves—lies close beneath the cortex of the angular gyre, and thus is likely to be unintentionally affected by either stimulation or extirpation of this region.

The particular sort of visual disturbance resulting from injury or disease within the occipital lobe varies greatly in different cases. In some cases it is described as "psychic blindness," under which head may be included several varieties, such as inability to recognize objects, or to read, or to perceive colors, or to utilize vision for

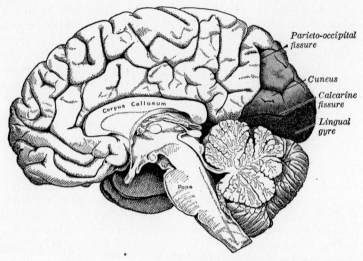

Fig. 105.—The Visual Area in the Occipital Lobe.

purposes of orientation. All of these symptoms may occur without blindness in the strict sense; in such cases, the patient can still see, but has lost the uses of sight, or some of them. In another class of cases, there is complete blindness for a certain part of the field of view. If the occipital lobe is destroyed in the right hemisphere, for instance, the patient cannot see what lies to his left, or, more precisely, what lies to the left of the vertical meridian of his eyes. It is as if the right half of each retina were blinded. This form of blindness is called "hemianopsia." The peculiar distribution of such blindness is well explained by the semi-decussation of the optic nerves at the chiasm (compare pp. 91 f.). In hemianopsia, however, central or foveal vision is not destroyed in either eye, which leads to the supposition that the fibres from the fovea of each eye are distributed to the occipital lobes of both hemispheres. In hemianopsia, blindness for the affected half of the field of vision is complete; all that is left, in man's case, is the pupillary reflex.

§ 13. Clearly, hemianopsia is a more radical form of blindness than is "psychical blindness." It must, therefore, be considered as the sign of destruction of the primary receiving station for nerve impulses from the eye, or of the fibres leading from the eye to that receiving station. The localization of this primary visual area is therefore the first step required toward a more precise localization of visual functions within the wider limits of the occipital lobe. To Henschen[1] is due the credit for a sharper localization of this primary visual area. On the basis of clinical cases, he located it in a relatively small portion of the occipital lobe, a portion which lies, in man, almost entirely on the mesial surface, and in the immediate neighborhood of the calcarine fissure. Later observers have on the whole confirmed Henschen's conclusion that hemianopsia, when it is due strictly to injury of the cortex, is dependent on lesion of the calcarine region (Fig. 105).

Anatomical evidence of convincing character is available in confirmation of this localization It will be recalled (see p. 92) that the optic nerves, after their semi-decussation, terminate in the interbrain, and for the most part in the external geniculate bodies. The fibres which arise from the geniculatum have been traced by Flechsig, Vogt, and others, by the method of myelinization; they are found to pass back, underneath the angular gyre and the lateral portion of the occipital lobe, and to terminate in the lips and immediate neighborhood of the calcarine fissure. Other methods of tracing fibres have led to concordant results. The facts, however, that some few fibres pass from the lower optic centres to other parts of the occipital lobe, and that central vision is often preserved after the destruction of the calcarine region, would seem to favor the view of Von Monakow.[2] He holds that central or foveal vision has no sharply defined cortical centre.

§ 14. Within the calcarine region, some degree of more minute localization is indicated by the observations of Henschen and others. Apparently the posterior part of the primary visual area is connected with the lower part of the retinas, and the anterior part of the visual area with the upper part of the retinas. It would appear likely that the retinas are projected, point for point, though perhaps not quite so minutely as this, upon the visual cortex. The projection of corresponding points of the two retinas must be superimposed in the visual areas, the right half of each retina being projected on

---

[1] *Klinische und anatomische Beiträge zur Pathologie des Gehirns* (Upsala, 1890–1892); "On the Visual Path and Centre," *Brain*, 1893, p. 170.

[2] *Ergebnisse der Physiologie*, 1902, I, part 2, pp. 653, 661.

the right visual cortex, and the left half of each retina on the left visual area.

Excitation of the occipital lobe gives rise to movements of the eyes, and Schäfer[1] found that different movements were obtained by exciting different portions of this lobe; for example, excitation of the posterior part gave an upward movement of both eyes. This result is harmonious with that of Henschen just stated, since an upward movement of the eyes is what occurs when a bright light from above suddenly shines into the eye, striking the lower part

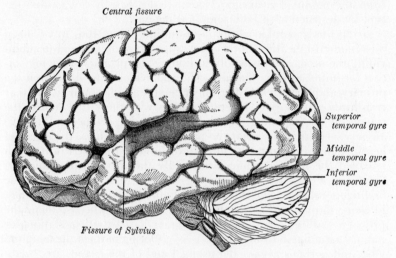

Central fissure

Superior
temporal gyre

Middle
temporal gyre

Inferior
temporal gyre

Fissure of Sylvius

Fig. 106.—The Auditory Area.

of the retina. It is probable that our ordinary movements of the eyes in looking at an object, i. e., in directing the centre of clear vision upon it, are reactions through the visual area, and not through the motor area. And motor fibres leading downward from the visual area toward the mid-brain have been demonstrated by von Monakow.

If the calcarine region is the receiving station for optic impulses, it is probable that neighboring portions of the occipital lobes are concerned with those more complicated visual functions, the loss of which is betrayed by the different sorts of "psychical blindness."

§ 15. The evidence in favor of an auditory centre is of the same kind as that in favor of the visual centre; and the history of its localization is much the same. There has been general agreement, from an early period of the study, that the auditory functions were spe-

[1] *Brain*, 1888, XI, 1; *Textbook of Physiology*, 1900, vol. II, p. 755.

cially connected with the temporal lobe. The symptoms which result from lesions here cover much the same range as the visual
symptoms which attend lesions of the occipital lobe. They are in
some cases of the "psychic" variety, such as "word-deafness"
(inability to understand spoken words) or as "amusia" (inability
to apprehend melodies); or such as loss of memory for words or
for melodies. In other cases, there is genuine deafness in the opposite ear; but the findings here seem not to be perfectly clear, perhaps because of an incomplete decussation of the incoming fibres
from the organ of hearing. Complete deafness is not caused except by destruction of both temporal regions.

Given this general localization of auditory (Fig. 106) functions in
the temporal lobe, the efforts of investigators were devoted to subdi-
viding the area, and especially to finding the primary receiving station for impulses from the ear. Clinical evidence tends to limit the
primary auditory area to the upper temporal gyre, and to the rear
two-thirds of this gyre. Here again, as with the visual centre, the
tracing of the incoming path is of decisive importance. We have
already seen (pp. 90 f.) that the path from the cochlea, the organ of
hearing, is traced up to the inter-brain, and to that part of it which
is called the internal geniculatum. By the myelinization method
(Flechsig, Vogt), the fibres arising thence are seen to pass to the
first temporal gyre; and, indeed, to a limited portion of it, which lies,
in man, mostly within the fissure of Sylvius. This is, then, the
primary auditory area, the receiving and distributing station for
impulses coming in from the ear. Neighboring parts of the temporal
lobe, and perhaps also of the parietal and of the island, are "elab-
orative," combinational, or perceptive with respect to the auditory impulses. Excitation of the temporal lobe, in animals, gives
rise to movements of the ears, and to turning of the eyes and head
to the opposite side. These are, in appearance, "listening" movements, and their occurrence indicates that the primary motor adjustment to sound occurs through the auditory area rather than
through the motor area.

§ 16. Regarding the cortical representation of the sense of smell,
we have already mentioned the evidence afforded by comparative
anatomy that the archipallium is concerned with this and allied
senses. The fibres from the olfactory part of the nose pass to the
olfactory lobe; and fibres can be traced back from this lobe to the
pyriform lobule, which, accordingly, is regarded as the receiving
station for olfactory impulses. The pyriform lobule usually shows
a high development in animals which make great use of the sense
of smell. In man, it is comparatively small. There is not much
pathological evidence regarding the localization of smell in the

human cortex, and the fibre connections just mentioned, on which
the localization of the olfactory area is based, have been traced in
animals not closely related to man. But what pathological evidence exists points, for the most part, to the pyriform lobule or to
its neighborhood. Excitation of this general region, by Ferrier,
gave movements of the nostrils—an adjustment of the sense-organ
analogous to those which are got by exciting the visual and auditory
areas.

§ 17. Little of a definite nature can be stated regarding the cortical representation of the sense of taste; but it is believed to lie somewhere within the archipallium or its immediate neighborhood.

§ 18. On reviewing the localizations which have been established,
we find that the retina is connected most directly with the calcarine
region; the organ of hearing with that portion of the first temporal
which lies in the side of the Sylvian fissure; the organ of smell with
the pyriform lobule; and the cutaneous and muscular senses with
the postcentral gyre; while the principal motor pathway arises from
the precentral gyre. Other special motor pathways, controlling the
adjustment of sense-organs, arise from the visual, auditory, and
olfactory areas. In addition, there is an area in the frontal lobe,
the connections of which are not as yet well made out, but which,
on excitation, gives movements of the eyes. With the exception of
this last area, the receiving and departing stations are of limited
extent; they occupy a comparatively small proportion of the entire
surface of the cortex, especially in the higher animals. They are
relatively smallest in the human brain. But this relative diminution, as we ascend the scale of animals, is owing to increase in the
intervening areas, which are not so directly connected with the sense-
organs or with the muscles.

What, now, are the functions of these "silent" areas? It is easy
to call them "intellectual centres"; but if such a term is used, the
implication of the word "intellectual" must be made very broad.
It must be made broad enough, for example, to cover the mental
performances of the dog, since even in the dog there is much "silent"
space left between the primary sensory and the motor areas. Flechsig proposed to call such areas "association centres"; but—here
again—if this term is used, it should, for the present, be understood in an anatomical rather than in a psychological sense. It
should have reference, namely, to the association fibres; and the
idea conveyed should be that the association centres are those areas
whose connections are provided by these fibres; that is to say, their
connection with the organs of sense and of movement is indirect.
Even this cannot be stated as an absolutely valid distinction; for,
though the principal bundles of projection fibres are traceable to

the sensory and motor areas, there seems to be a scattered distribution of similar fibres over a large portion of the whole cortex.

§ 19. With regard to the specific functions of other parts of the cortex, not thus far discussed, we have little definite information; and yet we are not wholly without grounds of conjecture. It is obvious, for example, that the areas surrounding the calcarine region are necessary for the proper utilization of visual data; that portions of the temporal lobe, near the primary auditory station, are necessary for the utilization of auditory data; and that parts of the parietal lobe, adjoining the somesthetic area, are necessary for the utilization of cutaneous and muscular sensation. These outlying regions are richly connected by short association fibres with their respective sensory distributing stations. Most of the evidence for these statements has been obtained from observation of human patients suffering from brain diseases, but some evidence is also to be got from the results of extirpation in animals. Munk found that excising small portions of the temporal lobe, in dogs, resulted not in deafness, for the animals would still prick up the ears at a sound, but in what he called "psychic deafness," as shown by the loss of habitual reactions to words of command, etc. Removals of small parts of the occipital region were followed, similarly, not by blindness, but by failure to recognize familiar objects, such as food, or the master's hand extended as if to "shake hands."

Losses of function which follow destructions of limited portions of the human cortex have been grouped under a considerable number of descriptive terms. These defects seldom occur singly; usually a number of them occur together; yet cases of isolated loss are not unknown, and are properly regarded as specially important, because they afford the best opportunity for purposes of localization, and for analysis of complicated mental functions into component functions of less complexity.

§ 20. A number of defects have been distinguished, which result from injury of the occipital lobe or of the adjacent part of the parietal lobe. The principal ones are given below.

Alexia is inability to read, occurring, of course, in a person who previously could read, and in one who has not become blind. In such cases, the printed characters are seen clearly enough, but have lost their significance. In "pure" cases, the individual can understand what is spoken, and may even be able to write, though unable to read what he has just written.

Asymbolia. The use of this term varies, at present, between a strict definition, covering cases in which numerals, or other conventional signs, are no longer grasped, and a wider definition, according to which it includes cases of "object blindness." In the latter cases, the patient is unable to recognize familiar objects; the visual impression is no longer for him a sign of the object, though he may know the object at once on handling it.

Achromatopsia. Occasionally there occurs, without blindness, a loss of color vision in half of the field of view.

In some cases, there is, without blindness, a loss of the power to perceive depth, or of the power to orientate oneself in familiar surroundings. In other cases, there is deficiency in the clearness of central vision; and in still others, a loss of visual imagination. Two or more of these various defects are likely to be combined in the same individual; but there is no necessary connection between any two of them, nor between any one of them and hemianopsia. Nor is it possible as yet to connect any of them with destruction of any particular limited area; but, when taken together, they give some notion of the function of the cortex in the neighborhood of the visual area.

§ 21. Analogous defects are met in certain cases of lesion of the temporal lobe and neighboring parts of the island and parietal lobe:

Amusia is a loss of ability to apprehend melodies and other musical complexes; it has been observed in musicians afflicted with brain disease.

Word-deafness is a similar inability to recognize the meaning of spoken words.

Verbal amnesia and *paraphasia* belong to the aphasias. In the former, there is abnormal difficulty in finding the right word to express one's meaning. Resort must be had to round-about modes of expression, or absurdly general terms, such as "the what-d' you-call-it." In paraphasia, there is less hesitation, but much substitution of wrong words, or of jargon.

§ 22. Injuries to the parietal lobe, in the neighborhood of the postcentral gyre, are often attended by

Astereognosis. This is a loss of the "stereognostic sense," or, better, of the ability to recognize the size, shape, and consistency of objects by handling them. Such judgments must depend on utilizing a combination of impressions from both the cutaneous and the muscular senses.

From a survey of these defects, and of the location of the lesions which cause them, we may properly reach the general conclusion that the immediate neighborhood of the receiving station for each sense is concerned with functions which are closely related to that sense.

§ 23. Similar defects occur on the side of movement, and pass by the general name of *apraxia*, of which several forms are recognized. In general, "apraxia" may be defined as a loss of ability to perform learned or skilled acts, in the absence of paralysis, or ataxia, or pronounced sensory or perceptional defect. The patient knows what he wishes to do, but cannot make his hands do it; yet his hands are not paralyzed, and may be able to perform very simple acts, and to take part in instinctive movements, such as locomotion, or as pointing toward an object at which he is looking. Often, indeed, there is paralysis of the right hand, with apraxia of the left hand, which is not paralyzed. Sometimes the apraxia is associated, not with motor paralysis of one hand, but with object-blindness; but in these cases, the difficulty consists rather in not knowing what is to be done, than in inability to carry out an intention. Sometimes, also, the difficulty lies in the combination of the single movements which, in proper sequence, make up a skilled act. In this connection, it is worth noting that even very familiar and apparently simple acts, such as lighting a candle or picking a flower, are really composed of an orderly sequence of movements, and therefore need to be learned, in childhood, by a long course of training. The results of this training are lost, in some forms of apraxia, in consequence of localized disease of the brain. There are other cases in which apraxia is associated with a "general" defect of intellect.

The close study of apraxia is only of recent date, and has been prosecuted with special vigor by Liepmann[1] and Pick.[2]

One case, narrated by Liepmann, is of special interest; because the patient, while free from paralysis or ataxia on either side, was apractic on the right side only. He was also free from "general intellectual" defect, as was shown by his ability to describe the act which he wished to perform, and by his performing it himself with his left hand. With his right hand, however, he could not successfully perform even simple learned acts. The post-mortem examination of the brain in this case revealed destructions of the white matter in such situations as to separate the two central gyres of the left hemisphere from the rest of that hemisphere, and also, through injury of the callosum, from the right hemisphere. Being thus isolated, the motor area for the right hand was beyond the influence of other parts of the cortex concerned with the intention and the proper ordering of separate movements into a skilled act.

Agraphia, or inability to write, may be regarded as a special form of apraxia. It seldom occurs alone, but usually in associa-

[1] H. Liepmann, *Das Krankheitsbild bei Apraxie* (Berlin, 1900); *Der weitere Krankheitsverlauf bei dem einseitig Apraktischen* (Berlin, 1906); *Ueber Störungen des Handelns bei Gehirnkranken* (Berlin, 1905).
[2] A. Pick, *Studien über motorische Apraxie* (Leipzig and Vienna, 1905).

tion with some form of aphasia. In the few recorded cases where it has occurred alone, examination of the brain has revealed destruction of the cortex in the middle frontal gyre, just forward of the motor centre for the arm and hand. This localization is disputed by many authorities, and is to be accepted only tentatively.

§ 24. No class of learned and skilled acts is more highly specialized than the various linguistic performances, such as using articulate language in speaking, understanding what is spoken, reading and writing. No losses of learned acts are, therefore, easier to detect than are those of language. For this reason, the study of *aphasia*, or loss of speech, has a much longer history than has the study of apraxia or of asymbolia. And since aphasia is a result of localized brain lesions, it has been, and is still, one of the chief concerns of the student of cerebral localization.

For about a decade, however, previous to the discoveries of Fritsch and Hitzig, in 1870, the facts which seemed definitely to connect the loss of speech with a certain region of the left cerebral hemisphere were nearly all to which any advocate of the localization of the cerebral function could confidently appeal in behalf of his theory. As long ago as 1825, Bouillaud located the articulation of words in the frontal lobes. Subsequently (1836) M. Dax maintained the proposition that "lesions of the left half of the encephalon are coincident with forgetfulness of the symbols of thought."

In treatises of the years 1861–1865, Broca first announced the substantially true discovery that the *gyrus frontalis inferior* on the left side of the cerebrum is especially concerned in using the power of speech. This circumstance he connected with the fact that men generally use the left hemisphere more than the right for the expression of thought with the right hand and arm, whether in writing or in the mechanical arts. The literal meaning of the statements made by Broca—such as that this part of the brain is "the seat of the faculty of articulate language"[1]—is, however, not simply inappropriate to the facts; it is even absurd. There is no one "faculty" of language which can, in any possible meaning of the word, be regarded as having its "seat" or locality confined to some particular region of the brain. Speech involves, in a very complicated and large way, all the faculties; strictly speaking, then, it cannot be located, with all its attendant operations of self-conscious, rational mind, in any one cerebral area. But that the phenomena of *aphasia* show some special connection of certain cerebral centres with the complex process of apprehending and ex-

---

[1] "Sur le siège de la faculté du langage articulé," etc., *Bull. de la Soc. anat.*, August, 1861; "Du siège de la faculté du langage articulé dans l'hémisphère gauche du cerveau," *Bull. de la Soc. d'anthropol.*, June, 1865.

pressing articulate language, seems entitled to credit as an induction based upon a wide range of facts. Of course, in this particular attempt at localization of function, no real help can be derived from experiments upon the lower animals.

§ 25. The phenomena of various classes, among which the truly aphasic cases must be discriminated, vary all the way from those resembling the results of momentary inattention—such as that of the German professor who certified in writing, "A. B. has attended my remarkable lectures in chemistry with inorganic assiduity"—to the impairment and utter loss of speech in progressive paralysis with dementia. A few of the more curious and instructive instances furnish facts like the following: The aphasic patient may be entirely speechless, and yet understand what is said to him, and be able to write his wishes down on paper. Some thus afflicted retain the power to pronounce words of one syllable, but are obliged to resort to writing in order to communicate anything further. Others possess a small stock of words, which they make more serviceable with expressive gestures. Others, still, are simply able to speak "a few senseless, and often very extraordinary, syllables and words."

Among the surprising phenomena of the disease of aphasia, none are perhaps more so than those occasioned by the ability to utter certain syllables or words, when accompanied by an utter inability to put the same letters into slightly different combination. One patient, who could say "Bonjour, monsieur," tolerably well, could not pronounce the word "bonbon" at all. Another, whose vocabulary was almost entirely limited to the meaningless syllables, "cousisi," was quite unable to utter either "coucon" or "sisi." The celebrated case of the aphasic Le Long, reported by Broca, was that of a man confined to five words for his entire vocabulary. These words were, "oui, non, tois, instead of trois, toujours, and Le Lo instead of Le Long." The first two and the last were used with their appropriate meaning; "tois" indicated all ideas of number whatever; and "toujours" was the word used when the patient could not express his meaning by gestures and the other four words. It appears, then, that Le Long could pronounce the r in "toujours," but not in "trois," and the nasal sound in "non," but not in his own name. In another class of cases, the aphasic person can utter only a few or no words spontaneously and correctly, but can repeat and write without difficulty words that are spoken before him. Such inability is somtimes called "simple aphasia of recollection." Different classes of words, as a rule, slip from the memory in succession, as it were. Proper names are most frequently forgotten; then substantives generally, and sometimes verbs, adjectives, pronouns, and all other parts of speech.

"The more concrete the idea," says Kussmaul,[1] "the more readily the word to designate it is forgotten, when the memory fails." Many cases of disease occur where the patient has lost the power mentally to *find* the appropriate words, although his power of articulation is unimpaired. Such disturbances of speech may, or may not, be accompanied by a corresponding impairment of general intelligence. This complication increases the difficulty of studying the phases of this disease.

Aphasia may also be accompanied by so-called "word-deafness" and "word-blindness." Persons thus afflicted hear words as con-

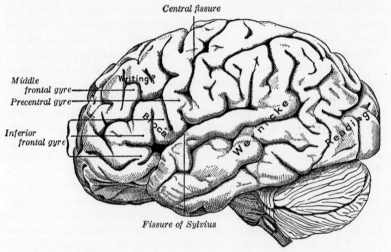

Central fissure

Middle frontal gyre
Precentral gyre

Inferior frontal gyre

Fissure of Sylvius

Fig. 107.—Areas of the Cortex Supposed to be Specially Connected with Speech.

fused murmurings, or see them as blurred images. The individual letters may be intelligently heard or read, but their combination has become unintelligible. The same thing sometimes happens with figures; as in the case of the accountant who could read the sum 766, figure for figure, but did not know what the figure 7 meant as placed before the two 6's. At other times the disturbance of speech takes the form of grammatical ataxy, as it were, or of verbal delirium—a medley of words, partly in themselves significant and partly unmeaning.

§ 26. In the analysis of these varied defects of speech, an important step was taken by Wernicke,[2] who, in 1874, made a distinction between motor aphasia and sensory aphasia (compare Fig. 107). Accepting Broca's localization as correct for the motor

[1] *Ziemssen's Cyclopædia*, XIV, p. 759.
[2] *Der aphasische Symptomencomplex* (Breslau, 1874).

form, he assigned for sensory aphasia quite a different seat—namely, in the temporal lobe of the left hemisphere. The distinguishing symptom of motor aphasia is inability to combine articulatory movements into spoken words, in the absence, however, of paralysis of the muscles of articulation. The distinguishing symptom of the sensory form, according to Wernicke, is a loss of the auditory images of words. Now, since speech is before all an auditory affair, loss of the auditory images of words is equivalent to a loss of memory for words, and so of the use of speech. So reasoned Wernicke. Whether the psychological terms in which he expressed his theory are correct, or not, the distinction between motor and sensory aphasia has proved to be valid; and also the separate localization of the two forms. Even in milder cases, in which both the sensory and the motor aphasic patient have retained some use of speech, there is still a difference between the two. The motor aphasic shows much hesitation and effort in enunciation, and speaks disjointedly, having lost his hold on grammatical form; whereas the sensory aphasic may speak fluently enough, and with preservation of grammatical form, but with the wrong use of words, and in some cases in a perfect jargon. Wernicke also introduced the conceptions of "cortical," "subcortical," and "transcortical" aphasia—a subdivision which can be applied to both main types. In the cortical varieties, the centre itself is supposed to be destroyed, and therefore the loss of function is complete. In the subcortical variety, the centre, remaining intact, allows of an internal speech, which, however is disconnected, by subcortical lesion, from the ear, in the one case, and from the muscles of articulation, in the other; so that the patient becomes either word-deaf or else incapable of actually enunciating. In the transcortical or associative variety, the centre, by severance of the association fibres, is thought to be isolated from other parts of the cortex concerned in the use of language. Though it is not difficult to find cases presenting these varieties of symptoms, the anatomical findings do not, as yet, clearly substantiate the interpretations indicated.

§ 27. In the recent history of the aphasia problem, great importance attaches to the work of P. Marie.[1] This authority concludes, from extensive material of his own, and from a review of cases pre-

---

[1] Marie's original articles appeared in the *Semaine médicale*, in 1906. His point of view, and the evidence for it, are well presented in the extensive monograph of his pupil Moutier, *L'Aphasie de Broca*, Paris, 1908. Marie's contentions have provoked wide-spread discussion among authorities. Reference may be made to the reviews and discussions by C. von Monakow, *Ergebnisse der Physiologie*, 1907, VI, 334–605; and by A. Meyer, *Psychological Bulletin*, 1907, IV, 181–193; 1908, V, 275–282.

viously published, comprising the original cases of Broca, that actual injury always extends beyond the limits of Broca's "speech centre," and that the assignment of special speech functions to this region is entirely unjustified. He even goes so far as to deny any speech function to the third left frontal convolution. He holds that the motor symptoms in aphasia are due, not to any cortical lesion, but to destruction of parts lying beneath the Broca region, especially the lenticular nucleus and the neighboring white matter. The motor symptoms, taken alone, would not, in his view, constitute a true aphasia, but simply a defect in the co-ordination of the speech muscles. True aphasia, he believes, is always of the Wernicke or "sensory" type, and is due to injury of "Wernicke's region," namely the rear of the temporal lobe and adjoining parts of the parietal. He objects, however, to calling this aphasia "sensory," insisting that it is, rather, to be called intellectual. In support of this last contention, he points out that practically all cases of true aphasia show other intellectual defects.

Without doubt it is time to inaugurate a much needed reform in the study of aphasia, especially on the anatomical side. Above all, do the negative cases, of which there are many with regard to the Broca region, need to be taken much fuller account of than has previously been done. The fact of a negative case is, however, always hard to establish; since defects of speech may be recovered from after a brain injury, and may never form part of the record of the patient's clinical history.[1] The anatomical examination of the brain of aphasic patients has usually been quite superficial, from a modern stand-point, which demands that the underlying portions, as well as the cortex, be microscopically examined in "serial sections." This laborious method is only beginning to be applied to cases of aphasia, and for this reason, most of the older attempts to localize its various symptoms are subject to suspicion.

Marie's view of aphasia as essentially a loss of general intellectual power corresponds indeed to the fact that patients who suffer from disturbances of speech usually show also some degree of apraxia or asymbolia, and are often mentally inefficient. In most cases, they are persons of advanced years, and often with a more or less diffused disturbance of cerebral circulation, or with other diseased

---

[1] Compare, in this connection, the case recorded by Liepmann, in *Journal f. Psychologie u. Neurologie*, 1907, IX, 284, in which almost complete destruction of Broca's region appeared on post-mortem examination of the brain of a man whose hospital record showed no evidence of aphasia, but whose previous history revealed a "shock," ten years before, which had been followed by temporary aphasia. Cases like this are likely to be frequent among those which are reported as completely negative.

conditions which affect a considerable area of the cortex. Intellectual deficiency in other directions, however, may be slight in comparison with the disturbance of speech; and in surgical cases, in which local destruction has been brought about in healthy brains, it is not uncommon to find aphasia unattended by any marked intellectual defect.[1]

§ 28. The conclusion seems warranted, then, that there is a group of functions, which are indispensable for language, but not equally essential for all kinds of intellectual performance; and that these functions may be disturbed or destroyed by partial destruction of the cerebrum. This is to express the conclusion very cautiously. There can be scarcely any doubt, further, that the part of the cortex which is most vulnerable as concerns the linguistic functions is "Wernicke's region," in close proximity to the receiving station for auditory impulses. Adolf Meyer,[2] who has studied the subject, both clinically and anatomically, with great thoroughness, concludes that the special symptom, word-deafness, or, as he prefers to call it, "word-imperception," is the result of destruction of the primary auditory receiving station in the left hemisphere; whereas paraphasia "jargon-aphasia," and verbal amnesia are associated with destructions within the rest of Wernicke's region. This region contains nervous mechanisms which are essential to orderly speech, and which are more closely related to the understanding of heard speech than to co-ordination of the muscles of articulation. We may then properly speak of a speech area in the temporal lobe, with the understanding that the area is too broad to be a unit in function; although special localizations within it are not yet clearly made out.

§ 29. To return now to the historic speech area of Broca, which has been assailed with such energy: Marie's attempt to show that the injury which causes the motor symptoms of aphasia is located in the neighborhood of the lenticular nucleus has not met with much favor; and clear cases have been brought forward[3] in which the destruction involved Broca's region, without affecting deeper-lying parts. Such negative cases are, indeed, not fully convincing (see p. 259), because of the possibility of recovery later. But the fact of restitution of motor speech, after extensive or even complete destruction of the third left frontal gyre, is an undoubted fact; and it is not exceptional. Restitution of function is as puzzling a fact here as in the case of injury to the motor area (compare p. 241). It cannot be interpreted as due to the assumption of linguistic func-

---

[1] C. v. Monakow, op. cit., p. 395.

[2] *Journal f. Psychologie u. Neurologie*, 1908, XIII, pp. 203 ff.

[3] See Liepmann, *Journal für Psychologie u. Neurologie*, 1907, X, 280.

tions by some part of the cortex which previously had nothing to do with them; for the recovery is often very sudden; and besides this objection, such an elaborate system of reactions cannot be easily learned at the time of life of most sufferers from aphasia. Usually, after restitution in case of injury to the Broca region, there are some residual defects, such as difficulty in pronouncing long words, slow and hesitating speech, with perhaps stuttering, spasm, easy fatigue; also difficulty in managing the grammatical constructions.[1] The amount of restitution depends, in part, on the general condition of the brain and of the bodily health. In some cases, with poor general condition, loss of the Broca region alone has brought about complete motor aphasia, without later recovery. Also, there is good evidence that the Broca region is the most vulnerable part of the cortex, as regards the motor co-ordination of speech.

There seems, therefore, on the whole, to be good ground for still retaining Broca's speech centre; while relieving it of part of its supposed duties. It is probable that the rearmost part of the third frontal gyre, in the left hemisphere, is intimately connected with the adjoining part of the precentral gyre, from which issues the motor pathway to the muscles of speech. It is further probable that this part of the third frontal has something to do with the combination of elementary movements of the organs of speech into those highly practised sequences which constitute words. Psychological analysis of the exceedingly complex mental activities involved in all the uses of human spoken and written language tends to confirm the conjecture of such writers as Campbell and Von Monakow, that speech functions cover a somewhat wider area in the frontal lobe. Among such functions might be those combinations which are of a higher order than that of elementary vocal movements into spoken words, such as phrasing, inflection of the voice, syntactical forms, etc., etc. Indeed, the entire cerebrum would seem to be, of necessity, involved in man's linguistic attainments and uses.

§ 30. A writing centre in the second frontal gyre, in close proximity to the motor area for the hand, has been asserted as the teaching of a few strikingly positive cases; but the negative and mixed cases have sufficient weight to prevent a general acceptance of this localization. Since the neighborhood of each sensory receiving station is concerned with the impressions received at that station from its sense-organ, it is a tempting conjecture that the writing area lies close to the motor area of the hand. This conjecture is fortified by the analogous case of the localization of the organs of speech. And there is some, but not as yet conclusive, evidence that the frontal

[1] Von Monakow, op. cit., p. 528.

region, just forward of the motor area, in the left hemisphere, is of special importance in all learned and skilled movements.

§ 31. Even after adding to the primary sensory areas those neighboring areas that are probably concerned in the utilization of sensory data, and allowing a similar bordering zone along the motor area for the combination of elementary movements into learned actions, there remains a considerable part of the cortex of the human brain without known relationship to any special function. Considerable portions of the parietal and temporal lobes are still unaccounted for; also the island; and, especially, a large part of the frontal lobes. The frontal lobes, because of their superior development in man, have long been regarded with special interest. They have been by many suspected of being the great intellectual centres. Statistics of the symptoms accompanying brain tumors in different regions[1] have shown intellectual disturbances in 80 per cent. of the cases, when the tumor was in the frontal lobes, as compared with 54 to 66 per cent. when the tumor was located elsewhere on the cortex. Bolton,[2] after examining many cases of dementia and idiocy, found that the cortex was usually thinned out, especially in the frontal lobes; and from this fact he concluded that the frontal region is the organ of attention and general "orderly co-ordination of psychic processes." Loss of power of attention and of inhibition has been claimed by several observers to be the result of injuries to this region. "Witzelsucht," or an addiction to practical jokes of a weak order, with lack of respect for propriety or the rights of others, has been frequently observed. Some authors use terms as broad and vague as "loss of character" or "of personality," in attempting to formulate the symptoms of frontal injury. Indeed, all of the clinical observations are rather vaguely formulated as regards the mental symptoms. On the contrary, in some remarkable cases of destruction of large parts of the frontal lobes, no marked symptoms whatever have appeared. Injury of the right frontal lobe has more frequently been attended by no marked mental symptoms than has injury of the corresponding area in the left hemisphere.

§ 32. Of experimental investigations of the frontal lobe in animals, we may recall the existence of an area, which on excitation responded with movements of eye, ear, and head. Changes in the rate of breathing and of the heart beat, were also sometimes observed.[3] This excitable frontal area is not yet fully understood. Of work done by the method of extirpation, the most promising is

---

[1] Compare Schuster, *Psychische Störungen bei Hirntumoren* (Stuttgart, 1902).
[2] *Brain*, 1903, XXVI, 215–241; *Journal of Mental Science*, 1905, 1906.
[3] Langelaan and Beyerman, *Brain*, 1903, XXVI, 81–93.

that of Franz, performed by a combination of physiological and psychological methods. Having first taught a cat or monkey certain specialized acts, such as getting into a cage by turning a certain button or pulling a certain string, Franz[1] removed parts of the frontal lobes, and later tested the animal to see if it retained the recently learned act. In general the act was not retained after the operation. The objection that the shock of operation, or the mere removal of a certain quantity of brain substance, no matter from what locality, was sufficient to explain the loss, was met by operations in other regions, which were not followed by loss of the learned act. Sometimes removals of parts of the frontal lobe itself were not followed by such loss; and the act could be relearned after the frontal operation, the new learning taking about the same time as if the previous learning had not occurred. Habits of long standing, on the other hand, were not disturbed by such extirpations. Injury to only one of the frontal lobes caused, indeed, a slowing of the act, but not a loss of it. The author concludes that the frontal lobes are concerned in the acquisition of new performances of the sort used; but that no one spot is indispensable for the acquisition of a particular act; and that long-continued practice in a performance reduces it to an automatic or semi-reflex condition, in which the frontal lobes are no longer necessary.

§ 33. Attention should be called to the predominance of the left hemisphere in right-handed persons. The various defects which have been described as resulting from injury to different portions of the cortex usually result from injury to the left hemisphere. Simple paralysis or loss of sensation may result, indeed, from injury to either hemisphere. But object-blindness, word-blindness or word-deafness, the various aphasias and apraxias, usually result from injury to the left hemisphere. From a study of ninety cases of hemiplegia (one-sided paralysis due to injury to the motor area or the white matter beneath it), Liepmann[2] found that injuries to the left hemisphere which caused paralysis of the right hand caused also awkwardness and disturbance of skilled movements in the left hand. Injury of the callosum by severing the connection between the two hemispheres resulted in disturbance of skilled movements of the left hand, but not of the right.

It would almost seem, from the evidence obtained, that the left hemisphere so completely takes charge of acts of skill, and of the intellectual processes concerned in them, as to leave nothing for the great bulk of the right hemisphere to do. Such a conclusion is,

[1] "The Frontal Lobes," *Archives of Psychology*, 1907, No. 2.
[2] *Münchner medicinische Wochenschrift*, 1905, reviewed in *Journal f. Psychol. u. Neurol.*, 1906, VII, 190.

of course, in itself extremely improbable, especially in view of the nearly equal size and inner development of the two hemispheres; but it must be admitted that the role of the right hemisphere, aside from the simplest sensory and motor functions, is not at all clearly made out. In general, it may be that of assistance, or in case of need, of substitution, for the more constant and important functions of the left hemisphere: and for this view there is a considerable accumulation of evidence. This special culture of the left hemisphere—if we may so express the fact—may well enough be connected, both as cause and effect, with the prevalent right-handedness of the human species.

§ 34. We have now passed in review all of the localizations of function in the cortex which have much claim to attention. With the exception of the sensory and motor areas, the localizations so far established are somewhat vague, as respects both their extent on the cortex, and also the exact function which is performed by any given area. What is needed, before a more satisfactory apportionment of functions over the cortex can be attained, is, on the physiological side, a more detailed knowledge of the structure of the cortex as a whole, and in its different parts; and, on the psychological side, a thorough analysis of such vague and gross so-called functions as "speech," or "skilled movement," or "perception of objects," or "orientation in space," into their elementary functional ıactors. It is highly probable that any concrete mental performance involves, physiologically, a complex of activities of various parts of the brain; the performance as a whole, therefore, cannot be localized, although the elementary functions may—and, without doubt, do—each depend on certain particular nervous connections that have a definite location. It is certain, psychologically, that all these mental activities involve a vast and tangled complex of simpler factors, which have either never come before us for conscious inspection, or have already been quite lost out of consciousness, for purposes of such inspection. But to this view of the whole subject we shall return again.

§ 35. On the histological side, the mapping of the cortex into areas of different structure has recently made great advances.

The picture seen on examining a cross section of the cortex under the microscope differs greatly according to the dye with which the tissue has been stained. Some dyes stain the cells, some the fibres. Prominent, for example, among the cell-stains is Nissl's methylene blue stain; prominent among the fibre-stains is the hematoxylin of Weigert. The Golgi stain shows cells with their dendrites and axons, but usually stains only a few of the whole number of cells present, thus, however, making it easier to trace out those that do show themselves. The silver-reduction methods of Cajal and of Bielschowsky show the fibrils within the cells, and altogether give the most complete pictures of the intricacy of the cortex. Each of these methods has its peculiar advantages, and a combination of the results of all is necessary in order to get an adequate notion of the minuter intricacies of cortical structure.

§ 36. To begin with the cells, let us consider a picture like that given in Fig. 108. The cells here are seen to be of several shapes, and of a considerable range of sizes. Prominent in the cerebral cortex are the "pyramidal cells," or "pyramids," cells of generally triangular appearance, with a long apical dendrite extending upward toward the outer surface of the cortex and several basal dendrites, extending horizontally and obliquely downward. The axon of a pyramidal cell emerges from the base and usually passes downward into the white matter, giving off a few collaterals as it goes. The pyramids differ in size from small to large.[1]

Besides these radially arranged cells, there are many others of different orientation. Some send their dendrites downward and their axon upward into the outer layer; some have short axons which split into fine branches close to their cell; some present a general horizontal arrangement of dendrites and axons. Examples of these varieties are shown in Fig. 109.

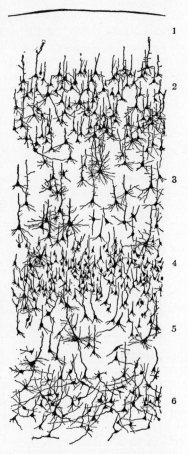

FIG. 108.—Section through the Cerebral Cortex, Stained by the Golgi Method. (Kölliker.) The numbers refer to the layers mentioned on p. 266.

§ 37. For purposes of histological examination and description, it is convenient to divide the cortex into layers. The boundaries between some of the layers are not perfectly definite, and authorities have disagreed both as to the number to be recognized, and also

[1] Cajal, *Studien über die Hirnrinde des Menschen*, Heft 2, pp. 27–28 (Leipzig, 1900).

as to their names. A division into six layers has very high authority, and is defended by Brodmann[1] as being the fundamental type throughout the neopallium of all orders of mammals. The six layers are, he states, clearly visible everywhere at an early stage of development; but he admits that they become obscured in the adult condition. These six layers, arranged in their order from the external surface to the white matter, may be named:

(1) The zonal or plexiform layer.

(2) The outer granule or small-celled layer.

(3) The outer pyramidal layer.

(4) The inner granule layer.

(5) The inner pyramidal layer.

(6) The spindle or multiform layer.

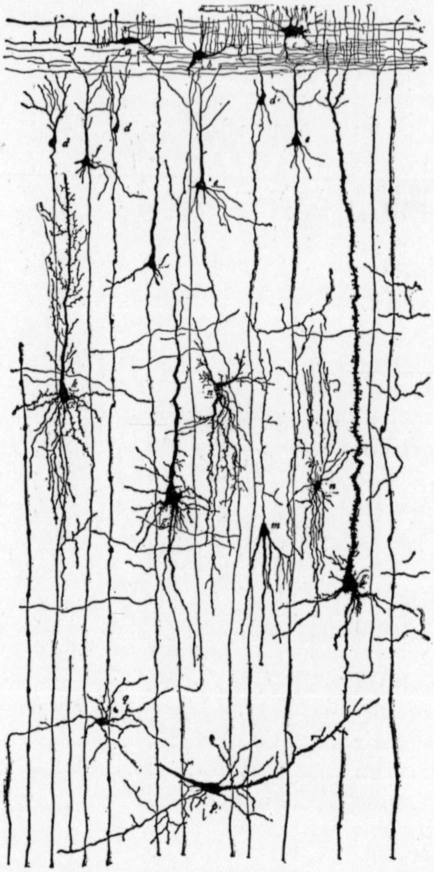

The plexiform layer, though it contains cells, especially the so-called "horizontal cells," consists mostly of fibres. According to Cajal,[2] some of these, the "tangential fibres," arise from the horizontal cells of this layer, and may be regarded as association fibres, and others are axons from cells lying in the deeper layers, or dendrites from the pyramidal cells. The plexiform layer is therefore a place in which numerous synaptic connections are formed between the various cells of the cortex. But the plexiform layer is not the only plexus of nerve-fibres in the cortex. Intricate networks

FIG. 109.—Different Types of Cells Found in the Cortex. (Starr, Strong, and Leaming.)

---

[1] *Vergleichende Lokalisationslehre der Grosshirnrinde in ihren Principien dargestellt auf Grund des Zellenbaus*, pp. 14–42 (Leipzig, 1909).

[2] Op. cit., p. 23.

of fibres, medullated and unmedullated, exist in the various layers. When the cortex is stained for medullated fibres (Fig. 110), some layers are seen to contain many such fibres, and some only a few. In the deepest layers, near the white matter, the network of horizontal and oblique fibres is specially dense. Those layers which show but few medullated fibres are not, however, free from a net-

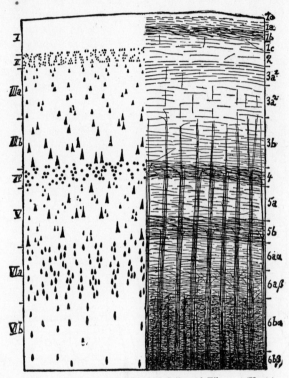

Fig. 110.—Layers of the Cortical Cells and Fibres.   (Vogt.)

work of fibres; for on treating the cortex with the Golgi stain, dense plexuses are seen. Cajal[1] describes what he calls the sensory plexus, which is very dense in the sensory and motor areas, and exists also, with less density, in the rest of the cortex. His tracing of the fibres which give rise to this plexus leads him to believe that they form the path of incoming impulses to the cortex (see Fig. 111). The outgoing path is, he thinks, provided by the axons of the pyramidal cells; and the inner connections within any minute portion of the cortex are provided partly, but not exclusively, through

[1] Op. cit., p. 83.

the plexiform layer.   Numerous interweavings of fine dendrites and terminations of axons and their collaterals occur at all levels.

§ 38. Certain areas of the cortex—especially the precentral gyre,

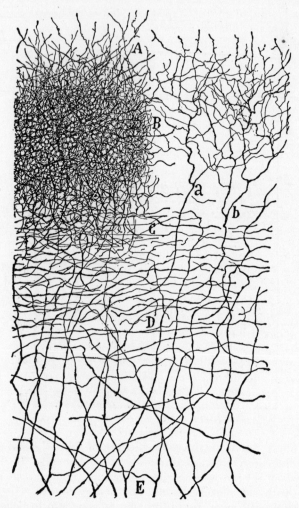

FIG. 111.—The Sensory Plexus of the Cortex.   (Cajal.)   *A* is the zonal layer.

the calcarine region, the pyriform lobe, and parts of the limbic lobe—are strikingly peculiar in structure (see Figs. 112 and 113). The precentral gyre is characterized by the large size of its pyramids, some of which are real giants, and are so named.   These giant pyramids are the chief origin of the long fibres of the cortico-spinal tract. The calcarine cortex is marked by a very prominent stripe, which is here called the stripe of Gennari, from the observer who

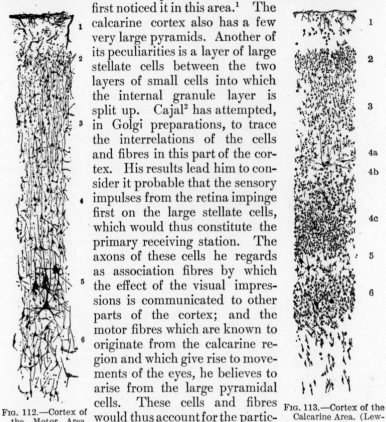

first noticed it in this area.[1] The calcarine cortex also has a few very large pyramids. Another of its peculiarities is a layer of large stellate cells between the two layers of small cells into which the internal granule layer is split up. Cajal[2] has attempted, in Golgi preparations, to trace the interrelations of the cells and fibres in this part of the cortex. His results lead him to consider it probable that the sensory impulses from the retina impinge first on the large stellate cells, which would thus constitute the primary receiving station. The axons of these cells he regards as association fibres by which the effect of the visual impressions is communicated to other parts of the cortex; and the motor fibres which are known to originate from the calcarine region and which give rise to movements of the eyes, he believes to arise from the large pyramidal cells. These cells and fibres would thus account for the particular functions of the visual area.

Fig. 112.—Cortex of the Motor Area. (Lewis, from Ferrier's *Functions of the Brain*.)

Fig. 113.—Cortex of the Calcarine Area. (Lewis, from Ferrier's *Functions of the Brain*.) The splitting of layer 4 into three layers is characteristic of this area. The fibre-stripe of Gennari comes in layer 4b.

§ 39. It has long been known that the internal structure of the cortex differs in different parts; but not till quite recently has the laborious work of examining systematically the whole cortex, and mapping out the limits of each variety of its structure, been attempted. This has now been done, independently, by different observers, with results that are in close agreement; and this work is one

---

[1] This stripe is visible, on close inspection, in most areas of the cortex, and bears in general the name of Baillarger.

[2] *Studien über die Hirnrinde des Menschen*, Heft 1, pp. 62–70 (Leipzig, 1900).

A

B

of the greatest recent additions to our knowledge of the brain. Campbell made a complete examination of several human brains, and also of the brains of the anthropoid ape and of the dog, cat, and pig. His examination was directed both to the cells and to the medullated fibres.[1] A yet more extensive program is now in process of execution in Professor Vogt's Neurobiological Institute at Berlin, the work being divided among several collaborators, and extending to all orders of mammals. Brodmann[2] has published his studies on the cells of the cortex in various mammals. Mauss[3] has issued a study of the medullated fibres of the cortex in monkeys; and Vogt[4] has given a map of the frontal lobes in man as divided on the basis of the medullated fibres. The maps of the cortex afforded by these different studies agree in the main, although Campbell did not subdi-

Fig. 114.—Medullated Fibres in Two Regions of the Cortex. (Campbell.) *A* is from the precentral or motor area, which is extraordinarily rich in fibres; *B* is from the prefrontal area, which is comparatively poor in medullated fibres.

[1] A. W. Campbell, *Histological Studies on the Localization of Cerebral Function* (Cambridge, 1905).
[2] *Vergleichende Localisationslehre der Grosshirnrinde* (Leipzig, 1908), and several papers in the *Journal f. Psychol.*
[3] *Journal f. Psychol. u. Neurol.*, 1908, XIII, 263–325
[4] Ibid., 1910, XV, 221–232.

vide so minutely as did the Berlin observers; and among the latter, Vogt has been able, by studying the fibres, to make more subdivisions than were recognizable from the study of the cells alone.

§ 40. The principles that have guided all these investigators in marking the boundaries between the cerebral areas may be illustrated by a few examples. The precentral area is characterized by the giant pyramids, and these stop abruptly at the bottom of the central fissure, thus establishing the posterior border of this area; its anterior border is less abrupt, but can be determined within a

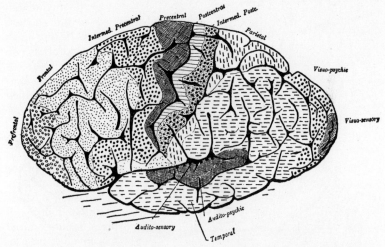

FIG. 115.—Histological Map of the Cortex. Lateral Surface. (Campbell.) The areas extend down into the fissures: thus, the precentral and postcentral meet at the bottom of the central fissure; and the audito-sensory lies almost entirely within the fissure of Sylvius.

millimetre or two. Another characteristic of the precentral area is its lack of a well-defined inner granular layer, and the consequent fusion of the outer and inner pyramidal layers. The granule layer appears promptly behind the central fissure. The thickness of the cortex in the precentral area is very great, and medullated fibres exist in extraordinary richness; the wealth of fibres is one of the distinctive marks of this area.

The calcarine area is distinguished by a splitting of the inner granular layer into two, with a layer of large stellate cells between (see p. 269); and in fibre preparations, by the distinctness of the stripe of Gennari, which can be seen with the naked eye; hence this area is named also the "*area striata*." The boundaries of this area are perfectly sharp; the stripe appears suddenly, and the subdivision of the granular layer is also very sudden.

There are other instances of sudden transitions between one type of structure and the adjoining types; but as a rule, the transitions are less abrupt. The distinctions between neighbouring areas are based partly on the fusion or subdivision of layers, and partly on quantitative grounds, such as the thickness of the whole cortex and of the separate layers, the size and frequency of the cells, the calibre of the single fibres, and the density of the fibre network.

§ 41. Some of the areas thus marked out in terms of structure by the accompanying histological maps (Figs. 115 and 116) are

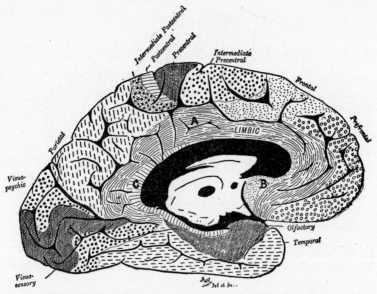

Fig. 116.—The Same, Mesial Surface. (Campbell.) Brodmann's map differs from this of Campbell in that it subdivides many of the areas into two or more.

already familiar in the localization of function. The precentral area, for example, coincides almost exactly with the motor area as delimited by Grünbaum and Sherrington; the only difference is that the excitable area extends a millimetre or two further forward than the area of giant pyramids. The *area striata* coincides with the visual area as marked out by the termination of the optic radiation, and hence is named by Campbell the "visuo-sensory" area; and there is an area in the temporal lobe corresponding to the end-station of the auditory fibres. This correspondence of differences of structure with the known differences in function lends force to the view that the other differences in structure, over parts of the cortex whose function is not known, may also be taken as indications of differences of function.

§ 42. It is a reasonable conjecture, then, that these structural maps of the cortex are functional maps as well. We cannot, indeed, as yet infer the function from the structure; but it is certainly significant that the motor area and the sensory areas present the appearance of fuller development than do most of the other areas. These other areas are also later in becoming myelinated in the individual, and later in making their appearance in the race. They are, therefore, probably concerned with functions which are less used and less essential than the elementary functions of sensation and movement.

Another important suggestion is afforded by the fact that it is possible to mark out areas which possess a nearly or quite uniform structure. The fact that a uniform structure exists over any considerable area of the cortex, giving place at its borders to areas of other structure, would seem plainly to indicate that within each area the elements have something in common in the manner of their functioning. Another fact may be brought forward, which points in the same direction. Rich provision seems to be made, both in the plexiform layer and by the dense plexuses in deeper layers, for causing neighboring cells to act together. It seems impossible, then, that the cells in these areas should be thrown into action singly; they must act in groups or neighborhoods. Some of these neighborhoods may, indeed, be microscopic in size, much smaller than the structural areas which are mapped out; also, it is probable that these neighborhoods are not sharply limited in extent, but that the co-operating cells, in any given function, are most active in a certain part of each neighborhood, and less and less active the further we go from this centre out. In this case, the neighborhoods concerned in different allied functions would certainly overlap.

If such a conception as the foregoing is even half-way true, contiguous spots of the cortex must possess related, and even overlapping functions; so that the transition from one function to another would be gradual over a certain area; and this area would accordingly be the seat of a certain *group or range of related functions*. Such considerations make it seem highly probable that the structural areas which the histologists have mapped out are, indeed, areas for different groups of functions.

§ 43. But what are the "groups of functions" which we have a right to expect to be thus localizable? As to this, little that is definite and satisfactory can be said at present. It is a question to the answer of which psychology must make the preliminary, directing if not determining, contribution. And the analysis of mental functions into their elements, in a manner suitable for physiological use, has scarcely been begun. The so-called "faculties" of memory, imagination, attention, and reasoning, are scarcely to be thought of in this connection. They are gross, unanalyzed terms of a popular psychology, having no claim to represent elementary functions of the mental life. The results of local injury to the cortex show that memory for visual objects is dependent on the integrity of the occipital lobes; for auditory objects, on the temporal lobes, etc.; and the same thing is true with respect to the imagining of these objects. As for attention, which some [1] have sought to localize in the frontal lobes, experience shows that any sort of thing may, on occasion, claim the attention and drive out, or inhibit, other claimants to control. In studying spinal inhibition (see pp. 172 f.) the fact was noted that different reflex functions exert a *mutually* inhibitory influence; any one can, on occasion, inhibit the others. But this is apparently the case with mental functions, when studied from the point of view of introspection, as well; any one can, on occasion, be dominant and inhibit others which are antagonistic to it. No one centre of attention, or of inhibition, can therefore be expected to be discovered. In general, instead of seeking to localize such so-called "faculties," it is necessary to start with complex and concrete acts and processes, and by a study of analysis discover the more simple and elementary acts and processes which have a value for the ends of physiological psychology. Such analysis, however, is extraordinarily difficult; and it is probable that in the future, as in the past, the efforts of normal psychology will need to be supplemented by the study of mutilated functions, as they are offered for observation by disease and injury.

In spite of the fact that it has, of late, been much decried and even ridiculed in certain quarters, we shall follow this method of careful and minute analysis in the part of the work to which we now proceed. In this part it is our purpose to point out certain more specific forms of correlation which exist between our psychical experiences and the functions of the nervous mechanism, when under different kinds and degrees of external stimulation and variously influenced by acquired habits and associations. But, first, it is in place to summarize our conclusions as to the mechanical nature of this system, taken as a whole.

[1] Most prominently Wundt, *Physiol. Psychol.*, 6th ed., 1908, I, 378.

CHAPTER XI

MECHANICAL THEORY OF THE NERVOUS SYSTEM

§ 1. The nature of the process by which the nervous system is developed, as well as the nature of the developed structure and its functions, so far as physical science can go at all, points in the direction of a mechanical theory. But in respect to both, such a theory is at present in an exceedingly fragmentary and uncertain condition. Further investigations may largely remove the present limitations. But the most complete theory possible can scarcely be more than a statement of the order and extent of physical changes, the real causes and meaning of which it lies beyond the power of a mechanical theory to give.

The impregnated ovum does, indeed, become converted into the developed organism by an evolution that, at every step in its course, appears as an alteration in the arrangement of material molecules, under conditions derived from the original nature of the molecules themselves, from their necessary relations to each other, and from the action of their total environment. By division of that which was single into several parts, by bending of that which was straight, by stretching in one direction and compressing elsewhere, by swelling and dilating in the various outlines under the influence of pressure, by folding and tucking in so as to close up an opening here and form another there, by laying down cells of the same kind in right lines or grouping them in masses, etc.—in brief, by motion of particles of matter in such a way that the motion of each is conditioned upon that of the others, the nervous mechanism is built up. What it can accomplish in the way of further molecular motion, after it is thus built up, depends of course in large measure upon what it is made to be by the very process of building. How far it is possible even to propound a mechanical theory of the building process belongs to the speculations of embryologists to consider. It is our problem, at present, to consider as a whole the few data upon which it has been thought possible to base a mechanical theory of the behavior of the nervous system after it has once been constructed as a result of the embryonic process.

§ 2. The machine-like nature of much of the structure and movement of the human body does not escape the most ordinary observation. When this body, either as a whole or with respect to some of its parts, changes its position in space, its various masses support and act upon each other in essentially the same manner as the masses of matter which compose the parts of any machine constructed by human skill. Such movement is possible for it, because its framework of bones has a rigidity sufficient to sustain the other less rigid organs; and because the bones are so divided, and yet articulated, that they can assume different relations toward one another in accordance with the simplest principles of mechanics. The laws of the lever, of the pulley, the ball-and-socket joint, etc., need no modification when applied to this particular machine of the human body.

The action of certain other of its parts, which do not belong to the bony framework but which are of muscular or epithelial structure, is also plainly of the same machine-like character. The movement of the heart, for example, is in part to be explained as that of a pump with chambers and valves; and the flow of the blood through the arteries as that of a fluid pumped through conduits, of unlike and changeable sizes. So, too, the lungs may be, with considerable propriety, compared to bellows which alternately suck in and expel the surrounding atmosphere. The optics of the eye and the acoustics of the ear are special only so far as the structure of the organs makes necessary a special application of the general laws of those sciences. Moreover, the distribution of the fluids among the tissues of the body takes place—in part, at least, if in part only—under the laws which govern the distribution of fluids generally when separated by membranes which they can permeate. Nor is the chemistry of the same tissues and fluids by any means wholly unlike that with which the experiments of the laboratory make us familiar. When, however, we begin to speak of those changes of relative position which take place at extremely minute distances among the molecular elements of which the larger masses of the body are composed, we seem compelled to drop the conception of a *machine* and to seek both another conception and another title.

The very attempt, then, to explain the motion of the more purely machine-like parts of the human body, leads us to consider certain activities of other parts for which the word "mechanism" is more appropriate. The movement of none of the more or less rigid organs of the body originates within these organs themselves. The changes of relative position in the parts, with which the ordinary laws of mechanics deal, imply antecedent molecular changes in other parts with which these laws cannot deal. The motion which finds its final expression in the swing of the arm, or of the leg, in the lifting of a weight, and even in the contraction of the heart, or in the rising and falling of the chest, does not begin in arm, or leg, or ribs, or diaphragm, or cardiac muscles. The change of position of so considerable masses of matter is but the summing-up of innumerable minute molecular changes which began within the body, but outside of the masses themselves. If, for example, we inquire as to what causes the bones to move—however strictly their motion, once begun, may follow the laws of mechanics—the answer is to be found in the pull of the tendons, or cord-like structures, which are attached to them. And if we then inquire, What causes the tendons to pull upon the bones by means of their attachment? the answer must be, That it is the contraction of the muscles which pulls upon the tendons.

The next step in following this chain of causes, however, introduces us to a different class of considerations from any of the foregoing. For we cannot say that the contraction of the muscles is caused by the pull of the nerves upon them. The movement of muscular fibre in contraction is an altogether different affair from the movement of the bones as they are pulled by the muscles; nor do the nerves act upon the muscles as the muscles act upon the tendons. The elasticity of the muscles is, indeed, a mechanical quality, like that of which we avail ourselves in the construction of machines. But the quality of elasticity does not fully explain the behavior of the so-called muscle-nerve machine when its muscular tissue is contracting or relaxing. Yet the living muscle, in itself considered, may certainly be looked upon as a molecular *mechanism*. It is a system of minute particles of matter which act upon each other at indefinitely small distances; and which, when any motion is set up at one part of it, propagates such motion according to laws that are given in the very constitution and arrangement of the particles themselves. This is precisely what we understand by a physical molecular mechanism. The office of the nerve with respect to the muscle is simply, as we know, to start that molecular activity which it is the function of the irritated muscle itself to exercise. The nerve, however, cannot perform its office of irritating the muscle without being in a state of molecular commotion called the "excitement" of the nerve. And, further, this excited condition of that part of the nerve which is in immediate contact with the muscle is itself a state of the nerve which has been propagated from a distant point of the nervous matter. All the machine-like movements of the masses of the body require us, therefore, to look for their origin in minute molecular changes that originate in its *nervous elements*. And for the further account of these neural molecular changes we are to look to a mechanical theory of the nervous system.

§ 3. The basis for a general view of the nervous system as a mechanism has been laid in all the preceding examination; and it cannot be denied that the results of this examination are such as to dispose us favorably toward the attempt to develop such a view into a complete mechanical theory. Physical science, as a matter of course, strives to establish such a theory. It knows no other way of considering any group of phenomena when brought before it for examination. To deny totally the application of the conception of a mechanism to the action of the nervous system would be to refuse to apply to its phenomena the same scientific treatment which we apply to all other physical phenomena. To limit, *a priori*, such application would be to restrict improperly, on merely theoretical grounds, the area of the phenomena with which such science is entitled to deal. The fact that molecular changes here are correlated with another class of phenomena which we call "mental," in no wise destroys the propriety of pushing our physical science of the nervous system to its furthest possible limits. The movements of all material bodies, whether in the elemental shape of the molecules, or in the shape of the same molecules when aggregated into masses, as well as the laws under which such bodies in movement act and react upon each other, constitute the legitimate sphere of physical science. But it is to a system of interacting molecules that the conception of mechanism especially applies. The aim of physical research with regard to any given system of this kind is, therefore, not accomplished until all the movements of its different parts are explained in the light of a consistent mechanical theory. This general principle of all physical science neither needs nor permits a special exception in the case of the human nerves, organs of sense, and brain.

On the other hand, the very unsatisfactory condition of the data for a mechanical theory of the human nervous system has been implied in each of the preceding chapters. It will appear all the more plainly now as we present briefly a statement of two or three such theories in the form in which it has been found possible for different investigators to state and to defend them. Nor can we express much confidence that physics and physiology combined will ever be able to point to a complete theory of so intricate and delicate a mechanism as this nervous system. Moreover, we do not by any means affirm that a purely mechanical treatment, however complete, would of itself suffice to furnish a satisfactory understanding of all the phenomena; or even that the phenomena in general could by any possibility be brought solely under the terms of such treatment. We only affirm the unrestricted right of physical science to attempt, in the light of the conception of mechanism, an explanation of the nervous system as well as of all other physical objects; and also its right to its persistent faith that—*So far as physical science can explain any object,* all the special difficulties of the nervous system can be fitly considered only in this way.

§ 4. The *chemical constitution* and *structural form* of the elements of nervous matter require that the system which they compose should be regarded in the light of the conception of mechanism.   It is true that physical science cannot give an accurate description of the chemical processes which take place in the formation of the nerve-fibres and nerve-cells, or during their functional activity; it cannot do so much as this for the living tissues generally.   But it finds here the same chemical elements which exist elsewhere in nature, especially the four elements, oxygen, hydrogen, nitrogen, and carbon.   It nowhere finds these elements behaving differently in the nervous system from the way in which it is their nature to behave elsewhere, under similar circumstances.   And the fact that precisely similar circumstances do not occur to induce the same combination and interaction of these elements outside of the nervous system, is traced back to its causes in a succession of occurrences that all have the character belonging to the chemistry of living tissues.   We know of no sap which is suitable for forming organisms in general, but which is itself a perfectly homogeneous fluid.   Nucleated granules in the very chemical constituents which give conditions to all the subsequent activity of the molecules, are revealed by microscopic examination of those cells from which the whole body springs.   This fact, together with the character of the subsequent process, may lead some to insist that a certain special form of energy (called "vital force," or by some less obnoxious title) is marshalling the minute particles under its superior control.   But such way of considering the phenomena—whether admissible or inadmissible—does not at all help us to dispense with the purely mechanical point of view.   In the original living germ with which the organism began, and in all its subsequent development, every chemical change in nervous matter is nothing more than a movement of physical molecules, strictly under the conditions furnished by their constitution and previous arrangement.

§ 5. The general significance of the form and chemical constitution of the nervous tissue is by no means wholly obscure.   Especially is this true in regard to the form of the minute structures which compose the system.   The long wire-like form of the nerve-fibre is understood by reference to its function of conduction.   Since the nerve-fibre does nothing which is directly beneficial to the body, but simply serves to transmit "impulses" which shall arouse activity in the muscles and other effective organs, the smaller the size

of the nerve-fibre, the better. Within the central organs, the rami-
fying of the fine branches of the fibre and of the cell seems fitted for
the function which the centres are known to exert,—namely that of
providing for co-ordinated action, and also for action which can
vary according to circumstances.[1]

In regard to chemical composition, less is perhaps known that
affords an insight into the mechanism of nervous activity. The
protoplasmic portions of the cell-body, dendrites and axon, seem to
differ only in minor respects from the protoplasm of other tissues.
The lipoids of the sheath seem to play a part as insulators or non-
conductors.

§ 6. There can be no doubt that the *arrangement of the nervous
elements* into a system corresponds to the conception of mechanism.
A certain work of *concatenating* the different physical systems of
the body, and of adjusting its relations to the changes in its environment, requires to be accomplished. This problem demands a
three-fold exercise of function; it is a problem in the construction
of a mechanism. The nervous system actually is of threefold construction; its threefold construction is the answer which it practically makes to the above-mentioned problem. One part of the
complex problem consists in the conversion of certain of those
molecular motions which take place in nature outside of the living
organism into molecular motion within the tissues of such organism.
The solution of this part of the problem is furnished by the end-
organs of the nervous system. The end-organs are those special
mechanisms which are adapted to convert the molecular motions
called stimuli into the molecular motions called neural excitation.
That by far the larger portion of the eye and ear, for example, acts
in a purely mechanical way, there is no doubt. It is the office of
the great mass of the eye to transmit and refract the rays of light;
of the ear to transmit and condense the acoustic waves. But when
the nervous elements of the retina and of the organ of Corti receive the physical processes transmitted to them, they transmute
these physical processes into physiological neural processes; in
doing this they act as special molecular mechanisms.

The second part of the complex problem before the nervous system consists in the conduction in all necessary directions of these
neural processes; only on this condition can distant parts of the
nervous system act, as it were, in view of each other, and thus the

[1] It is true that we cannot describe the peculiar place in the mechanism, or the
specific chemistry—if such there be—which belong to the different locations and
shapes of nerve-cells, bipolar, multipolar, stellate, etc. But all that we are learning about the minute structure and detailed functions of the nervous elements
seems to indicate that these more obvious mechanical characteristics are *of
value* in the entire complex working of the nervous system.

whole body be bound into a living unity under the influence of changes in its environment, and in the ideas and impulses of the mind. The nerve-fibres solve this part of the problem. This they do by acting as mechanisms, which have such a molecular constitution and function that a commotion, started at any point in the physical elements of the system, spreads from molecule to molecule, in accordance with the laws of the system.

The third part of the same complex problem requires for its solution structures and functions still more intricate and inexplicable. Incoming molecular disturbances must be modified and redistributed so as to give rise to outgoing molecular disturbances along definite tracts, in order that definite groups of muscles may be made to contract. Only in this way can the whole physical organism, by a so-called reflex activity, adjust its condition, in view of the presence of given kinds and degrees of stimuli. Moreover, the vital functions the movements that control respiration, digestion, circulation of the blood and of other fluids, etc.—must be united so as to work to a common end, and with the modified forms and degrees of their respective energies, which the changing circumstances require. Still further, not only must the neural processes set up by the end-organs and conducted inward by the afferent nerves have a place of meeting in proximity with the centres of origin for the corresponding efferent impulses; but all the neural processes in this place of meeting must also be so modified and made mutually dependent that they can be correlated, under psycho-physical laws, with the processes of mind. It is the central organs which alone possess the molecular construction and functions necessary for such wonderful reflex and automatic activities. In their highest form— the hemispheres of the human brain—they solve the problem of providing a system of molecules, whose constitution and changes may be immediately related with the phenomena of mind. These central organs are extremely intricate physical structures. It cannot be pretended that even a beginning has been made toward a satisfactory theory of their functional activity considered as a special case in molecular physics. But this fact does not affect the confidence which is based upon what is known of physical structures in general, that in these organs, the changes which take place are essentially of the same order as are those with which the science of molecular physics has elsewhere to deal. They are modes of motion in which the behavior of each molecule, regarded as a constituent element of the system, is conditioned upon the constitution and behavior of the other members of the same system. That is to say, the central organs must be regarded in the light of the conception of mechanism.

§ 7. The general office of the nervous system may, then, be described in somewhat the following manner. The development of a rich and varied life, both animal and intellectual, requires a great store of sensations and of motions. The sensations are primarily designed to serve as signs of changes in the environment of the animal to which his condition must be adapted by movement of his bodily parts; but they are also to serve as a basis for intellectual attainment and development. The forces of external nature continually storm the peripheral parts of the animal's body. In order that any of these forces may act as the stimuli of sensations, they must be converted into molecular motions within the tissues of this body. In order, further, that the masses of the body may constantly be readjusted to the external changes of which the sensations are signs, the molecular motions must, in turn, be converted into movements of these masses. In other words, a process of constant interchange must take place between the animal organism and external nature.

Disturbances in one part of the body, by the play upon it of nature's energy, instead of becoming injurious or destructive, are thus made serviceable through inducing the needed disturbances of other parts of the same body. The equilibrium on which life depends is maintained. Moreover, the material necessary for self-conscious development, for a growing knowledge of the so-called outside world, is furnished through the conduction of these disturbances to their common meeting-places in the central organs. The nervous system, especially in its supreme central organs, must therefore be the kind of mechanism that can—so to say—be " trained " into co-ordinated forms of action, so as to serve as a basis for the mental activities involved in processes of learning.

§ 8. To accomplish the general work of *equilibrating the interaction of the different parts of the body*, of readjusting its condition to the changing condition of its surroundings, some special construction and arrangement of material molecules is necessary. If the work is to be done in a highly elaborate way, a very intricate arrangement of an indefinitely great number of chemically complex molecules is necessary. Such an arrangement is the human nervous system. But just because its arrangement and function are of this kind, it is a *"mechanism."* As a highly complex molecular mechanism it utilizes the disturbances which arise from the environment. It binds together all the other systems of the body in living reciprocity of energies and functions. Its superficial parts are so constructed that they can be set in motion by various forms of physical energy—by light, heat, sound, chemical change, etc.; they are also adapted fitly to modify the impressions thus received.

The molecules of its conducting nerves are so constituted and arranged that they can indicate the path along which the disturbance thus occasioned must pass; they can dictate the conditions and laws under which its course must be completed. The molecules of its central organs are capable of assuming inconceivably varied relations to each other, of thus transmuting and redistributing the nerve-commotions which reach them along the incoming tracts, and even (it would seem) of starting automatically outgoing disturbances in response to self-conscious sensations and ideas.

But all the foregoing offices of the nervous system are nothing but the movements of physical elements, in constant reciprocal dependence upon each other, though in response to excitations lying outside of the system itself. To move thus is the function of a molecular mechanism. So far as science can control the different parts of the nervous system for experimental purposes, it finds them behaving in such a manner as to make a plain demand for a physical and mechanical theory in explanation of their behavior.

§ 9. The foregoing description of the nervous system as a mechanism, like all similar descriptions, undoubtedly lacks scientific quality. It is neither exact nor in such form as to admit of experimental verification. It is largely based upon conjectures, full of gaps and assumptions; and were it pressed at every point for proof, it would be obliged to rely much upon general principles in mechanics (the special applications of which to the case in hand are by no means certain or obvious), and even to indulge in hopes and promises with reference to the future rather than present demonstration. May we not know more precisely the nature of the molecular changes which constitute the functions of nerve-fibres and nerve-cells? Cannot physical science help us to complete these beginnings of a theory?

§ 10. In answering the question just raised, we have to consider separately the case of the nerve-fibre and that of the nerve-centre. The former is much the simpler problem, and there is more of experimental knowledge to form the basis of a theory for its solution. In a preceding chapter (pp. 135 ff.) we noted the disagreement between physiologists as to whether the activity of a nerve is to be conceived of as a chemical process, which involves the consumption of fuel, and the setting free of potential energy; or whether, on the contrary, the nerve impulse is a purely physical process, like the transmission of a wave over the surface of water, or of electricity along a wire. It appears that in the former case, the amount of catabolism in the nerve must be exceedingly slight, and the recovery of the fibre exceedingly prompt. This absence of signs of chemical change in the active nerve, we then saw, has led a group of physi-

ologists to regard the nerve-impulse as an electrical affair, similar
to a movement of ions along a "core conductor." In the interest
of reconciling these views it was suggested (foot-note, p. 143) that a
mechanical theory of the nerves and their functions, which shall account for all the phenomena, is entirely feasible and consistent with
what is known of chemical change, as related to electrical conduction,
in other cases. It is a reasonable hope, then, that in the not distant
future the facts of "summation," "interference," "facilitation," etc.,
may be statable in terms of such a combination theory. It is significant that these very terms are applicable only to phenomena
which admit of a mechanical explanation.

§ 11. Bound up with this is the further question, whether the
nerve-impulse in all nerve-fibres is of the same quality; or whether
different nerves have different "specific energies," to use a term
introduced by the celebrated physiologist, Johannes Müller. Müller called attention[1] to the fact that the optic nerve, whether excited
normally through the action of light on the retina, or artificially by
the passage of an electric current through the forehead, or by a blow
on the head, always gives rise to a sensation of light. Similarly,
each of the sensory nerves, however excited, gives rise to a specific
sensation. He accordingly interpreted these facts to mean that
"Either the nerves themselves may communicate impressions
different in quality to the sensorium"—or brain—"which in every
instance remains the same; or else the vibrations of the nervous
principle may in every nerve be the same and yet give rise to the
perception of different sensations in the sensorium, owing to the
parts of the latter with which the nerves are connected having different properties. The proof of either of these propositions I regard as at present impossible." Müller, however, inclined to the
former opinion—namely, that each sensory nerve has an action peculiar to it, a "specific energy," differing from the energy of all
other nerves. With the progress of the study of the nerves, the apparent similarity in the action of all of them has led most physiologists to the second member of the alternative, according to which
the specific quality is no longer believed to inhere in the action of
nerve-fibres, but rather in the organs, central or peripheral, with
which they are connected. Thus, in the case of motor nerves, the
nerve-fibres which run to the biceps muscle seem not to differ in
their mode of action from the fibres running to the triceps, or to
any other muscle. These nerves are, accordingly, regarded as indifferent conductors; and the difference in the motor results of their
activity is believed to inhere simply in the muscles to which they

[1] In 1844, in his *Physiology*. See the English translation, 1848, pp. 1059 ff.

lead, and in the attachments of these muscles to the bones. This may be affirmed to be true, in general, of motor nerve-fibres.

§ 12. Strong additional evidence in favor of this view is obtained by "crossing" two nerves. If, for example, the nerve A leads to the muscle *a*, and nerve B to muscle *b*, and if both nerves are cut, and the central end of A sutured to the peripheral end of B, and *vice versa*, then, after time has been allowed for the regeneration of the peripheral ends, nerve A excites muscle *b*, and nerve B muscle *a*, so that muscle *a* contracts when muscle *b* should contract, and *vice versa*. That is to say, the impulses issue from the nerve-centres in the normal way, but, the nerves being crossed, the impulses are conveyed to the wrong muscle. It appears, however, that, with practice, a fair degree of co-ordination can be newly learned. But the conclusion from the experiment, from our present point of view, is that nerves are capable of exciting other muscles than those to which they normally lead. The motor nerves are thus, to a large degree at least, interchangeable, and have no specific energies of their own, but differ, as was said, only in their connections.

In regard to the sensory nerves, equally conclusive evidence does not seem to be at hand; but the prevalent view is, probably, that the action of the fibres of the optic nerve differs in no essential respect from the action of the fibres of the auditory nerve, or of other sensory nerves; the same principle, therefore, holds here as in the case of the motor nerves—namely, that the difference between them lies in their connections. In the case of the sensory nerves, the connections to be considered are central—the connections of the incoming sensory fibres with motor fibres or with central cells. The differences in conscious sensation between the sensory nerves would, accordingly, be associated with differences, not in these nerves themselves, but with differences in the cortical centres to which these nerves lead. Visual sensations, that is, would result from the activity of the visual area, no matter by what means it is excited; and the same for the other sensory areas. It has been objected by Hering[1] that transferring the specific quality from the nerves to the sensory areas does not make the differences between sensations any more intelligible, and that our methods of studying nerve-fibres are much too crude to detect fine differences in the character of their activity, should such exist. The objection does not, however, counterbalance the evidence derived from more recent cases of anastomosis, where mixed nerves are involved. For it has been found that, when the juncture between the cut ends of the two nerves is made perfect, and time is allowed for healing

[1] *Zur Theorie der Nerventätigkeit* (Leipzig, 1899).

and for the effects of practice, both the sensory and the motor functions of such a nerve can be performed by another nerve, whose normal connections commit it to quite a different and even distant area of the body (compare p. 243).

§ 13. In regard to the mechanism of the nerve-centres, a considerable change of opinion seems to be taking place in the minds of students on the subject. In the early days after the microscope had revealed the cell elements in the gray matter, and after the fact was established that the gray matter constituted the real central organs of the nervous system, it seemed almost self-evident that the nerve-cells were the essential structures of the nerve-centres; and that, therefore, the mechanics of the centres was the mechanics of the nerve-cell. These cells were regarded as exercising control over the motor nerves and so over the muscles, much as a general, seated in his tent, exercises control over an army. *Co-ordination* was supposed to be the special function of the nerve-cells. They were also believed to contain large stores of potential energy which they, at the time of their activity, discharged along the nerve-fibres leading from them. The cells in the sensory areas of the brain were regarded as the essential termini of the sensory nerves, and the activity of these and other cells in the brain was supposed to be correlated with consciousness. Memories were spoken of, metaphorically, as being "stored" in the cell;—the meaning being that modification of the cells by any experience is the physical condition of the later revival of the experience. In all respects, the nerve-cells were regarded as the organs of reflex and mental activities.

§ 14. With the progress of histology, it became evident, however, that the nerve-cells are only a part of the gray matter, and, in bulk, a small part. The branches of the cells were seen to be fully as characteristic a feature of the gray matter, and to fill much more of the cranial space. As the conception of the nerve-fibres and their branches as conductors gained precision, the view came into prominence, that the connections established by the fine branches of cells in the gray matter are the important fact. This view assigns more importance to the branches by which the connections are made than to the cell-bodies themselves. The neurone conception, too (see pp. 110 ff.), added force to the same view; for it holds that the branches of the different cells simply come into contact or close proximity with each other, so that the surfaces of contact would be, in all probability, the most critical points in the system of nervous communication. Within any one neurone, all parts—cell-body, axon, and dendrites—are in continuity, and apparently conduction is free throughout. Between one neurone and another, conduction is less free, because of the lack of perfect continuity. Nerve-impulses must indeed pass from one neurone to another; but the passage would probably be more difficult than from one part to another of a single neurone. Therefore the delay which occurs in the transmission of a nerve-impulse through a nerve-centre is localized in the passage from one neurone to another. That is, the delay occurs at the "synapse."

§ 15. Now, delay in transmission is a type of several of the peculiarities of central nervous action. One of these is the "blocking" of nerve-impulses. In general, this seems due to the fact that the impulse can pass from the terminal branches of an axon over to the dendrites of another cell, but not in the reverse direction. This fact means that the synapse is the place at which such a peculiarity of central conduction occurs. Oftentimes, also, an impulse is blocked in the forward direction. This is the case when anæsthetics act on the centres; and since nerve-centres are more susceptible than nerves to the action of ether, chloroform, and alcohol, the probability is that the loss of function brought on by anæsthetics is due to the blocking of the synapse. Still other instances of blocking a nerve impulse on its way through a nerve-centre are seen in the phenomena of inhibition; and here, again, the continuity of structure between the various parts of a neurone makes the view probable that all these blocks occur at the place of separation between one neurone and another. In fine, it seems possible to conceive of the action of the nerve-centres as a process of the transmission of nerve-impulses that is subject to the peculiarities of central conduction.[1] Most of these peculiarities can be stated in terms of resistance—resistance in general high, but variable with many conditions. If the highest resistance in the path of a nerve-impulse through the centre lies at the synapse, then this would be the critical and typical part of the centre. Thus, for example, memory would not consist so much in a modification of the cell-bodies as in the improvement of synaptic connections between different cells.

§ 16. Our reasoning on this subject, it is admitted, has about it much that is vague and uncertain. It is founded partly on the apparent structure of the gray matter, and partly on the conception of nerve-action as being essentially that of conduction. There are, however, a few experiments which throw additional light on the mechanism of the nerve-cells. If nerve function, even in the gray matter, is essentially conduction, then the cell-bodies might be dispensed with, were it not for the fact that they are usually interposed between dendrites and axon, and so form a link in the chain of conduction; and were it not for the further fact, that they are

[1] For a fuller account of these peculiarities, see Sherrington, *Integrative Action of the Nervous System*, p. 11.

certainly necessary for the nutrition and continued life of all parts of the neurone. If, however, the cell-bodies could be cut out of a nerve-centre without interrupting the continuity between the dendrites of each cell and the axon, such an operation would not necessarily at once destroy the function of the nerve-centre. Even the conception of such an operation seems wild enough when only the vertebrate cord and brain are considered; but in some invertebrates the motor neurones are unipolar—dendrites and axon being directly continuous—while the cell-body, with its nucleus, lies off to the side, connected with the rest by a slender strand. In the crab, for example, the cell-bodies are bunched together at the outside of each ganglion, and can be destroyed without seriously injuring the axons and dendrites with their fine branches and connections. The experiment has been tried by Bethe,[1] with the very striking result that the reflex functions of a ganglion are retained after its cell-bodies have been removed. To be sure, the function is not retained permanently in the absence of the cells, but it is retained for a few days; and even if it were only retained for a few hours, the evidence would be conclusive to show that *normal activity of the ganglion can occur without the presence of nerve-cells.* Accordingly the activity of a nerve-centre is not essentially the activity of the cell-bodies in it. The evidence applies in the first instance only to the crab, but we have nothing of a contrary teaching in regard to vertebrates.

§ 17. If, then, the query should be raised anew as to what is the function of the nerve-cells, the answer may be found by recalling that the condition of the centre slowly deteriorates after the removal of the cell-bodies. A nerve-fibre, too, when cut off from its cell of origin, undergoes degeneration. Similar facts are true of other than nervous tissue. The nucleus of a cell is necessary to the nutrition and good condition of the whole cell, and any part severed from the nucleus suffers and usually degenerates. Now the cell-body of a neurone—the "cell" as we usually call it—is principally distinguished as the part of the neurone containing the nucleus. We may then be sure that the cell-body has the highly important function of serving the nutrition of the whole neurone; it is necessary for maintaining the axon and dendrites in proper condition for work, even though it may take no peculiar part in the actual doing of the work.

§ 18. If we accept the view that the synapse is the locus of the most important peculiarities of central function, our inquiry becomes: Is it possible to form a reasonable conception of the mechanics

---

[1] "Das Zentralnervensystem von Carcinus Maenas," in *Archiv. f. mikroscop. Anatomie*, 1897, L, 629 ff.

of the synapse? In answer to this question, a theory which has the merit of simplicity and tangibility has been put forward by Duval[1] and others. Duval supposes that the fine branches of axons and dendrites, which by their close proximity to each other form the synapse, have the power of motility, in much the same way as that shown by the amœba (compare pp. 14 f.). As, then, the amœba puts out temporary branches, but retracts them under certain conditions, so, according to this theory, the fine branches of axons and dendrites can be thrust out under certain conditions and retracted under others. When they are thrust out they come into closer contact; when they are retracted they separate. As the conduction across a synapse would naturally be better the closer the contact between the branches forming it, the protrusion of the branches would mean better conduction through the centre, and the retraction of them poorer conduction, or even a blocking of the path. Special application of this theory has been made to the case of unconsciousness from anæsthetics or from fatigue. It has been claimed that the retraction of the dendrites would block the path of impulses, and thus reactions to stimuli would be prevented. The promoters of this theory also believed they had evidence that the fine branches of the dendrites were shorter in animals subjected to ether, than in animals killed suddenly without the use of anæsthetics. In general, however, the evidence is against any power of motility in the nerve-cell or its branches; and the theory does not command the assent of the best authorities. It may, however, serve a useful purpose as giving a sort of rough diagram of what goes on in the synapse. There need be no actual motion of the branches as wholes; but there may be molecular motions within them, or chemical changes within them, which would have the same effect of increasing or decreasing the conductivity of the synapse.

§19. In view of the attractiveness of the electrical theory, as applied to the nerve-fibre, it will be of much interest to see whether the same theory can be extended to give a reasonable account of the action of the synapse. This has been attempted with considerable success by Sherrington[2]. There is a certain degree of discontinuity at the synapse; it is a boundary between cells, as is seen in this fact, among others, that the degeneration which occurs in a nerve-fibre on being separated from its cell-body extends to the fine branches of that fibre, but does not pass over the synapse into another neurone. The synapse is a cell boundary, or surface of separation between cells. It should have, therefore, the physical

---

[1] *Comptes rendus de la Société de Biologie*, 1895, p. 74.
[2] *Integrative Action of the Nervous System*, 1906, pp. 15–18.

properties of other cell boundaries, one of the most important of which (see above, p. 14) is the resistance interposed by it to free diffusion and to the passage of electricity. The position of the synapse as such a boundary would therefore account for the fundamental fact that conduction through a nerve-centre is less free than along the nerve-fibre. The allied facts mentioned above regarding the peculiarities of conduction through the nerve-centres are susceptible of possible explanation in the same terms. The strange fact of the irreversibility of conduction through a nerve-centre becomes a little less mysterious when it is recalled that some degree of irreversibility of diffusion is characteristic of cell boundaries. The fact that ether, chloroform, etc., have a powerful effect on conduction through nerve-centres is also partly cleared up by the well-known influence of these chemical substances on cell membranes. Cell boundaries can have their permeability altered by many causes, and their variability in this respect may well be brought forward in explanation of the variability of conductivity through a nerve-centre.

The synapse or cell-boundary theory of the action of nerve-centres seems, therefore, when worked out in detail, to be more capable of giving an expression in physico-chemical terms to most of the known peculiarities of central function than any other theory which has been put forward.

§ 20. Of other theories,[1] the most prominent have conceived the action of nerve-centres as essentially a chemical and metabolic process, and have laid stress on assimilation and dissimilation, or anabolism and catabolism, as the fundamental processes involved. The most thoroughly worked out of these metabolic theories are those of Wundt[2] and of Verworn.[3] It does not seem possible, with present knowledge, to fit these theories to the details of the function of nerve-centres so nicely as has been done for the cell membrane theory. As affecting all these theories, the fundamental question concerns the evidence of catabolism in central activity. This is the same question which was raised before in regard to the activity of the nerves (pp. 135 ff.); but the answer here would seem, at first, to be very different from that reached in the case of the nerves. There, the evidence showed unmistakably that the catabolism of the nerve-fibres is, at most, very small in amount. In the case of

---

[1] See a critical discussion of the theories of central function by Bethe, in *Ergebnisse der Physiologie*, 1906, V, 250–288.

[2] *Untersuchungen zur Mechanik der Nerven und Nervenzentren*, 1876; and in the successive editions of his *Physiologische Psychologie*.

[3] See the chapter, "Vom Mechanismus des Lebens," in the various editions of his *Allgemeine Physiologie*, and also many special papers.

the centres, however, the prevailing view has been that much ca-. tabolism occurs during their activity. Perhaps the chief fact in favor of this view is the rich blood supply of the brain and cord, and the great dependence of their functions on their blood supply. Stoppage of the arteries to the brain results in speedy unconsciousness. The brain must have blood, must have plenty of oxygen. And it uses up this oxygen, for the blood returning from the brain by the veins has been deprived of its oxygen. The conclusion seems almost self-evident that this oxygen was used by the brain in processes of combustion; and that much combustion was needed to supply the energy consumed in brain activity. But the matter is not so simple. For much blood circulates through the brain even in conditions of mental quiescence, sleep, in anæsthesia; and even in these conditions the blood returning from the brain has lost much of its oxygen and become venous. Respiration experiments on men performing hard mental work have failed to detect any increase in the consumption of oxygen, or in the production of carbon dioxide, over the amounts consumed and produced, respectively, in conditions of rest.[1] Other tests for the consumption of oxygen by brain work have yielded no conclusive evidence. On the whole, it seems that brain work is not a strongly catabolic process, and that the mechanics of brain activity, and of nerve-centre activity in general, is of the same general sort as the mechanics of the nerves. All this is, however, no conclusive argument against our recognizing the evidence for the view that chemical processes in the form of catabolism, are an essential part of the mechanics of the nervous system. And modern discoveries are constantly showing more clearly what enormous amounts of promptly available energy may be stored in very small amounts of material substance. Among such kinds of substance, the structure of the nerve-fibres and cells seems to have a distinguished, if not a pre-eminent position.

§ 21. Our main contention—namely, that science must view the structure of the nervous system in the light of a mechanism, and its functions as a species of mechanics, in the most vague and general meaning of these terms—would not be in the least impaired or altered, if it should continue forever impossible to explain the phenomena in terms of pure chemistry and physics. Let it be found necessary to revive the conception of "vital force," or of a considerable group of so-called "vital forces." This would not at all essentially change the conditions of the problem. Structural changes in material substances, and forces assumed to account for the performances of such substances, can be described and explained

[1] Atwater, *Ergebnisse der Physiologie*, 1904, III, part 1, pp. 609 ff.

only in terms of a mechanical theory. Considered as a mechanism, the human brain, with its marvellous outfit of fibres and cells, is no more worthy to be dubbed spiritual, or have applied to it terms that are derived from the phenomena of consciousness, than are the most obvious and grossest forms of matter.

§ 22. Our review of the various molecular theories proposed to account for the nervous mechanism, either as a whole or in any of its parts, has made plain the important fact that such theories are all obliged to assume the origin and continuance of a peculiar molecular structure for this mechanism. In other words, no attempt to explain how the nervous system *acts* can avoid the conclusion that the determining factor in the explanation must be found in what the nervous system *is*. The physiological functions of the nerve depart when the nerve dies. The nerve dies when it is severed from the ganglion-cell. Both cell and nerve must, therefore, constitute a living molecular unity, in order that their normal physiological functions may be performed. The explanation of these functions assumes the molecular constitution of the organs themselves. But how shall we explain, in accordance with the known laws of molecular physics, the origin and preservation of such a molecular constitution? It is the business of biology rather than of physiology to attempt an answer to this question. But the question itself asks from science the performance of a task no smaller than that of framing a mechanical theory of life. Biological science can, as yet, do little toward framing such a theory. Throughout our entire discussion of the nervous mechanism we have carefully avoided raising any inquiry as to the nature of life, as to the source and conditions of that very molecular constitution which determines the nature and working of this mechanism. We have simply assumed and argued that, taking the nervous system for what it really is and really does, its structure and functions admit of scientific explanation, so far as such explanation is possible at all, only when they are regarded as belonging to a molecular mechanism. The question of a mechanical theory for the origin and constitution of living organisms in general lies outside of the inquiries of Physiological Psychology.

§ 23. One other important question has also thus far been avoided. What is the relation of the mind to the working of the nervous mechanism? Can the mind set this molecular mechanism at work, or can it in any way determine the character of its functions? As far as our consideration of the nervous system has gone hitherto, all might very well have been the same without the existence of a single act of conscious thought or feeling occurring in any relation whatever to this system. Given the molecular mechanism as it is constituted and conserved by the forces which control as long as life continues; and given the necessary impact of outside forces upon the end-organs, and the proper changes of blood within the central organs; and it has been assumed that this mechanism would exercise its functions in ways thus far described. But the consideration of another class of phenomena is now to be introduced; these are the phenomena of human consciousness, the phenomena of *Mind*. The question whether such phenomena can be true causes of any of the changes in the molecular mechanism is a part of the general question as to the correlations that exist between two classes of facts. The answer to such general question belongs to the following divisions of our work.

PART SECOND

CORRELATIONS OF THE NERVOUS MECHANISM AND MENTAL PHENOMENA

CHAPTER I

THE QUALITY OF SENSATIONS

§ 1. A considerable change in the point of view, and a corresponding change in the methods of investigation, will be found necessary for effective treatment of the subjects which are to occupy our attention from this time onward. Thus far we have endeavored, as much as the nature of the subject made possible, to look at the nervous system from a purely objective point of view, and to arrive at an understanding of its structure and functions by employing the methods of the physico-chemical and biological sciences. In a word, this system has been examined as a material mechanism, which like everything known to human minds, must be known in terms of the human consciousness, but which may be known, as other material structures are known, without any preconceived opinions, or preconceived theories, as to its special relations to this consciousness. Viewed in this way, the nervous mechanism is an *object*—to have its constitution determined by the dissecting knife, the microscope, and the various means for physical and chemical analysis; while its functions consist of molecular changes and chemical processes, that are in all important respects assumed to be like those with which science is familiar in other living bodies.

It can scarcely have escaped observation, however, that this promise to keep clear of all the more strictly psychological implications and complications has not been completely fulfilled. And, indeed, no amount of painstaking, or even of distinct aversion to all that has a remote connection with psychological topics, could possibly have resulted in its complete fulfilment. No treatise of the human nervous mechanism is possible, that does not admit somewhat freely implications derived from the science which has for its subject-matter the mind's conscious states; or that does not adopt some provisional attitude toward a number of complicated psychological problems. And in giving the results of modern researches as to the functions of certain parts of the nervous system, the language which it is found necessary to employ is, strictly considered, often much more psychological than physiological.

Examples illustrating our contention will readily occur to any one who passes before his mind in review the descriptions given,

297

theories favored, and laws demonstrated, in Part First of this book. For instance, in tracing the development of the nervous system in the animal series, and the phylogenetic peculiarities of different species, it was found that a certain at least rough and indefinite, but no less real, correlation must be assumed between this development and the development of what, from the psychologist's point of view, we speak of as the "mind." In studying the development of the nervous system in the individual man, we found it necessary to assume a yet more strict, if not more complicated network of correlations between the two kinds of development. The different main parts of this system in man were seen to be plainly adapted to the performance of functions which, if not employed in the immediate present, would before long be needed to serve as the physical correlates of the main classes of mental activities that are involved in the more elaborate processes of learning. Provision must be made for the individual's becoming consciously aware of the nature of his environment, and for his reacting on that environment with different kinds and degrees of consciously directed activity. Moreover, it was found impossible to avoid the conclusion that the complexity and size of the nervous system, and, *in a very special way*, of the cerebral hemispheres, are correlated with the complexity and the extent of a possible mental development.

§ 2. It was, however, when we came to consider the so-called "localization of cerebral function," that we found ourselves compelled to receive the terms, the analyses, the conclusions, and even the conjectures, of psychology, as derived from a study of consciousness, into our fullest confidence. Indeed, the functions described as cerebral, and located in different parts of the cerebrum, are, properly speaking, not *cerebral* at all. They are different factors, or phases, or aspects, of conscious acts. *They* can only be described as such, in a relatively satisfactory manner. Modern science, by a skilful combination of the methods of histology, pathology, and experimentation, has established in some cases, what parts of the cerebral areas are in some manner concerned in furnishing the conditions or accompaniments of these factors, phases, or aspects, of the mental performances; and it has a few rather uncertain conjectures as to the physical and chemical changes in which these conditions and concomitants consist. But it is these latter alone, that are, strictly speaking, localized in the cerebral areas. Without psychology—that is, without a study of the states of consciousness—we should not even know where to look for any of those physical and chemical reactions which are the special performances of the nervous system. And did we not see that a more complete and satisfactory analysis, from the psychological point of view, is at present a prime requisite for clearing up the very puzzling counter evidences and contradictions which still cling to the doctrine of cerebral localization?

The same thing is even more obviously true of all our treatment of those portions of the nervous mechanism which serve the purposes of end-organs of sense. It might almost be said that there is no physiology proper of the end-organs of sense. There is increasing knowledge as to their histology; and there is some growth to our knowledge of the physical and chemical changes which they undergo when subjected to the various forms of stimuli to which they, specifically, respond. But as "end-organs of sense" we know them only through our conscious sensations in dependence upon their integrity of structure and normal ways of functioning. This fact results in making the physiology of the special senses, too, very largely psychological rather than distinctly physiological —a description and analysis of how we feel, rather than of how a piece of mechanism looks and acts, when examined in a purely objective fashion.

§ 3. It will be seen, then, that after all, the change which is to take place in our point of view, and the corresponding change in the methods of investigation, are by no means absolute and complete. We have all along been getting some very decided and fixed, if not always definite and mathematically accurate, impressions as to the correlations which exist in fact, between the structure, functions, and development of the nervous system in man, and the nature, activities, and development of man's mental life. But having obtained a sufficiently full and clear notion as to what sort of contrivance this nervous mechanism is, in fact, and of how it can operate, with its three-fold outfit of receptors, conductors, and central organs, we wish now to set it agoing, so to say. In this way we can study the results, as they appear in consciousness, of the action upon it of various kinds and degrees of stimulus, and the laws of mental life, as it develops in dependence, more or less remote, upon these results. It is thus much of change which has seemed to us to justify the beginning here of a "Part Second" of our treatise on the one subject of Physiological Psychology.

§ 4. A study of the correlations which exist between the nervous mechanism and the mental life in man, requires a certain amount of preliminary analysis of experience. The first topic to be approached in this way is our experience in the use of our senses.

The world as known to us by our senses consists of a great number of so-called "things" that are believed to be separate existences, but possess certain common characteristics, and stand in certain relations to each other, of space, time, and action. It is with the *things*, their common qualities and mutual relations, that unreflecting practical life is chiefly concerned. But even without special reflection, every one learns that his knowledge of such external objects depends upon the kind and degree of the effect they exercise upon his consciousness through the senses. Attention is thus turned from the things themselves to the sensations produced in us by their action. The variety of such sensations, at first bewilderingly great, is soon reduced to some order by a classification which refers them to the different organs through which they come. Thus, certain sensations are received through the nose, others through the mouth, the ear, the eye, or the skin—especially as covering that part of the body (the *hand*) which is most active in touch. Smell, taste, hearing, sight, and touch are the five classes of sensation, as the grouping is made by the unprejudiced judgment of all; and until recently this was considered sufficient for scientific purposes.

A further rough and scientifically inadequate classification takes place among the sensations of the same sense. Those of smell, indeed, defy classification, whether popular or scientific. Among tastes, the most familiar are easily distinguished; such are the sweet, the sour, and the bitter. The two principal classes of sensations of sound are easily discriminated, as either noises or musical tones; the former are further classified as respects the character of the feeling which accompanies them, and the latter as high or low in pitch. The different more prominent colors—including black and white—are recognized by all persons of normal vision as modes of the sensations of sight; hence the colors commonly named, and the various so-called "shades" of these colors. That more than one class of sensations arise through the skin is shown by the popular use of the word to "feel." Things *feel* hard and soft, smooth and rough, as well as warm and cold. But things are also said to feel heavy or light. The feeling by which their weight is estimated, however, is only ascribed in a very indefinite way to the parts of the body that are chiefly concerned in passively supporting, or actively lifting, or pushing against their weight. The particular use of tactual feeling, as well as the general use of the muscular sense, in gaining this class of sensations is little noticed by ordinary reflection.

§ 5. All the sensations are also regarded as having some place in a scale of degrees of sensation; they are either strong or faint, or else lie somewhere between the two extremes. They are also habitually thought of as related to time, and as being connected with the motion in space of the objects that occasion them. Of the molecular action of their stimuli upon the end-organs of special sense; of the hidden chemical, electrical, or other processes connected with the activity of the peripheral and central nervous system; of the physiological, psycho-physical, and psychological laws under which the mind reacts in the form of simple sensations, and combines these sensations into the composite objects of sense; of all these and other similar matters, the unreflecting conception of sensation takes no account.

§ 6. It is obvious that the analysis of sense-percepts which suffices for working-day life will in no respect answer the demands of science. Its "common-sense" character is a distinct mark of its inadequacy. An adequate scientific treatment of this branch of Physiological Psychology requires at least four things: (1) to distinguish the simple sensations from those complex objects of experience with which alone our adult consciousness is familiar; (2) to point out the varieties of quality and degrees of quantity which belong to these sensations, and to discover the laws which relate them to changes in the form and intensity of their stimuli; (3) to show how the simple sensations are constructed by the mind into the so-called "presentations of sense" under mental laws of time-form and space-form; and (4) to indicate how far, if at all, the higher mental activities of association, memory, will, and judgment may be brought under laws similar to those upon which the formation of these presentations of sense depends. It is upon these four heads of inquiry that modern psychology, as studied from the psycho-physical point of view, has expended most of its painstaking researches. Its success has been by no means complete. All these fields of inquiry still include many unanswered questions; all of them present the results of researches that seem in various respects conflicting. Yet it is precisely in these fields that modern psychology has achieved its most brilliant successes.

§ 7. The distinctions with which scientific analysis begins are to a large extent received from ordinary experience. Some of the most essential of the distinctions are confirmed by the results of this analysis. They all, however, require to be carried farther and to be fixed with much more of accuracy than belongs to the impressions of common life. New distinctions also have to be introduced. For example, scientific investigation maintains the difference between sensations of smell and sensations of taste; but it points out what is not ordinarily apparent—namely, that certain results commonly referred to the latter sense really belong to the former. It also adds the sensations of the muscular sense to the classes popularly described; and it discriminates more clearly between the several kinds of sensations that have the skin for their organ. As we have already seen, it assigns two very different classes of sensations to the ear.

Psycho-physical science, moreover, accepts the common distinction between the quality and the quantity of the different sensations. But it describes with all possible accuracy the limits within which alone this distinction can be carried out. It shows that the quality and quantity of sensation are inseparably connected; that, as Lotze held (a view confirmed by von Kries and others), changes in quality can be distinguished from changes in intensity, with perfect confidence, only in the case of sensations of hearing. It is possible that even here the distinction is largely made on the basis of complex experience. Very intense sensations of heat and cold so far change their specific character as to tend to pass into each other, or, perhaps, to become submerged in a common tone of painful feeling. Minimum sensations of heat and pressure are difficult to distinguish from each other; maximum sensations of pressure are likely to lose the characteristic quality of touch and be displaced by sensations of pain. To treat scientifically of the quality of sensations requires, then, a large amount of the most careful analysis.

§ 8. It is essential, in the first place, to distinguish "simple sensations" from "presentations of sense," or those complex objects of consciousness which result from an act of mental synthesis on the basis of several simultaneous affections of sense. As respects developed experience, *the simple sensation is a necessary fiction of psycho-physical science.*[1] Consciousness is scarcely more able directly to analyze a presentation of sense into those factors out of which it originated than it is to analyze a drop of water into its component oxygen and hydrogen gases. Simple sensations, therefore, are not objects which can be examined in the direct light of introspection. Yet they are factors which, as scientific analysis shows, actually enter into all such objects as can properly be spoken of under the term "presentations of sense." Any sensation which is absolutely unanalyzable with respect to distinctions of quality, and which, therefore, cannot be considered as consisting of component parts, is called *simple*. It is distinguished as a *sensation* from all other elementary forms of feeling or knowledge, by the relation which it sustains to the presentations of sense. A sensation, unlike the feeling of grief, of desire, or of weariness, etc., is a

---

[1] All our subsequent work will be completely misunderstood unless this statement is constantly borne in mind. On the one hand, the scientific study of sense-experience is impossible without the analysis which employs this fiction; on the other hand, to give reality to the fiction, as though it were an experienced element in consciousness, is to favor an atomistic theory of mental life.

potential factor of a material object. Through the senses we know "things"; not, indeed, as though they appeared before the mind by immediate apprehension in the form of exact copies of extra-mental realities. But every sensation is an affection of the mind recognized as connected with an extra-mental reality, through the activity of the senses. Simple sensations are those elementary factors, themselves indecomposable, out of which the presentations of sense are composed. The objects of sense, however, do not have the character of *mere* compounds of simple sensations. Sensations must not only be associated and compounded, but also localized and projected without (that is, set in systematic relations of space-form), in order to constitute the objects of sense.

§ 9. The foregoing remarks suffice to indicate, in a preliminary way, what is the nature and value of the psycho-physical investigation of sensation. We inquire, in the next two chapters, as to the Quality of Sensations. The inquiry, when conducted from the psycho-physical point of view, involves an answer to three questions: (1) What is the precise locality in the organism where the specific excitation which occasions each kind of sensation originates; and what is the nature of the action of the stimulus in producing such excitation? (2) What are the kinds of sensations which appear in consciousness as the result of the various excitations? (3) What are the laws by which the quality of the sensations is related to the kinds of excitation? Neither of these three questions can be answered completely. The investigation of the first is much restricted by our almost complete ignorance of those processes in the central organs that are in all cases the proximate internal stimuli or immediate antecedents of the sensations. Moreover, as has already been made apparent, our knowledge of the intimate structure of the end-organs of sense, and of the nature of the physical processes which excite them, is still very incomplete. The detection of obscure but important differences in the qualities of conscious states of sensation is by no means easy; it requires great skill, strict and trained attention, and unwearied repetition of experiment. But these conditions of success have a great effect in altering the quality of the sensations themselves. Besides all this, remarkable idiosyncrasies not infrequently appear; and language can only imperfectly describe even the most common factors of the varied and living experiences with which science tries to deal.

In investigating the laws that define the relations between our subjective experience, called sensation, and objective phenomena in the shape of physical energy acting upon the nervous mechanism, there is often the greatest doubt as to what manner of laws are being investigated. They may be considered as purely physiological, or as psycho-physical, or as purely psychological. It is not strange, therefore, that different theories exist for accounting for all the more important groups of facts, depending upon the emphasis laid by different investigators upon the value of each of the three possible modes of explanation. The truth is, that each sensation is separated by a series of intricate physiological and psychical processes from the application of the stimulus in the gross, as it were, to the end-organ of sense.

§ 10. What has already been said regarding the "specific energy of the nerves" (compare pp. 284 f.) must be assumed in discussing the quality of sensations. The possession of common functions cannot, indeed, be denied to the nerve-fibres in general. Conduction has been seen to be the one universal property of all the nervous elements; and even the end-organs, or receptors, of sense-impressions are made up of elaborate and ingenious combinations of these elements. But the phenomena of sensation require a further extension of the conception of specific functions, on whatever physical or physiological basis this differentiation is founded. Consciously made distinctions in the quality of sensations depend upon the excitation of specific corresponding elements of the nervous mechanism. Sensations of light and color depend upon different species of the excitation of the optic nerve; and similar specific quality cannot be denied to the functional activity of the nerves of smell, taste, hearing, and touch. But the nature of the evidence and the conclusions which must be drawn from it will be much better appreciated at a later period in the discussion.

§ 11. Little of a scientific character is known concerning *Sensations of Smell*, considered as respects their specific quality. The physical and nervous structure of the apparatus employed in exciting this species of sensations, and the way in which the stimulus is customarily applied, have already been described (see p. 176). Under ordinary conditions the stimulus must act in gaseous form, or else be vaporizable, with the existing degree of temperature. The degree of temperature at which different substances become vaporizable, and therefore odorous, varies greatly according to their physical characteristics. Arsenic, for example, which at ordinary temperatures is inodorous, when raised to a dark-red heat excites intense sensations of smell by the vapor it gives off.

Whether an odorous substance must actually reach the olfactory mucous membrane in a vaporous form or whether a solution will in any case excite sensations of smell, cannot easily be ascertained; since neither the positive nor the negative results which have been obtained by different experimenters can withstand all criticism. In the case of negative results, such as those of Weber, who found that when the head was tilted back and the nostrils filled with a ten per cent. solution of eau de cologne, the sense of smell was not excited, attention must be directed to the fact that treatment of the membrane by soaking it in a liquid disturbs the function of the olfactory apparatus for a considerable time. In the case of the positive results, the difficulty is that of being sure that the narrow chink in which the end-organs are situated is actually filled with the liquid; if it were not, but some air remained, then the odorous particles might really reach the olfactory surface in the form of a vapor. On the other side, it may be argued that, since at least a thin layer of liquid must cover the olfactory membrane, the odorous particles must finally be dissolved or suspended in this liquid, and so excite the sensations of smell.

§ 12. Whatever decision may be reached as to the possibility under highly abnormal conditions, the ordinary and "adequate" stimulus of smell is rightly assumed to consist in certain exceedingly minute particles contained in the odorous gas or vapor which is drawn in with the current of air over the mucous membrane of the *regio olfactoria*. The question is as yet scarcely decided, whether other forms of stimulus, besides these odorous particles— mechanical, electrical, thermic, or so-called subjective—can excite the sensation of smell. The older experimenters (Volta, Pfaff, Fowler, and Humboldt) failed to obtain any certain proof that the electrical current is an excitant of this sense. In one place, however, Pfaff speaks of a sensation resembling the smell of sulphur as caused by the application of electricity to the sensory passages of the nose. Ritter (in 1798) experimented by using bits of graphite and zinc thrust into these passages, and also by holding one pole of a battery in the hand and placing the other in the nostril. In the latter way he thought that he excited a genuine specific sensation of this sense. He describes the positive pole in the nostril as producing an inclination to sneeze and a trace of a smell like that of ammonia; the negative pole placed there does away with this inclination and produces a kind of "sour" smell. Such phenomena are probably, however, all to be assigned to the nerves of taste, touch, and common feeling. More recent investigations have done little to remove the reasons for doubt.[1] The smell of phosphorus which is developed by the action of the electrical machine is probably due to the ozone set free; it is not a case, then, of the direct excitation by electricity of the sensation of smell. Some physiologists (notably Valentin) have observed that this sensation may be awakened by mechanical stimulation, such as strong vibration of the nostrils, violent sneezing, etc.; others have failed

---

[1] See W. Nagel, *Handbuch d. Physiologie des Menschen*, 1905, III, 602.

to produce this specific sensory effect in such ways. It does not appear that thermic stimulation will excite the sensation of smell.

Experiments to prove that subjective sensations of smell may be produced by injecting odorous substances into the veins of animals are very uncertain. Human pathological cases, in spite of the customary indefiniteness of the patient's testimony as to the nature of his sensory affection, tend to show that compression of the olfactory nerve by tumors, etc., may produce sensations of smell. Disturbances of the central organs, such as occur in cases of disease, may doubtless have the same result. The powerful effect which some odors have upon the brains of some persons, so that nausea, giddiness, and other disturbances of feeling result, scarcely needs mention; but it cannot easily all be resolved into mental associations connected with the sense impressions. Hallucinations of smell are among the prominent and persistent symptoms of certain forms of insanity.

§ 13. As concerns the varieties of odors, from the psychological point of view, the important scientific problem is that of attempting to reduce this manifold to order. In other senses, particularly in sight and taste, such attempts have already met with a considerable degree of success. The great variety of colors can be ordered by reference to a few primary colors; and the tastes can be reduced to mixtures of a few elementary tastes. There are some indications that a similar "component theory" is moving in the right direction in the case of smell also. This theory would hold that there is a relatively small number of primary odors, each aroused by a specific physico-chemical stimulus, while the great variety of other odors have their complex nature due to their being aroused by mixed stimuli. But owing to the uncertain and vague character of the evidence, a designation of the primary sensations of smell, or of their specific stimuli, is still very far from an accomplished fact.

Introspectively, odors by no means separate themselves into elementary and compound, but all seem simple. It is, however, possible to draw a line between smell proper and tactile sensations of the nasal organ. The interior of the nose is supplied not only by the olfactory nerve but also by a branch of the trigeminus; and many sharp "odors" are in part stinging sensations from the end-organs of the latter nerve, and persist in individuals who are, through injury or congenital absence of the olfactory nerve or similar causes, completely *anosmic*, or lacking in the sense of smell. It is also possible to draw a line between smell and the sensations of taste which sometimes arise from vapors, as the sweet taste of inhaled chloroform, which is properly due[1] to excitation of taste-buds on the soft palate and in the larynx. Even these distinctions are not easy for introspection; and in common life we ascribe the mixture of smell, taste, and touch sensations which may result from sniffing a vaporous substance, all to the sense of smell.

§ 14. If all these extraneous sensations are excluded, the introspective analysis of the sensations of smell proper seems impossible. About all that can be done is to notice resemblances and differences between odors, and so to arrive at some sort of classification. None of the classifications of odors which have been offered are thoroughly satisfactory, however; nor do any of them afford much promise of leading to the discovery of the elementary smell-stimuli. The only one which has any claim to attention has come down to us from Linnæus, the great naturalist of the eighteenth century; it has been adopted and somewhat developed by Zwaardemaker, who ranks as the leader among contemporary students of the sense of smell. Zwaardemaker's classification is as follows:

(1) Ethereal odors, including the odors of fruits.

(2) Aromatic or spicy odors.

(3) Fragrant odors, including the scents of flowers, and also vanilla, tea, balsam, etc.

(4) Ambrosial odors, of which musk is the most familiar example.

(5) Alliaceous odors, including onion, india rubber, chlorin, and iodin.

(6) Empyreumatic or burnt odors, including burnt foods, and also tar, gasoline, etc.

(7) Hircine or goaty odors, including cheese, rancid butter, etc.

(8) Repulsive odors, as of certain insects and plants.

(9) Nauseous odors, as of decaying flesh.

Some of these classes seem broader than others; especially do we notice that numbers 8 and 9 include, for many individuals, smells that might be selected from all the other classes; and all are capable of subdivision into subordinate classes. More important still is the fact that some odors do not readily find a place in the scheme at all. If it were possible to discover any chemical community between the members of any class or sub-class, which should set that class off, as stimuli, from the other classes, a long step would be taken toward a scientific understanding of these sensations; but, so far, there is little sign of a common chemical character among resembling odors. Perhaps more hope of advance is afforded by

[1] W. Nagel, *Handbuch der Physiologie*, 1905, III, 611; Zwaardemaker, *Physiologie des Geruchs*, 1895.

the results of examining the odors of closely related groups of chemical substances. It is found, in the first place, that odorous substances, with few exceptions, contain elements belonging to only three of Mendelejeff's groups, namely the fifth (of which nitrogen, phosphorus, and antimony are members), the sixth (including oxygen, sulphur, and chromium), and the seventh (including chlorin, bromin, and iodin). When similar compounds of the elements of one of these groups are arranged in the order of their atomic weight, the odors are found to run along a scale, shading off from one to another. Thus, the odors of chlorin, bromin, and iodin can be regarded as arranged along a linear scale, and the same is true of like compounds of these three. Similar scales are found on arranging the fatty acids in order, or the monatomic alcohols, or other like series of organic compounds. The members at each end of such a series are often odorless; and the intensity as well as the quality of the odor is likely to change in a gradual manner along the series.[1]

§ 15. On the psychological or physiological side, more light can be expected from studying the results of mixture of odors, of fatigue of the organs, etc., than from attempts to classify odors introspectively. Partial anosmia—a condition in which the nose is insensitive to certain odors but not to all—is not infrequent; and the distinction draws a physiological line between some odors and others. It is well known that prolonged action of an odorous substance results in a condition of fatigue (or adaptation), in which the odor can no longer be perceived. In this condition, it is found that the nose becomes insensitive to certain other odors besides the particular one which has been acting, while it remains sensitive to still other odors of a different character. The odors which are fatigued together would seem to belong together physiologically, and they are also likely, in fact, to be subjectively similar.

Somewhat analogous results have been obtained by studying mixtures of different stimuli which excite sensations of smell. Care must be taken, in such experiments, to avoid the possibility of a chemical union between the two vapors, and this is perhaps best accomplished by Zwaardemaker's device of conducting one vapor to the right nostril and the other to the left, each through a separate tube. The effect of such mixed stimulation is, in some cases, the production of an intermediate odor, but in others the masking of one odor by the other, or even the complete neutralization of each by the other so that no odor is perceived from the mixture. Similar

[1] See Haycraft, *Brain*, 1889, II, 166, and in Schäfer's *Textbook of Physiology*, 1900, II, 1254. The results appear to be an entering wedge into the tough problem of the classification of the stimuli of sensations of smell.

effects of the blending, or contrast, or opposition of sensations are obtained in other classes of our sensory experience. It is along these lines that the unravelling of the intricacies of the sense of smell may be expected to make most progress.

§ 16. The condition of scientific attainment as to *sensations of taste* and their stimuli is somewhat better than that as to the allied sense of smell. The adequate specific stimulus for the nerves of this sense consists in certain tastable substances; such substances, however, do not excite the end-apparatus unless they act upon it under definite conditions. Only fluid bodies, or such as are at least to some small degree soluble in a fluid or menstruum, excite sensations of taste; absolutely insoluble bodies are, without exception, tasteless. This fact may be due to the concealed position of the inner cells of the gustatory flasks, which is such that they cannot be reached by substances undissolved. By no means all soluble substances, however, have a taste. No known law regulates the relation between the solubility of bodies and their power to excite sensations of this class. The adequate stimulus of taste is thus chemical; and taste-buds are "chemo-ceptors." Whether they can be aroused by other classes of stimuli—mechanical, thermal, electrical—is not yet ascertained with certainty. But thermal stimuli, at least, are probably without any effect on the taste end-organs. As to mechanical stimuli, some good observers have reported sensations of taste resulting from pressing or tapping the tongue; but others have been unable to obtain the same results. Sensations of this class are certainly aroused by the passage of a current of electricity through the tongue. If, for example, the positive pole or anode is applied to the tongue, the sensation is sour; if the negative pole or cathode is applied, the taste is not so easy to describe, but is called sharp, alkaline, or bitter, by different observers. Whether the sensations produced in this way are the direct result of the action of the current on the end-organs of taste is a question which, after a hundred and fifty years of study, is not yet settled. The insufficiency of the evidence is due to the fact that the passage of a current sets up electrolysis; and though this may be prevented from taking place in the saliva of the mouth, there is no way to make sure that electrolysis is not going on within the taste-buds, or at some polarizable surface through which the current has to pass. Now electrolysis of the salts dissolved in the saliva or body fluids would set free acid ions at the anode and alkaline at the cathode; and thus the tastes actually observed could be accounted for as due to chemical stimuli generated by electrolysis, rather than to electrical stimuli. This view has considerable probability as an explanation of the "electrical tastes"; it is at least not excluded by any results yet obtained.[1] Apparently, therefore, we have in the taste end-organs a striking example of the general characteristic of special receptors— namely, that, though highly sensitive to one special stimulus, they are rather obtuse to all other sorts of stimuli.

§ 17. In attempting to delimit, analyze, and order the sensations of taste, we are met with the same difficulty as that which confronted us in the case of smell—namely, that tastes usually occur in close combination with other sensations. The tongue and mouth possess the tactile, temperature, pain, and muscular senses as well as taste; and the "feeling" of food contributes largely to its apparent "taste." For example, astringent and oily "tastes" are really tactile sensations. It is difficult to distinguish between taste and smell, except by artificially excluding smell. A simple experiment for accomplishing this is due to Chevreul (1824), and consists in holding the nose while taking into the mouth substances of various flavor, but reduced to like consistency so as to avoid help in discrimination from the side of the tactile sense. Under these circumstances, the surprising fact comes to light that it is impossible to distinguish, by taste alone, between coffee and quinine, or between apple and onion. The conclusion from this experiment, when fully carried out, is that most so-called tastes are really odors.

Excluding the sense of smell does not, however, interfere at all in the perception of the following four tastes: sweet, sour, bitter, saline. These four are universally recognized as simple tastes, and it is very doubtful whether any others should be added to this list. Metallic and alkaline are added by some authorities, and there is still some question regarding them; but it is clear that they are at least partly composed of mixtures of sweet, sour, bitter, and saline, along with sensations of touch and smell.

§ 18. The following question now arises: Does each of the four elementary tastes have a special end-organ? Histologically, no difference appears between the various taste-buds which can be taken as an indication of functional differentiation. Yet it is clear from experiment that the taste-buds are not all equivalent. The fact is familiar that bitter is best tasted at the back of the tongue, and sweet best at the tip; while the edges of the tongue are the most sensitive to sour. Experiment has made these results more precise by sharply localizing the stimulation. If weak solutions are applied to individual fungiform papillæ by means of a camel's-hair brush, it is found that the sensitivity of the papillæ varies considerably; although it is impossible to localize the stimulus to single taste-buds. A few papillæ are found which respond only to sweet,

[1] See the summary of evidence by Nagel, in his *Handbuch der Physiologie*, 1905, III, 630.

or only to sour, etc. Others respond to two, and others to three, some to all four, classes of the sensation of taste; while some do not respond at all.[1] These facts, so far as they go, are favorable to the hypothesis that individual taste-buds are specialized, each for one taste.

The physiological relations maintained between the four elementary tastes are not yet clearly made out. A condition of partial *ageusia*, or lack of taste, can be produced by chewing gymnema leaves; the sense for sweet and for bitter is thus temporarily destroyed, while that for sour and saline substances remains. The mixture of two taste-stimuli does not give rise to a series of clear intervening qualities, as does, for example, the mixture of red and yellow, but the two tastes in some cases remain side by side and distinct; in other cases they alternate; and in still others, the two neutralize each other. Kiesow has, however, found that a mixture of weak solutions of sugar and common salt gives a flat alkaline taste, weaker than that of either of the components of the mixture, and not like either of them. Contrast effects, such as the extreme sourness of an acid fruit after a sweet substance has been eaten, are well known; but it seems at present impossible to utilize this experience in explaining the dynamic relations of the four simple sensations of taste. There is no clear indication that the tastes can be arranged in a linear scale, as the primary colors are, nor that any taste stands to any other definitely in the relation of opposite or complementary. On the whole, it appears as if the four tastes were rather isolated from each other, each representing almost an independent sense. There is much blending, to be sure; but the amount is apparently no greater between one taste and another than between tastes and odors.

§ 19. Little can be said regarding the nature of the chemical stimulus which arouses any of the sensations of taste. It is true that bodies of similar chemical composition usually evoke similar tastes; though a curious exception to this rule is found in the fact that sweet and bitter are often evoked by bodies of very similar composition, or even by the same body. On the other hand, substances of very different chemical composition—such as, for example, cane sugar and sugar of lead—sometimes excite the same sensation of taste. Since it is in solution that substances act on the end-organs of taste, the theory of solutions needs to be taken into account. It may be that dissociated ions are the essential stimulus; and there is some positive evidence that acid

---

[1] Öhrwall, *Skandinav. Archiv f. Physiol.*, 1890, II, 1; Kiesow, Wundt's *Philosoph. Studien*, 1898, XIV, 591.

taste is due to the action of hydrogen ions, and alkaline taste to hydroxyl ions.[1]

§ 20. On passing to the consideration of *sensations of sound* much more help is received from the science of physics. But modern investigations, in the form in which they concern us, do not go back of the great work of Helmholtz,[2] who made the entire field peculiarly his own. Since the first appearance of this work, the subject has also been greatly enriched by the original researches of Oettingen, Mach, Preyer, Hensen, Stumpf, and other still later writers. In speaking of the stimuli of these sensations, we are compelled to refer chiefly to the vibrations of air, which are only remote excitants of the end-organs of this sense. Neither physics nor physiology has yet been able to fix the precise locality in the organism (the nervous structure of the cochlea) where the immediate stimulation of the end-apparatus takes place; or to tell what is the exact nature of its action. We are obliged, then, to confine ourselves in the main to considering a relation between the vibratory energy of the air and certain states of consciousness, without attempting to explain the many intermediate links.

All sensations which arise in the mind by means of the irritation of the auditory nerve are called sensations of sound. The word "sound" is thus used by psychology for a wholly subjective affair, which has no more resemblance to those vibrations which physics designates by the same word than has the taste sweet to the unknown physical properties that produce it. The trained mind, or "trained ear," as we say, has indeed the power directly to analyze a compound musical sound into its constituent elements. But each of these elements is purely a sensation, a subjective affair. It carries in itself no token that it has been produced by vibrations of any kind; or that it sustains any numerical relation whatever to the vibrations of which some other sensation of sound is composed. We know nothing directly, through sensations, either of the structure of the ear or of vibrating strings and particles of air, or of the mathematics and physics of music.

§ 21. Sounds are of two classes—*tones*, or musical sounds, and *noises*. The former are due to periodic motions of sonorous bodies; the latter to non-periodic. Noises are those sounds which, objectively considered, are wanting in the periodic regularity of stimulation which characterizes all musical sounds, and, subjectively considered, in the peculiar, pleasant modification of consciousness

---

[1] Richards, *Amer. Chem. Journal*, 1898, XX; Kastlé, *ibid.*; Höber and Kiesow, *Zeitschr. f. physicalische Chemie*, 1898, XXVII.

[2] *Die Lehre von d. Tonempfundungen als physiolog. Grundlage für d. Theorie d. Musik* (Braunschweig, 1st ed., 1862; and several subsequent editions).

which the latter produce. But noises accompany almost all tones; and, conversely, tones may be detected by the trained ear as mingled with the noises of every-day life. No player of the violin avoids all noise of scraping from the bow; no stroke of a workman's hammer, or slamming of a door, that does not start and catch up into itself some trace of musical tone. The interest of science has hitherto been almost wholly concentrated upon musical sounds, and little has been done by either physics or physiology toward the analysis of noises. It is characteristic of a noise, according to Helmholtz, that there is a quick and irregular alternation of different kinds of sensation of sound. This distinctive character can generally be detected "by attentive aural observation without artificial assistance." We can compound noises out of musical tones; as, for example, by striking together all the keys of an octave on the piano. Hensen[1] distinguished three "categories of unmixed noises"—the "beats" or pulsations which disturb the purity of musical tones; the crackle, crack, or crash; and hissing sounds. These three shade into each other, and, when mixed with different kinds and quantities of musical sounds, make up the noises which we hear on every hand.

It is possible, therefore, to analyze tonal elements out of most, if not all, kinds of noises. And although no one has succeeded in completely analyzing a noise into such elements, success has been great enough to encourage the opinion that a complete analysis of all noises might break them up into combinations of various inharmonic tones.

§ 22. Musical sounds differ, not only in quality, but also in quantity or intensity of sensation as dependent upon the amplitude of the vibrations which produce them. With respect to their *quality* they are distinguished as either simple or complex, according as they result from one set of regularly recurrent (periodic) vibrations of a given number in a given unit of time, or result from a combination of two or more sets of such vibrations. The musical sounds of ordinary experience are complex. The blending of the simple tones into the complex tone is not so complete, however, that it cannot be at least partially analyzed directly by a trained ear. The complex sound, which results from this compounding of the contrasts or coincidences of several simple musical sounds, may be called by the term "clang"—in this meaning borrowed from the usage of the German. The quality of tones considered as simple sensations is their *pitch*, which varies according to a scale of states of consciousness that are immediately apprehended and compared with each other, and that are discovered by objective meth-

[1] In Hermann's *Handb. d. Physiol.*, III, ii, pp. 3–142, and works by the same author there referred to.

ods to correspond to a scale of changes in the number of the vibrations of the waves which occasion them. The pitch of tones is therefore spoken of as "high" or "low," according to the place which we assign to the resulting sensations in this scale. Such place in the scale may be considered either with respect to the relation of any particular tone to the upper or lower limits of the scale, or with respect to the relation of the different tones to one another. "Clangs," or complex tones—the musical sounds with which we are made acquainted by all ordinary experience—have also a variable quality called timbre, or "tone-color"; the timbre of the clang is dependent upon the pitch, number, and relative intensity of the simple tones which compose it. Thus a note having the same place in the musical scale (for example, *a* of the once-marked octave—440 vibrations) *sounds* differently, as we say, on the piano, violin, cornet, or when sung by the human voice. The pitch of the tone as produced by all these different methods is the same; but its tone-color is determined by the character of the overtones which are blended with the fundamental tone.

§ 23. The *pitch of tones* depends upon the rapidity of the periodic vibrations (the number in a given unit of time—usually one second) which occasion them, or—what is the same thing—upon the length of the sound-waves. This class of sensations, however, has both an upper and a lower limit; that is to say, vibrations either below or above a certain number per second, or—what is the same thing—wave-lengths that are either shorter or longer than a given limit, produce no sensations of musical sound. The difficulty of determining these limits is great, because the intensity of extremely low or high tones has to be enormously increased in order that they may be heard at all; because the perceptions of the acoustic sense are so very blunt near the limits that the different sensations are almost certain to be confused; because distracting sensations of common feeling mingle in these ranges of tone with the sensations of sound, and because near the lower limits the over-tones—especially the octave above—become so strong as to be mistaken for the fundamental tones. On account of these difficulties the older investigators made numerous mistakes.

Individual peculiarities are also very important in determining sensations of pitch. Some persons can hear tones below or above those audible to most others; and, in general, the range of audible pitch decreases somewhat with age—beginning in some cases with the twentieth year. This difference in individuals is illustrated by the judgment of Helmholtz, who thought that sensations of tone begin to cease when the vibrations fall below 34 per second; some tuning-forks of great size, which vibrated only 28 times per second, seemed to him, however, to have a trace of tone in the form of a "weak drone." But Preyer[1] found that while 14 vibrations produced no tone that he could hear, at 16 vibrations he was able to hear a tone; others could distinguish a musical sound only at 19 or 23 vibrations. The same observer experienced as a sensation of musical sound more than 40,000 vibrations per second; Turnbull found that the majority of those with whom he experimented could not hear more than about 20,000 to 22,500 vibrations per second, and only one—a musician—heard 30,000; Despretz succeeded in producing with tuning-forks audible tones that had 32,000 vibrations. Of late years, the Galton whistle (a little organ pipe, of adjustable length), especially in the improved form introduced by Edelmann, has been much used in determinations of the highest audible tone. Edelmann reports that tones of 50,000 vibrations are sometimes heard, while Bruner,[2] who tested a large number of individuals, finds an average of 32,000, with individuals of apparently normal hearing varying from 22,000 to 43,000.

Setting aside the evidence from more or less exceptional cases, it appears that vibrations slower than 28 to 30 per second produce in most ears only a buzzing or groaning sound; the more acute tones are unpleasant, or even painful, and finally inaudible to all ears. These results cannot be considered as very concordant or precise. They show, however, that the range of the average human ear is not far from ten octaves, reaching from about A_2 of the sub-contra octave ($27\frac{1}{2}$ vibrations per second) to about c^8 of the eight-times-marked octave (33,792 vibrations per second).

The table[3] on next page gives the pitch of all the musical tones audible to the human ear, in the key of C major, on a scale in which a^1 is fixed at 440 vibrations. Only about seven of the rather more than eleven octaves of the table are, however, usable in music; these seven reach upward from C_1 of the contra, or from A_2 of the subcontra octave, to b^4—namely, the seven or seven and a half octaves of the modern piano.

§ 24. The sensitiveness of the ear to *differences of pitch* also varies greatly with different individuals, and for the different octaves of the musical scale. Preyer found that unpractised persons, within the octaves from c to c^3 (132–1,056 vibrations by the table, but 128–1,024 by the scale adopted for his experiments), distinguish

---

[1] *Grenzen d. Tonwahrnehmung*, p. 23 f.

[2] *Archives of Psychol.*, 1908, No. 11, p. 11; this work contains references to the older authorities.

[3] Taken from Stumpf, *Tonpsychologie*, I, p. xiv, and giving the German scale; for the purposes of physics and psychology, C_1 or "middle C," is usually fixed at 256 vibrations.

a difference of from 8 to 16 vibrations as producing a distinct difference in the sensation of pitch. Extreme cases of deafness to differences in pitch are recorded; as, for example, that of the man who, in the middle part of the scale, could not distinguish an interval of less than a third, and, in the higher and lower parts, of less than a seventh. Persons insensitive to differences of a tone or half-tone, who are sometimes said "not to know one note from

	C	D	E	F	G	A	B	
Subcontra octave........	$16\frac{1}{2}$	$18\frac{9}{16}$	$20\frac{5}{8}$	22	$24\frac{3}{4}$	$27\frac{1}{2}$	$30\frac{15}{16}$	C_2, D_2, etc.
Contra octave...........	33	$37\frac{1}{8}$	$41\frac{1}{4}$	44	$49\frac{1}{2}$	55	$61\frac{7}{8}$	C_1, D_1, etc.
Great octave............	66	$74\frac{1}{4}$	$82\frac{1}{2}$	88	99	110	$123\frac{3}{4}$	C, D, etc.
Small octave............	132	$148\frac{1}{2}$	165	176	198	220	$247\frac{1}{2}$	c, d, etc.
Once-marked octave.....	264	297	330	352	396	440	495	c^1, d^1, etc.
Twice-marked octave....	528	594	660	704	792	880	990	c^2, d^2, etc.
Thrice-marked octave....	1,056	1,188	1,320	1,408	1,584	1,760	1,980	c^3, d^3, etc.
Four-times-marked octave	2,112	2,376	2,640	2,816	3,168	3,520	3,960	c^4, d^4, etc.
Five-times-marked octave	4,224	4,752	5,280	5,632	6,336	7,040	7,920	c^5, d^5, etc.
Six-times-marked octave.	8,448	9,504	10,560	11,264	12,672	14,080	15,840	c^6, d^6, etc.
Seven-times-marked octave	16,896	19,008	21,120	22,528	25,344	28,160	31,680	c^7, d^7, etc.
Eight-times-marked octave	33,792	38,016	42,240	....	....	....	....	....

another," are by no means infrequently met. Sensitiveness to pitch is, however, generally capable of rapid cultivation, and may reach a high degree of perfection in persons who have what is called "a good natural ear" for musical tones, if the ear be also highly trained. Such persons may become able to discriminate differences in the sensations caused by changing the number of vibrations not more than a third of a single vibration per second, in the region of the scale between c and g^2. In the octave from a^1 to a^2 more than 1,200 tones are distinguishable. But above and below this region the distinctions possible are less fine; above c^5 even well-trained ears commit errors in identifying two notes that differ by 100 or even by 1,000 vibrations. Not only the musical quality of tones, but also the power of distinguishing differences in them, diminishes rapidly as we approach the upper limits of the scale.

It appears, therefore, that sensitiveness to pitch is, in general, greatest in the most used part of the musical scale; or, in other words, in that part which falls within the common range of human voices. Within this range, the least perceptible difference is a constant quantity, when expressed in number of vibrations.[1]

§ 25. The fineness of the possible distinctions of *purity of interval* also differs for different individuals and for different inter-

[1] On this whole subject compare the lengthy and interesting discussion on "Individualität des Sinnes und Gedächtnisses für Tonqualitäten," in Stumpf, *Tonpsychologie*, I, pp. 262 ff.

vals. The results of experiment on this point have been tabulated by Hensen as derived from data drawn from Preyer's investigations. This investigator found the degree of sensitiveness to be greatest in the case of the octave, next of the fifth, next the whole tone, and so on to the minor third, where it is least of all. The figures which give the number of vibrations off from the pure interval which is distinguishable, for the above intervals, are respectively, 0.13; 0.23; 0.85, and 1.90. Other investigators have obtained somewhat different results.

Immediate *judgment of absolute tone* (as the a^1 carried in mind by musicians) is possible; judgment between two tones as to which is higher or lower in pitch is also immediate, and may be exercised independently of everything except the two sensations themselves. The latter judgment is the common power of mind belonging to this sense; the former is, as a rule, exercised only by skilled persons, and by them only very imperfectly. Experiments of Stumpf,[1] upon himself and three other musicians, showed that the mistakes in judgment of absolute tone amounted, in the lower region of the scale (from C_1 to B_1), to 15%–100% of the trials; in the middle region (from a–g^1, or from g–e^2), to 0%–70%; in the upper region (from g^3–f^4, or from f^3–a^4), to 7%–80%. Only one of the four persons experimented upon seemed to approach the point of infallibility. Judgment of absolute tone is, therefore, a different matter from that which makes distinctions in intervals or in the least observable differences of pitch, and is much more precarious.

§ 26. Those psychologists appear to be in the right who claim that some power of the mind immediately to judge differences of quality in pitch, purely as such, must be assumed in order to account for the foregoing phenomena.[2] Such judgment, however, may be, and ordinarily is, much assisted by auxiliary discriminations of other sensations which blend with those of musical tone. Among such secondary helps the most important are the muscular sensations which accompany the innervation of the larynx and other organs used in producing musical tones. For we ordinarily innervate these organs (at least in an inchoate and partial way)—that is, we sound the tone to ourselves—when trying carefully to judge of its pitch. But the niceness of these muscular sensations is not great enough, even when most highly trained, to account for the discriminations of the "good ear." The trained musician can de-

---

[1] *Tonpsychologie*, I, pp. 305 ff.
[2] On this subject compare Lotze, *Medicin. Psychologie*, pp. 265 ff., 480 f.; Stricker, *Studien über d. Association d. Vorstellungen*, 1883, pp. 2 f.; G. E. Müller, *Zur Grundlegung d. Psychophysik*, pp. 276 ff., Berlin, 1878; and Stumpf, *Tonpsychologie*, I, pp. 134 ff.

tect by ear a difference in quality between two tones of 400 and 400⅓ vibrations per second; but the most skilful singer—Jenny Lind, for example—scarcely succeeds in singing in quarter-tones. Fairly good singers often err by 5–10 vibrations in striking a note, and cannot prevent the voice from varying by as much as this in attempting to sustain the same tone for a second or two.[1] Moreover, the relative powers of larynx and ear by no means keep pace with each other in the same person. It should also be remembered that all our ordinary discriminations of musical sound apply to composite tones, or "clangs"; in discriminating these we are aided by the tone-color, or tone-feeling, which belongs to each note as sounded by some sonorous body with whose peculiarities we are previously more or less acquainted.

It follows, then, that the judgment is supplied, by the varying qualities of musical tones, with the means for arranging them in a continuous series which may be symbolized by different positions assigned along an uninterrupted straight line. Of any three unlike tones, one *must* be, and only *one can* be, arranged as respects pitch between the other two. And whenever any two tones, as m and n, are given, another sliding tone, which begins with m and ends with n, is possible. Moreover, within the bounds of our experience of tones, as we advance along the scale toward either the upper or the lower limit, we see no tendency in the qualities of the sensations to approach each other. In this respect the scale of sound-tones is wholly different from that of color-tones. There are not two ways, for example, of getting from a^1 to c^3 (one through b^1, c^2, etc., and the other through g^1, f^1, etc., around to e^3, d^3, and then c^3), as there are two ways of going from yellow to blue (i. e., through green and blue-green, or through orange, red, and violet). We speak, then, of the series of tones as a constant and infinite series; although, of course, no series of states of consciousness is really infinite, and although the upper and lower limits of the musical scale, as well as the limits of the least observable differences between two tones, are not constant but variable for different individuals.

The symbolism taken from relations of space, which we employ when we speak of certain acoustic sensations as "high" and of others as "low" in pitch, or when we distinguish so-called "intervals" between the tones as large and small, is strictly applicable only to the complex tactual, visual, and muscular sensations that accompany the acoustic. In sounding the lower tones with the voice the organs are depressed; in sounding the higher, they are elevated. Low tones have a certain breadth and gravity which

[1] Cameron, *Psychol. Rev. Monogr. Suppl.* No. 34, 1907, p. 227.

correspond to the foundations of a spatial structure; as sensations they require more time to come into and depart from consciousness, as it were. A great intensity and slower *tempo* belong to the bass-viol than to the violin. We read *up* for the notes of highest pitch, and *down* for those of lowest pitch, in the written musical scale.

§ 27. We have seen that tones, like rays of light, come to us as compounded into "clangs"; these really composite tones being esteemed as single tones in ordinary experience. The nature of such composition determines the so-called "timbre," or "tone-color," of the compound tone. In a word, each sensation of a clang is a summing-up in consciousness of several absolute qualities of musical sound; the stimulus which occasions this complex subjective state is a complex sound-wave made up of the contrasts and co-incidences of several single waves that have the character of simple pendular vibrations. The quality of each clang depends upon the combination of simple waves, of different lengths, within this complex sound-wave.

In the interests of psycho-physical science, or the study of the various qualities and combinations of sensations of sound from the point of view held by physiological psychology, it is not necessary to consider with any detail the mathematics and physics of the waves, whether simple or in combination, which act upon the organ of hearing and so become the stimuli of these sensations. To afford some explanation of those acoustic sensations which appear in consciousness as having an æsthetical value, and which, when combined and arranged in certain ways, give rise to the art of music, it is enough to recall the physical fact that a sounding body, such as a piano string, gives forth when struck not only the "fundamental" pitch to which it is tuned, but also a series of "overtones," the vibration rates of which are 2, 3, 4, 5, 6, 7, 8, 9, 10, etc., times the vibration rate of the fundamental. The string may be said to be vibrating, not only as a whole, but simultaneously in halves, thirds, fourths, etc. The vibrations impressed by the string on the air and by the air on the drum of the ear, are therefore highly compound; and a fundamental fact in the physiology of hearing, as noted in an earlier chapter (see p. 206), is that overtones can, with training and attention, be heard out of a clang, and that therefore the ear must act as an analytic organ. Ordinarily, however, we do not consciously analyze a clang, but experience it as a whole.

Of the whole series of overtones, some are favored by one instrument, and others by another instrument, and thus the tones of the instruments differ. It was an achievement of Helmholtz to analyze the clangs of different instruments, and to show that it is the difference in overtones which gives the peculiar quality to the tone of each instrument, each human voice, each vowel, etc. Instruments which give off few and weak overtones have a soft but rather dull tone; those which favor the lower overtones have a rich but mellow tone; those which favor the higher overtones tend toward shrillness. Besides the overtones, other elements contribute to the peculiar quality of an instrument; e. g., the noises made in operating it, the suddenness with which its sound begins and ends, etc.

§ 28. Of the very numerous pitches which are distinguishable, music makes use of only a small selection. It is not so much the absolute pitches, as the intervals between the notes of the scale, that determine the qualitative effects of the music. The scales in use among the different peoples differ greatly: Chinese music, for example, uses quite a different scale from European music; and the scale used in the native Japanese music may be called "indefinitely pentatonic." The scale of European music has come down from the Greeks, and perhaps from the Egyptians; it is said to have been reduced by the Pythagoreans to a mathematically exact form, according to which the relative vibration rates of the tones of the diatonic scale are as follows:

1st	2d	3d	4th	5th	6th	7th	Octave
C	D	E	F	G	A	B	C^1
1	$\frac{9}{8}$	$\frac{5}{4}$	$\frac{4}{3}$	$\frac{3}{2}$	$\frac{5}{3}$	$\frac{15}{8}$	2
8	9	10	$10\frac{2}{3}$	12	$13\frac{1}{3}$	15	16

That is to say, while the tone C makes one vibration, D makes nine-eighths, and E makes five-fourths, etc.; or while C makes 8 vibrations D makes 9, E makes 10, etc. Of these relations in the number of vibrations, the simplest is, of course, that of the octave, 1 : 2; and the octave seems to be present in almost, or quite, all musical scales; whereas the other intervals are less universal. Even in European music, the practical necessities of instruments with keyboards (the piano, etc.) have led to the abandonment of the strict mathematical ratios, and the substitution of the "equally tempered" scale, in which the octave is first divided into twelve equal semitones, and the different intervals of the scale then built up as well as possible out of these semitones. The result is that all the intervals except the octave are slightly mistuned by comparison with the Pythagorean relations; yet the effect is satisfactory to even musical ears which have become accustomed to this scale.

Indeed, European ears, to which Oriental music seems at first devoid of musical quality, are able, after practice with the Oriental scale, to find beauty in it; and this fact, as well as the fact of the equally tempered scale, suggests that the use of a particular scale is partly a matter of custom. It does not seem possible, in view of all the facts, to lay so much stress on "simple ratios" as was done by the Pythagoreans and many later theorists; yet, on the other hand, it is not possible, at present, to substitute any other theory of the psychology of scale formation which would meet with the general approval of authorities.

§ 29. Modern European music makes great use of the simultaneous sounding of two or more tones, forming chords and discords. A chord or consonance may be described as a combination of tones which gives a smooth and agreeable impression; a discord or dissonance as a combination which gives a rough and disagreeable impression. Among the combinations of two tones, the most perfect consonance is no doubt presented by the octave, with vibration rates of 2 : 1; other recognized consonant pairs are the Fifth (theoretical ratio 3 : 2), the Fourth (4 : 3), the Major Third (5 : 4), Minor Third (6 : 5), Major Sixth (5 : 3), and Minor Sixth (8 : 5). That custom or habituation has much to do with the agreeableness or disagreeableness of many of these combinations is evidenced by the history of European music; for the older music rejected Thirds and Sixths as dissonant, whereas they are extremely satisfactory to modern ears; while recent music makes great use of Seconds, Sevenths, and Ninths, in combination with other notes of the scale. It seems more proper, however, to speak of these dissonances as "tolerated," and to regard the æsthetical pleasure as consisting in an appreciation of this contrast with preceding or following consonance.

Such facts as the foregoing make it difficult to formulate a theory of consonance and dissonance—and yet consonance and dissonance certainly are phenomena which call for explanation, in view of their importance in music, which is, psychologically considered, the most highly developed system of sensory qualities, treated as such, rather than for their associations or meanings. A partial explanation of some of the phenomena of consonance and dissonance is found in a fact brought forward by Stumpf,[1] that if a tone and its octave are sounded together, they not only produce a smooth and agreeable impression, but fuse or blend to such an extent that even a musically trained ear may be in doubt whether one or two tones are being sounded. If, on the contrary,

[1] C. Stumpf, "Konsonanz und Dissonanz," in his *Beiträge zur Akustik und Musikwissentschaft*, 1898, I, 1.

a tone and its Second or Seventh are sounded, the fact that two tones are being sounded is evident, usually, even to an untrained ear. In general, the degree of fusion corresponds to the perfection of the consonance; Stumpf, therefore, suggests that the fusion is the source of the consonance, or, in other words, that the unity of the impression is the measure of its harmoniousness. The physiological basis for the blending of certain tones and the comparative refusal of others to blend, remains to be worked out.

§ 30. It is important in this connection to bear in mind the complexity of the stimulus when two or more tones are sounded together. Each single tone is a clang with overtones. The overtones of one of two complex tones may coincide, to a greater or less extent, with the overtones of the other. In the case of a fundamental tone and its octave, all the overtones of the upper tone coincide with overtones of the lower; but in case of the smaller intervals, the correspondence of overtones is less complete. Thus the degree of consonance runs parallel, to a considerable extent, with the amount of coincidence of overtones; and Helmholtz and others have laid stress on this point in their theories of consonance, and of the relatedness which is felt between the various tones of the scale.

Now we know that when two sounding bodies, of different vibration rates, act on the same body of air, the waves from the one periodically strengthen and weaken the waves from the other; and the number of such "interferences" per second is equal to the difference between the two vibration rates. Thus, if tones of 200 and 201 vibrations are sounded together, the compound tonal effect will wax and wane once a second. This change in intensity can be distinguished, and is called a *beat*. As the difference between the vibration rates becomes greater, the beats become more frequent, and also rougher and more unpleasant, reaching the maximum of unpleasantness at about 30 per second. Beyond this point, the effect of beats becomes less marked, and disappears at a difference in the vibration rate of about 50–60. Rough, unpleasant beats are inconsistent with consonance; this fact, therefore, forms the basis of a negative theory of consonance, which defines dissonance as the presence of beats, and consonance as the absence of dissonance. Helmholtz, who bases his theory of consonance in this way, calls attention to the disagreeableness of other intermittent sensations, such as a flickering light, for example. It is, however, not only the beats of the fundamental tones which have to be considered; for, even if the fundamentals do not beat, their overtones may do so; and in general, the consonances which appear the most perfect are those in which the overtones do not beat observably, whereas the Minor

Third and Minor Sixth, for example, have overtones which produce audible beats.

§ 31. Another element of the complex mass produced by the simultaneous sounding of two tones is the *difference-tone*. If two preferably high tones are sounded together, attentive observation reveals a low tone sounding with them; this low tone is not heard when either of the high tones is sounded alone, but only when the two sound together. The pitch of this additional tone is equal to the difference in vibration rate of the two inducing tones. This induced tone is called the *first* difference-tone, to distinguish it from others of like character but of lower or higher pitch. The external stimulus which gives rise to the difference-tone is the same as that which gives rise to beats—namely, the periodic interference between two sets of waves of different vibration rates; but the starting-point of the difference-tone, as a separate series of vibrations, is apparently in the ear, either in the tympanic membrane or in the fenestra rotunda or ovalis. Difference-tones are, therefore, of importance in connection with theories of hearing; and also in connection with theories of consonance, especially in the explanation of the discordant effect of slightly mistuned intervals. In such intervals, the difference-tones of different order are likely to beat with each other.[1]

When we consider the great complexity of the acoustic effect of a chord of even two tones, with its overtones, beats, difference-tones, and the degree of fusion of all these elements, it is not to be wondered at that students of this branch of psychology have not yet been able to come to a generally acceptable theory of the cause of the harmonious or inharmonious effect of the chord.

[1] See F. Krueger, "Beobachtungen über Zweiklangen," in Wundt's *Philosophische Studien*, 1900, XVI, 307, 568.

CHAPTER II

THE QUALITY OF SENSATIONS (Continued)

§ 1. The analysis of the qualities of different Sensations of Sight is much more intricate than that of any of the other senses. They may all be described as sensations of color and light; but an indefinite number of colors is known to experience, and many degrees of the sensation of light. Moreover the quantity of the white light which acts as stimulus upon the eye has an important effect upon the quality of the resulting color-sensation; in other words, the tone of the color is dependent upon the amount of white light which is mixed with the "*saturated*" spectral color. The size of the colored object and the resulting breadth of the sensation, as well as the intensity of the stimulus and the time during which it acts, also affect the quality of the sensation. Still further, the same stimulus produces different sensations as it falls upon different portions of a normal retina; while a considerable class of persons are color-blind, or incapable of certain kinds of color-sensations. The previous condition of the retina, and the relations between the contiguous portions when any considerable area of it is under stimulation, must also be taken into account. The fundamental laws governing sensations of sight can, therefore, be discovered only by excluding for the time many of those variable elements which, in fact, always enter into the determination of the exact character of our experiences in the use of our eyes. Thus defining the first problem before us, we find that it may be stated in the following terms. What sensations result from the stimulation of a sufficiently small, but not too small, area of the most central part of the normal retina, for a given time, when it is not fatigued and the eye is at rest, and with neither too great nor too small intensity of a given kind of light? Such sensations may be called (though somewhat ineptly) *normal* sensations of color. When the foregoing question is answered we may go on to consider the most important variations possible on account of various forms of departure from the so-called normal conditions of sensation.

§ 2. The ordinary stimulus, the application of which to the eye gives rise to the sensations of sight, is light—or certain exceedingly rapid oscillations of luminiferous ether. Some forms of mechanical and electrical stimuli also produce the same sensations. Any violent shock to the eye, such as a blow upon the back of the head, may fill the whole field of vision with an intense light. The action of mechanical pressure of moderate intensity upon a limited part of the retinal elements may be studied by rolling the eyeball inward and using the fingernail, or a small, blunted stick, upon the outer surface of the closed lids. By such stimulation disks of light (called *phosphenes*), with darkly colored edges, are produced in the field of vision of the closed eye. Some observers have claimed that very strenuous exertion of the apparatus for accommodation occasioned in their eyes similar phenomena ("phosphenes of accommodation"). On making or breaking a weak electrical current sent through the eye, the entire field of vision is lighted up; the constant current also seems to excite the optic nerve. The quality of the sensations thus excited is found to depend upon the direction of the current through the nerve. When the current is ascending, the place where the nerve enters the retina appears as a dark disk upon a field of vision that is brighter than it, and of pale violet color; when it is descending, as a bright bluish disk on a field of dark or reddish-yellow color. The retina has also a "light of its own" (*Eigenlicht*); for its nervous elements are rarely or never inactive, but have a continuous *tonic* excitation. Hence some persons see the most gorgeous and varied coloring, when the eyes are closed in a darkened room. This normal light of the retina is not constant either in degree or in quality; both the form and the color of the different minute parts of the field of vision, as lighted by it, are very changeable. It may be said to have the rhythmic movement of all tonic excitation. Such excitation is supposed to be due to chemical effects, wrought by the changing supply of blood, upon the nervous elements of the retina and (perhaps, also) of the central organs of the brain. The peculiar action of the ascending and descending electrical current has been thought by some[1] to be due to its catelectrotonic or anelectrotonic effect upon the central organs by way of the optic nerve. Aubert has estimated the retina's own light to be about equal (in his case) to half the brightness of a sheet of white paper when seen in the full light of the planet Venus.

§ 3. The place where the light acts (and here, as is supposed, only indirectly through photo-chemical—and perhaps electro-motive—changes in the pigments of the eye) upon the end-organs of vision must be located at the back of the retina in the rods and cones. The argument by which we have already (see p. 194) connected

[1] See Fick, "Physiolog. Optik," in Hermann's *Handb. d. Physiol.*, III, i, p. 230.

the analytic power of vision with the structure of this nervous layer may be carried yet further into details. It appears likely that each element of the structure—at least in some parts of the retina—should be regarded as an isolated sensitive spot, which corresponds on the one side to definite excitations from the appropriate stimuli, and on the other side to the smallest localized sensations of color and light. Accordingly, in order that two visual sensations may be seen as separate, yet side by side, in an object, two neighboring retinal elements must be excited by the stimulus. This implies that the breadth of retinal surface stimulated must be, at least, about that of the distance between two such elements.

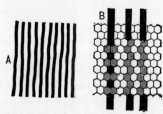

FIG. 117.—*A* shows the appearance of lines drawn very closely together, which is supposed to be due to their falling upon the nervous elements of the retina in the manner shown by *B*.

With this hypothesis the facts of histology and experimental physiology agree fairly well.

The degree of accuracy which sight can attain seems to be related to the size of the retinal elements directly affected by the light. Certain individual differences, either native or due to training, in the fineness of visual discriminations must, apparently, be allowed. Hooke observed that no one can distinguish two stars as two, unless they are apart at least 30″; few, indeed, can distinguish them when less distant from each other than 60″. E. H. Weber could not perceive as separate two lines whose distance did not cover at least 73″ of the angle of vision; Helmholtz puts the limit of his sharpness of vision at 64″. The numbers 60″, 64″, and 73″, in the angle of vision, correspond to a size of the retinal elements varying from 0.00438 mm. to 0.00526 mm.; and this agrees very closely with the calculated breadth (by Kölliker) of the thickness of the cones in the yellow-spot—namely, 0.0045 mm. to 0.0055 mm. (0.000177 in. to 0.0002165 in.). If white lines be drawn on a dark ground so closely together as to approximate this limit of vision, they will appear, not straight, but knotted and nicked. This fact is due to the action of the stimulus on the mosaic of rods and cones, as seen by the accompanying figure (No. 117). The diminishing sharpness of vision as we move away on the surface of the retina from its most central area corresponds to the comparative paucity of the nervous elements, especially of the cones, which enter into the structure of the peripheral parts.

§ 4. Excluding consideration of those changes in the quantity, as such, of visual sensations which are produced by changes in intensity of the light, and confining our attention to what has already been defined as the normal action of the eye, we treat scientifically all the different sensations of sight when we describe (1) the wave-lengths of the different kinds of colored light, or pure color-tones, and (2) the relations in which the different colors stand with re-spect to the amounts of white (or colorless light) and saturated light (or light of pure color-tone) which enter into them. The fore-going distinctions in the quality of our color-sensations may be con-firmed by an appeal to experience. Red is unlike yellow in "color-tone," and both are unlike blue; but orange is more like either red or yellow than it is like blue, while violet is more like blue than it is like either yellow or red. Yet we distinguish colors of the same class (red, green, or violet) as being like or unlike with respect to their "brightness"; and in respect of *brightness*, a certain shade of red may differ more from another shade of red than it differs from some shade of yellow, green, or blue. The brightness of a color is, scientifically speaking, dependent both upon the degree of saturation which the color possesses and upon the total inten-sity of the light.

§ 5. A *color-tone* is said to be "pure" or "saturated" when it is free from all admixture of other color-tones. Pure or saturated color-tones can be obtained only by the use of the spectrum, which, on account of the different refrangibility of the different colored rays that compose it, analyzes the compound ray of white light into its constituent color-tones. By stimulating with different simple rays those nervous elements which have the same local situation at, or very near, the pole of the eye, we test the question whether each special color-sensation corresponds to a special physical con-struction of the stimulus. It is thus discovered that the compound ray of sunlight, so far as it stimulates the human eye, is made up of components formed by oscillations varying all the way between about three hundred and seventy billions and about nine hundred billions per second; and that the color-tone of the sensation changes as the number of these oscillations changes. The table[1] on next page exhibits these facts on the scale of Fraunhofer's lines, which mark those portions of the spectrum where its principal colors ap-pear most obvious to the normal eye.

Rays of light which have a number of oscillations less than four hundred and seventy billions per second, so far as they affect the retina at all, occasion the sensation of Red; and this sensation does not vary essentially in quality when the oscillations are four hundred and forty to four hundred and sixty billions. But when their number

[1] Taken from Fick, "Physiolog. Optik," in Hermann's *Handb. d. Physiolog.*, III. i. p. 173.

increases beyond four hundred and seventy billions (*C*) the quality of the sensation changes rapidly, takes on a yellow tone (Orange-yellow), and finally, at about five hundred and twenty-six billions (*D*), corresponds to what we definitely call Yellow. This yellow becomes greenish as the oscillations increase in number, until they reach about five hundred and eighty-nine billions (*E*), when Green appears. (Changes from yellow to green occupy only a small zone

Name of the line	Number of vibrations per second	Wave-length in the air
	Billions.	Millimetres.
B	450	0.0006878
C	472	0.0006564
D	526	0.0005888
E	589	0.0005260
F	640	0.0004843
G	722	0.0004291
H	790	0.0003928

in the spectrum.) The green in turn becomes bluish; at six hundred and forty billions (*F*) Blue begins to appear. From this point to seven hundred and twenty-two billions (*F–G*) the color-tones that lie between blue and violet are run through; beyond the latter number Violet comes to view.

The color-tones of the spectrum are, therefore, not sharply separated, but pass gradually into each other. The nearer together two colors are situated in the spectrum, the more nearly do they correspond in the quality of their sensations. Nor has the spectrum any sharply defined limit at either end, but passes gradually into black —more gradually at the violet than at the red end. The energy of the *ultra*-red rays, as measured by their physical and chemical action, is greater than that of the more highly refrangible rays. The fact that these rays do not excite visual sensations must, then, be due to the structure of the retina. The *ultra*-violet end of the spectrum has been made visible for a certain extent by experiment;[1] it produces the sensation of a glimmer of lavender-gray color. Our inability to perceive these *ultra*-red and *ultra*-violet rays is not to be considered an imperfection of the eye, as Tyndall thought. It is rather purposeful, and of the greatest importance for vision; since, if these *ultra* rays were visible, the clearness of objects would be much disturbed by the chromatic aberration of the refracting apparatus of the eye.

[1] See Helmholtz, *Physiolog. Optik*, pp. 232 f.

§ 6. Besides the foregoing distinctions of color-tones, the impression made by the green-yellow of the spectrum (*D–E*, and immediately about *D*) is by far the strongest; or, as we should say, this color is naturally the "brightest" of the spectral colors. From

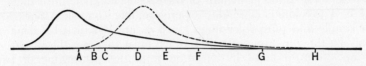

A   B C   D   E   F   G   H

FIG. 118.—(From Fick.) The letters on the horizontal line stand for Fraunhofer's lines. The ordinates of the interrupted curved line show the brightness of rays as seen; the ordinates of the dark curved line, the intensity of the rays as measured by calorific effect.

the region immediately around *D*, the brightness of the color-tones diminishes toward both the red and the violet ends of the spectrum —at first slowly, then more quickly, and then more slowly again. Such a relation cannot be due to the spectrum as an objective affair; for if we measure by other physical means the amount of energy belonging to its different regions, we find that of the red rays (which are by no means brightest) to be strongest. We must, then, seek an explanation in the structure of the retina, and conclude that it is peculiarly sensitive to stimulations by oscillations of about five hundred and fifty billions per second (compare Fig. 118). The sensitiveness of the retina to slight variations in color-tone, as dependent upon differences in the wave-lengths of the stimulus, is also different at different portions of the spectrum. It is greatest in the green and blue-green regions (*D* and *F*).

The following table represents both the foregoing laws. The numbers of the second and third columns show the relative bright-

	Fraunhofer	Vierordt	Mandelstamm and Dobrowolsky	
Red, *B*	32	22	*B*	$\frac{1}{113}$
Orange, *C*	94	128	*C*	$\frac{1}{167}$
Reddish-yellow, *D*	640	780	*C–D*	$\frac{1}{331}$
Yellow, *D–E*	1,000	1,000	*D*	$\frac{1}{7½2}$
Green, *E*	480	370	*D–E*	$\frac{1}{246}$
Blue-green, *F*	170	128	*E*	$\frac{1}{340}$
Blue, *G*	31	8	*E–F*	$6\frac{1}{5}$
Violet, *H*	5.6	0.7	*F*	$\frac{1}{740}$
			G	$\frac{1}{272}$
			H	$\frac{1}{146}$

ness with which the different colors of the spectrum appear to the eye, as calculated by different methods and by two observers. It will be seen that the results agree substantially, though by no means perfectly. In the last two columns the letters stand for Fraunhofer's lines, and the figures give the fractional variation in the wave-lengths which produces an observable variation in the color-tone for different regions of the spectrum.

§ 7. The colors of every-day experience, like its musical tones, are not simple and pure color-tones, such as are obtained by spectral analysis; they are composite. Inquiry must therefore be raised as to the effect produced in sensation from the co-working of two homogeneous rays of light upon the same elements of the retina under all the normal conditions to which reference was previously made. In pursuing this inquiry no direct assistance can be obtained from the discriminations of consciousness; for sensations of color, unlike those of musical clang, cannot be mentally analyzed into their constituent elements. The science of optics makes us acquainted, however, with the following facts: When the wave-lengths of the two colors mixed vary but slightly (a few billions of oscillations in a second) from each other, the color resulting from the mixture lies between, and may be recognized as a "shade" of, the colors mixed. By selecting for mixture color-tones that lie apart at the various distances possible along the spectrum, an indefinite number of impressions of color may be obtained, which all differ from those obtained by the homogeneous colors. These *mixed color-impressions* classify in such a way, however, that the number of the qualities of resulting sensations is far less than that of the compound physical processes which stimulate the retina.

The character of the colors making up our ordinary visual experience depends both upon the place in the spectrum from which the simple color-tones are selected for mixture, and also upon the relative intensity of the ones selected. For example, if a ray of four hundred and fifty billions of oscillations per second (red) be mixed with one of seven hundred and ninety billions (violet), a new series of impressions of color (the purples) is attained by varying the intensities of the two. These impressions are more or less like red or like violet, according to the relative amounts of the rays of four hundred and fifty billions and of seven hundred and ninety billions which enter into the mixture. Moreover, there are found to be two ways of advancing by this process of mixing color-tones toward any one of the composite colors. Thus, we may pass from yellow to blue either through green-yellow, green, and blue-green, or through orange, red, purple, and violet. The table[1] on next page is of interest in this connection. Where two colors are given as

---

[1] Made according to investigations by J. J. Müller. and taken from Fick, in Hermann's *Handb. d. Physiol.*, III. i, p. 14.

resulting from the mixture, the variation is to be understood as dependent upon the prevailing intensity of one of the two components.

§ 8. The *number of colors* distinguishable by the human eye is
not easily stated with accuracy; like the number of musical tones,
it varies with different individuals. The usual number of seven

Components	Tone of the color obtained by mixture	Degree of saturation
Red and Yellow............	Orange.....................	Spectral.
Orange and Yellow-green....	Yellow.....................	Spectral.
Yellow and Green...........	Yellow-green...............	Whitish.
Yellow-green and Blue-green.	Green......................	Very whitish.
Green and Cyanic Blue......	Blue-green.................	Whitish.
Blue-green and Indigo.......	Cyanic Blue................	Spectral.
Cyanic Blue and Violet......	Indigo.....................	Spectral.
Red and Yellow-green.......	Orange or Yellow...........	Spectral.
Red and Green.............	Orange or Yellow or Yellow-green....................	Whitish.
Violet and Blue-green.......	Indigo or Cyanic Blue.......	Spectral.
Violet and Green...........	Indigo or Cyanic Blue or Blue-green....................	Whitish.
Violet and Orange..........	Red........................	Whitish.
Red and Cyanic Blue.......	Indigo or Violet............	Whitish.
Red and Indigo............	Violet.....................	Slightly whitish.

fundamental colors, as fixed by Newton, with the intent of forming
an octave in the scale of color-tones, has no sufficient claim to
acceptance. Six of the seven—namely, red, orange, yellow, green,
blue, violet—are indeed names in common use. But indigo, as an
intermediate tone, or kind of semi-tone, between blue and violet
has perhaps no more real right to recognition than various other
intermediate color-tones. Donders put the number of color-tones
distinguishable in oil-colors at one hundred; Von Kries the recognizable number of spectral tints at about two hundred and thirty.
But, as has already been said, colors also differ according to the
degree of their saturation or purity, due to freedom from admixture of white light. Another series of variations of sensation must
be allowed for, which are due to differences in "brightness" or
intensity. Introducing these two variable elements, Von Kries
calculates the number of distinctions of color-sensations, possible
for all degrees of purity of tone and intensity of light, at about five
hundred thousand to six hundred thousand. This number stands
midway between the "many millions" of which Aubert speaks and
the five thousand allowed by Donders. Herschel thought that the

workers on the mosaics of the Vatican must have distinguished at least thirty thousand different colors.

§ 9. Experiment also shows that if certain color-tones with a given intensity are united on the retina, the result is a sensation unlike that of any other of the colors, whether pure or mixed. This sensation we call "white," and the two colors which by their admixture produce it are called "complementary." *Complementary colors* may be mixed upon the retina in various ways; either by allowing two spectral rays properly selected to be superimposed at the same spot, or by blending the reflected images of two colored wafers, or by blending the direct visual impressions of colored surfaces on a swiftly revolving top or wheel, etc. But however mixed, the resultant sensation is that of a so-called "white" color, in which all trace of the constituent elements is lost. Following is a table of complementary colors [1]: the wave-lengths are given in millionths of a millimetre.

Color	Wave-length	Complementary color	Wave-length	Relation of wave-lengths
Red...............	656.2	Green-blue.......	492.1	1,334
Orange...........	607.7	Blue............	489.7	1,240
Gold-yellow	585.3	Blue	485.4	1,206
Gold-yellow.......	573.9	Blue............	482.1	1,190
Yellow...........	567.1	Indigo-blue......	464.5	1,221
Yellow...........	564.4	Indigo-blue.......	461.8	1,222
Green-yellow......	563.6	Violet...........	433. {and less}	1,301

It will be noted that no complementaries are assigned for the colors between green-yellow and green-blue, with wave-lengths from five hundred and sixty-four to four hundred and ninety-two. In other words, the central greens have no complementary colors within the limits of the spectrum. In the series of color sensations, however, green has a complementary, namely purple, the stimulus for which is a mixture of long and short wave-lengths.

§ 10. If the foregoing facts and laws are held to be true of the "normal" connection between light and visual sensations, then various classes of circumstances must be taken account of as "abnormal," which, nevertheless, enter into all our daily experience with this sense. Indeed, the connection between stimulus and sensation is not the same for different individuals who possess substantially the same color-sensations; frequently the complementary colors for two different individuals are not precisely the same.

[1] From Helmholtz, *op. cit.*, p. 277.

Even the two eyes of the same individual often differ perceptibly in this regard. Important changes in the quality of the sensations, other than those directly ascribable to changes in the wave-lengths of light, take place when the intensity of the light approaches either a maximum or a minimum. At the maximum intensities of the stimulus all sensations of color-tone cease, and even homogeneous rays appear white. Previous to reaching this maximum, red and yellowish green pass over into yellow, and bluish green and violet into blue. At the minimum intensities of light every color-tone except the pure red of spectral saturation appears colorless when seen alone on a perfectly black ground.

In other words, light of any wave-length can be weakened till it gives no sensation of color, while still giving a sensation of light. There is, accordingly, a "photo-chromatic interval" between the threshold for the perception of light and the threshold for the perception of the color of the light; but this interval is extremely small or absent in the case of the longest waves which give the sensation of red. This phenomenon is closely connected with the process of dark-adaptation, which has been described in an earlier chapter (see p. 195) and may be restated as follows: With decreasing illumination, the retina becomes "adapted," or gets into a condition in which it is sensitive to very faint lights, but does not respond with sensations of color to these very faint lights.   Moreover, this adaptation, or increase in sensitiveness, varies greatly with the different wave-lengths; and, indeed, scarcely exists at all with those which produce sensations of red.

§ 11. Changes of color also take place when *the time* of the action of the light is reduced to a minimum. Sensations of saturated color can be produced by instantaneous illumination of the spectrum with the electrical spark. More time is needed, however, to produce these sensations with smaller intensities of the light. The different colors, even when of the same brightness, appear to require different amounts of time in order to reach the maximum of their effect—red, 0.0573; blue, 0.0913; green, 0.133 of a second. The tone of the color varies with the duration of the impression as well as with the intensity of the light. Very minute objects, too, appear of a different color on account of their size.   In general, the larger the surface, the less the intensity of the light necessary to produce the sensation of any particular color-tone; the greater the intensity of the light, the smaller the surface which will suffice for such sensation.   Fick[1] showed that the color-sensations derived from small *distinct* points support each other, as it were, in the same way as the contiguous points of a colored surface.   For if we make

[1] *Pflüger's Archiv*, XVII, p. 152.

with a fine needle a single hole (of about 0.6 mm. in diameter) in a sheet of paper and look through it at colored paper distant some six and a half metres, the color of the paper cannot be distinguished. But if the number of holes be as many as sixteen, the color can be distinguished at the same distance, even when the holes through which we look are smaller. Subsequent experiment has shown that the smaller the distance between the single perforations, the greater the distance at which the eye can recognize colors through them. In general, then, two weak sensations, both of which belong to one eye, may fuse together into one stronger sensation.

§ 12. Very important changes in the visual sensations occur as dependent on *the part of the retina* which is stimulated. In this respect a great difference exists between the central and the peripheral parts. The entire field of this organ may be somewhat indefinitely divided into three zones—a central or polar, a middle, and an outer or peripheral. It is probably true that the peripheral parts of the retina produce no sensations which cannot be produced by stimulating the central zone. But it is equally true that, under the same circumstances, the same stimulus produces a markedly different effect upon sensation when applied to different localities of the retina. Rays which, falling on the polar zone, produce the impression of red, yellow, or green, all make an impression of yellow when they fall on the surrounding zone (a few millimetres from the *fovea centralis*); and this yellow is so much the paler, the greener the impression on the polar zone. Rays which make on the polar zone the impression of blue or violet make on the outer zone the impression of blue; and this blue is so much the paler, the nearer the impression on the polar zone is to green.

Any conclusions which we might be tempted to draw, as to physiological differences in the different parts of the retina, in dependence upon histological differences, are somewhat complicated by the fact that a *certain* red, a *certain* yellow, a *certain* green, and a *certain* blue can be found, which do not undergo this change of color-tone in passing from the polar to the intermediate zone; but the yellow and the blue remain unchanged, while the red and the green change directly into gray, without first changing to yellow or blue. These four special color-tones are, therefore, called the *stable colors:* the stable yellow and blue are about what we should ordinarily call a typical yellow or blue; but the stable red is a somewhat purplish red, lying outside of the spectrum; and the stable green is a somewhat bluish green, as described in customary terms. The stable blue and yellow are complementary, and this is true also of the stable red and green.

The so-called stable colors are clearly of great theoretical importance; and the more so because of the following curious fact: If the stable yellow and blue are made of such relative intensity that, when mixed, they give a white or gray, the limit at which they lose their color and become gray, on being moved toward the periphery, is the same for both; and, similarly, if the stable red and green are of such relative intensity as to give gray when mixed, both change to gray at the same limit, on passing from the polar region outward.[1]

§ 13. A certain proportion of persons (from three to five per cent. of males, and apparently a much smaller proportion of females) have a defect of vision which is known as "color-blindness." There are several forms of color-blindness, in one of which (very rare) no distinctions of color are possible, but only of brightness; and the spectrum appears to such persons as differing, from part to part, only in intensity. Light of any color appears to them identical with light of any other color, provided the intensities be rightly proportioned. In dim light, the vision of these individuals is the same as that of normal persons, who also, it will be recalled (see p. 333), lose color-vision under similar conditions. With the increase of light, the normal eye begins to distinguish colors, i. e., to observe qualitative differences between different parts of the spectrum; but this the totally color-blind eye fails to do. The further fact that, often at least, the yellow spot of the totally color-blind eye yields no visual sensations whatever, suggests that such an eye possesses only rod-vision and no cone-vision (compare pp. 195 f.).

Much more common, however, are the cases of blindness to certain colors, or, more correctly expressed, of inability to distinguish certain colors which are readily distinguished by the normal eye. It should be said that, though we speak of the normal eye as distinguished from the color-blind, there is no diseased condition present in the color-blind eye. The defect is inherited, and is perfectly consistent with normal vision in all other respects except that of distinguishing certain colors. In the form which is called "red-green blindness," the colors which are most frequently confused are shades of red and green, or of purple and greenish blue. By properly adjusting the intensity and saturation, it is possible to produce confusion, in these persons, of any of the color-tones that lie between red and green, and also of any lying between purple and greenish blue. More precisely studied, the color-vision of these individuals is found to reduce—apart from matters of intensity and

[1] See a review of the somewhat conflicting literature on this point, and an experimental research establishing the above results, in Baird's *The Color Sensitivity of the Peripheral Retina* (Washington, 1905).

saturation—to a single qualitative distinction; and this is the distinction between two colors that are excited, respectively, by the long waves and by the short waves of light. From the red end of the spectrum to a point in the green (wave-length about 490–500), all visual sensations are with such persons shadings of a single color; and any part of the scale may be matched with any other provided the intensities are rightly selected. In similar manner, from this point in the green to the violet (and purple), all is a shading of a single color. Colors taken from opposite sides of this limiting point in the green are, however, clearly distinguished. This boundary itself is indistinguishable from gray; and the particular mixture of long and short wave-lengths, which produces in the normal eye the impression of a purplish red complementary to this green, to the color-blind eye is also indistinguishable from gray.

What precisely are the color-sensations of the red-green blind individual—whether his white and gray look the same to him as white and gray look to the normal individual, and whether the red half of the spectrum seems to him shaded in red, or in yellow, the blue half in blue or in violet—is a difficult question to approach; since evidently normal and color-blind individuals cannot "compare notes" on such a matter. There have been examined one or two cases of color-blindness confined to one eye, while the other saw normally; and the testimony of these individuals seems to indicate that, to the color-blind eye, gray and white appear the same as to the normal eye, but that the red end of the spectrum is shaded in yellow, and the blue end in blue.

Under the head of red-green blindness are recognized two subclasses, sometimes called the red-blind and the green-blind, the difference being that the red-blind are comparatively insensitive to reds near the end of the spectrum. A few (pathological) cases have also been observed of a different form of color-blindness, called blue or yellow-blue blindness. This form of color-vision, like that in red-green blindness, is dichromatic, and apparently the two colors retained are red and green. In these cases, the neutral point in the spectrum falls in the yellow.

§ 14. Color-blindness is evidently of great importance for an understanding of normal color-vision; we may even say that dichromatic vision, from its greater simplicity, is better understood than the normal, polychromatic form. The evidence, so far as it goes, shows that the color-vision of the red-green blind agrees exactly with that of the intermediate yellow-blue zone of the normal retina; the two agree, at any rate, in being dichromatic.

§ 15. Important modifications of the normal action of the retina are also produced by *previous excitation*. The most important of these changes is the adaptation to dark or to light which has already been described.   Let us assume that the eye has been exposed for some time to light of a moderate intensity, and that it is then turned upon a much brighter light, with prolonged fixation, and the latter will appear to grow less bright; but if, after this, the eye is turned back on its previous moderate light, this appears darker than before. If, however, the eye is turned from moderate light to a dark field, the latter seems to grow brighter with continued fixation; and if then the eye is returned to the moderate field, this appears brighter than before.   These effects can be seen more strikingly, if only a part of the field of view is bright or dark.   After gazing steadily, for example, at a bright patch on a medium background, and then turning to a uniform medium surface, a dark patch appears on this, corresponding to the light patch previously fixated; and this dark spot moves about on the background, as the eyes move.   If, similarly, a black spot on a gray ground is gazed at, and then the eye turned to a plain gray ground, the place of the black spot is now taken by a bright spot.   If a figure containing both bright and dark parts is fixated, and the eyes are then turned to the gray field, an image of the figure appears, bright where the figure was dark and dark where it was bright.   This residual effect of excitation is called the *negative* after-image.

Negative after-images of colors are also seen, the colors of the image being complementary to those of the stimulus.   If, for example, a green spot is steadily fixated, it appears to lose some of its color, becoming less saturated; and if then the eye is turned to a plain gray field, there appears, in place of the green, its complementary purple.   If the eye is turned from green to a purple ground, the after-image of the green is still seen, in the form of a spot of still deeper purple; it is in this way that the most saturated color effects possible can be obtained.   These after-images can be explained in terms of adaptation, or in terms of fatigue.   A full explanation, however, would need to take account of many curious details, one or two of which are worth mentioning.   When a patch of color is being steadily fixated, it not only grows less saturated, but also changes its color-tone; under such conditions, it seems to approach either yellow or blue—the colors which are nearer to yellow approaching yellow, and those which are nearer to blue approaching blue.   Yellow and blue, themselves, however, do not change their color-tone on prolonged fixation; nor do two other colors—namely, a bluish green and a purplish red.   These four colors are stable here as they were in passing from central to peripheral vision.[1]   A further detail is that the color of the after-image,

[1] Voeste, *Zeitschrift f. Psychol.*, 1898, XVIII, 257.

after strong stimulation, changes from moment to moment, and passes through a series of colors.

§ 16. Another difficulty in the way of a simple conception of the after-image is the existence of *positive* after-images, between which and the negative it is not easy to draw any valid distinction. The names positive and negative are indeed justified by the fact that the positive after-image presents both color and light-and-dark sensations as they appear during the direct action of the stimulus; whereas the negative after-image reverses everything. In order to study the positive after-image we need only to look for a second or two at some luminous object, and then close the eyes or turn them toward a dark ground. A bright image of the luminous object will be seen for a few seconds. Longer fixation favors the negative image; when both are obtained, the positive precedes, though, in case of the prolonged images which follow looking at a very bright object (as the sun), changes occur from negative to positive and back again as the background is changed from light to dark. Thus the whole series of facts becomes rather complicated, and this is still more the case when minute examination is directed to the immediate after-effects of the stimulus. These effects can be best examined when the stimulus is moved at a moderate rate over a dark ground, while the eye remains fixed in position; the after-effects then appear strung out behind the moving light. Three images appear, separated by dark spaces; of these, the first image corresponds to the sight of the light itself; the second is fairly sharp, and often called the "ghost"; the third is less sharp and passes over gradually into black. Translating the spatial relations of this experiment into terms of time, we conclude that, when a light acts on the retina for an instant, the first, wholly positive effect outlasts the stimulus for a small fraction of a second, and is succeeded by a brief interval of no effect, then by a recurrence of light effect, then by another interval and another recurrence of light which gradually fades out and gives place to a negative effect (black). The three images may all be called positive, except that the "ghost" is negative as regards color.[1] Many other details have been observed, but these are sufficient to show something of the intricacy of the reaction of the retina to light, and the difficulty of forming a clear conception of what takes place. Individual peculiarities appear to count for much in these, as in all other details, of our visual experience.

§ 17. The different parts of the retina are interdependent in the production of sensation; or—to employ the statement of Wundt[2] —"The sensation which arises through the stimulation of any given

[1] See W. McDougall, *British Journal of Psychology*, 1904, I, 78.
[2] Quoted from the *Grundzüge d. physiolog. Psychologie* (2d ed., I, p. 439).

point of the retina is also a function of the state of other immediately contiguous points." Hence arise, in part at least, the phenomena of *contrast*, which are of two kinds—contrast of brightness and contrast of color-tone. The fundamental fact in the first class of contrasts is this: every bright object appears brighter with surroundings darker than itself, and darker with surroundings brighter than itself. These phenomena are explained by Helmholtz[1] as deceptions of judgment, such as we are accustomed to in our estimates of distances. To this explanation, however, Fick,[2] Hering[3], and others oppose strong and apparently conclusive objections. They would explain the same phenomena by the modifying influence of the excitation of one part of the retina upon the excitation of contiguous parts.

When colored instead of white light is used in experimenting under the law of contrast, phenomena similar to those of complementary colors are obtained   A small square of white on a surface of green, when covered with a transparent sheet of tissue-paper, appears as red on a surrounding surface of a whitish hue; on a red ground it appears as green, on a blue ground as yellow, and *vice versa*. More complicated illustrations of this principle of interdependence may be obtained in various ways. For example, if on a pale-green background, in size 36 mm. by 44 mm., which is divided into squares of 1.8 mm. by lines of white 0.4 mm. in width, a red letter E, 21 mm. by 34 mm. in size, be constructed out of similar squares, on observing the figure for a few seconds with a fixed gaze, some of the red squares will disappear and be replaced by green squares similar to the background.[4] Or if on sheets of different colored paper, 20 cm. by 30 cm. in size, small strips, 1 cm. by 20 cm., of various colors are laid, as on a background, and the whole then observed at a distance of about 3 m. with a fixed gaze, exceedingly varied illusions of disappearance and substitution may be obtained.[5]

These, and similar phenomena, of which a great variety might be mentioned, certainly cannot be explained as *deceptions* of "judgments" in any justifiable meaning of the term. They do, however, all seem to imply some physiological explanation which ascribes to each part of the retina an influence on contiguous parts. Still less in accordance with the facts of experience would the view of Helmholtz appear to be, in the cases of those individuals who can

[1] *Physiolog. Optik*, pp. 388 ff.
[2] Hermann's *Handb. d. Physiologie*, III, i, 231 f.
[3] *Sitzgsber. d. Wiener Acad.*, June, 1872; Dec., 1873.
[4] Fick's *Lehrb. d. Augenheilkunde*, 1897, p. 50.
[5] Ladd, "A Color Illusion," *Yale Studies*, VI, 1898.

by an act of will produce, with eyes closed, simple colored shapes in the retinal field, which upon opening the eyes will cast their complementary images upon a white background.[1]

§ 18. It will by this time readily be seen that a *theory* which shall satisfactorily account for all the complicated phenomena of visual sensations is difficult to establish. Though ingenuity of the highest order has been employed in the development of theories of color vision, not all the phenomena are well explained by any one theory. Among the more significant facts which must find a place in any adequate explanation are the following: (1) The colorless vision which occurs in dim light, in the outer zone of the retina, and over the whole retina in cases of total color-blindness. The conception of two kinds of vision, one making no distinction of colors, and provided for, probably, by the rods, the other distinguishing colors and provided for by the cones, serves admirably to explain these facts, and a number of other details. This theory is associated principally with the name of Von Kries (compare pp. 195 f.). With colorless vision thus explained, as the function of the rods of the retina, there remain to be explained only the facts of color-vision.

(2) The principal facts of color mixture are, first, the discovery of Newton that all the colors of the rainbow, when mixed in proper proportion, produce the sensation of white; then the fact of complementary colors, i. e., that pairs of colors, suitably chosen, mix to produce the sensation of white; and further the fact that all color-tones can be produced by the mixture of three (or more, but not less than three) properly chosen colors.

(3) To these two classes of facts must be added the facts of after-images and of contrast; and (4) The existence of dichromatic vision, in the intermediate zone of the retina, in red-green blindness, in intense illumination, and (partially at least) in the prolonged exposure of the eye to light of a fixed color. In explanation of the effect of intense light, and of the dichromatic zone of the retina, we know that the two colors to which vision is reduced are yellow and blue; in the case of color-blindness we are not so sure, but the indications point to the same two colors; in the case of prolonged fixating of one color, again, the color tends to change toward yellow or blue, i. e., there is a tendency to dichromatic vision with these two colors remaining. In all these cases, moreover, special interest attaches to a certain bluish green, and its complementary, a purplish red, since these are "stable," not being reduced completely to, or in the direction of, yellow and blue, but changing directly to gray or white.

[1] See Ladd, " On the Direct Control of the Retinal Field," *Psychol. Rev.*, July, 1894; Mar., 1903.

(5) The psychological simplicity of white, i. e., the fact that it cannot be introspectively analyzed into colors, though its stimulus is always a complex of color stimuli, is also of prime importance. Black, too, seems a positive and elementary sensation. It should be noted that the occasion on which this sensation arises is not, precisely (as was formerly held), the absence of all light; for prolonged absence of light gives rather the sensation of gray, and deep black comes always as an effect of contrast or as an after-image. All of the colors, to many psychological analysts, appear equally elementary; though others assert that orange, for example, seems to them, introspectively analyzed, to consist of red and yellow components.

§ 19. Of the theories which attempt to account for the facts of our experience with color sensations, it will be sufficient to refer to the two most prominent; but this must be done with the understanding that, as neither of these has yet proved itself perfectly adequate, constant attempts are still required to supplement or modify them both, when taken singly and together. One of these theories is called the Young-Helmholtz theory, having been propounded by Thomas Young, and elaborated and defended by Helmholtz; the other bears the name of Ewald Hering. The Young-Helmholtz theory approaches the matter from the side of physics, i. e., primarily from the facts of color mixture; the Hering theory takes its start rather from physiological and psychological facts, such as the apparent simplicity and positiveness of white and black, the facts of contrast, etc.

Since all color-tones can be produced by mixing no fewer than three of the number, there must apparently exist at least three sorts of receptors or sensitive substances in the retina, each of them attuned to ether vibrations of different wave-lengths. The Young-Helmholtz theory supposes that there are, in fact, three such substances, one of them attuned to the long waves of the red end of the spectrum, one to the short waves of the blue end, and one to waves of intermediate length. Since, however, color-sensations arise from stimulation by waves of any length, within the limits of the visible spectrum, each of the three substances must be excitable, not simply by waves of one length, but also, in diminishing degree, by waves differing from this length. The relative sensitivity of the three substances to light-waves of different lengths would be somewhat as indicated by the curves in the accompanying diagram, in which the horizontal distances denote distances in the spectrum, the lettered lines indicating the prominent lines of the spectrum. The height of the curve G over any part of the spectrum, indicates the sensitivity of the "green-receiving substance" to light from that part of the spectrum; and the same for the curves

R and *B,* which show the varying sensitivity of the red and of the blue (or violet) receptors. Light of any wave-length, according to this diagram, would stimulate all three receptors, but in varying degrees according to its length. White light would excite all of them equally, we may suppose.

§ 20. The theory of Hering is even more ingenious. It supposes, first, that white light is not, physiologically, a mixture of colors, but is due to the excitation of a special "brightness-receptor," which responds, though in unequal degrees, to light of any wave-

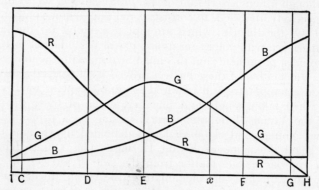

FIG. 119.—Diagram from Fick, illustrating the Young-Helmholtz Theory.
(For explanation, see the text.)

length. The whole white-black series, including all the shades of neutral gray, is therefore due to the activity of this receptor, which is accordingly named the "white-black substance." But the sensation of black, according to Hering, is not due to the total inactivity of the white-black substance, but to a form of activity opposed to that which occurs in response to bright light. This one receptor is supposed to have two opposite forms of activity, which give the sensations of the opposites, white and black. What the two forms of activity may be, is not of so great consequence; Hering supposed them to be anabolism or assimilation, and catabolism or dissimilation—the latter resulting from the action of bright light, and the former from the action of lights more dim than that to which the retina is, at any particular time, adapted. Other opposed chemical or electrical processes would, however, do as well.

Now if white and gray are due to the activity of a special receptor, and not to the mixture of color-impressions, it follows that color stimuli, when mixed, as they are in sunlight or in complementary colors, must have the power of neutralizing each other; and so allowing free play to the white-black process. The so-called primary colors must, therefore, exist in pairs, the members of each pair being antagonistic. Hering therefore assumed, in addition to his white-black substance, two other receptors, one for yellow and blue, the other for red and green. The red must be slightly purplish and the green slightly bluish, in order that they may be exactly complementary and thus antagonistic. Light of long wave-length excites in the yellow-blue receptor a process which gives us the sensation of yellow; but the short wave-lengths arouse in it an opposite process, which gives us the sensation of blue. If both long and short waves reach the receptor at once, the one neutralizes the other, and the receptor remains at rest, leaving the white-black receptor to act. Most colored lights excite simultaneously all three receptors, and the resulting sensation is compounded of so much light (or dark), so much yellow (or blue), and so much red (or green).

§ 21. Without attempting to evaluate these opposing theories by applying them in detail to the many facts which have to be explained, we may say that both are equally good as applied to the facts of color mixture; while neither seems inconsistent with the main facts of contrast and after-images. The psychological analysis of colors as simple or as positive is perhaps of no conclusive weight; but of all the facts, the most crucial seem to be those of dichromatic vision. The most promising way of approaching an explanation of these facts, with either theory, is therefore to suppose that color-blindness is due to the absence, or lack of functional power, of one set of color receptors; since, in either theory, the subtraction of one set of receptors would leave dichromatic vision. This same explanation could also be applied to the intermediate dichromatic zone of the retina. The Young-Helmholtz theory has a certain advantage in dealing with the two classes of the red-green blind, which it supposes to be due to the absence, respectively, of the red-receptors and of the green-receptors, and accordingly names red-blind and green-blind. But other facts strongly favor the Hering theory. For in the intermediate zone of the retina it is certain, and in red-green blindness rather probable, that dichromatic vision is yellow-blue vision. Now if yellow and blue are two of the primary colors, since they are complementary, no other single primary would suffice; for white light could not be secured by the mixture of two complementaries with any other single color; nor could all the colors be produced by the mixture of three such colors. In fact, only half the range of color-tones could be produced by such mixtures. The facts of dichromatic vision, therefore, apparently make impossible any three-color theory for normal vision. There must, accordingly, be at least *four* primary colors; and if four, the two besides yellow and blue must themselves be complementary, in order that the mixture of all four may give white. This turns our minds back to the two stable colors—colors which, each singly, become gray in dichromatic vision—the bluish green and its complementary purplish red. These are the red and green which Hering chose for primaries, and there can be no doubt that the peculiar behavior of these two particular colors, as revealed in the studies of recent years, has done much to strengthen the Hering theory, at least as far as concerns the selection of the primary colors.

§ 22. Much ingenuity and painstaking have been expended in devising some form of *symbolism* which should represent to the eye in geometrical relations the laws of the sensations of light and color. Obviously the sensations of this sense cannot, like those of hearing, be symbolized by the relations of points along a straight line. Color-tones, unlike musical tones, form a series of qualitatively different sensations that, at certain places in the scale, separate from each other with varying degrees of rapidity, and then toward the broken ends, as it were, of this scale, tend to approach each other again. Such relations are, perhaps, most successfully set forth by a triangle in which the different color-tones may be regarded as lying together along a curved line, from red to violet, and the difference in any two color-tones as measured by the angle which two lines make when drawn from a point within the triangle through the points occupied on the curve by the two color-tones.

§ 23. Of sensations arising from excitation of the Skin, introspection enables us readily to distinguish those of *temperature* as different in quality from those of *contact* and *pressure;* and to separate sensations of warmth as different in quality from those of cold. Further, the sensation of pain which comes from pricking the skin can scarcely be regarded as anything but a distinct quality of sensation (i. e., in the narrower meaning of both words, "pain" and "sensation"). These introspective distinctions are corroborated in a most interesting way by experiments with minutely localized stimuli applied to the skin. Such experimentation[1] reveals the existence of what are called "touch-spots," "warmth-spots," "cold-spots," and "pain-spots." If a small area of the skin, free or freed from hairs, is explored, first with a bristle or hair which requires very little force to bend it, no sensation is felt at most points on pressing the end of the hair against the skin, but at certain points,

---

[1] Since it was inaugurated by Blix in 1882, by Goldscheider in 1884, and by Donaldson in 1885, this work has been continued by Von Frey, Kiesow, Alrutz, and many others. See Goldscheider's *Gesammelte Abhandlungen, Physiologie der Hautsinnesnerven* (Leipzig, 1908), also Sherrington in Schäfer's *Textbook of Physiology*, 1900, II, 920–1001, and Thunberg in Nagel's *Handbuch der Physiologie*, 1905, III, 647–733.

a clear sensation of touch emerges. These are the touch-spots (Fig. 120); and if they are marked for identification and retested on another day, careful exploration finds their arrangement unchanged. If, next, the skin is explored with a brass cone, cooled a few degrees below the temperature of the skin, and applied with its (somewhat rounded) point against the skin, no temperature sensation will be felt at most points; but at certain points a clear sensation of cold appears. These cold-spots are not identical with the

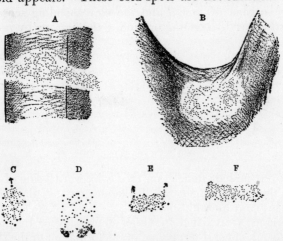

FIG. 120.—Arrangement of Pressure-spots (Goldscheider). *A*, dorsal and radial surface of the first phalanx of the index finger; *B*, membrane between thumb and index finger; *C*, dorsal surface of forearm; *D*, back; *E*, inner surface of forearm; *F*, back of hand.

touch-spots (see Fig. 121). Exploration with a warm cone brings out, though with more difficulty, the existence of another series of spots specifically sensitive to warmth; and exploration with a fine-pointed needle or stiff bristle reveals numerous spots which give a sharp, minute, pricking sensation. The pressure needed to excite these pain-spots is much greater than that needed for the touch-spots.

The skin thus resembles a mosaic of differently sensitized spots; it differs from a mosaic in this, however, that there are insensitive spots between those which are sensitive. No great care is required to convince oneself of the general truth of these observations; but, on the other hand, great care is necessary to reach precise results, largely because of the difficulty of properly confining the stimulus to the point which it is desired, at any moment, to examine; if the pressure, the warmth, or the cold, is too great, it spreads quickly to neighboring regions and the observations become uncertain and confused.

§ 24. The number of spots of the four varieties already mentioned is, in general, very unequal,—the warmth-spots being the fewest, and the pain-spots the most numerous. The relative numbers may be roughly stated as 1 warmth-spot to 10 cold, 10 touch, and 40 pain-spots. This proportion varies, however, in different parts of the skin. From the cornea, for example, it seems that only sensations of pain arise; while from certain areas on the inner surface of the cheek, over against the gums, no sensations of pain can be elicited.[1] Hairs are organs of touch, and the corresponding sensation can be aroused either by bending or pulling the hair, or by pressure on

Fig. 121.—Arrangement of Temperature-spots. A, cold-spots; and B, warmth-spots—
from the palm of the left hand (Goldscheider).

the skin over the hair follicle, on the "windward" side of the point of exit of the hair. In general, the arrangement of the spots seems to be irregular within any small area.

Touch-spots are excited by either depressing or by pulling out the skin, or, in general terms, by any deformation of the skin; they can also be excited by electricity. Pain-spots can be excited mechanically, electrically, chemically, or thermally; they seem to be adapted to receive any stimulus which is intense enough, or almost intense enough, to injure the skin. Cold-spots can be aroused, not only by cold objects, but also by warm objects ("the paradoxical sensation of cold"); warmth-spots cannot, perhaps, be aroused by anything but warmth.

§ 25. Concerning the exact nature of temperature stimuli, two theories are in the field. The one (that of Weber) holds that the warmth organs are excited whenever the temperature of the skin is rising, and the cold receptors whenever the temperature of the skin is falling. The other theory, by Hering, holds that any portion of the skin is, at any moment, adapted to a certain temperature, which may be called its zero or indifference point;[2] and that temperatures above this zero point excite the sensation of warmth, and temperatures below the sensation of cold or cool. The difference between the two theories will become clearer when applied to the fol-

[1] Kiesow, in Wundt's *Philosophische Studien*, 1898, XIV, 567.
[2] More properly speaking, not a "point," but a zone extending for about the space of one degree (Fahrenheit).

lowing experiment. Suppose that the temperature of the skin of both hands is 80° Fahrenheit, and feels neither warm nor cool. Immerse one hand in water at 100°, the other in water at 60°, and, after leaving them there for a minute, plunge both into water at 80°. This will now feel warm to the hand which has been in the cold water, and cool to the hand which has been in hot water. The explanation, according to the first theory, is that the temperature of the hand which has been heated is now lowered, that of the other hand raised by the same water. The other theory says that immersion of one hand in hot water has adapted it to a temperature above 80°, i. e., that its zero point has been raised, so that 80° is now below its zero and feels cool; and the opposite for the other hand. Such an experiment does not, however, enable us to decide between the two theories. A more crucial instance is afforded by prolonged exposure to warmth or (moderate) cold. If one is in a hot bath, or sitting before a fire, or has a fever, the sensation of warmth persists, though perhaps in diminished degree, for a very long time. The first theory would have us suppose that the temperature of the skin is constantly rising during all this time—which is hardly possible. The other theory has simply to argue that the process of adaptation to temperature has limits—i. e., that the zero point, though it can be raised or lowered, cannot be raised or lowered very far. The latter, or "adaptation theory" has the better of it in this case; as it has also in the case of a sensation of warmth which lasts for a time after emerging from a hot bath, in spite of the fact that the skin at this time is cooling off. However, such every-day observations have not the precision needed for a convincing test of either theory; and experimental observations,[1] in which care has been taken to excite a limited portion of the skin continuously and without allowing neighboring parts to be affected, have been more favorable to Weber's theory; inasmuch as prolongation of the stimulus did not prolong the sensation beyond a minute or at most three or four minutes.

§ 26. Other sensations from the skin are apparently compounds or modifications of the four classes already mentioned. Hard and soft, rough and smooth, moist and dry, are judgments regarding objects, founded on a combination of cutaneous sensations and of these with muscular sensations. Itch seems closely akin to pain; tickle, at least one form of it, seems closely related to touch proper, since it can be aroused by brushing the hairs, which are organs of touch. The sensation of heat or of burning has clearly an element of pain, and probably arises from the excitation of pain-spots along with warmth-spots. It is also probable, from what was said above

---

[1] By Holm, *Skandinavisches Archiv f. Physiol.*, 1903, XIV, 242; cited by Thunberg in Nagel's *Handbuch*.

regarding the paradoxical sensation of cold, that a hot object excites the cold-spots as well, so that a burning sensation would be a blend of three elementary sensations.

Regarding pain, the view has long been held and is still entertained by some authorities, that this sensation is the result of excessive stimulation of *any* sensory nerve; and the painfulness of very loud sounds, or very bright lights, and of high temperatures, was regarded as good evidence in favor of this view. The evidence is not, however, conclusive, since it is impossible to prevent excessive stimulation from involving other end-organs besides those of the special sense supposed to be under stimulation. Very bright light affects not only the retina, but causes a strong reaction in the iris and eyelids. Loud sounds cause strong reactions in the middle ear; and high temperatures, as we have just seen, affect the pain-spots as well as the warmth-spots. If we distinguish, as we certainly should, between mere unpleasantness and pain, we can hardly doubt that there is a specific cutaneous pain, which arises from the excitation of certain definite points; and accordingly it has become customary to speak of a pain sense, as of a warmth sense, a cold sense, and a touch sense. There are, however, several different qualities of sensory pain and ache, as from the bones, teeth, fatigued muscles, etc.

§ 27. Quite recently a new line of study of the cutaneous senses has been opened through the work of Head and his collaborators.[1] When a nerve supplying the sense-organs in any area of the skin is severed by accident, a certain region of the skin is entirely deprived of sensibility; but, bordering this region is a zone in which sensibility is impaired in a definite way, without being entirely destroyed. This border region may be insensitive to light touch or to minor degrees of warmth or cold, and be deprived of spatial discrimination; a prick may be felt, but not be localizable, since it gives rise to only a diffuse, tingling sensation. In the area in which the skin is totally insensitive, a deep or subcutaneous sensibility is still retained. Pressure through the skin is felt here; but, if the skin is lifted from the underlying tissue into a fold, no stimulus applied to this fold of skin is felt. The pressure which is appreciated by the subcutaneous sense can itself be localized, and yet spatial discrimination, as between the point and the head of a pin, or between two points and one point of the compasses, is impossible with the deep sensibility alone. Dull pain is produced by strong pressure on the subcutaneous organs.

[1] Head and Sherren, "The Consequences of Injury to the Peripheral Nerves of Man," *Brain*, 1905, XXVIII, 241; Rivers and Head, "A Human Experiment in Nerve Division," *Brain*, 1908, XXXI, 323.

Such phenomena show that the severance of the cutaneous nerve has served to isolate the subcutaneous sense, and thus they lead to a distinction between the tactile sense of the skin and the pressure sense of the subcutaneous tissue; and also to a distinction between the pain sense of the skin (pricking) and the duller pain of the subcutaneous sense. Besides this isolation of the subcutaneous sense, Head believes that the partial sensibility of the intermediate zone of the skin represents the isolation of a rudimentary form of cutaneous sensibility, which is sensitive to pricking and to extremes of heat and cold, from the perfected form of the normal skin, which is sensitive to warmth and coolness and to light touch, and which has the power of spatial discrimination. The more rudimentary form he calls "protopathic" sensibility, and the more perfect form, "epicritic" sensibility. This separation of two distinct forms of cutaneous sensibility has been called in question; since it has been shown by Franz[1] and by Trotter and Davies[2] that the transition from one to the other is really gradual. But the sufficiently sharp delimitation of the subcutaneous sense appears to be correct, and a certain region in which the transition appears gradual is precisely what we should expect. The discovery, therefore, represents a considerable advance in our knowledge of these classes of sensation.

§ 28. The subcutaneous sense merges with the so-called muscular sense. Sensory end-organs are found in muscles and tendons, about the joints, and in the bones (see p. 181). Goldscheider[3] and others have shown that cutaneous anæsthesia alone does not destroy nor much impair the power of perceiving the movements and positions of the different members of the body, nor the power of accurately co-ordinated movement, which latter, as well as, of course, the former, is destroyed by complete anæsthesia of a member. At one time, there was much disposition to believe in a definite joint-sense, with end-organs in the articular surfaces, excited by the rubbing of these surfaces over each other; but evidence is lacking of sense-organs in these surfaces. Yet the region of the joints must be the location of end-organs important in the perception of movement, for Goldscheider found that anæsthetizing the joint, by passing a current through it, greatly impaired the perception of motion. The observations of Pillsbury[4] indicate that the sensibility of the joint region is closely connected with the tendons which pass over the joint. It is apparently the movement of these tendons in their

[1] *Journ. of Comp. Neurol. and Psychol.*, 1909, XIV, 107, 215.
[2] *Journ. of Physiol.*, 1909, XXXVIII, 134.
[3] See Goldscheider's *Gesammelte Abhandlungen, Physiologie des Muskelsinnes* (Leipzig, 1909).
[4] *American Journ. of Psychol.*, 1901, XII, 346.

grooves, rather than the movement of the articular surfaces over each other, which gives rise to sensations of movement. Of the qualities of sensation belonging to this "muscle" sense it is less easy to speak than of the perceptions of motion, position, and resistance which are founded on them. We may, however, distinguish with certainty between the unpleasant sensations of muscular fatigue and soreness and the more matter-of-fact sensations of movement and resistance. Of these latter, several varieties can be observed;[1] but nothing like a complete analysis or system of such sensory qualities has yet been attempted.

§ 29. From the labyrinth of the inner ear—the semicircular canals and vestibule—arise a class of sensations which may be named "labyrinthic" (see above, p. 206). Here again, though it is easy to mention the perceptions and the reflex movements which result from the stimulation of these organs, it is not possible as yet to say much regarding the sensory qualities belonging to the labyrinthic sense. The swimming sensations in the head in dizziness, and the milder degrees of the same which can be observed in rotation, and in going up or down in an elevator, belong here without doubt.

§ 30. Under the head of visceral or organic sensations may be grouped hunger, thirst, nausea, suffocation, and probably a host of other sensory compounds which contribute much to our feeling of well-being or illness and in general to the "coenæsthesia" or "common sensation" of the organism. Analysis here is difficult, for it is never easy to analyze a sensory complex into its elements unless we can control and isolate the stimuli. Little can be done at present toward a physiological explanation of these sensations, except to call attention to their existence.[2]

§ 31. In closing the subject treated in the last two chapters, attention is again called to the large amount and cumulative character of the evidence afforded by the special sensations, considered as respects their quality, for the law of the *Specific Energy of the Nerves*. It is impossible to account for the above-mentioned phenomena without carrying this law to a great length in its application to the special senses. We may not be able at present to affirm that two sensations are distinguishable as respects quality *only* in case they are occasioned by two individually different elements of the nervous system. For, as we advance in our investigations we shall see even more clearly that the quality of sensations depends upon their quantity, upon their relation to preceding and con-

[1] See Woodworth, *Le Mouvement*, pp. 25 ff. (Paris, 1903).
[2] For a more extended treatment of the entire subject of qualities of sensation, reference may be made to Titchener's *Textbook of Psychology* (New York, 1909).

temporaneous sensations, and upon innumerable considerations other than merely the one of what particular nerve-fibre or element of the end-apparatus was acted upon by the stimulus. Moreover, there is no warrant for saying that identically the same nervous apparatus cannot be excited variously according to the nature of the stimulus which acts upon it, or according to the combination with other parts of the system into which it enters for the time. It is obvious, however, that the differentiation of function, and the assignment to specifically distinct apparatus of particular nervous impressions corresponding to particular mental states, is carried to a great length in the special senses. In this differentiation of function it is not wholly or chiefly the nerve-fibres, as such, which should be taken into account; it is also the minute subdivisions of the end-organs of sense, and the connections set up within the corresponding regions of the central organs. In accounting for those complex sensations which appear in ordinary consciousness, the law of permutations and combinations has, of course, to be considered. A vast variety of such sensations may be made up by changing the relations to each other of comparatively few simple elements. But in each of the senses our analysis, when carried to its utmost limit, leaves a number—in some of the senses very large—of simple sensations, which apparently must have their normal physical basis in the excitation of specifically distinct elements of the nervous mechanism.

The sense of smell apparently requires that the law of the specific energy of the nerves should be carried to such a length as almost to reduce it to an absurdity. Histology has discovered only one essential kind of olfactory end-organ, and that of comparatively simple structure; and yet experience gives, as the result of its excitation, a bewildering variety of sensations so specifically different as to baffle all our attempts to classify them. From the case of this sense an argument may then be derived which leads in either direction. It may be objected to the law that it is absurd to suppose a complexity of the end-organs of smell such as to correspond to each specific kind of olfactory stimulus with a specific sensation —for example, the smell of musk, or of sulphuretted hydrogen. It may be replied to the objection that, in the case of the ear, there are at least 16,000 or 20,000 distinct units of auditory end-apparatus corresponding to the different musical tones; and it is therefore by no means impossible that the entire *regio olfactoria* may contain enough specifically different forms of its own peculiar end-apparatus to suffice for all the simple sensations of smell.

The sense of taste does not occasion so many difficulties in relation to the law of the specific energy of the nerves. We have seen that physiologists incline to reduce all the sensations of taste to four, or at most six, different species. It is easy to suppose as many specifically different forms of the nervous apparatus corresponding to the different classes of sensations—sweet and sour, salt and bitter, alkaline and metallic. On combining these with sensations of smell and of touch, it is assumed to find an explanation for all the varieties of the tastes of our daily experience. But even if we have greatly to increase the number of primary sensations of the gustatory species, the theory of specific functions for different nervous elements and combinations of such elements would seem able to meet the demand.

The strongest defence of the most extreme form of the theory of the specific energy of the nerves has hitherto been found in sensations of musical sound. Here we undoubtedly have a wide range of qualitatively distinct states of consciousness which are apparently dependent upon the excitation of a correspondingly large number of distinct nervous elements.

The recent discoveries as to the existence of pressure-spots, warmth-spots, and cold-spots in the skin add important evidence to that already existing in favor of the law under discussion.

It is, undoubtedly, still difficult to make any thorough-going application of the law of specific energies to the case of the color sensations. The principal reasons for this are twofold: first, histology has revealed no such differentiation of the cones as would enable us to divide them into organs for the several primary colors; and, second, the peculiar, antagonistic relations of white and black, yellow and blue, and red and green, are hard to explain by any theory of specific energies. The Hering theory, as we have seen, interprets these relations to mean that the same end-organ is capable of two antagonistic reactions. Accordingly, it would seem that the nerve-fibres connected with these end-organs must transmit two kinds of impulses to the brain. The theory of their specific energy, therefore, needs further testing before it can be satisfactorily fitted to the facts of our vision of color.

It will further appear, when we consider the process of localization in the so-called "geometrical senses" of the eye and the skin, that the very possibility of such a process demands a somewhat strict and far-reaching application of the law of the specific energy of the nerves. Precisely how we are to state and limit this law, neither its opponents nor its advocates have as yet been able satisfactorily to show. The exact expression of the theory waits for further evidence from experiment, although there can be little doubt that in its main features it is already secure.

CHAPTER III

THE QUANTITY OF SENSATIONS

§ 1. By an act of mental analysis, which all men readily perform, changes in the amount of sensation are distinguished from changes in its quality. This distinction, in itself considered, obviously requires for its performance nothing beyond what is immediately given in consciousness. The simple fact of experience is, that all sensations appear to differ among themselves, not only with respect to the nature of the impression which serves to classify them into groups (as sensations of sight, sound, etc.), but also with respect to the *degree* in which each particular impression possesses the sphere of conscious attention and feeling. The best illustration of an alteration in the intensity of sensation, while its characteristic quality remains unaltered, may be derived from musical tones. The dying-out of a single tone when the bow is drawn with decreasing force across the string of a violin, or a single key of the piano is struck and the pedal held, may be considered as a change in the quantity of sensation, while its quality is unchanged. A more complex case is the experience we have when approaching or receding from a bell that is sounding or a steam-whistle that is blowing. Noises of a certain complex quality—such as slamming, hissing, grating, etc.—are continually described as very loud, moderately loud, or of weak intensity. So, too, when approaching a white or colored light, with our attention fixed upon it, we generally disregard almost wholly the changes in its color-tone which take place, and consider chiefly the changes in its intensity and apparent size. The pressure of different weights upon different parts of our skin is ordinarily regarded as the same in quality and as varying only in amount and locality. The same thing is true, in almost precisely the same way, with sensations of temperature. The thing we touch is called slightly cold or very cold, somewhat warm or very hot, our attention being directed chiefly to our judgment of the *quantum* of sense experience which it calls forth. In other words, it is generally the same *kind* of pressure and temperature, with a varying degree of intensity, of which we believe ourselves to be conscious.

It is more difficult, however, even in the most indefinite way, to discriminate between the quantities of our sensations of smell and taste and the changes in specific quality of the same sensations. A concentrated sweet or acid so strongly excites a variety of forms of feeling which mingle indistinguishably with the sensations of taste that we are compelled to attend to the very decided qualitative changes which are taking place. The increased intensity of the sweet or sour we may indeed speak of as *"very"* much of the same sensation which was excited in less degree by the diluted form of the stimulus; but we are more likely to regard it as constituting a complete change in the kind of taste. In the same manner, attention is forcibly directed toward the *kind* of sensation which results from increasing the *quantity* of any specific sensation of smell.

It is further obvious that the distinction which we make between changes in the quantity and changes in the quality of our sensations is to some extent applicable for comparing the sensations of different senses. And here the distinction, when applied to sub-species under certain specific forms of sensation, affords us a means of transition for such comparisons. Some yellows are bright and others dull; and the same thing is true of the reds and the blues. The sours, the sweets, the bitters, may be compared with each other as respects the degree of intensity which they possess. We may next, in a very indefinite way, compare the quantities of the sensations of the different senses as they appear side by side, or successively, in consciousness. We are ordinarily satisfied, however, with simply describing the varying degrees of intensity possessed by our different sensations as "weak" or "strong" (with or without the emphatic *"very"*) or as only "moderate." Thus we may judge that both the light which we see and the tone which we hear (either simultaneously or one immediately after the other) are, or are not, to be classed together under the same one of these three popular forms of discriminating degrees of intensity.

§ 2. That changes in the intensity of our sensations are not, in fact, wholly independent of changes in their specific nature has already been stated. Only in the case of musical tones are we able at the same time to attend carefully to both the quantity and quality of our sensations, and so discover with perfect confidence that the former is changing while the latter remains unchanged. Even in this case, since the tones which we ordinarily hear are composite, any considerable alteration of their intensity changes also their tone-coloring, through the alteration which it produces in the comparative intensities of the overtones. Any increase in the brightness of a particular color invariably changes its characteristic color-tone. A white of less intensity is not merely less white, but it has become a gray; and by constantly diminishing its intensity white can be shaded through the different grays toward black, which is certainly not a feebler degree of the sensation of white. The same dependence of quality on quantity is true in all sensations of smell, taste, pressure, and temperature. It is no less than an inexcusable psychological blunder, however, on this account to consider "quantity" of sensations as only another name for shades of quality; or to deny that we can apply terms of measurement to these reactions of the mind upon the excitation of the nervous apparatus of sense. Scientific analysis confirms the distinction made by ordinary experience between "the *way*" we feel and "*how much*" we feel in any particular way.

§ 3. All descriptions of the changing intensities of sensations, when made on the basis of ordinary experience solely, leave the subject in a very indefinite and unscientific form. That a certain noise is louder or weaker than another of precisely the same kind, one may be quite ready to affirm; one may even be ready to say that one judges this noise to be about twice or three times as loud as the other. But when more precise estimates are demanded, one is obliged to hesitate before giving them. Is this musical tone ten (or a hundred) times as loud as the other; or is it only nine and nine-tenths (or ninety-nine and nine-tenths) as loud? Few would venture so nice an estimate with any confidence. Yet the case of sound is much more favorable than that of most of the other senses for forming an exact judgment as to its intensity. It would be difficult under the most favorable circumstances to affirm that the sensation of the light *a* is twice or three times as bright as that of the light *b;* or that of the shadow *x* one-half or one-third as bright as *y.* The comparative intensities of different color-tones are yet more difficult to fix subjectively—even in the most indefinite way. This particular yellow may seem *about* as bright a color, of its kind, as does the red near it, of its kind. But the precise moment could not readily be told when the blue of the sky appears exactly twice as intense as the green of the grass. Still further, all estimates of the quantity of sensation approach the point at which they lose their meaning and tend to become absurd, when we compare, for example, sensations of smell or taste with those of pressure, temperature, or sight. We never say: The rose smells as sweet as it looks red; or the lemon is twice as sour as the sky is blue. And yet each qualitatively different sensation is assumed to have its place somewhere in that scale of intensities through which the different qualities may run; each may, therefore, be compared with every other, with respect to the general position which it occupies in its characteristic scale.

§ 4. The variation of sensations in intensity, though it is an obvious fact of the commonest experience, leads, when we attempt to give it exact scientific form, to a host of difficulties, which have been the occasion of an immense amount of discussion among psychologists. All the resources of the higher mathematics have been employed in order to discover and demonstrate some law of universal applicability, which shall regulate satisfactorily the quantitative relations existing between the functions of the nervous mechanism, on the one hand, and on the other, the states of consciousness to which psychology gives the name of sensations, or "sensation-complexes." In some cases, as notably that of Fechner, the attempt has even been made to raise this alleged psycho-physical law to the dignity of a universal metaphysical principle. Meantime, the fact has become more and more apparent that what we have, on the one side, is certain largely unknown but always highly complex chemico-physical and nervous reactions, and on the other side, even more complex, and often unanalyzable, conscious experiences, in which the faculty of discrimination always plays the leading part, and which are quite uniformly influenced by individual conditions of mental habit, fatigue, specific sensitiveness, either congenital or acquired, and even individual idiosyncrasies. We do not expect, then, to reach anything like an exact and universal formula, statable in terms of mathematics, after the fashion of the results obtainable by a successful research in physics or chemistry. As students of psychology from the physiological point of view, it is our duty (so we have always held) first to discover the data, and then as far as possible give them that kind of interpretation of which alone the science of psychology admits.

§ 5. The fundamental characteristic of the intensity of a given sensation, that which fits it for scientific study and *measurement*, is this: its various degrees can be arranged in an ordered series, from less intense to more intense; and thus every intensity can be judged, with reference to any other, by comparing it with a standard, or some one simple category of magnitude. Such well-ordered series can be found, not only in reference to intensity, but also in reference to extent and duration; and, in some instances, in reference to quality. Tones, for example, can be arranged in an ordered series as regards their pitch; lights, as regards their color-tone. The scientific problems which arise in connection with such series are (1) to assign the limits of the series; and (2) to discover, if possible, the customary, or fixed, relations between the different terms of the series. As applied to the pitch series, these problems lead to the determination of the lowest and highest pitch, the measurement of the least noticeable difference of pitch, and the examination of the "intervals." As applied to color, however, the problems of measurement are reducible to the determination of the limits of the colored spectrum, the least noticeable difference in color, and such relations as that of complementary colors.

As applied to the intensity series, these same problems call for (1) the determination of the weakest and strongest sensations, of any given quality, of which we are capable; (2) the relation between neighboring members of the series which is indicated by the least noticeable difference in intensity; and (3) the relations (if any of interest can be found) between distant members of the series.   In all this kind of work, it is clearly impossible to deal with sensations apart from the stimuli which give rise to them.   The stimuli are needed to arouse the sensations; control and identification of the stimulus is necessary in order to control and (approximately) identify the sensation; and furthermore measurement can be applied directly to the stimulus, but not to the sensation.   It is clear, then, that quantitative statements regarding the intensity of sensation must always be based on quantitatively determined stimuli.

§ 6. The quantitative problems which arise in connection with the intensity of sensation may then be somewhat crudely generalized as follows: (1) To determine how little and how much of each kind of stimulus will produce respectively the least and the greatest quantity of each kind of sensation of which the mind is capable, or to find the quantitative limits within which sensations of each sense are possible; and (2) to determine the law of the relation under which changes in the intensity of sensations, as estimated in consciousness, are dependent upon changes in the intensity of the stimuli.

§ 7. Two methods of determining the *lower limit*, or minimum of stimulus producing a sensation, are possible.   In the use of one method, a weak stimulus, but somewhat above the amount needed to produce a sensation, is applied; its intensity is then diminished by minute gradations until the exact point is reached and noted at which it ceases to produce any sensation at all.   In the use of the other method a stimulus too weak to produce any sensation is first applied; its intensity is then very gradually increased until it begins to produce the smallest observable sensation.   Both ways may be combined, and thus the "sensitiveness" of each organ of sense, and of each part of each organ, may be determined.   Such sensitiveness increases, of course, in inverse ratio to the amount of stimulus necessary for producing any sensation at all, or for producing a sensation estimated as having a definite degree of energy.   The effort to determine the lower limit of sensations of sight and of sound is embarrassed by the facts that the retina is always under excitation from the chemical changes going on in its pigments, and therefore has a certain quantum of so-called "light of its own," and that such a thing as "absolute stillness" cannot probably be secured for the ear. Total absence of sensation in the ear, could it be secured, would not be comparable to the black which we see with the eyes closed.

The *upper limit* of the intensity series would be determined if we should find that increasing the stimulus beyond a certain limit gave no further increase in the sensation. Practically, however, such a determination is scarcely ever possible, both because of the danger to the sense-organs, and also because very intense stimuli affect other organs besides that whose sensations we wish to examine and so lead to confused results.

§ 8. The invention of methods for determining the least perceptible difference in intensity, and other relations between members of the intensity series, has been one of the main tasks of experimental psychology, and has engaged the attention of many of the ablest students of this specialty. The greatest contributions, in this matter of method, were made by Fechner in his *Psychophysik* (1860).[1]

We cannot enter here into the technical details which must be attended to in any actual use of these methods, but will simply attempt to characterize them briefly. The following are the principal ones: (1) The "method of just noticeable differences" determines that difference in the intensity of two stimuli which is just large enough to be recognized as such. Of two lights, for example, which are at first equally bright, one is made brighter by slow degrees, till it is first judged brighter; then a second determination is made, starting with one light obviously the brighter, and diminishing this one till it no longer seems brighter than the other. The mean of these two determinations gives a measure of the least noticeable difference, or, it may also be called, the *threshold* of difference. It is not true, however, as the name might imply, that this threshold is a perfectly fixed quantity, below which all differences are unperceived, while above it all are perceived; for perception is a variable process, and a difference which at one moment may be clearly detected will pass unnoticed at another moment. It is necessary, therefore, to repeat the determinations a number of times, and to take an average, according to the well-known rules regulating such experimentation.

(2) In the "method of average error," as in the preceding method, there are two stimuli, one of which is fixed in intensity, and the other

[1] Next to Fechner, the development of these "psychophysical methods" owes most to G. E. Müller: *Zur Grundlegung der Psychophysik* (Berlin, 1878); *Die Gesichtspunkte und die Tatsachen der psychophysischen Methodik* (Wiesbaden, 1904). For both an elementary account of these methods and a full history and discussion of the subject, see Titchener, *Experimental Psychology, Quantitative* (New York, 1905).

adjustable. In the use of this method, however, the effort is made to adjust the second stimulus so that it shall appear equal to the first. Some slight error is sure to be committed; the error will vary from trial to trial, and the average error is determined, and also any constant errors which may appear; and, as well, the variability of the performance. In some respects the variability is the most important of all of these determinations, since it gives a measure of the variation which a stimulus can undergo without ceasing to appear the same.

(3) In the "method of right and wrong cases," neither of the two stimuli is adjustable, but they are fixed at a difference too small to be perceived with certainty and regularity, but not too small to be detected most of the time. With this fixed difference, a long series of judgments is made, and the per cent. of right judgments gives a measure of the perceptibility of the chosen difference between the stimuli. If, for example, a weight of 105 grams is judged heavier than a weight of 100 grams 70 per cent. of the time, while 205 is judged heavier than 200 only 60 per cent. of the time, it is clear that the difference 200–205 is less perceptible than the difference 100–105; and if 200—210 is, like 100–105, judged correctly 70 per cent. of the time, then these two differences are equally perceptible. Mathematical analysis, based on the theory of probability, enables us to go further than this, and compute, from the observed per cent. of right cases with a given difference, the difference which should give any desired per cent. of right cases.[1]

While the three preceding methods deal with the perception of small differences—differences at or near the threshold—the two which remain to be noticed deal with larger, supraliminal differences.

(4) The "method of mean gradations" uses three stimuli, two of which are fixed, while the third is to be so adjusted as to seem midway between the other two. The point is to see whether the stimulus which gives this "middle sensation" is the arithmetical mean between the extreme stimuli, or the geometrical mean, or some other proportion. Various similar problems, involving the relations of distant members of the intensity series, can be approached in the same way.

[1] It would seem that the "method of right and wrong cases" can scarcely be freed from certain inherent difficulties; the chief of which concern, first, the proper treatment of those cases in which the judgment is undecided; and second, the relation of the values found by this method to those found by the method of the least noticeable difference. Neither of the solutions hitherto proposed for these difficulties seems altogether satisfactory. For a discussion of the relations of the two methods of measurement from the point of view of their comparative value, the student of the subject may refer to Fullerton and Cattell, *On the Perception of Small Differences*, pp. 10, 35 (Philadelphia, 1892).

(5) What may be called the "discrimination time method" is of recent introduction.[1] It consists in determining the time required to judge of a difference between two stimuli. If, starting at the threshold, we gradually increase the difference between the stimuli, requiring the observer to make his judgments as promptly as possible, we find the judgment rather slow near the threshold, and more and more prompt as the difference is increased. The impulse to judge, or the "steering force" exerted by the pair of stimuli, goes on increasing far beyond the threshold; and this is a fact of some theoretic moment, as showing the artificiality of the threshold. Now differences that are judged rightly and in equal times may be called subjectively equal; they are equal in their effect on perception, or equally perceptible—this is the basis of the method.

§ 9. The problem to which these methods have chiefly been applied is that of determining equally perceptible, or equal-appearing differences, at all parts of the scale of intensities. The commencement of this study, which soon took on the proportions of one of the most important topics of experimental psychology, dates from about 1830, and is due to the physiologist E. H. Weber.[2] Desiring to determine the power of the skin and of the muscle-sense to discriminate weights, Weber devised the method of least noticeable differences, and found that, when poised in the hand, a weight of 30 ounces could just be distinguished from one of 29 ounces; but that if he started with 30 drams instead of ounces, the least noticeable difference was one dram. It seemed that the least noticeable difference was not itself a fixed quantity, but varied with the stimulus, being always a certain fixed fraction of the stimulus. Weber found, however, that the fraction which gave the least noticeable difference was not the same for all the senses: it was larger, for example, in case of pressure on the skin than in case of the lifting of weights; but in the case of judging the length of lines it was much smaller, or only about $\frac{1}{100}$ —i. e., a line of 100 units could barely be distinguished from a line of 101 units. Weber therefore concluded, on generalizing from his results, that the least noticeable difference, in each kind of sense-perception, is a constant fraction of the stimulus.

Some years later, Fechner became acquainted with this general-

[1] Henmon's *The Time of Perception as a Measure of Differences in Sensations* (New York, 1906) is the most important study made by the use of this method, and contains a history of the method.

[2] An account of Weber's experiments can be found reprinted in his collected works (1851) and also in his article in Wagner's *Handwörterbuch der Physiologie*, 1846, III, ii, 481.

ization, and being greatly impressed with its importance, he named it *Weber's law*, and made it the corner-stone of his *Psychophysics*. Fechner tested this law by extensive series of experiments, which he conducted according to several of the above-mentioned methods. And he further sought to utilize it as a means for attaining to a scientific measure of all our sensory experience.   To accomplish this, he had to make one or two assumptions.   He must, of course, assume that every sensation is a measurable quantity, and this implies that sensations can be subdivided, added and subtracted; and he further assumed that the least noticeable difference corresponds to a genuine unit of sensation, and that all least noticeable differences, within the same kind of sense-perception, represent equal steps or units of sensation.   With these assumptions, Fechner could express Weber's law in either of the two following ways: (1) The addition of equal units of sensation is accomplished by the successive multiplication of the stimulus by a constant fraction; or (2) to make sensation increase in arithmetical progression, the stimulus must increase in geometrical progression.   Now when two quantities are related in this way, the one increasing in arithmetical progression while the other increases in geometrical progression, the former is proportional to the logarithm of the latter; and thus Fechner reached the most compact form of his modification of Weber's law, which reads that sensation is proportional to the logarithm of the stimulus.[1] This modification is called Fechner's law; and it is to be noted that, as it involves certain assumptions from which Weber's law is free, the latter is the more empirical expression of the facts, so far as, indeed, the facts are found to agree with it.

§ 10.   That Weber's law is at least an approximation to the truth is borne out by our most common experiences.   These evince the simple fact that an amount of difference which is easily percepti-

---

[1] For the detailed mathematical discussion and expression of Weber's law the reader is referred to the technical works, especially of Fechner and G. E. Müller. A simple statement of Fechner's principle may be given as follows: Let $H=$ the intensity of the light of one-half of a white field; $\frac{H}{100}=$ the smallest fraction of stimulus added to H that will produce an observable increase in this intensity; and $H + \frac{H}{100}=$ the intensity of the other half of the same field.   Then let $S=$ the sensation produced by H; $S+s=$ the sensation produced by $H+\frac{H}{100}$; and s will, of course, represent the so-called least observable difference at this point in the scale.   We have, then, H produces S; $H+\frac{H}{100}$, or $\frac{101}{100} H$, produces $S+s$; $\frac{101}{100} H+\frac{\frac{110}{100}}{100} H$, or $\frac{101}{100}.\frac{101}{100} H$, produces $S+s+s$; and so on.   That is to say, if s is to be kept of the same magnitude, then H must be *multiplied* by the same magnitude ($\frac{101}{100}$).

The three fundamental formulas which Fechner has employed to state and demonstrate the law are the following: Let S be the magnitude of the sensation caused by the stimulus Σ, and ΔS a just observable increase in this sen-

ble when the stimuli are weak becomes imperceptible when the stimuli are strong. If, for example, when a single electric bulb is burning, one more is turned on, the increase in illumination is very marked; but when a hundred are burning, the addition of one more is barely perceptible; and when a thousand are burning the addition of one more is quite unnoticed. To hear the pin drop, the room must be very quiet. But such every-day observations are not a sufficient test of the law, which states something definite and exact—namely, that the least perceptible difference is a constant fraction of the stimulus; or, when somewhat generalized, that equally perceptible differences require the stimuli to be in a constant ratio. Moreover, while the empirical data upon which the advocates of Weber's law rely are very numerous, their value and trustworthiness are often much diminished by the fact that many of these experimenters have failed to isolate sufficiently the exact problem which it was desired to solve. Nevertheless, the data show that *the law summarizes many facts reasonably well within a certain range of sensations lying near the middle of the scale of quantity*. The same general fact of experience, which this law attempts to summarize, holds, roughly, of our perception of magnitudes of space and time, as well as of our estimate of intensities of sensation. Near both the upper and the lower limits the law fails to prove applicable; even in the regions and under the circumstances which are most favorable it is only approximately true. Many fluctuations of unknown significance and origin occur in all the senses.

§ 11. In the following brief summary of the empirical results of a study of the intensity of sensation, we shall group together under each sense the data on the two chief problems:—that of the least observable stimulus; and that of the least observable difference between two stimuli. Weber's law is concerned only with the latter;

---

sation which is caused by an increase of the stimulus$=\Delta\Sigma$. Let C be a constant dependent on the units chosen for S and Σ. Then $\Delta S = \frac{C\Delta\Sigma}{\Sigma}$. Let it be further assumed that ΔS remains constant whatever values for S and $\Delta\Sigma$ are assumed; then $dS = C\frac{d\Sigma}{\Sigma}$, and by integration $S = C$ log. Σ, which is Fechner's "fundamental formula." But if the stimulus is just *below* the least observable amount, and be $=\Sigma°$, then substituting in the above formula we have $0 = C$ log $\Sigma°$; from which Fechner derives formula No. 2 (the formula of measurement)— namely, $S = C$ log. $\frac{\Sigma}{\Sigma°}$, which means that the magnitude of the sensation is "*negative*," in case the stimulus sinks below the least observable. If two sensations (S and S') are observably different, then $S - S' = C$ (log. Σ — log. Σ') $= C$ log $\frac{\Sigma}{\Sigma'}$; this is called the "formula of difference," and means that the difference in the intensity of two sensations is proportional to the logarithm of the quotient of the magnitudes of their stimuli.

and wherever this law is empirically true, it is possible to express the result, in regard to the least observable difference, or the discriminative sensibility of the sense in question, in the form of a single fraction. It should be noted, however, that a single sense may furnish more than one intensity series, and that Weber's law must accordingly be tested in each such series separately.

§ 12. We begin where Weber began, with the perception of weight. Weight is appreciated partly by pressure on the skin and subcutaneous pressure organs, and partly by the muscular sense, as in lifting and poising the weight. One of Weber's results was to the effect that a smaller difference between weights can be detected when they are lifted than when they are simply allowed to press on the skin, and this result is now generally accepted. Weber also decided that the discriminative sensitivity, for lifted weights, was expressible as a constant fraction, about $\frac{1}{40}$, of the total weight. His experiments were, however, confined to a narrow range of weight.

Biedermann and Löwit, by the method of just observable differences, obtained results departing widely from Weber's law.[1] By experimenting with weights varying from 10 to 500 grams they found that the sensitiveness to pressure rose with the increase of the weights from 10 to 400 grams, and then fell off rapidly, as the following table will show:

Absolute weight Grams	Least observable difference Grams	Quotient of sensitiveness
10	0.7	$\frac{1}{14}$
50	1.7	$\frac{1}{29}$
100	2.4	$\frac{1}{42}$
200	3.6	$\frac{1}{56}$
300	4.6	$\frac{1}{65}$
400	5.2	$\frac{1}{77}$
450	6.5	$\frac{1}{89}$
500	25.5	$\frac{1}{20}$

The trustworthiness of these results is impaired, however, by the fact that no method, except the doubtful one of directing "attention" exclusively to the sensations of pressure, was employed to exclude the disturbing effect of the muscular sensations. The same observers concluded, also, that the fineness of the *muscular* sense, when isolated, does not vary according to Weber's law. They fixed it at $\frac{1}{21}$ for weights of 250 grams, $\frac{1}{114}$ for weights of 2,500 grams, $\frac{1}{98}$ for weights of 2,750 grams.

[1] See Hering, *Sitzasber. d. Wiener Acad.*, LXXII, iii, 342 f.

The absolute sensitiveness of the complex sensations dealt with in the above experiments differs greatly for different localities on the surface of the body. This kind of sensitiveness was at one time thought to be chiefly dependent upon the number of the nervous elements present in the skin, its thickness, the character of its tension over the underlying parts, etc.; but its variations are by no means parallel with those of the sharpness of the sense of locality. The foregoing and similar conclusions all need to be revised in the light of Goldscheider's determinations of the pressure-spots.

Several other authors have tested Weber's law in the perception of lifted weights, and have regularly found the least perceptible fraction of the stimulus to decrease as the total weight increased. The least perceptible difference of weight does, indeed, increase in absolute magnitude as the total weight increases, but it increases more slowly than the weight, contrary to Weber's law. The same is true of other forms of perception depending on the muscle-sense, such as the extent or force of a movement. In all these varieties of muscle-sense perception, the least noticeable difference increases more slowly than the total magnitude; the fraction which should remain constant grows smaller as the magnitude increases. It is rather disappointing to find that the sphere of perception which first suggested the formulation of Weber's law should prove to be the sphere, of all others, to which it is least applicable.

§ 13. Let us now turn to the determinations of the least observable stimulus in the realm of the muscle-sense. Such determinations have been chiefly carried out by Goldscheider,[1] who has measured the least perceptible extent of movement at various joints. This varies greatly for different joints. The most sensitive joints, i. e., those at which the least angular rotation is perceived, are the wrist, shoulder, and the joint between the hand and the finger; at these joints a rotation of .30 to .40° can be perceived. Less sensitive are the elbow, hip, and knee, with thresholds of .40 to .80°; still less sensitive are the ankle and the two joints within each finger (.75–1.50°); and least sensitive of all are the joints within the foot (2–4°). The measure of sensitivity varies with the speed of the impressed movement, the joints being more sensitive for rapid than for slow movements. For active movements (that is, movements made voluntarily by the observer's own muscular action), the sensitivity is perhaps slightly greater than for passive or impressed movements; but the difference, if any, is very small.

§ 14. If we next turn to the skin and subcutaneous pressure organs, we easily observe that the absolute sensitiveness of different

[1] *Gesammelte Abhandlungen,* II.

parts differs greatly. Aubert and Kammler found the lightest weight which produced a sensation of touch to be 0.002 gram on the forehead, temples, and dorsal side of the forearm and hands; 0.003 gram for the volar side of the forearm; 0.005 gram for the nose, lips, chin, eyelids, and skin of abdomen; 0.005–0.015 gram for the volar side of the fingers; and 1 gram for the finger-nails and skin of the heel. Later observations have to some extent varied these results; and it has come to be recognized that the most significant experiments are those which determine the least perceptible pressure on single touch-spots. Von Frey[1] concludes that individual touch-spots differ comparatively little from each other in sensitiveness, the threshold ranging from .5 to 4 grams pressure per square millimetre of the surface pressed on. Kiesow[2] has determined the sensitivity of touch-spots in various regions of the trunk and limbs, and finds it to vary little within the limbs, but to be comparatively blunt on the chest and back. The presence of hairs or hairlets greatly increases this kind of sensitivity.

The sensitivity to differences of pressure also varies from one area of skin to another, being greatest on the face, where the least noticeable difference may be as low as $\frac{1}{30}$ of the total pressure, whereas on the leg the fraction rises above $\frac{1}{10}$.[3] Probably the most thorough test of Weber's law in this field has been made by Stratton,[4] who found that the fraction expressing the least observable increase in an existing pressure was large for such small pressures as 10 grams, and decreased considerably up to 75 grams, but from here on remained fairly constant up to 200 grams; accordingly, Weber's law held good for a medium range of stimuli but not for weak stimuli. The skin, as well as the joint sense, is more sensitive to rapid than to slow changes.

§ 15. Extraordinary difficulties accompany the attempt to apply Weber's law to sensations of *temperature*. As has already been seen (compare p. 346), we do not know exactly what to measure—whether the rising and falling of the thermic apparatus, or its actual temperature in relation to its own zero-point—as constituting the quantitative changes in the stimuli. Even Fechner admits that Weber's law does not apply to the sensitiveness of the hand to changes in temperature when it is itself cooling off; but he thinks the law holds good approximately for degrees of warmth varying between 25° and 37.5° C. (77°–99.5° Fahr.), if 18.71° C. (65.66° Fahr) be

[1] Pflüger's *Archiv f. d. gesammte Physiol.*, 1900, LXXXII, 399.

[2] Wundt's *Philosophische Studien*, 1902, XIX, 307.

[3] Eulenberg, *Zeitschrift f. rationelle Medecin*, 1861, X, cited after Sherrington in Schäfer's *Textbook of Physiology*, 1900, II, 929.

[4] Wundt's *Philosophische Studien*, 1896, XII, 525.

taken as the zero-point. The assumption of this zero-point is, however, arbitrary. No general rule for the quantity of sensations of temperature can well be given except this: *the skin is most sensitive to changes which lie near its own zero-point.* In comparing two temperatures it is most favorable to nice discrimination that one should lie slightly above, the other slightly below, this point. The degrees of the thermometer between which the maximum of sensitiveness is attainable are given differently by different observers: By Nothnagel, 27°–33° C. (80.6°–91.4° Fahr.); by Lindemann, 26°–39° C., by Alsberg, 35°–39° C.; by Fechner, 12°–25° C.—where it is so great as not to be easily measurable by a good quicksilver thermometer (about $\frac{1}{10}$° Fahr.). Cold and heat alike, when applied for some time, reduce greatly the sensitiveness of the skin to minute changes of temperature; by heat it can be so dulled as not to distinguish alterations of less than $\frac{1}{2}$° or $\frac{3}{4}$° Fahr.; by cold it can be rendered insensible to changes measuring from 2° to $5\frac{1}{2}$°.

Another complicating circumstance is that the sense of temperature depends for its fineness upon the extent and locality of the surface excited. Weber found that water at $29\frac{1}{2}$° R., in which the whole hand was immersed, seemed warmer than that at 32° R., to a single finger. Nothnagel placed the following values upon the fineness of discrimination, for minute variations in temperature, of different parts of the body: Middle breast, 0.6° C.; sides of the same, 0.4°; middle of the back, 1.2°; sides of the same, 0.9°; hollow of the hand, 0.5°–0.4°; back of the same, 0.3°; parts of upper and lower arm, 0.2°; cheeks, 0.4°–0.2°; temples, 0.4°–0.3°.

More recent investigations have shown that the table of sensitiveness for the different parts of the body must take account of the division of the temperature-sense into two species, and of the locality of the warmth-spots and cold-spots in all such different parts. On the basis of experiment with areas of the skin whose topography with respect to the temperature-sense had previously been investigated, Goldscheider has given a lengthy statement[1] of the sensitiveness of different parts of the body. Thus he finds that the skin of the head is, in general, little developed for the sense of cold, and only in a few places for the sense of heat. The sensitiveness of the forehead to cold is intense, but to heat only moderate; that of the breast to cold moderate along the sternum, and elsewhere very intense, while to heat it is only moderate except near the nipples; that of the back everywhere very intense to cold, and only moderate to heat; while in all parts of the hand the intensity of sensitiveness

[1] See the *Archiv f. Anat. u. Physiol., Pysiolog. Abth.*, 1885, Supplement-Band, pp. 60 ff.

to both cold and heat is alike.   In general, the skin in the median line of the body seems much less sensitive to changes in temperature than at its sides; and the number of thermic elements (according to Goldscheider, the distributory fibrils of the temperature-nerves), the thickness of the skin, etc., are determining factors.

§ 16. The possibility of executing or appreciating a musical passage in which the intensity of the successive tones is brought to a certain standard of memory, or in which these tones are nicely shaded so as to constitute a crescendo or a diminuendo, appears to depend upon applying to sensations of *sound* some law resembling that of Weber. It is partly by comparing such sensations with their images in memory that the singer or player reproduces certain notes previously executed, with about the same stress of tone. Moreover, in order to shade the relative intensities of successive tones, our appreciation of their differences needs to be much greater for those that have a low degree of intensity. Many obstacles, however, stand in the way of determining either the lower limit or the least observable difference for sensations of sound. The greatest difficulty is of a physical nature—namely, to obtain a source of sound which shall be free from disturbing variations in pitch and clang, both of which greatly affect the apparent intensity of sound; and especially to secure a physical measure of the intensity of the stimulus. If sound is generated, as has frequently been the case in tests of Weber's law, by dropping a metal or hard rubber ball upon a block of wood or slate, it is easy to calculate the energy of impact from the weight of the ball and the height of its fall. But the real stimulus is not this impact, but the vibrations of air which strike the tympanic membrane; for a full determination of the stimulus, we should therefore need to know how much of the energy of impact went into the production of vibrations of the air, and how the amplitude of these vibrations decreased in its passage to the ear. In regard to the latter point, the law of inverse squares would prob- ably hold in a space that was perfectly open, and so free from all reflection; but in a closed room reflection and resonance make it impossible to deduce the intensity at the ear from the distance be- tween the ear and the sounding body. Comparative tests may, how- ever, be made by keeping both the apparatus and the observer at the same places in the same room throughout. In regard to the question as to how the intensity of the sound varies with the height of the fall, there has been much difference of opinion, but perhaps it is safe to assume that, for a given piece of apparatus, the intensity varies as the height of the fall (and therefore as the energy of im- pact).[1] If this is granted, the least perceptible difference in inten-

[1] See Kämpfe, *Philosophische Studien*, 1893, VIII, 526.

sity of sound (noise) as produced by this apparatus, is about $\frac{1}{3}$; i. e., the two noises can just be distinguished when the heights of fall are as 3 to 4. This ratio remains fairly constant within a moderate range of intensity, in confirmation of Weber's law.

§ 17. Such an experiment as the above, though it does not measure the real stimulus at the tympanic membrane, is satisfactory for the testing of Weber's law; but not for determining the least stimulus which can be perceived. Through the work of several authors, among whom may be mentioned Lord Rayleigh and Max Wien, an approximation to the desired measure can now be given. The sound given out by a telephone receiver can be calculated if the excursions of the telephone plate are known; and these excursions can be measured by direct microscopic examination. If now a telephone receiver be held to the ear, and actuated by an electric current which causes the plate to vibrate with a known amplitude, as well as a known frequency, the amplitude of the vibrations entering the ear is known, and it can be assumed that this does not change much in the passage to the tympanic membrane. By such means, Wien[1] has found that a tone is barely audible when the energy of the atmospheric vibrations is from .00032 to .000,000,000,002,5 *ergs* (per second, over an area of one square centimetre). Now the *erg* is itself a small unit; and since the air vibrations need not act for a whole second, a small fraction of a second being long enough, the above figures would need to be considerably reduced in order to express the minimum stimulus which will produce the sensation of sound. Other authorities, it should be said, have not assigned values as small as the smallest of Wien, but they all lie within the range of those cited from this author.

Individuals differ greatly in absolute sensitivity; Bruner[2] found the energy of the least noticeable stimulus to vary in the ratio of 1 to 400, among normally hearing individuals of the white race. The sensitivity to sound varies also, and greatly, with the pitch. The largest of the numbers, quoted above from Wien, is the energy required for a low tone (50 vibrations per second); the smallest is for tones of 1,600 and 3,200 vibrations. The ear is, accordingly, more than 100,000,000 times as sensitive to the high tones as to the low ones; but the threshold is nearly constant in the interval from 800 to 6,400 vibrations. It increases rapidly above and below this range. It will be seen that the ear is most sensitive to decidedly high tones (from "high G," or g^2, up for about three octaves). This may appear strange in view of the fact that these high notes lie beyond the ordinary use of the human voice; but the importance of

[1] Pflüger's *Archiv f. d. gesammte Physiol.*, 1903, XCVII, 1.
[2] *The Hearing of Primitive Peoples*, p. 95 (New York, 1908).

overtones in the appreciation of the clang, or complex character, of a sound, should be borne in mind in this connection. The ability to distinguish different noises, voices, vocal sounds, etc., is as important as anything in hearing, and requires that the ear shall be sensitive to high and faint overtones.

§ 18. Wien also employed the telephone method for determining the least noticeable difference of intensity of tones. He found the fraction expressing the least noticeable difference to vary with the pitch of the tone ($\frac{1}{5}$ to $\frac{1}{3}$ from a to a^1); but for each tone it preserves a fair equality over a considerable middle range of intensity. There is, therefore, good ground for concluding that Weber's law is fairly applicable to intensity of sound.

§ 19. Attention was early called to the law of judgment in estimating the quantitative relations of sensations of sight, on account of its connection with astronomical observation. In the eighteenth century French physicists had already begun to investigate the sensitiveness of the eye to varying intensities of light. Bouguer, in answer to the question, What force must a light have in order to make a more feeble one disappear? placed the fraction of least observable difference in the intensities of two shadows at $\frac{1}{64}$. That the magnitudes of the stars are not to be classified according to their absolute brightness as determined by photometric observations, was, of course, assumed by Sir John Herschel when he made the latter vary in the series $1 : \frac{1}{4} : \frac{1}{9} : \frac{1}{16}$, while the former vary in the series $1 : 2 : 3 : 4$. That the least observable difference in the intensity of two sensations of sight is absolutely much smaller for those of the lowest grade of intensity is a truth needed to explain many every-day experiences. For example, the finer gradations of shade in a lithograph or photograph are not lost when we take it from the open sunlight into a rather dimly lighted room; we can also observe them through smoked glass, if it be not too black. Through the same media we can measure rather delicate shades of brightness on the clouds. We observe, however, that in all such cases either too great or too weak intensity of the light destroys our power to distinguish the finest gradations of its intensity.

§ 20. It has already been shown (p. 325) that the retina is never free from light of its own which has a varying intensity; this fact greatly increases the difficulty of fixing accurately either the lower limit or the least observable difference of visual sensations. In the effort to apply Weber's law to sensations of color, the laws of change in the quality operate to obscure the laws of change in the quantity of the sensations. Experiments with shadows for the sake of testing Weber's law were first conducted by A. W. Volkmann and others, under the direction of Fechner.[1] By measuring the distance to which a candle must be removed from an object in order that the shadow produced by its light might disappear in that of another candle of like intensity situated at a fixed near distance from the object, the quotient for the least observable difference was found to be $\frac{1}{100}$. This quotient was also found to remain nearly constant for absolute intensities varying from 1 to 38.79. If, however, the light of the background diminished to 0.36 in intensity, marked variations in the law occurred; the difference in the brightness of the two shadows had then to be greater than $\frac{1}{100}$ to be observable. Later experiments of the same observer yielded results less favorable to Weber's law.[2] The quotient was found to vary from $\frac{1}{65.6}$ for weak intensities of light to $\frac{1}{195}$ for stronger intensities.

By using rotating disks and comparing the grayish circles made upon them when revolving rapidly, through the admixture of small black stripes with the white of their surfaces ("Masson's Disks"), Helmholtz[3] found the medium value of the quotient of least observable difference to be $\frac{1}{133}$; this quotient is not constant, however, and increases, especially for sensations near the upper or the lower limit. By changing the method somewhat, Aubert obtained a variation of $\frac{1}{186}$ to $\frac{1}{120}$ in the degree of sensitiveness to differences in the brightness of lights, even when not going above the middle of the scale of intensity. Experiments with such intensities as lie nearest the limits showed much greater departures from Weber's law. Just above the lower limit, an addition of even $\frac{1}{4}$ to $\frac{1}{3}$ to the stimulus might be necessary in order to produce an observable difference in the resulting sensation. Similar results have been obtained by Delboeuf, but, on the whole, more favorable to Weber's law than the results of Aubert.

§ 21. Of the many experiments which have been undertaken with the object of testing Weber's law in the comparison of intensities of light, those of König and Brudhun[4] apparently cover the greatest range of intensities and so afford the most complete test. These experimenters used intensities varying in the proportion of 1 to 50,000,000, and found the least perceptible difference to be a nearly constant fraction (.017 to .018 of the total intensity) over a considerable range of medium intensities. But the fraction became considerably larger for very feeble, or for very intense, light (.036 for the most intense employed, and .695 for the weakest). We may accordingly regard Weber's law as verified for the middle range:

[1] See *Elemente d. Psychophysik*, pp. 148 f.
[2] A. W. Volkmann, *Physiolog. Untersuchungen*, I, pp. 56 f.
[3] *Physiologische Optik*, pp. 315 f.
[4] *Sitzungsberichte der Berliner Akad. d. Wissensch.*, 1888 and 1889.

of intensity of light. The fraction which expresses the least perceptible difference varies greatly, however, with the special conditions of observation; it is smallest when the two lights to be compared appear side by side with no intervening space, so that the effect of contrast helps discrimination. When the lights are separated, comparison is much less precise, and if one light is seen a second after the other has been removed[1] the fraction may rise as high as $\frac{1}{4}$.

Older experiments seemed to show that the sensitivity of the eye to differences in intensity varies according to the color of the light; but the authors just quoted found that this was not the case, within the same range of brightness. The comparison of the brightness of one color with that of a different color is, however, difficult and uncertain.

§ 22. The minimum of the intensity of light appreciable by the eye is dependent on many circumstances, of which the most important is the condition of *adaptation* to light or dark (see p. 195). The color or wave-length also makes a great difference, as also the part of the retina stimulated, and the extent and duration of the stimulus. The eye is much more sensitive to rays from the middle of the spectrum, especially yellow and green, than to rays from near the red or the violet end. The central area of clear vision of the retina is less sensitive to very dim light than is the region lying just about it; this difference appears during dark adaptation. Lights of very small area or duration will make no impression, although the same intensity, with greater extent or duration, would suffice to give a sensation. S. P. Langley[2] sought to determine the energy of the least quantity of light which could, under the most favorable conditions, produce a perceptible impression, and reached a figure of .00000003 *ergs*. Though this is a very small quantity of energy, it is considerably greater than the minimum determined by Wien as required to excite an auditory sensation.

§ 23. Weber applied his own law to so-called extensive sensations of light. He showed that in judging of the comparative length of lines the least observable difference is, for each person, a tolerably constant fraction of the absolute length of the line with which the comparison is made. This fraction is different for different persons; and has a range from $\frac{1}{50}$ to $\frac{1}{100}$. Fechner[3] defends the validity of the law for lines of lengths varying between 10 and 240 mm. ($\frac{2}{5}$ to $9\frac{1}{2}$ in.), with the eye removed from 300 to 800 mm. (12–32 in.). The lower limit for such cases has been fixed by A. W. Volkmann at lines of length from 0.2 to 3.6 mm. It is obvious,

---

[1] See Fullerton and Cattell, *The Perception of Small Differences*, 1892, p. 140.
[2] *Philosophical Magazine*, 1889, XXVII, 1.
[3] *Elemente d. Psychophysik*, I, 211 f.

however, that we are here not dealing with pure quantity of visual sensations, but with judgments of local relation which, in case the eyes are moved, have their basis, at least partly, in our power to discriminate minute differences in the sensations of the muscular sense connected with such movements.

§ 24. The law of Weber can, of course, derive little or no support from sensations of taste and smell. In the case of these two senses our knowledge of both series of quantities—of the intensity of the stimulus and of the amount of specific sensation which results from its application—is altogether too inadequate to admit of trustworthy comparison. We cannot measure forms of energy like those by which smellable particles and tastable solutions act on the end-organs of sense, until we have a unit of measurement and some information as to what the object is to which the standard should be applied. Nor can we compare amounts of sensations that are so largely matters of individual origin and capricious change, and that are so overlaid with other forms of feeling, as are the sensations of these senses. Moreover, the element of time—both as respects the interval elapsing between the two sensations compared and also the order in which the sensations follow each other —is here a very important influence.

The *intensity of taste* depends upon a variety of circumstances besides the objective quantity of the stimulus. Among these circumstances is the extent of surface excited. Camerer[1] found by experimenting with common salt in solutions of different degrees of concentration that the number of correct guesses increased almost in exact proportion to the number of gustatory papillæ upon which the solutions were placed. Certain mechanical and thermic conditions also have a great influence. Substances even in fluid form, when quickly swallowed, have little taste; pressing and rubbing against the gustatory organs, movement of the tastable matter in the mouth, increase the excitatory effect of the stimuli. It is doubtful whether this effect is due solely to the mechanical result of spreading the stimulus over the surface and urging it into the pores against the end-organs of the sense, or in part also to some direct physiological cause. The influence of temperature on the intensity of sensations of taste is well known. Weber showed that if the tongue is held for $\frac{1}{2}$ to 1 minute in very cold water, or in water of about 125° Fahr., the sweet taste of sugar can no longer be perceived. Cold also destroys for a time the susceptibility to bitter tastes. Keppler[2] endeavored to test Weber's law by determining the sensitiveness to minute changes in the four principal kinds of

[1] See *Zeitschr. f. Biologie*, 1870, VI, pp. 440 f.
[2] Pflüger's *Archiv*, 1869, II, 449 f.

taste; and arrived at a negative result. Fechner, however, considers that Keppler's experiments with common salt confirm Weber's law, and that his other experiments were not adapted to yield any assured result. We can only repeat the statement that other causes than mere increase in the quantity of the stimulus so largely determine the intensity of the resulting sensations as to discredit any arguments from the experiments either for or against applying Weber's law to sensations of taste.

§ 25. The experiments of Valentin and others, to determine how weak solutions of various substances will excite the end-organs of taste, are chiefly valuable as gratifying our curiosity. The figures are not to be accepted as exact, but as showing in general the extreme fineness of this sense, and the great difference of different substances in their power to excite it. Valentin found, for example, that 0.24 gram of a solution containing 1.2 per cent. of cane-sugar excited the sensation of sweet; a solution containing $\frac{1}{426}$ part of common salt was scarcely detectable; of sulphuric acid $\frac{1}{100000}$ could be discerned, $\frac{1}{1000000}$ not; extract of aloes containing $\frac{1}{900000}$ could be distinguished from distilled water; $\frac{1}{33000}$ of sulphate of quinine was plainly observable, and the observer thought he could detect a slight trace of bitter when the solution was diluted to $\frac{1}{1000000}$ of this substance. In general, a smaller absolute quantity of stimulus, when in a relatively concentrated solution, will suffice to excite the end-organs of taste. It will readily be seen that the minimum of some of these substances which will give rise to a sensation under the most favorable circumstances is exceedingly small.

§ 26. The *intensity* of sensations *of smell* is also largely dependent on other causes than changes in the quantity of the stimuli. The amount of sensation appears to be largely governed by the extent of surface excited; since it is greater when we smell with both nostrils, and with the current of inspiration which carries the exciting particles over more of the sensitive membrane. No assured results on this point, however, have yet been reached. Valentin supposes that a smaller number of odorous particles will excite sensation if presented in a concentrated rather than a dilute form. When the intensity of the stimulus increases beyond a certain point, the character of the resulting sensation changes—oftentimes from a pleasant to an unpleasant tone of feeling. All are familiar with the fact that a large increase of some smells—for example, musk—does not give the same kind of sensation.

This sense has a great degree of "sharpness," or power to be excited by small quantities of stimulus, as distinguished from "fineness," or power to distinguish minute variations in the sensations.

It is undoubtedly different in different species of animals, as dependent upon unknown differences in their psycho-physical constitution; but it is tolerably uniform among men where there is the same cultivation of it, and the same concentration of attention. It is well known that certain animals have an astonishing fineness of smell, and are able by it even to detect the individual variations that are quite imperceptible to man. Little value can be attached to the results reached by experiments to fix the least quantity of smellable substances which can excite the human end-organs of this sense. In general, we can say that incredibly small quantities of some substances will suffice. Valentin found that a current of air containing $\frac{1}{200000}$ of vapor of bromine excited a strong unpleasant sensation. Atmosphere polluted with even $\frac{1}{1700000}$ of sulphuretted hydrogen could be detected. It was calculated by this observer that $\frac{1}{2000000}$ of a milligram of alcoholic extract of musk is about as little as can be perceived; of mercaptan, a still smaller quantity is perceptible, since the odor can be detected when a litre of air contains only $\frac{1}{230000000}$ of a milligram of this substance; and it is probable that only a small part of a litre would be inhaled in snuffing the air.

Zwaardemaker[1] has devised an olfactometer, which, though not measuring the stimulus in absolute units, permits of relative determinations, and has applied his instrument to the testing of Weber's law. The results were necessarily inexact, but the law was believed to be approximately verified.

§ 27. A review of the facts bearing on the validity of Weber's law shows, first, that the law is regularly departed from at both the lower and the upper extremes of the scale of intensities; next, that it holds very well for an extensive middle range of intensities of light; further, that it seems to hold approximately for the middle range of intensities of sound, smell, and pressure on the skin, though in none of these cases has anything like the full range of intensities been brought under examination. In the perception of lifted weights, and generally in perceptions dependent on the muscular sense, the departures from the law, even within the middle range, are great and all in the same direction, so that it is impossible to regard the law as holding for these kinds of perception.

§ 28. The value of Weber's law is so restricted, even as stating a general fact of experience, that it would seem scarcely necessary to discuss at length its higher significance. Three possible modes of explanation have all had their defenders; these are the physiological, the psycho-physical, and the psychological. The first of the three assumes that the physical construction of the nervous

[1] *Physiologie des Geruchs*, 1895.

system, including chiefly the end-organs of sense and their central representatives and connections, is such as to supply the reason for this relation between the intensity of sensations and that of their stimuli. And certainly, if we were to adopt off-hand the simplest assumption, it would be that the quantitative relation between the last antecedent molecular changes in the brain and the mental changes to which they give rise, is one of simple proportion; the more work done by means of the excitation in the appropriate cerebral centres, the more of physical basis laid, as it were, for a resulting quantity of psychical movement.

If, then, the sensations vary in quantity in an arithmetical proportion, while their external stimuli vary in a geometrical proportion, the explanation of the fact must be found somewhere in the chain of events between the external stimuli and the nerve-commotions set up as a result in the appropriate centres of the brain. And without doubt, in all of the senses, the end-organs profoundly modify the intensity of the stimulus they receive. In the so-called chemical senses (smell, taste, sight) a profound quantitative modification takes place, even before the stimulus reaches the fibrils of the sensory nerve. In the case of the mechanical sense of hearing we cannot say how much of the effect stated in Weber's law may not have been gained even before the acoustic waves set agoing the nervous elements of the organ of Corti. As to profounder modifications in the same direction by reason of the interaction of different nerve-elements in the brain we are yet more ignorant.

The psycho-physical explanation of Weber's law is that adopted by Fechner. This explanation insists upon making the law one of the utmost generality and of the highest import as stating the relations between organic and spiritual activities. Although Fechner's view confessedly grew out of his speculation that body and mind are only two phenomenal aspects, as it were, of one and the same underlying reality, it has been defended by him with a great amount of mathematical science and experimental research. No other form of explanation, however, takes us so much into the regions of utter obscurity. Why the quantitative relations of body and mind should be such, and such only, that a geometrical series of changes in the one should invariably be represented by an arithmetical series of changes in the other, must indeed remain an ultimate mystery. And the experimental proof of Weber's law is as yet much too incomplete to make us ready to accept it as an ultimate psycho-physical principle.

The psychological explanation of Weber's law resolves it into a special case under the greater law of the relativity of our inner states. It is not so much, then, a law of the absolute quantity of sensations as dependent on stimuli, but rather a law of our apprehension in consciousness of the relation of our own feelings. In general, it may be said that *every mental state has its value determined*, both as respects its quality and its so-called quantity, *by its relation to other states*. It is the amount of change rather than the absolute amount of feeling which the mental apperception estimates. That some psychological explanation is needed to account for the facts there can be no doubt when we consider how important are the elements of attention, mental habit, power of acute discrimination, etc., in determining our estimates of the quantitative relations of our sensations. *Estimates*—that is, acts of the comparing judgment—are involved in the experience upon which reliance is placed for a demonstration of Weber's law.

§ 29. It does not seem possible, however, to make a strict deduction of Weber's law from the principle of relativity alone; for the proportionality required by Weber's law is not the only form of relation that can hold between quantities. Wundt has laid some stress on the "method of mean gradations" as being specially suited to test the view that, in comparing different intensities, we judge by ratios rather than by additions and subtractions. If we judge by ratios, the subjective mean between two intensities should be given by the geometrical mean between the stimuli. The results, on application of the method, have been uneven: in some cases the subjective mean has corresponded rather closely to the geometrical mean of the stimuli, and in others to the arithmetical mean. This has led Wundt to offer the suggestion that two kinds of comparison are possible—by ratios and by absolute differences—according to the psychological attitude induced in the observer by the conditions of the experiment. This importance of the psychological attitude he regards as good evidence in favor of the psychological interpretation of Weber's law.[1] The prevailing opinion at the present day probably favors some form of physiological interpretation for Weber's law. In this connection a suggestion of Fullerton and Cattell[2] is of interest. They would interpret the least noticeable difference, like the average error, as belonging to the class of "errors of observation," and as due, fundamentally, to the variability which the process of discrimination shares with all other organic processes. In general, the variability of a large phenomenon is greater than that of a small; and the perception of a strong stimulus may probably be regarded as involving a larger organic response than the perception of a weak stimulus, and thus as involving more sources of variability. Accordingly, the error of observation, and

[1] *Physiologische Psychologie*, 1902, I, 544; 6th ed., 1908, I, 635.
[2] Op. cit.

the least noticeable difference, would increase with the stimulus. It need not, however, increase as fast as the stimulus; and indeed these authors suggest that it should typically increase according to the general law of composition of independent variations—namely, according as the square root of the stimulus. This formula fits the facts better than Weber's law, in the case of perception of weight and bodily movement, and the deviations from Weber's law in the other departments of sense-perception are usually toward the law of the square root.

This ingenious hypothesis may be helped out by ascribing the departures from Weber's law to the peculiarities of structure in the end-organs and to the complexity of the physiological process involved in different sense-experiences. It is to be noted, however, that it does not do away with the required psychological explanation, but, the rather, involves it as its necessary correlate. For *conscious discrimination* is involved in all the experiments, of every kind and by whatever method tested, that are cited in the interests of Weber's law. And conscious discrimination, as viewed from the introspective point of view, is an exceedingly complex and variable process.

§ 30. As an experimental problem, our confidence in the scientific accuracy of Weber's, or indeed of any other law looked upon as an invariable rule of our sense-experience, quantitatively considered, would be much increased, if there could be any agreement as to exact standards of measurement, and as to the values of the different ways of treating the experimental data. But, as yet there is no such agreement.

Fechner interpreted Weber's law as affording a measure of sensations, and so modified the more empirical expression of Weber as to express the quantity of sensation in terms of the logarithm of the stimulus. This conception implies the possibility of adding one sensation to another, and of treating the least noticeable difference as a certain quantum of sensation. Against this it has been argued, with much force, that the least noticeable difference is not a sensation, but simply a fact about perception; that every sensation, be it of great or small intensity, is, for consciousness, a unit and not made up of smaller sensations; and that, in short, a sensation is not a measurable quantity, but that what we call a difference in intensity is merely a difference in one of the many directions along which sensations differ—a certain kind of qualitative difference. Probably this general point of view has been rather generally accepted, in opposition to Fechner. But it has been found possible to retain Fechner's logarithmic formula, while revising the interpretation of it.[1]   Granted that it is no longer considered as giving a measure of sensation; it may be retained as indicating the position of a sensation in the scale of intensities.   Any convenient intensity can be taken as the zero or centre of reference, and any convenient unit can be chosen, and then the location of any intensity can be indicated in multiples of the unit above or below the chosen zero.   This view does not require us, as Fechner's did, to conceive of a sensation as made up of smaller sensations, but only to conceive the scale of intensities of any kind of sensation as marked off in equal units.   Fechner's formula then shows the relation of points in the intensity series to the corresponding points in the series of stimuli which produce the sensations.

It is doubtful, however, if even this improved interpretation of Fechner's law can be regarded as a justifiable way of stating the facts discovered in measuring least noticeable differences.   One difficulty may be expressed as follows: If a least noticeable difference is taken as a unit, the difference in intensity between any two sensations must be equal to a certain number of these units.   The units must therefore be additive; they must fit together, one after another, without loss.   But this, in general, they will not do, because of the adaptation of the sense-organ to different intensities of the stimulus.   In the case of sensations of sight, for example, on account of the adaptation of the eye, it may even happen that the same intensity of sensation is aroused by stimuli of widely different strength, in spite of the fact that, in passing gradually from one to the other, we have perceived many successive increases of intensity.   Our units have telescoped; we have been like a man on a ship, carefully pacing off the distance between two points on the neighboring shore, unmindful of the fact that the ship is moving in the opposite direction.   The same difficulty would be met in other senses besides sight, since all have some power of adaptation.

§ 31. It seems better, then, to drop Fechner's logarithmic law, and abide by the more empirical expression of Weber.   The facts which are discovered in experiments on the least noticeable difference are not, directly at least, facts regarding the intensity of sensation, but facts regarding the discrimination of intensities of the stim-

---

[1] Those who have contributed to this revision are principally Delboeuf, *Elements de psychophysique*, 1883; Stumpf, *Tonpsychologie*, 1883; and Ebbinghaus, *Sitzungsberichte d. Berl. Akad. d. Wissensch.*, 1887.   Convenient references are Ebbinghaus, *Grundzüge der Psychologie*, 1905, p. 529, and Titchener, *Experimental Psychology, Quantitative, Instructor's Manual*, 1905, p. cxvi.

ulus;[1] and Weber's law, where it holds good, expresses an important truth regarding the perception of intensities, the interpretation of which, as already explained, probably must involve both physiological and psychological factors. Indeed, we shall have to return to the discussion of the whole subject of our sense-experience, from higher points of view.

[1] That all the studies which have been considered in this chapter are, properly speaking, studies in the process and limitations of sense-perception, and not simply in the intensity of sensation, is a growing conviction among psychologists, and has been presented with special force by Müller, in *Die Gesichtspunkte und Tatsachen der psychophysichen Methodik*, p. 234 (Wiesbaden, 1904), and by Aliotta, in *La Misura in Psicologia Sperimentale*, p. 103 (Firenze, 1905).

CHAPTER IV

PRESENTATIONS OF SENSE, OR SENSE-PERCEPTIONS

§ 1. It has already been made clear that those hypothetical elements which we have called "simple sensations," and whose variations in quality and quantity have been found to be dependent on the locality, structural peculiarities, and characteristic physical and cl.emical processes, of the nervous system, have themselves no real existence in our sensuous experience. We are never consciously aware of simple, unlocalized sensations, as such. Even our most carefully prepared means of scientific analysis do not succeed in disentangling them from the intricate complex of experience in which we find them to be actually engaged. For this experience of feeling, smelling, tasting, hearing, and seeing things, is of something infinitely more complex. And to it, when viewed from the psychological point of view, such titles as the following have been given: "Sense-perceptions," or "apperceptions," "presentations of sense," "sense experience," or when designated in a manner seeming to imply less of introspective theory, "objects of sense."

It is the ambition of physiological psychology, as it is of course the aim of psychological science from whatever point of view its problems may be approached, to explain experience. And explanation here, as elsewhere, would involve an analysis of these compounds (if we may be pardoned a somewhat inappropriate figure of speech) into their simpler elements; or better, a descriptive history of the genesis and growth of the more complex from the simpler and more nearly primitive: a study of the causes which have given rise to the process of development, and of the relations which have been called into existence between its different products; and, finally, as far as possible, the establishment of those most general facts of relationship, or so-called laws, which have presided over the whole course of this development.

§ 2. But while our study shares to the full in the desire to accomplish this aim of all psychological science, it has its own somewhat special stand-point to maintain, its special obligations to fulfil, and its somewhat special problems to investigate. All these have been sufficiently many times over defined. We are studying the whole subject from the point of view of one who lays emphasis

380

on the relations existing between the development of mental life and the growth and increasingly complicated functionings of the nervous mechanism. Our special ambition, accordingly, is to discover, or to conjecture, the most plausible explanation of the development of the mental life of the human individual by correlating it with the genesis and growth of the human nervous mechanism.

It is plain, however, that from this time onward we must be more than ever dependent for our problems, for suggestions as to the best manner of approaching the study of them, and even for suggestions as to the directions in which to look for their answer, upon introspective psychology. It is *conscious experience* which we wish to explain. And since the particular kind of experience, which we obtain through the use of our senses, by no means consists in the mere having of simple, or of indefinitely complex, sensations, we must constantly bear in mind the fact that—as everybody knows—attention, association, memory, discrimination, judgment, are all involved in gaining a knowledge of things. All these so-called faculties, however, have a genesis and development which, while it involves a constant and ever more complicated system of actions and reactions, may in many respects be made the subjects, each one, of a special investigation from the physiological point of view.

§ 3. We shall now briefly summarize some of those conclusions, or suggestions from introspective psychology, which have most bearing on every attempt to build up a theory of the presentations of sense, or so-called sense-perception.

(1) Sensations are, when considered from the introspective point of view, modes of *our* being affected. There is a wide interval between our consciousness of being ourselves affected and the perception of "things" as objective and having qualities of their own. This interval is filled, in nature, by the development of mental life as conditioned upon its environment of sense-stimuli; it must be filled in psychological theory, by a description of the process of development. But how shall such a description be obtained? The psychologist does not remember by what stages he first learned to see or feel the extended and external objects of sense. The child cannot describe the process to the psychologist. The infant's first sense-experience is already exceedingly complex; and in all stages of human growth the analyzable contents of consciousness represent only very imperfectly the nature of the basis upon which they rest.

(2) The forms of being and happening in the world, outside of the body, furnish in themselves no adequate explanation whatever of the presentations of sense. This is as true of the colored or smooth extension of an object as it is of its sweet taste or disagreeable smell.

Whatever exists *extra*-mentally, so far as its pure existence goes, is of no account to the mind. It is only as so-called "things" act upon us, or—in other words—get themselves expressed by causing changes in our mental states, that any theory of knowledge by the senses can make use of them. What is true of all that exists and happens outside of the body is just as true of all the bodily conditions and processes. Strictly speaking, they can in themselves furnish no adequate explanation for the rise and development of the presentations of sense. *Only psychical factors can be built into mental products.* The simple sensations have no theoretical value except as they may be considered as *psychical* elements. The image on the retina, for example, is a necessary physical condition of the clear vision of outside objects; it may also become an object for the inspection of another observer. But the retinal image never becomes a kind of inner object for one's own brain or mind. The mind is never to be conceived of as contemplating a spatial picture of its object formed somewhere within the cerebral substance.

Even more obvious is the worthlessness, for purposes of strictly psychological analysis, of all theory as to the precise spatial arrangement of the fibrils of sensory nerves within the skin or muscular fibre. We have nothing approaching an immediate cognition of the extended network of sensory fibrils in the skin or muscles; much less of the extended muscle or area of the skin. No copy in space-form of the various simultaneous or successive rubbings and stretchings of these peripheral fibrils is propagated to the brain; and if it were, the mind could not be regarded as taking account of any of these neural processes.

(3) A further negative statement may be made with entire confidence. The place at which each organ of sense is found in the periphery of the body, or the place at which any such organ is acted on by the stimulus, cannot of itself furnish a reason for the spatial perception of such place or for distinguishing it from other places near or remote. The locality where a stimulus is applied, except as this locality affects the mental coloring or qualitative shading of the sensations which result, is a matter of complete indifference to the mind.

§ 4. In contrast to all theories like those just rejected, the following positive affirmations are to be held firmly. (1) *Sensations,* as the elements of so-called "presentations of sense," *are psychical states whose place*—so far as they can be said to have one and to speak figuratively—*is in consciousness.* The transference of these sensations from mere mental states to an interpretation of physical processes located in the periphery of the body, or of qualities of things projected in space external to the body, is a mental act. It may rather be said to be a mental *achievement;* for it is an act which in its perfection results from a long and intricate process of psychical as well as physical development.

(2) The presentation of sense, or rather, the thing perceived, has "space-form"; it is extended, and consists of an indefinite number of visible or tangible parts that are systematically arranged beside each other into a continuous whole; it is related with respect to position, magnitude, etc., to other similar objects of sense. And, indeed, the one most important characteristic which the presentations of sense possess is *space-form.* "Space-form" (whatever metaphysics may decide to be the nature, origin, and validity of our idea of space) must be regarded by psychology simply as the mental form of the presentations of sense. The problem which physiological psychology has to solve in this direction may then be stated as follows: *On the basis of what combinations of physical and nervous processes do the different resulting sensations come to be combined into presentations of sense under the characteristic of space-form?*

§ 5. The most complete answer possible to the question just raised is obliged to recognize the following particular truths:

(1) A combination (or "fusion," or "synthesis," or "association") of two or more qualitatively different series of sensations is ordinarily —if not absolutely—necessary in order that presentations of sense in space-form may be constructed. A series of sensations of one kind only, like the pure differences in pitch of musical tone, or of degrees of brightness and saturation of color-tone, or of pressure, temperature, or muscular innervation, is not adapted to form the material for constructing extended objects of sense.

(2) The characteristic differences in quality of the sensations of some of the senses, and so their adaptability to form graded series, are such as to fit these sensations for combination with other similar sensations into the presentations of sense under space-form; the sensations of other senses have not,—at least, to the same extent,— these characteristic differences and this adaptability. We may then speak of peculiarly "*spatial* series" of sensations, and of other series of sensations as—at least, relatively—non-spatial. The sensations of smell, for example, are manifestly not fitted to form a so-called spatial series; indeed, they are incapable of being arranged in any series at all. On the contrary, the various series of complex sensations that come through the eye and skin (including those of the muscular sense) are qualitatively adapted to enter into such relations to each other as shall give a ground in their combined existence for a perception of things. Accordingly the eye and skin are the so-called "geometrical senses."

(3) The locally different parts of the organ of sense—if this organ is itself to become known (as in the case of the skin), or if through its being stimulated an extended object outside of the body is to be perceived (as in the case of both skin and eye)—must have some mental representative in the sensations which stimulation of each calls forth. It is therefore assumed that every complex sensuous experience, besides its general characteristic quality as belonging to this or that particular sense, must have a peculiar "local stamp," or shade, or mixture of quality, dependent upon the place of the organism at which the stimuli are applied; otherwise such experience cannot serve as a factor in the construction of an extended object of sense. This peculiar local stamp, or shade, or mixture of quality has been called a "local sign." It is to Lotze that we owe the first elaborate theory of "local signs," and of their relation to the formation of the presentations of sense.

(4) Various stages in the process of elaborating the objects of perception must be recognized. Thus the knowledge of the things we handle—the fork, the tool, the pen—stands at a farther remove from the simplest perceptions of touch than does the discrimination of one area at the surface of the body as warmer or under more pressure than the surrounding spots. Two noteworthy stages, or "epoch-making" achievements, in the process of elaborating the presentations of sense would seem to require a special consideration. These have been spoken of as "*localization*," or the assigning of the sensuous experience to more or less definitely fixed points or areas of the body; and "*eccentric projection*" (sometimes called "eccentric perception"), or the recognition by the senses of the qualities of objects as situated within a field of space and either in contact with, or more or less remotely distant from, the body.

(5) The entire process of elaborating the presentations of sense, or objects of perception by the senses, presupposes for its explanation a constant activity of the mind in reacting upon the stimuli which produce various forms of molecular disturbance in the nervous system; and, furthermore, its activity in combining the sensations into ever more complex forms. This combining activity is best called "*synthetic*," or *constructive*.[1] It may, indeed, always have a physical basis in some central organic combination of the

---

[1] The word "synthesis" for this mental activity is employed and defended by Wundt (*Physiolog. Psychologie*, 2d ed., ii, pp. 28 f., 164 f., 177), who justly objects to the word "association" and the theories which have used the word, because of their concealment of the truth that the process imparts *new* properties to its product. He also calls attention (p. 175) to the fact that John Stuart Mill, a chief defender of the "association hypothesis," virtually admits the theory of a mental synthesis by using the term "psychical chemistry."

neural processes which result from stimulating, simultaneously or in the right succession, the different end-organs and areas of the end-organs of sense. And, indeed, our science assumes that this is so; although about this, as a matter of accurate knowledge, we are almost wholly in the dark.

§ 6. It follows, then, that *an analysis of the presentations of sense leads us to find our explanation of certain primary facts and results in the nature of the Mind itself.* It is in vain to object that to do this leaves the subject, ultimately, still shrouded in mystery. As a matter of fact, the analysis of psycho-physical science does end in the recognition of ultimate mystery. This is no reproach to it; nor is it a failure or fault peculiar to it alone. All physical science, even, is obliged to accept the same result from its keenest analyses when most vigorously pushed.

The foregoing remarks indicate what is the correct attitude of the science of physiological psychology—so far as it is necessary for it to take any position whatever—toward the two rival theories as to the nature and origin of presentations of sense. These theories have been named the "nativistic" (or intuitional) and the "empiristic." Properly speaking, they are not two fundamentally different theories, but rather two tendencies which appear in the attitude assumed by two classes of observers toward the admission of certain alleged facts, or in the manner of explaining such facts as are admitted by all. These different tendencies are largely due to differences of position on certain fundamental philosophical questions. Thus influenced, the advocates of the so-called "Nativistic School" prefer to emphasize the intuitional and underived activities of the mind.

The so-called "Empiristic School," on the other hand, is inclined to give little or no place to the mind's native intuition; it prefers to fill the gaps in the explanation as based on experiment, with probable conjecture and hypothesis. It often aims to show how what we call "mind" is itself rather the result of a genesis induced by the activity of things through the nervous system. The one school is inclined to look upon the space-form, which presentations of sense possess, as the mind's form, in some large sense *native* to it and not to be explained as the result of a development. The other is inclined to look upon space-form as wholly a form which "things" have come to acquire, and which will be fully explained when science has described the empirical process by which solely this acquisition is gained for them.

§ 7. Certain principles adopted both by the empiristic and by the nativistic school have their undoubted rights; and no satisfactory theory of sense-perception can be framed without admitting them.

There can be no doubt that the presentations of sense which so largely constitute our every-day *adult* experience are not direct results of untrained organic and mental activities; they are not simple intuitions dependent solely on the native and inherent powers of the mind. With whatever speed and certainty they are formed, and however the impression they make is characterized by a perfect "immediateness," they are really extremely complex products, involving not only the organic habit of the species and individual peculiarities of mind and body, but also the acquisitions of experience through memory, attention, association, and so-called "instinctive inference." All this is as true of the unhesitating localization of a burning or cutting pain in some area of the skin as it is of the most deliberate judgment about the distance of a mountain.

On the other hand, however far the "empiricist" may succeed in resolving these "intuitions" of sense into more nearly primitive elements, and however minutely he may describe the processes and laws of their *development*, he will never succeed in withholding from the mind itself the ascription of all its so-called native powers. The elements reached by his most complete analysis must always be considered as reactions of the mind upon the stimulation of the nervous centres through the end-organs of sense; they all imply a *native* disposition and ability of the subject of the sensations. And both theories must alike admit that the nature of the elements and of the synthetic process is conditioned at every step upon the action of the central nervous mechanism as sensitive and excited through stimulation of the end-organs of sense. Nevertheless, the triumphs of scientific research all lie along the line of the construction of a more and more perfect genetic theory.

§ 8. Before proceeding to illustrate and confirm in detail the principles already laid down, several questions raised by the mere statement of these principles require an answer. And first: What are those characteristic differences in quality which the sensations belonging to some of the senses possess, and which adapt them to combine into presentations of sense under space-form? In other words, what kinds of sensations are fitted to constitute a so-called "*spatial series*"? Plainly, it is not necessary that those elements of the complex objects of sense, which make the objects appear to be composed of parts set together side by side, should themselves be immediately known as side by side. What is really necessary is that both series of sensations, if they are to be combined into one presentation of sense, shall be capable of clearly and reciprocally determining each other as series of sensations. They must both have, that is to say, the common qualities and mutual relations of a so-called "spatial series."

(1) Of the qualities which characterize *spatial series* the following are the most important: *Series of sensations of like quality, which are adapted to combine into extended objects of sense, must admit of easy, rapid, and frequent repetition in varying order of arrangement.* If a portion of the body be moved, as, for example, a finger, an arm, a leg, or the bending of the back—a graded series of sensations, due to the varying quality and quantity of strain upon the different muscles, joints, etc., is the result. This series is composed of individual compound sensations that shade into each other with no apparent interruption, each of them having a certain value and temporal position in consciousness. In adult experience the series is rapidly concluded, and instantaneously interpreted as a whole. But they may be reproduced in a measure by slowly moving a limb in any direction, and endeavoring to pay strict and exclusive attention to the succession of feelings which results. Every motion of each limb, from about the same position a to about the same position m, relative to the whole body, with similar energy, speed, and other concomitant circumstances, yields a nearly identical series of sensations (a, β, γ, . . . μ). Other motions of different limbs, or differing otherwise (in energy, speed, point of starting or of conclusion, etc.), yield series differing in the value and ordering of their individual members. What is true of the muscular sensations that result from the movement of the limbs is also true of the accompanying sensations of the skin, such as arise from changes in its tension, etc. These sensations, however, largely blend with the series of muscular sensations so as to be nearly or quite inseparable in consciousness. The same thing also holds good of the series of tactual sensations (sensations of light pressure or touch proper) developed by moving an object over the skin, or by moving a tactile organ (especially the hand) over an object at rest. The muscular and tactual sensations which result from motion of the eye also have the qualities of a graded spatial series.

Accordingly, senses like those of the eye and hand, which have organs capable of rapid and precise motion, are equipped with a peripheral mechanism adapted to the production of so-called spatial series of sensations. The succession of sensations of light and color which accompany the movement of an object in the field of vision, or of the glance from one object to another, are of the kind favorable to forming a spatial series. In all these cases the rate of the sensations is important. Either too slow or too rapid movement of the organ will not yield a spatial series of sensations. Moreover, such series are capable of repetition, not only forward, as a, β, γ, δ, . . . μ, or in inverse order, as μ, λ, κ, . . . β, a, but also in an endless variety as an intersecting network of sensations.

(2) The second class of qualifications which must be possessed by a spatial series of sensations secures their habitual combination with other series, also of a spatial kind. They must be in nature *comparable* and *associable* with each other, and, in fact, simultaneously experienced by the mind. In singing a musical scale a series of sounds is accompanied by another series of muscular and tactual sensations occasioned by the use of the vocal organs; both series may be produced in inverse order by singing the same scale backward. Thus we know not only that *we* are singing the scale *with* the vocal organs, but also that we are at the same time hearing it with the ear. We know both these facts, however, through sensations of muscle and skin that have already become inseparably associated and localized in our own body.

On the contrary, from the dawn of consciousness onward through all the development of experience, series of sensations of light and color are constantly accompanied by, and combined with, other series of tactual and muscular sensations of the eye. So, too, the different series of sensations that arise from the irritation of the nerves in muscle and skin are, of necessity, habitually combined. In forming the field of touch, the fact that certain parts of the periphery of the body so frequently come into contact with other parts is of the highest significance. Two series of complex sensations, corresponding to the terms "touching" and "being touched," are thus brought into *juxtaposition*, as it were, in consciousness. This "juxtaposition" in consciousness is not itself, of course, a *spatial* juxtaposition; the former is, however, the necessary precondition of the latter.

(3) The third characteristic of the spatial series of sensations is the possession of a *system of local signs*. It may safely be assumed that on neither side—that of an active nervous mechanism, or that of a conscious, sensuous experience—are the means that make an interpretation of the locality of our body as affected by the stimuli, of the spatial relation one to another of its parts, of the whole body to its environment, and of the different objects in this environment one to another, a simple affair. On the contrary, those feelings, on the interpretation of which, as "local signs," our sense-perceptions all depend, are always exceedingly complex. And correspondingly complex are the quickly changing and combining functions of the nervous mechanism. For this reason, if no other, it is uniformly difficult to submit them to a complete analysis. Several views, for example, are possible as to the nature of the *local signs of the skin*. It has been held that they are not qualitative differences at all, but differences in the intensity and time course of the tactual sensations. Again, it has been held that the local

signs of touch are qualitative differences of sensation dependent upon the modifications which the stimulus undergoes on account of the changing character of the skin with respect to tension, nature of the substance of muscle, tendon, and bone over which it is stretched, etc. Finally, it may also be held that the local signs of the skin are qualitative differences of sensation peculiar to the different nervous elements existing in different parts of this organ of sense. They are the direct result, that is, of the mind's reaction upon the specific energies of the nervous elements as called out by the stimulus. This is, of course, to fall back upon the ultimate mystery involved in the original nature of that reaction which the mind makes as dependent upon the locally individual nervous elements being stimulated.

What is certain of the feelings, or "sensation-complexes," in dependence on which this class of objects of sense becomes known to us, is yet more certain of those on the interpretation of which all our knowledge of visual objects is dependent. Here, not only is it true that no one theory among the several proposed seems adequate to account for all our experience, but something may possibly be taken from them all which will prove of assistance. And more refinements borrowed from the psychology of association, memory, habit, and judgment, must be added in order to approximate, even somewhat remotely, a satisfactory theory of the local signs of the eye.

§ 9. In view of all the evidence, it would seem that the general theory of local signs must be constructed in somewhat the following way: Within certain limits, which it is impossible for science as yet definitely to fix, the irritation of the different nervous elements of certain organs of sense gives rise to sensations which differ in the *shading* of their quality according to the locality in the organ at which the elements are situated. This is probably true of both peripheral and central areas of the total organ. It is true of the latter areas as dependent on the excitation of the former. The simultaneous irritation of several locally related elements of the organ (and the irritation is seldom or never confined to a single element) results, then, in a certain *mixture of feeling* dependent upon the number and local relation of all the elements thus simultaneously irritated. For example, the color-tone of the complex sensations aroused by irritating together the retinal elements a, β, γ, δ, etc., differs from that aroused by irritating the elements γ, δ, ϵ, ζ, etc. The same thing holds true of locally related nervous elements of the skin. Just how much in every case of the local coloring is due, on the physiological side, to differences in structure and how much to differences in processes, how much to peripheral elements and how much to central nervous connections, it may be impossible to say. Each of the spatial series of sensations is characterized by this shading of its elements. We must, therefore, hold that every sense which is the medium of space-perceptions has a system of local signs of its own.

Further: not only each "geometrical sense," but also each of the "spatial series" of sensations arising through the total operation of that sense, consists of members that have a local coloring peculiar to the series. Thus the spatial series of tactual impressions produced by moving an object from a to d on the hand differs from that produced by moving it from a to n; the series of muscular sensations developed by raising one pound differs, with respect to the color-tone of its members, from that developed by raising two pounds, with the hand.

But another important consideration remains. The local signs of the different spatial series which frequently combine in the operation of the same organ must necessarily modify each other. Hence there arise ever more complex admixtures of feeling dependent upon the combined specific energies of the nervous elements simultaneously excited, with a given amount of energy and with given relations to preceding conditions. We define the local sign, then, as *that mixture of feeling which gives to the sense-experience its peculiar coloring, and is dependent upon the combined result of exciting the nerves of a given locality of the organ.*

§ 10. The most noteworthy stages, or "epoch-making" achievements, in the process of elaborating the presentations of sense, have been declared to be "localization" and "eccentric projection." The first, primarily, gives us the knowledge of our own body, mainly by passive sensations of touch; the knowledge of our own body which comes through sight is by eccentric projection. We immediately feel the peripheral parts of the body as the places where the sensations are localized; we see some of the same parts as projected in space before our eyes. Objects that are not a part of ourselves are given to us as projected eccentrically, either by touch through their being in contact with the skin and occasioning sensations of muscular exertion, or by sight as having distance in its field of vision.

Localization and projection are not, however, to be regarded as two phases of one and the same process; we do not first have the presentations of sense as parts of the periphery of our bodies, and then, on further experience, push them beyond this periphery, either to an infinitesimal distance or to one remote. Localization and eccentric projection are rather two processes, largely unlike, which go on contemporaneously and are set up chiefly on the basis of different classes of sensations. Where two parts of the sensitive skin of our own bodies come together, the conditions for both of the above-mentioned processes are fulfilled.   Accordingly, one part has localized in it those complex sensations which make us aware that this part of our body is *touching* something; the other has localized in it those sensations which make us aware that this part is being *touched by* something.   Which of the two parts shall be regarded as touching, and which as being touched, depends on various considerations.   Those members of the body which are most used in active touch are generally known as touching, and the less active parts as being touched.

§ 11. Two things more must constantly be borne in mind in any attempt to construct even a fairly plausible theory of sense-perception in terms of physiological psychology.   First: so far as we can penetrate the mysteries of beginning mental life, there is never at any stage an experience corresponding to "pure sensations," or "simple sensations."   Such terms, if employed at all, must always be understood as applying to hypothetical elements of already complex psychoses, which are, however, of value, especially to the student of physiological psychology as enabling him *to correlate the mental life, in its development, with the increasing complexity of the secondary activities of the brain which result from the combination of its more primary reactions to the elementary sensory impulses.* That there is growth in knowledge as to the spatial and temporal relations of the bodily members, and of external objects and the sequence of events among things, there can be no manner of doubt. Our problem is to account for this growth.

But second: the so-called "higher faculties" of the mind are as truly implied in the very beginnings of sensuous experience as in its latest developments.   The infant attends, discriminates, judges, and so learns, as truly—and in all probability, in essentially the same way—as the adult man of science.   Indeed, the most astonishing and antecedently incredible thing about the whole of these earlier stages is the intensity, and the fine quality, of those mental activities which initiate, conduct, and control all the more primitive processes of learning to know, by the senses, the bodily organism and external things. *For these secondary and "synthetic" reactions, the highly developed, but as yet unused, cerebral hemispheres of the human infant seem especially adapted.*

The foregoing principles must now be illustrated and confirmed by a brief statement of facts which relate to the formation and development of presentations of sense by a synthesis of simple sensations.   Attention will, for obvious reasons, be directed almost exclusively to those presentations of sense which come through the eye and skin, including in both the influence of muscular sensations.

§ 12. *Perceptions of Smell* differ only in fineness, duration, and accompanying tone of feeling; they have no size or shape, no spatial properties of any kind. Considered apart from their accompaniment of muscular and tactual sensations, they cannot even be said to be localized. Fineness of smell, or power to make minute distinctions in quality, and so infer the presence or direction of an object previously known to excite such quality of sensations, differs greatly in different species of animals and in different individuals of the same species. The exploits of some animals give ground for the conjecture that every species, and even every individual, has an odor of its own. The direction and nature of the object which causes the sensations are judged by variations of intensity on turning the head, or on approaching or receding from the object. Sensations of smell are known to come through the nose, by localizing there the accompanying muscular and tactual sensations with their strong tone of feeling. This is readily done, since we draw the air through the nostrils and feel its double effects in producing the two classes of sensations. As to the simultaneous influence of two smells, little is known beyond the fact that the stronger overwhelms the weaker. The power of discrimination may, of course, be cultivated in this sense as in every other.[1]

§ 13. Most of the remarks just made as to perceptions of smell apply also to *Perceptions of Taste*. Sensations of taste, however, are much more closely connected with those of touch; since the tongue is a chief organ of active touch. It is the tactual and muscular sensations, and not the purely qualitative affections of taste, which are localized in the mouth. Concerning contrast and compensation of tastes, little is known which does not belong to ordinary experience. Valentin[2] alleges that when a sour mass is laid on one half, and a bitter mass on the other half, of the root of the tongue, the predominating taste may sometimes be determined by our choice. It is well known that certain tastes compensate each other, as it were, in experience, without any chemical equivalence of their properties. The sugar neutralizes the acid of the lemonade, not in the vessel that contains the mixture, but in the nervous system of him who drinks it. Brücke holds[3] that the neutralizing of one sensation of taste by the other takes place in the brain. The sensation of bitter is especially difficult to cover or neutralize.

§ 14. *Perceptions of Hearing* next demand consideration. More difficulty accompanies the effort to establish the proposition that

---

[1] On the whole subject see von Vintschgau's monograph in Hermann, *Handb. d. Physiol.*, III, pp. 225 ff.

[2] *Lehrbuch der Physiol. d. Menschen*, etc., Abth. ii, p. 308 (2d ed.).

[3] *Vorlesungen über Physiol.* (ed. 1884), ii, p. 262.

sensations of sound are not directly localized, but are projected in a space constituted chiefly by the eye and the hand, through complicated indirect inferences.

The chief facts which must be accounted for by a theory for the localization of sounds are the following: A sound can be recognized with certainty as coming from the right or the left side, or as coming from a point either to the right or left of the median plane of the head. Moreover, the angle at which the sound approaches the ear, as measured from the median plane, can be recognized with considerable accuracy. Or, if a sound is produced within this plane (extended into space), this fact can be well recognized. But as to the direction within this plane from which the sound comes—whether from above, before, or behind—judgment is uncertain and subject to large errors. And the same difficulty is experienced in judging the exact direction of sounds which come from the side. How much their direction differs from the median plane can, as was stated, be told; but whether from before, behind, up or down, is only poorly distinguished. In other words, if a sphere be conceived as surrounding the head, with the north and south poles located opposite the ears and the equator coinciding with the median plane of the head, then the latitude of a sound can be detected with considerable accuracy, but the longitude is subject to much error. Judgment of the latitude is, however, most accurate near the equator, and least accurate near the poles.[1]

§ 15. Another set of facts comes to light when different sounds are made to affect the two ears. If the two sounds are of different pitch or timbre, each is apt to be heard and localized separately; but if the two are alike, except that one is stronger than the other, they usually appear as one, which is localized on the side of the stronger stimulus; and if they are alike in intensity as well as in pitch and timbre, usually one sound is heard, which seems to come from the median plane. This last result, which is as instructive as it is curious, can be obtained by sounding two tuning forks of the same pitch, with equal loudness, one opposite each ear; or by conveying a sound through a branched tube, one branch being inserted in each meatus; or, finally, by employing a branched telephone circuit, with a receiver held to each ear. In the latter two cases, the sound is subjectively localized in the interior of the head. Similar results are obtained by applying the shank of a vibrating tuning fork to the skull at various points; the tone is localized in that ear which is more strongly excited, but if the fork is applied at a point

---

[1] See D. Starch, *University of Iowa Studies in Psychology*, 1905, IV, 1; and *Psychological Review, Monograph Supplement*, No. XXXVIII, 1908.

in the median plane, the sound is localized in the median plane, and often in the interior of the head. When sound is thus conveyed to the ear by bone conduction, closing the meatus of one ear by holding the palm against it increases the effect on that ear, and causes the sound to appear louder, and, therefore, to be localized in the ear that is closed (Weber's experiment). As such conduction is, in large measure, the means by which the sound of our own voices reaches our ears, the same experiment can be tried by humming a low note with closed lips, and observing the effect of closing the external meatus with the palm. If one ear is thus closed, the sound is localized in that ear; if both ears are closed at once, the sound appears to come from the interior of the head.

§ 16. The first step toward an explanation of the power of localizing sounds is thus made clear: evidently, as the last-mentioned experiment shows, each ear has a "local sign" of its own, by which a stimulus affecting chiefly one ear is distinguished from a stimulus affecting the other ear. It should be noted that sound never affects one ear alone, unless the other ear is totally deaf; for conduction by the bones occurs between the two ears to a surprising degree. Neither closing the external meatus of one ear, nor bringing the source of sound close to the other ear, suffices to produce strictly monaural hearing. These devices do, however, ensure a stronger excitation of one ear than of the other. There can be no doubt—as a second indication for a correct theory of the localization of sounds—that a sound which excites one ear more strongly than the other is localized on the more excited side; nor that when both ears are excited equally, the sound is localized in the median plane. It would seem, accordingly, that the decisive factor in localizing sounds to the right or left must be the relative intensities of the stimulation of the two ears. This factor would account for the more accurate element in localization. The much less accurate sense of locality for front and back may be dependent on the position of the auricle, which, in the human being, would seem to favor the entrance of sounds from the front; just as, in animals possessing movable ears, the localization of sounds certainly appears to depend on adjusting the position of the pinna most favorably for the direction of the sound.

§ 17. The principle of relative intensities can therefore be applied satisfactorily to the case of sounds originating near the ear; but difficulty arises in the case of sounds from distant sources, for here the difference in distance of the ears from the source of sound is too small, in comparison with the total distance, to account for a different intensity of excitation of the two ears. One ear is practically as far from the source as the other; both ears should therefore be equally excited, and the sound be localized in the median plane, instead of being, as it often is, very clearly and correctly assigned to one side or the other. The ear which is toward the source of sound is indeed exposed to the direct impact of the waves, whereas the other would seem to be shielded from them by the head. But here we meet a physical difficulty, for, as Lord Rayleigh has shown,[1] the head is too small a shield to cast a "sound shadow," at least when the sound is of low pitch and, therefore, of great wave-length with respect to the diameter of the head. Sound-waves bend readily around the head, and enter the further ear with, it would seem, little possible diminution of their energy. The waves entering the two ears would, however, be at any moment in different phases, and Lord Rayleigh believed that this difference of phase afforded a basis for distinguishing the direction of the sound—a view which appears rather improbable. Myers and Wilson,[2] taking account of bone conduction, are, however, able to show that the difference of phase must result in a difference in intensity at the two ears. It should also be noted that, as the orifice of the ear lies nearer to the back than to the front or top of the head, the path of sound-waves around the head is shorter in some directions than in others, and that, accordingly, the waves which reach the further ear will themselves vary in phase and therefore interfere with each other and have less effective intensity than the sounds which, approaching the nearer ear across clear space, act on it without this mutual interference. High tones, with short wave-length, would evidently be more subject to this interference than low tones. At any rate, there is no doubt that the nearer ear is more intensely excited than the further ear, for this can be proved by direct measurements of the least audible sound, coming from various directions.[3] A weaker sound can be heard when the source is directly opposite the right or left ear, than when it is situated in or near the median plane.

The quality or timbre of a sound is also affected by the angle from which it approaches the ear, and is different for the nearer and for the farther ear.

The shorter the waves, the more effectively does the head screen the farther ear; it thus cuts out the higher partial tones of a clang or noise more than the lower components, and changes the quality of the sound. This difference in the quality of sound to the two ears, according to the direction from which the sound comes, may be

[1] *Nature*, 1876, XIV, 32; *Philosophical Magazine*, 1907, XIII, 214.
[2] *Proceedings of the Royal Society*, 1908, A, LXXX, 260; *British Journal of Psychology*, 1908, II, 363.
[2] See Starch, op. cit.

of importance not only in the binaural localization of sounds to the right or left, but also in the (often considerable) power of localization as possessed by a one-eared person;[1] and, further, in the assignment of sounds to front and rear, above and below.

§ 18. What has thus far been said of localization of sound has referred to the perception of its direction. The judgment of its distance must be dismissed with a few words. If the sound is familiar, the distance of its source can be judged from its apparent intensity. But even when the intensity of the sound at its source is not known, it may still be possible to recognize the distance from which it comes. It is probable that the change in the quality of a sound with distance, due to the dropping out of the weaker overtones, has much to do with the recognition of distance. It is significant that simple tones are more poorly localized, both as to distance and as to direction, than clangs and noises containing an abundance of high partial tones.[2] In one-eared individuals pure tones are entirely unlocalizable.

The proposition would seem then to be established that the so-called perceptions of hearing are localized by means of the varying intensities and complex qualities (or "local signs") of the sensations of sound, in a field of space which has been "constructed"—so to say—out of other forms of sense-experience.

§ 19. An account of the process by which a *Field of Touch* is constructed, and extended objects are known as in contact with the skin at definite points or areas of it, must begin by enumerating the data which the mind has for such activity. The most important of these data are indicated by certain facts as to the fineness of the so-called "sense of locality" belonging to the skin. E. H. Weber first attempted a rule for measuring the degree of this fineness accurately; he also mapped out the entire field of the surface of the body into areas differing greatly in their fineness.[3] For a measuring instrument he used the two points of a pair of dividers, blunted so as to prevent the sensation of being pricked; the principle of measurement was that the minimum distance apart at which the *two points*, when touching the skin of any region, are felt as *two localized sensations*, is the measure of the sensitiveness to local distinction of that region. The following table gives some of the results of Weber's experiments; the figures indicate the number of

---

[1] See Angell and Fite, *Psychological Review*, 1901, VIII, 225, 449.

[2] On this point, see J. R. Angell, *Psychological Review*, 1903, X, 1. For general discussion and literature, see K. L. Schaefer, in Nagel's *Handbuch der Physiologie*, 1905, III, 573, and C. S. Myers, *Textbook of Experimental Psychology*, 1909, 286.

[3] *Annot. Anatom.*, vii, p. 4 f.; Wagner's *Handwörterb. d. Physiol.*, III, Abth. ii, p. 529 f.

millimetres[1] apart which the points of the dividers were when the given area of the organ was *just able* to distinguish them:

Tip of the tongue	1
Volar side of the last phalanx of the finger	2
Red part of the lips	5
Volar side of the second and dorsal side of the third phalanx of the finger	7
White of the lips, and metacarpus of the thumb	9
Cheek, and plantar side of the last phalanx of the great-toe	11
Dorsal side of the first phalanx of the finger	16
Skin on the back part of cheek-bone, and forehead	23
Back of the hand	31
Knee-pan, and surrounding region	36
Forearm, lower leg, back of the foot near the toes	40
Skin of the nape, and of the back in the five upper cervical vertebræ	54
Skin of the middle of the back, and of the upper arm and leg	68

Weber also found that the fineness of the sense of locality is greater in a transverse than in a longitudinal direction, on both arms and legs. On these surfaces of the skin the "sensation-circles," or areas within which the minimum distances of the dividers' points are felt as two points, have an elliptical shape, with their long axes up and down. That the size of the sensation-circles, or the fineness of the sense of locality, largely forms the basis for our judgments of the position, number, and magnitude of the localized sensations in the field of touch may be shown by a simple experiment. If the points of the dividers be separated somewhat less than is necessary in order to distinguish them as two on the cheek just in front of the ear, and then (the distance apart of the points remaining unchanged) be slowly moved until one point rests upon the upper and the other upon the lower lip, to a person blindfold, and unprejudiced by knowing what is to take place, the point first felt as one will appear to become two, and then the two recede from each other continually as the parts with a finer sense of locality are traversed. The same experiment may be tried upon any other part of the body. It appears, therefore, that the mental representation of the magnitude of the distance between two impressions varies in inverse proportion to the real magnitude of the smallest perceivable distance, on any given area of the skin. The same principle appears to hold good when all the space between the impressions is filled up, so as to make a *continuum* of localized sensations.

§ 20. The explanation of Weber's "sensation-circles" of the skin has been the subject of much debate. It is natural at first to as-

---

[1] The numbers were given by Weber in Parisian lines; in the table they are taken from Wundt, *Physiolog. Psychologie* (2d ed.), ii, p. 7, who has reduced them to even millimetres.

sume that each entire circle is provided with one and only one
nerve-fibre, whose terminal expansion covers the circle, and whose
excitation is represented in consciousness by a sensation of a specific value.   Doubtless certain anatomical differences in the nerve-
fibres of the skin, and certain corresponding physiological differences in their function, must be assumed as the basis of every theory to account for the skin's sense of locality.   But Goldscheider's
experiments show that a number of pressure-spots must be recognized within each sensation-circle, and each pressure-spot at least
should have a sensory fibre.   Moreover, every point within each
sensation-circle is itself sensitive (however large the circle may be),
and the limits of none of the circles are fixed as would be the expanse of a single nerve-fibre distributed over them.   Still further,
different individuals differ greatly in the size of these circles (and
we cannot well suppose a corresponding difference in the number
of sensory nerves of the skin), and practice suddenly and greatly
diminishes the area covered by a single circle.   It must at least be
admitted that "the smallest perceivable distance is not a direct
measure for the diameter of the sensation-circle."   Weber himself
assumed that sensation-circles always contain a number of isolated
nerve-fibres; and that, in order to have the impression of two localized sensations, several unexcited fibres must exist between the two
excited.   The number of these unexcited fibres serves the mind as
a kind of means for the approximate measurement of distances on
the skin.   The highly conjectural, and in general the unpsycho-
logical, nature of all these explanations renders them unsatisfactory.

§ 21.   When we attempt to apply the theory of local signs to this
subject, difficulty arises in assigning a conclusive reason why the
different areas of the skin should differ so greatly in the fineness of
their capacity for making *local distinctions*.   In the view of Lotze,[1]
this difference is chiefly due to the varying character of the areas
of the skin with respect to richness in nerve-fibres, thickness and
so sensitiveness, support and tension according as the skin is
stretched over underlying soft or hard parts—fat, muscle, tendon,
bone, etc.   Doubtless all such influences enter into the determination of that mixture of feeling which characterizes the local signs
of the skin.   The theory suggested by Vierordt,[2] on the basis of
experiments made by himself and his pupils, should also be mentioned.   This investigator concluded that the fineness of the sense
of locality belonging to any area of the skin increases in direct proportion with the distance of that area from the axes about which it

[1] See *Medicin. Psychologie*, p. 405 f.
[2] Pflüger's *Archiv*, 1869, II, pp. 297 ff.; and *Zeitschr. f. Biologie* VI, VII, IX,
X, XI.

is rotated. The relative fineness of the organ's local sense is a function of its mobility. Thus an uninterrupted increase of the power of localization exists in the arm from the acromion to the tips of the fingers; an increase of its movableness, on the whole, also exists. If a value of 100 be assigned to the power of discrimination exercised at the acromion, 151 will represent that of the upper arm, 272 that of the lower arm, 659 of the hand, 2,417 of the thumb, and 2,582 of the tips of the fingers. In estimating the relative movableness of these different parts, it should be remembered that they not only all move in an enlarging circuit from the shoulder-joint downward, but that each of them from the elbow-joint downward has its special increased circuit and more numerous forms of motion.

But even if Vierordt's law could be strictly demonstrated for every portion of the body, its meaning would have to be translated into other terms in order to be of any real service to psychology. It is therefore suggested by Funke that the increased power of discrimination which belongs to the more movable areas of the skin is really due to the superior facility which they thus have for exercise; it therefore falls under the law of habit. Furthermore—as we have occasion to remark concerning many similar functions of the mind in correlation with the nervous mechanism—the effect of acquired habit is not limited to the experience of the individual; it belongs also to the race. The superior fineness of local sense in some parts of the body may therefore be regarded as largely native to the individual.

§ 22. The view which must be taken of Weber's "sensation-circles," and of the entire subject of the localization of areas of pressure on the skin, has been largely changed by the more recent experiments of Goldscheider[1] and others. We have already seen (p. 344) that the finest point, when it touches a "pressure-spot," produces a sensation of pressure, and not one of being pricked; but touching other spots does not produce a sensation of pressure at all. It must be held, then, that the sensations produced by laying a single blunted dividers' point upon the skin, as in Weber's classical experiment, are really very complex, and are composed of the sensations from several pressure-spots blended with other sensations from the rest of the same area not covered by the pressure-spots. The fineness of discrimination possible in any area of the skin depends, then, upon how all the points irritated stand related to the specific pressure-spots. Goldscheider found that only when two irritating points touch two pressure-spots are they *felt as* two. But

[1] *Archiv f. Anat. u. Physiol.*, Physiolog. Abth., 1885, Supplement-Band, pp 1–104; especially, p. 84 f.

when one of the points touches a pressure-spot, and the other touches some place in the contiguous area of skin which is free from such spots, the two points are not both felt; in this case only the one resting on the pressure-spot is felt.

The table of minimum distances at which two points can be felt as two, when the exact nature of the area of the skin on which we are experimenting is known, and everything made as favorable as possible, consists of numbers very much reduced from those of Weber. Following are some citations from Goldscheider's table:

Part of the body	mm.	Part of the body	mm.
Back	4–6	Back of hand	0.3–0.6
Breast	0.8	I. and II. phalanges (volar)	0.2–0.4
Forehead	0.5–1.0	I. and II. phalanges (dorsal)	0.4–0.8
Cheek	0.4–0.6	Upper leg	3.0
Nose and chin	0.3	Lower leg	0.8–2.0
Upper and lower arm	0.5–1.0	Back, and sole of foot	0.8–1.0

§ 23. Yet more recent experiments by Von Frey[1] and his collaborators, Brückner and Metzner, differ considerably from those of Goldscheider in the absolute values assigned to the touch-spots. When two points are applied to neighboring spots, the threshold is indeed very small provided the points are applied successively, but not when both are applied simultaneously, as in the experiments of Weber. It had previously been known that a difference of location could be perceived with much less distance between the points stimulated when one was touched after the other than when both were touched at once.[2] Von Frey and Metzner, applying stimuli to previously identified touch-spots, concluded that a difference of location could be appreciated between any two touch-spots, no matter how near together they might be, when one was excited shortly (say ½ to 1 second) after the other, but not when both were excited simultaneously. In the latter case, the "two-point threshold" was not much less when touch-spots were specifically touched than when the compasses were applied in the usual indiscriminate manner. The perception of simultaneous double touch, therefore, is evidently a perception made under difficulties, and cannot give an ultimate measure of the fineness of the system of local signs. Other facts tend in the same direction. If two points are simultaneously applied to the skin at a distance too small to permit of a clear recognition of twoness, still the sensation aroused may differ from that of a single point, in possessing a certain breadth. In pathological cases, notably after injury to the nerves supplying some region of the skin, the power of discriminating two points

---

[1] *Zeitschrift für Psychologie*, 1901, XXVI, 33, and 1902, XXIX, 161.
[2] See Judd, Wundt's *Philosophische Studien*, 1896, XII, 409.

from one may be practically abolished, while nevertheless the power of localizing single touches may remain excellent, being provided for by the subcutaneous sense, which possesses good powers of localization but none of spatial discrimination.[1]

§ 24. We conclude, then, that the discrimination of two points applied to the skin is not simply related to the system of local signs, but is, as we should expect, closely bound up with other mental factors. Of these may be mentioned attention, practice, suggestion, and association. Under the head of attention we note that persons unfamiliar with the compass test suffer much more than trained observers from the strain to which they are subjected; previous mental or bodily exertion seems to make it difficult to adapt the attention to the rather unusual demands of the test. For this reason this method has been regarded by some as a suitable device for testing mental and muscular fatigue.[2] The *direction* of attention is also an important factor in determining the threshold; for if the observer seeks to interpret the impression of breadth that arises from two points which are applied close together, he may translate this into terms of double touch, whereas if he insists on a clear impression of doubleness, he needs to have the points much farther separated.[3] Such differences in the direction of attention probably account in part for the enormous individual differences which seem to exist in the fineness of this kind of perception. A. W. Volkmann[4] showed the remarkable effect of exercise upon the cultivation of the sense of locality. After fixing the value of the least perceivable differences of locality for a number of small areas in the field of touch, Volkmann found that each successive series of experiments with each area increased its fineness of perception, until within a few hours twice the original degree of fineness could be reached. The growth in perceptive skill of the skin was slower at first for areas not ordinarily used for touch; quicker for those accustomed to daily use. The improvement ceased at a certain limit, and was soon lost by disuse, so that a few months out of

---

[1] Compare Head and Sherren, *Brain*, 1905, XXIX, 109; Spearman, *British Journal of Psychology*, 1905, I, 286.

[2] Griesbach, *Archiv für Hygeine*, 1895, XXIV, and *Internationales Archiv für Schulhygeine*, 1905, I, 317. Griesbach introduced the two-point threshold as an index of mental fatigue, especially in school pupils. He asserts that the two points must be more widely separated after mental work, in order that they may be felt as two. Of others who have tried the method, some regard it as valid, but many have got only negative results. See a summary of this and other points in the recent literature by Spearman in *Archiv für die gesammte Psychologie*, 1906.

[3] Binet, *Année Psychologique*, 1903, IX, 199.

[4] *Berichte d. sächsischen Gesellschaft d. Wissenschaften*, 1858, pp. 38 f.

practice served to reduce the acquired tact of any area to its original condition. A most surprising discovery of this experimenter was, that the practice exclusively of a member of the body on one side resulted in improving the fineness of touch of the corresponding member of the other side. Thus, if the smallest perceivable distance for the tip of a left finger was, to begin with, 0.75 line, and that of the corresponding place on the right finger, 0.85, practice with the left finger exclusively reduced the distance for both fingers—for the left to 0.45 line, and for the right to 0.4.

It is well known that the blind, who have no spatial series of sensations or presentations of extended objects by the eye, attain by exercise a high degree of fineness for certain space-perceptions of the skin.[1] In the case of those who have sight, the most movable and discriminating organs of the skin—such as the tips of the fingers—are capable of being cultivated to great delicacy of touch; but Funke[2] did not succeed, even by an education lasting an entire month, in reducing the obtuseness of the skin of the back between the shoulder-blades and in the lumbar region more than by about one-fourth.

§ 25. These earlier results are subject to some modification in consequence of later work. The rapid improvement with training is ascribed by Tawney[3] to the influence of suggestion, while Judd and Von Frey and Metzner found that the improvement did not occur in the form of the experiment in which the two points are excited successively. Probably the improvement which occurs in the case of simultaneous application is due to the acquisition of skill in interpreting the broad impression produced by exciting two near-by points.

The influence of suggestion and of chance associations has been brought out clearly by Solomons[4] and by Messenger,[5] who, by systematically mistraining an observer, were able to induce a condition in which false judgments were the rule, and in which there might even be a complete reversal of the judgments "one" and "two." The fact is that the impressions derived from two points simultaneously excited appear in consciousness as a single, blended impression, which, however, differs slightly from that produced by the excitation of one point; and the more distant are the two points, the more the difference in the two impressions increases. When the two points are quite far apart, it becomes possible to single out

---

[1] Compare Czermak, *Sitzgsber. d. Wiener Acad.*, XVII, Abth. ii, pp. 563 f.
[2] See Hermann's *Handb. d. Physiol.*, III, ii, p. 382.
[3] Wundt's *Philosophische Studien*, 1898, XIII, 163.
[4] *Psychol. Rev.*, 1897, IV, 249.
[5] *Psychol. Rev.*, Monog. Suppl., XXII, 1903.

either of them and devote attention to it separately, and thus the perception of two is clear. When the points are too near to permit of either being singled out in this way, it may still be true that the total impression of the two-point stimulation differs perceptibly from that of one-point stimulation, and these impressions may then be associated with the numbers one and two, so that correct judgments of the stimulus will be established.

In the case of the blind, though their skill in judging the shape of objects by touch is highly developed, it does not appear that their two-point threshold is specially low.[1] Their skill in touch judgments must, therefore, be the result of practice in interpreting the *total* impressions derived from objects of different size and shape.

§ 26. Since our experience shows that localization of the different minute areas of the skin includes not only the existence of discriminable local signs, but also an active process of discrimination, any physiological theory of this class of perceptions must include some attempt to account for the nervous correlates of the process of discrimination itself. The fact that discrimination is easier when the stimuli are presented successively than when simultaneously holds good not only in the case here under consideration, but also in many others, such as the discrimination of weights or of tones. The transition from one stimulus to another following it may produce a "shock of difference"[2] even though the two stimuli blend when applied simultaneously. Physiologically considered, this blending may be related to the convergence and summation of two compatible stimuli which was seen to occur in the case of reflex action (see pp. 161 f.). The confluence of sensory impulses from two excited points must be less complete in the case of perception than in the case of reflex action; otherwise, it would seem, no discrimination would be possible. To account for the facts of the two-point threshold, Bernstein[3] proposed a theory which has much in its favor. He conceived that the sensory impulses reaching, let us say, the somesthetic area of the brain did not impinge simply on a single point, but were distributed over a certain neighborhood—most intensely, however, to a central point in this neighborhood, and less and less intensely to more and more distant parts of the same. The distribution of impulses from two near-by points in the skin might therefore overlap in the brain to a greater or less degree. Where the overlapping was but slight, there would be two points of maxi-

[1] Haines, *Psychological Review*, 1905, XII, 207.

[2] See James, *Principles of Psychology*, 1890, I, 495.

[3] *Untersuchungen über den Erregungsprozess im Muskel- und Nervensystem* (Heidelberg, 1870). See also Thunberg in Nagel's *Handbuch der Physiologie*, 1905, III, 720; and Myers, *Textbook of Experimental Psychology*, 1909, p. 235.

mum activity within the somesthetic area, and this condition would favor discrimination; where the overlapping was considerable, on the contrary, there would be only one point of maximum activity, and therefore no possibility of a true sense of double stimulation; though, if the combined distribution was broad, the total impression might be recognizably different from that of a single point, with its narrower cerebral distribution. To account for the fact that two points can be discriminated at a much less distance on some portions of the skin than on others, we make the probable assumption that the cortical area connected with a highly sensitive region of the skin is broad, and that connected with a less sensitive region narrow, in comparison with the corresponding areas of the skin. Accordingly, the cortical overlapping of impulses need be no greater from closely adjacent points on the finger-tips than from widely separated points of the back. Such a theory does not pretend to explain the process of discrimination, but only one of the nervous correlates or prerequisites of discrimination; other conditions also must be met in order that discrimination may occur, for two points *need* not be distinguished though separated by a very considerable distance. On the psychological side, the process corresponds to what, when exercised in a more deliberate way, we call the "weighing of data" before "making up the mind" to an act of judgment.

§ 27. Closely connected with the foregoing is the difference of different parts of the skin in furnishing data for discriminating the fact, the amount, and the direction of *motion* in contact with the body. Upon this point the experiments of G. Stanley Hall[1] are of special interest. These experiments seem to show that we are more likely, when in doubt, to judge motion on the surface of the limbs to be up rather than down their axis; on the breast, the shoulder-blades, and the back, the tendency is to judge motion to be toward the head. The discriminative sensibility of the skin for motion is much greater than that for separate touch, as determined by Weber's experiments. Thus, while at least a distance of 25 mm. between the dividers' points was needed on the volar surface of the right arm, in order to perceive them as two points, both the fact and the direction of motion could be discriminated at an average distance of between 6 and 7 mm. In judging the rate and distance of motion over the skin the liability to error is always great; but, as a rule, distances rapidly traversed are judged to be relatively shorter than the same distances more slowly traversed. Inasmuch, however, as the judgment of motion on the left arm was expressed by reproducing the rate and distance with the right hand, we have

[1] *Motor Sensations on the Skin*, by Professor G. S. Hall and Dr. H. H. Donaldson, in *Mind*, October, 1885, pp. 557 ff.

a double liability to error involved in regulating the muscular movement of this hand by means of its series of muscular and tactual sensations.

Hall found the motor sensibility of different parts of the surface of the skin to be different; but the differences do not appear to correspond to those belonging to Weber's sensation-circles. The average distance, in millimetres, which a metallic point of 12 mm. in diameter could move over the skin at a rate of 2 mm. per second before a judgment of direction could be formed was found, for one subject of experiment, as follows: forehead, 0.20; upper arm, 0.40; forearm, 0.44; shin, 0.60; palm, 0.74; back, 0.85. Motion can be produced so slowly as not to be discriminated at all, even when the body in contact has really moved from 6 to 12 centimetres. It can also be produced so rapidly as to make it impossible to tell when it begins and when ends. Heavy weights seem to move faster than light ones going at the same rate; but here other sensations are called out by the deep pressure, and combined with those of contact. Hall concludes that heat-spots and cold-spots traversed by the moving body are of great service in judging motion and its direction on the skin; the cold-spots more than heat-spots, "because of the fainter sensation and wider irradiation" of the latter.

Further experiments with a travelling metallic point that carried the stimulus of an electrical current over the surface of the skin showed an astonishing diversity of sensations developed at different points of the area thus traversed. Points of cutting pain, "thrill-points," "tickle-points," "acceleration-points" (or places where the rate of motion seems suddenly to increase without any real change in the speed of the moving metal), "blind-points" (or spots where all impression of contact is momentarily lost), are all to be differentiated. Yet the sharp differentiation of these sensations is rendered difficult by the fact that the various kinds are so impacted and run together, in a *tangle* of sensation. The experimenters also speak as though many dermal sensations may thus be partially disentangled, for the description of which language furnishes no adequate terms. All these facts agree exceedingly well with the theory of local signs already proposed. These dermal signs are complex "mixtures" of feeling, which give to each discernible locality a characteristic local stamp. The fact that our sensibility to motion is so much greater in each area of the skin than our susceptibility to the distance of stationary points accords with the same theory. Our ability to localize the dermal sensations is dependent upon the degree and rate of the *changes* in the color-tone of these sensations. Hall is undoubtedly right in holding that, by *moving* the touching surface over the surface touched, we do not simply multiply, but also diversify, our data for filling up the dermal blind-spots and judging the nature of impressions.

§ 28. The localizing of sensations of *temperature* in the skin is, in principle, the same as that of sensations of light pressure or of motion. The former, however, are in all our ordinary experience interwoven with the latter; they therefore have the help of the latter in getting a place assigned to them in the periphery of the body. Goldscheider[1] experimented to determine how far apart the heat-spots and cold-spots must be, respectively, in order that two of them, when stimulated, may be *felt as two*. Both kinds of sensations are localized, not as points, but as minute warm or cold drops in contact with the skin. By the following table, which gives the minimum distances for different areas of the body, it appears that the sense of locality connected with the cold-spots is about twice as fine, as a rule, as that connected with the heat-spots. The distances are given in millimetres.

Part of the body	Cold-spots	Heat-spots
Forehead, cheek, and chin	0.8	3–5
Breast	2.0	4–5
Abdomen	1–2	4–6
Back	1.5–2.0	4–6
Upper arm	1.5–2.0	2–3
Lower arm	2–3	2–3
Hollow of the hand	0.8	2.0
Back of the hand, and upper and lower leg	2–3	3–4

§ 29. Some basis seems to be laid in the foregoing facts for a system of local signs of the skin, that consist in a *mixture* of color-tones and temperature-sensations. Yet sensations of heat or cold, in themselves considered, differ chiefly, if not wholly, in intensity. In themselves, therefore, they are not well fitted to constitute a so-called "spatial series" of sensations. If, for example, a certain area of the skin be stimulated simultaneously by both heat and cold, at points too near together to be distinguished by touch, the result is neither a modification of one sensation by the other nor a localizing of the two sensations as lying closely side by side.[2] A wavering of perception rather takes place, similar to the strife of colors in vision; the experience is as though the skin were being touched with

[1] *Archiv f. Anat. u. Physiol.*, Physiolog. Abth., 1885, Supplement-Band, pp. 70 ff.

[2] See Czermak, *Sitzgsber. d. Wiener Acad.*, March, 1855, p. 500; confirmed by Klug and others.

a single body alternately hot and cold. Klug also found that the least observable distance between two points touching the skin at the same time depends upon their temperature relative to that of the skin. The fineness of our sense of locality, as well as of our sensitiveness to motion, is increased by exciting sensations of temperature up to the point where pain intervenes. But the localizing of these sensations is primarily dependent, to a great extent, upon their connection with localized sensations of touch. If we bring two parts of the skin, that differ considerably in temperature, into contact—for example, a cool hand and warm forehead, or a cool hand and a warm one—it is often difficult by strict attention to the sensations of temperature alone to tell which part is cooler, which warmer. The difficulty is doubtless largely due to the fact that each part which feels the temperature of the other is also changing its own temperature in the direction of the temperature of the other. A confusion of the data for judgment, accordingly, takes place.

Any localization of the sensations which occurs under such circumstances is largely dependent upon secondary considerations, and especially upon the direction of the attention. We judge of depth by sensations of temperature, indirectly, and through our ability to remove or change the intensity and locality of these sensations by changing the position of the body in space as related to what we know to be hot and cold bodies or surrounding media.

§ 30. The specific sensations of the *muscular sense* constitute another spatial series which combines with the foregoing in the localizing of areas at the periphery, and of external objects as projected in space and yet known as in contact with the body. Indeed, it is upon *this* particular system of local signs that the mind is chiefly dependent for its data—other than the visual—in the synthetic construction of its presentations of bodies that stand related to each other in three dimensions in objective space. Three principal theories have been held as to the nature of the so-called muscular sensations: (1) They are to be resolved into "central feelings of innervation," which differ only in intensity and not in specific quality, and which result from the changes, initiating movement of the bodily organs, that take place in the brain as correlated with impulses of the will; (2) they are not specific sensations, but are due to interpretations of those feelings in the skin which originate on account of its changes of position, tension, etc., as the underlying muscles are moved; (3) they are specific sensations dependent on a nerve-apparatus of sense, which has its end-organs in the muscle-fibre, and which is excited by the contraction of the latter in a manner dependent upon the kind, amount, and direction of the muscular movement taking place.

We have already given certain reasons for preferring the last of the foregoing views; other reasons are implied in considering the nature of what has been called the "feeling of innervation" or of "active energy." The muscular sense, like all the other senses which contribute to our presentations of objects extended in space, appears to have its own system of local signs. The muscular sensations are *qualitatively* (and not merely quantitatively) different, according to the combination of the muscles moved, and according to the extension over the muscular area of the stimulus imparted to the sensory nerve-fibres situated in the muscle by the changing condition of the latter as it contracts and relaxes. At each step in the flexing of the leg—for example—the muscular sensations have a specific quality and value as local signs, in our consciousness, of the position of the member. The same thing is true of the bending arm, back, or single toe or finger. These sensations are indeed intimately, and even inextricably, combined with the spatial series of specifically dermal sensations; but in themselves they have a different quality, and are not localized simply at the surface of the body. As the extent of the circuit of motion gone through by any limb increases, or the intensity of the strain becomes greater, the quality of the *mass* of resulting muscular sensations is perpetually changing. These sensations are, accordingly, localized over a broader area of the body and *deeper* in its substance, as it were. Every one knows what new mixtures of sensation are produced in consciousness by calling into vigorous exercise the unused more deeply lying muscles of the body.

The muscular sensations also assist the more strictly tactual in discriminating locality for all cases where the pressure upon the skin exceeds a certain small degree of intensity. In strong contact or heavy pressure the sensory nerves of the underlying muscle are excited; we have the feeling, not simply of being touched, but also of being pressed. The combination of these two spatial series gives to the mind a doubly constituted system of local signs; hence, as the experiments of G. Stanley Hall[1] show, our judgment of direction of motion is quicker as the weight resting on the skin is increased up to the limit where other disturbing sensations intervene. The superior discriminating power which any member of the body has when permitted to move—that is, to call forth familiar series of muscular sensations—is largely due to the help which the local signs of this system render to the mind. When the particular member (the hand) which is capable of the nicest tactual discrimination is also permitted to move over an object freely, and to acquire abundant data from all the sources described above, we have fulfilled the most advantageous conditions for the

[1] *Mind*, October, 1885, p. 567.

utmost nicety of knowledge possible to "touch," in the widest meaning of the word.

§ 31. In point of precision, judgments of extent of bodily movement far surpass judgments of extent based on cutaneous sensation alone, but are inferior, in their turn, to judgments of extent by the eye. The perception of extent of movement is one among several judgments which may be passed on the movement of a limb, since the direction, duration, and speed of the movement, the resistance encountered, and the end-positions of the limb can all be judged with considerable accuracy. The perception of any one of these characteristics of a movement is usually confused by introducing irregularities into any other of them. Thus, movements by different limbs, or by the same limb in different positions or directions, cannot be so accurately compared in regard to their extent as when the two movements to be compared are as nearly as possible duplicates of each other in all respects. Systematic or "constant" errors often creep in when judgments of extent are attempted in comparing diverse movements. Thus, a slow movement seems longer than a fast movement of equal extent.[1] But, curiously enough, a movement made against resistance seems no longer than a free movement of the same extent.[2] This last result seems to prove that the extent of the movement of a limb is not judged in terms of the muscular work performed in executing it; while the close interrelation of the speed of a movement and its apparent extent, along with other facts, has been thought to indicate that extent was judged in terms of the duration of a movement. On this point opinions have differed widely, but there seems to be no cogent reason for singling out the duration of a movement as that on which the judgment of extent is based. It is more probable that the judgment of extent, like that of duration and also of speed, is based directly on the entire complex of sensations which is produced by moving the limb.[3]

§ 32. The fineness of the spatial perception connected with the "muscle-sense" is of great significance in forming a just conception of "touch" as an organ of space-perception. Seldom, in the common use of touch for discovering the form and size of objects—as in the dark—do we attempt to rely on cutaneous impressions alone; we handle the object, bringing into play sensations of movement and position as well as sensations from the skin. Such

---

[1] Loeb, Pflüger's *Archiv für die gesammte Physiologie*, 1887, XLVI, 1; Delabarre, *Ueber Bewegungsempfindungen* (Freiburg i. B., 1891).

[2] Delabarre, op. cit.; Angier, *Zeitschrift für Psychologie*, 1905, XXXIX, 429.

[3] Compare Hollingworth, *The Inaccuracy of Movement*, 1909, p. 40.

perceptions are not tactile alone, but "stereognostic."[1] The perception of the shape of objects simply laid or pressed on the skin is much inferior to the judgment based on handling them. Hence there seems to be sufficient evidence for our view,[2] which is also that of Wundt[3]—namely, that *"touch space," in-so far as it can be conceived as independent of visual space, results from a union, fusion, or synthesis of cutaneous sensation with sensations of bodily movement and position.*

§ 33. It is unnecessary to illustrate further the process by which the mind's native activity of discrimination, with the help of qualitatively different sensation-complexes, or local signs, constructs its field of touch. The localization of certain points in the area of the body which are of marked local characteristics, and frequently recurrent in experience, is the first achievement in constructing this field. To these landmarks, as it were, other points or areas, subsequently discovered, are referred. One hand learns to know the other; the right hand chiefly explores the left arm and side and the upper right leg; the left hand, the right arm and side and the upper left leg. The finger-tips, especially of the right hand, have an office similar to that performed by the yellow-spot of the retina; they are the centre or hearth of clear perceptions of touch. But in order to bring them to their object they must be moved; through this motion fresh combinations of muscular and tactual sensations result. But long before the entire field of touch has been constructed with any considerable approach to completeness, the eye has already explored those parts of the body which are open to its inspection. It learns first to know the hand, which nature keeps constantly in motion before it. As objects rest on the hand, it notes the place where they rest; with its perceptions of sight certain combinations of tactual sensations thus become associated. As the hand moves over other objects, or especially over the other parts of the body, the eye marks its successive progress; combined sensations of muscular and tactual kind are thus associated with each position of the hand and with each area of the body which it touches. Very early in the development of a normal experience the eye comes to be the leader and critic of the discriminations connected with the muscular and tactual sensations. Its power of rapid movement over its total field, and its delicate judgment on account of the finely shaded complex local signs which it calls forth with a comprehensive simultaneousness, give a great superiority to the organ of vision as a geometrical sense. The results of such superiority it

[1] Hoffmann, *Stereognostische Versuche* (Strassburg, 1883).
[2] Compare Ladd, *Elements of Physiological Psychology*, 1st ed., 1887, 417 f.
[3] *Physiologische Psychologie*, 6th ed., 1910, II, 517.

constantly places at the disposal of the more slowly moving and less delicate sense of touch. For this reason, one born blind can never attain the same quality (of "comprehensive simultaneousness") for his spatial intuitions and ideas of spatial relations; even the field of touch, in spite of the greater refinement which the muscular and tactual sensations of such an unfortunate person acquire through use, cannot possess this quality as it is imparted by the eye.

The familiar experiments of trying to estimate the size, shape, and relation of objects, the amount and direction of motion, etc., when blindfold, show our dependence upon the organ of sight. It must not be forgotten, however, that the discriminations possible through the muscular and tactual sensations alone are wonderfully exact; and that in certain circumstances touch has sight at a disadvantage, as it were. Thus the player on the violin who should adjust his spacing of the strings by the sensations of the eye, with the unaccustomed and unfavorable perspective made necessary by its position in relation to the left hand, would not attain the art of making true and pure tones.

§ 34. Among the most complex perceptions of which the skin and muscles by their combined action are capable are the so-called "feelings of double contact." It is largely by means of these feelings that skill is acquired in the use of tools, weapons, and musical instruments. In these cases the process of projection goes so far that we seem to feel the object with which the implement is in contact, not so much in the hand (the feelings of contact being located there), by the external means of the implement, but rather as ourselves being in the implement and using it as a sentient part of the organism. The carver in wood feels his chisel move through the stuff he is shaping, and guides it as unerringly as he would his finger, so as to lay it with a given degree of pressure upon a given spot. We are all familiar with the experience of feeling the ground we are about to tread, with a cane or other stick. If the fingers be lightly brushed over the hair when it stands out from the head, it will be difficult to localize the sensations of pressure at the scalp rather than in the hair. We feel the touch of our finger at the end of the tooth, where the contact takes place, instead of where the sensory nerves really receive the stimulus and convert it into a nerve-commotion.

The management of the implement is, of course, really made possible by delicate changes in the shades of feeling called out by its changing pressure upon the nerves terminating in the skin and muscles of the hand, and by the accompanying feelings of strain and of effort that result from the movement of the arm which carries the hand. These feelings are aroused by the end of the implement which is in contact with the body, and are primarily localized in that part of the body; but they are felt through a more artificial and elaborate process of localization, as though directly dependent upon the other end of the implement. Upon the æsthetic and pleasurable uses of these feelings of double contact Lotze[1] has remarked at length.

At this point the further discussion of the development of our presentations of sense in general must be arrested, in order to consider more in detail the activities of the other great "geometrical sense."

[1] See *Microcosmus*, i, pp. 586 ff. (Edinburgh, 1885).

CHAPTER V

PRESENTATIONS OF SENSE; OR SENSE–PERCEPTIONS (Continued)

§ 1. The discussions of the last chapter as to the data furnished in the form of complex sensations, and as to the mental activities involved in the discrimination, association, and interpretation of these data, for the localization and knowledge of objects of sense through the skin and the muscles, must have convinced us that the problem which nature solves with such apparent ease in a practical way, is exceedingly difficult—perhaps impossible—of a complete theoretical solution. Moreover, the application of the general principles which control the development of our sense-experience to the particular case of *the eye* has many peculiar difficulties. The physiological psychology of visual perception is, therefore, a much controverted and very obscure domain. This fact is doubtless in part due to the amount of experimenting and speculating which has been bestowed upon it; but peculiar difficulties are intrinsic in the case of the eye. These are caused by the great complexity of its native activities, and by the speed with which it reaches a generous maturity of development. Nature has equipped this organ with superior means for furnishing to the mind a variety of data, as respects both quantity and quality, for the nicest discriminations; it has also provided it with such constant stimulation as to cause it to acquire an incomparable facility. The character of its structure, functions, and development is, therefore, such as to make it difficult to disentangle the simple factors from those complex forms into which the synthetic activity of the mind has constructed them.

It is affirmed by one authority[1] that no less than eight different data, or *motifs,* are used even in monocular vision by the adult for perceiving the third dimension of space and of visual objects in space. These are the changes with respect to (1) extent and (2) clearness, of the complex of the sensations of color and light, as dependent on distance; (3) the perspective elevation of the bottom

[1] Volkmann von Volkmar, *Lehrb. d. Psychologie,* II, p. 84.

413

of distant objects above the horizon; (4) the covering of known distant objects by those placed nearer; (5) the alterations of light and
shadow on the curved surfaces of the object, according as they are
nearer or more remote; (6) the perspective contraction of the retinal
image; (7) the change of the visor angle in proportion to the distance of the object; (8) the muscular sensations of the accommodation of the eye. To these eight data, two others at least must be
added for binocular vision—namely (9), the stereoscopic double
images, and (10) the sensations arising from convergence of the
axes. These ten sets of variable experiences may be combined, of
course, in an almost infinite variety of proportions.

Moreover, it is not improbable that we shall have to admit still
other data as entering into the complex perceptions of sight. The
question must be raised: Do not the visual sensations themselves
have a certain local coloring directly dependent upon the nervous
elements of the retina which are excited by the stimuli? If we
answer this question affirmatively, we shall have a system of local
retinal signs as constituting one of the most primary of the spatial
series of sensations entering into the space-perceptions of this sense.

§ 2. Several of the data just enumerated, however, are plainly of
only secondary rank and value; they do not necessarily enter into
every perception of a visual object as such. What does seem necessary to the most elementary form of visual perception may be stated
as follows: *Sensations of light and color, differing in intensity and
quality, but simultaneously present in consciousness, must be systematically arranged with reference to each other by being localized with
the help of retinal signs.* For any development of visual perception as the adult human being has experience of it, we must add:
*These sensations must be associated with other spatial series of mus-
cular and tactual sensations that arise from accommodation of the
eye and from its position and motion.* The complexity of the combinations arising in the normal use of the organ of vision is, of course,
increased by the fact that there are *two* eyes, and, therefore, two
retinas with their systems of retinal signs, two images of each object,
and two sets of motions. But the two eyes are (as we shall see subsequently) in a certain sense to be regarded as one eye—certainly
as constituting one organ of vision. So that, even when one eye is
closed, the other does not see what it sees without being influenced
by the closed and relatively inoperative part of the one organ. The
constancy with which the eyes act together explains, in part, why
they are one organ as the two hands are not; but the frequency with
which we voluntarily suppress the activity of one eye by closing it
explains, *in part*, why they are not one organ as are the two nostrils
or the two ears.

§ 3. Could we select an adult human being who had never seen, and proceed to develop his visual perceptions, experimentally, in the direct order of their complexity, we might possibly rely upon his description of his experience to solve certain problems that now seem unsolvable. At present, however, it is quite impossible to say what the experience of the subject of such experiments would be. Nothing remains, then, but to employ the data which physiological optics has secured, in order to make a theoretic reconstruction (confessedly imperfect and doubtful) of the process that nature is all the while successfully completing. In this effort we naturally follow the order of nature, so far as possible; beginning with the simplest conceivable case (this is substantially the course followed by Wundt), we find three things to be considered in explaining the developed perceptions of sight: (1) The retinal image of the eye at rest, and the *motifs* which it furnishes; (2) the single eye as moved, and the influence of these movements; (3) the conditions furnished by the existence and relations of the two eyes exercising their functions in common. But, in reality, from the very beginning of its activity the eye is in motion, and acts as a double organ.

Corresponding to the three sets of considerations just mentioned, we may speak of three fields of vision which are to be constructed in the order of their complexity. They may be called, respectively, the retinal field of vision, the field of monocular vision, and the field of binocular vision. In the "retinal field of vision" we mean to include only such a perception—or mental spatial arrangement of sensations of color and light as points lying side by side—as would be presented through the excited expanse of nervous elements constituting the retina of one motionless eye, in case there had been no previous vision with both eyes in motion. The field of monocular vision, when completely constructed, includes all that can be seen with one eye as the result of its experience, developed, but unaided by the other eye. The field of binocular vision includes all that can be seen by both eyes. The first two so-called "fields of vision" are, strictly speaking, fictitious and theoretically constructed in order to explain the process by which the mind reaches the construction of the third and last. Indeed, the question may be pressed, whether we can speak of a purely "*retinal* field of vision," and whether the excited mosaic of nervous elements on which the image is formed, without aid from previous experience of sensations of position and motion, could furnish any true presentations of sight, or visual perceptions of objects as they actually exist in space.

§ 4. The "retinal field" has no clearly defined limits, or boundary-lines; it may be described rather as having its expanse of sensations distinguished by a shifting, graded transition into a region of no-sensations. This fact is, of course, due to the constantly changing activity of the nervous elements of the retina. Yet the sensations which are massed in the foregoing experience constitute a true spatial expanse; that is, they are not simply recognized as differing in color-tone, or brightness or intensity of effect, but as having true local distinctions, and as being arranged into a system of points of color and light lying side by side. In other words, the different sensations do not fall together in consciousness so as to resemble the one sensation of smell produced by irritating simultaneously a number of fibres of the olfactory nerve; nor are they simply analyzable into several qualitatively different factors, as is the complex sensation of a musical clang. They are presented as *spatially systematized*. The "retinal field"—at least, as it appears in adult vision—may, then, be said to be extended in two dimensions; and the *minima visibilia* which compose it all have local relations to each other. It cannot properly be said, however, to have depth (as Stumpf[1] and Hering[2] hold that it does); for the different colored points are not projected as different in distance, nor can we be said to look *into* the colored space thus presented before the mind. It is true that the expanse of the retinal field is not like that of a darkly colored wall or curtain placed in front of the eye. But the quasi-appearance of depth is due to constant change in color-tone and brightness of the minute portions of the field, which has an effect somewhat like that we get on looking at a very dense mist of particles differently colored and drifting. In other words, the secondary and derived data give to it an appearance which we have learned to associate with the perception of depth.

On the other hand, the retinal field can scarcely be considered as two-dimensional in a way to distinguish it from the three-dimensional field of binocular vision, without implying a suggestion of the third dimension, as though it were itself seen *projected in* a three-dimensional space. The only safe conclusion from all this is, therefore, that this simplest (?) form of adult visual experience is so far removed from the form with which its own development began, as to be no adequate representation of it. In particular, it leaves the question of the influence, and even of the absolute necessity, of sensations of position and motion for any visual perception, still unsolved

---

[1] *Ueber d. physiolog. Ursprung d. Raumvorstellung* (Leipzig, 1873). Stumpf holds that "Space is just as originally and directly perceived as quality" (p. 115).

[2] In Hermann's *Handb. d. Physiol.*, III, i, pp. 572 f.

§ 5. Further experiment, however, with this so-called "retinal field" serves to show how complicated its apparently simple character really is. In the first place, even this field is the result of the combined action of the two retinas. If, with both eyes closed, a "phosphene" be produced in either eye by pressing upon its ball, the colored circle will be located in the corresponding part of the field; but the character of the entire field, as formed by the activity of both retinas, will be changed. It is, of course, impossible to suppress the action of one retina, and thus examine a monocular "retinal field," as it were. But it may easily be shown that, even in vision with one eye open and in motion, the character of the whole field of vision is under the influence of the retinal activity of the closed eye. Let one of the eyes—both hitherto closed and motionless—now be opened. Immediately a picture of all the objects falling within the field of monocular vision appears before us; each object seen with its position, magnitude, and spatial relations determined according to the laws of visual perception. This monocular field seems bounded on one side (the left side if the right eye is opened, the right side if the left) by the rather dim outline of the nose and lower line of the forehead. What has become of the retinal field of the closed eye? It has been submerged or overwhelmed by the field of the open eye, on account of the latter's stationary and clearly defined images and strong arrest and fixation of attention. But if a character to arrest and fix the attention be given to the field of the closed eye, it may be made in turn to overwhelm that of the open eye. This can be accomplished by producing strong "phosphenes" in the former. On pressing the closed eye brightly colored circles are presented in the corresponding part of the field; and by using sufficient pressure the objects seen as projected in space by the open eye are drowned in a shower of minute, vivid sparks.

The "retinal field" has its character determined also by associated muscular sensations dependent upon the movement of both eyes. It will be found impossible to make any definite area of this retinal field, which lies much to the right or left, to the upper or lower part, of its centre, a matter of regard without detecting slight movements of the eyes according to the direction in which the attention is to be fixed. The value of muscular movements in this case cannot consist in their enabling a clear image of objects situated in different relations to the eye to be formed on its retina; for with closed eyes no change is occasioned in the retinal images by motion of the eyes. Moreover, it will be found that the extent of this entire field and its prolongation, as it were, in any given direction are dependent upon the accommodation and motion of the eyes.

§ 6. The foregoing facts undeniably afford considerable support to the "empiristic" theory of visual perception; but they do not show that the considerations it brings forward are entirely conclusive. It would seem that, after excluding all the factors which combine into our ordinary presentations of sight—such as double images, accommodation, convergence of the axes of the eyes, and secondary helps by way of shadows, perspective, elevation, etc.— a certain spatial quality still remains to the simplest sensations of color and light which we are able to reproduce. It will naturally be objected that these sensations are the reactions of a mind that has had a long previous experience in localizing visual sensations by means of just such helps as the foregoing. The question then recurs: Is the fact that the sensations of light and color, which are produced by the simultaneous excitation of many nervous elements of the retina, appear as locally distinct (even when the eyes are closed and motionless) an otherwise unexplained datum due to an original activity of the mind under the law of the specific energy of these nervous elements; or is it a result of acquired experience, to be explained by the revival of images of previously associated impressions obtained when the eyes were both open and moving? To take the former position is to adopt, so far forth, the nativistic theory of visual perception; to take the latter is to espouse the empiristic opinion. Either position has its difficulties. The former seems to us, however, nearer to the ultimate truth.

§ 7. That the sensations of light and color occasioned by stimulating different elements of the retina have a *different value* in consciousness, and that the recognition of this value, and the presentation of the sensations as locally separate and arranged into a spatial system, is native to the mind, may be argued from the following among other reasons: The peculiar mosaic structure of the retina is obviously the fundamental cause for the pre-eminence of the eye as a "geometrical sense." It has already been shown (chap. VIII, § 15) that each element of this structure may be regarded as an isolated sensitive spot, which corresponds, on the one side, to individual irritations from the stimuli, and, on the other, to the smallest localized sensations of light and color. But the latter part of this statement could not be true unless each of the elements in this nervous mosaic had a certain peculiar representative value in consciousness. In other words, sensations of light and color are localized in part, at least, by means of the specific local quality which belongs to the result of the different points in the retina being simultaneously irritated. The very construction of this organ, as well as the correspondence between its construction and the nicety attained in its use for local distinctions, indicates that the spatial quality of our visual percepts depends upon its specific functions.

Moreover, unless the series of light- and color-sensations had an original spatial character, it is difficult to see how they could combine with the other spatial series of the eye into perceptions of extended colored objects. It is difficult to see what advantage they would then have over the series of musical tones varying in pitch. Still further, it is as impossible to *prove* experimentally as it is to make *seem* true to consciousness that the arrangement of the points of light and color which appears before us with closed and motionless eyes is only the *residuum*, as it were, of past sensations of a muscular kind. Such an appeal to consciousness could not be made, indeed, with any confidence, if scientific analysis were able to show that the color-sensations can be perceived simultaneously, as a system of points lying side by side, without having the characteristics of a spatial series. But in view of our inability to do this, we only account for the facts of consciousness by admitting what the very structure of the organ suggests, and what general psychological theory seems to confirm, when we hold that *spatial perception, at least in germinal form, is native to the mind as a synthesis of the qualitatively different sensations which result from stimulating simultaneously the retinal mosaic of nervous elements.*

The foregoing view is very different from that which assumes that we have an immediate knowledge of the retinal image; or that a knowledge of the direction from which the light falls upon the retina is an unresolvable intuition of the mind. To such mistaken statements it is a sufficient reply to show that the subjective image (or mental presentation) of the object does not correspond either to the image on the retina or to the real object as it is otherwise known to exist in space. The mental presentation, for example, has no blind-spot; it is a different representation of the real object from that offered by the retinal image, with more inaccuracies than belong to the latter as seen by an observer looking at it from without. To the question, then, whether sensations of light and color would have space-form if they came only from an excited but motionless retina, and were uncombined with other sensations of a spatial series, we can give only a tentative and partial answer. Doubtless the "presentations of sense" formed by combining such sensations alone would be indescribably different from those to which we now ascribe visual space-form. An animal with a single immovable expanse of nervous elements susceptible to irritations from light could not be said to have what we call "vision." But, on the one hand, the spatial quality which belongs to the visual sensations of man cannot all be resolved into muscular and tactual sensations of eye and hand; and on the other hand, sensations of light and color do have the quality which insures their arrangement in consciousness in spatial order. This fact is due to the working of the law of the specific energy of the nervous retinal elements in connection with the native activity of mind in synthesizing these sensations. The law as applied to the eye is essentially the same as that already demonstrated for the skin; the activity assumed as native to man is not essentially different from that ascribed to the lower animals in the use of their senses. That this *tact* for the individual has been largely won by the development of the race is a proposition to which our attitude is determined by more general conclusions. But physiological optics cannot account for the phenomena of vision without assuming both the original exercise of this tact and the theory of local retinal signs as data hitherto unresolvable by its analysis.

§ 8. Whatever may be thought of the foregoing assumptions, it is certain that ordinary adult visual perception involves *the motion of the open eye*—monocular vision, of one eye and binocular of both. The sensations which accompany such motion must be combined with sensations of light and color to make the complete presentations of sight. The consideration of the simplest case requires that we should recur to the physiology of the eye. Only one small spot in the retina (the so-called "*fovea centralis*," see p. 193), is capable of giving a perfectly clear image of an object. When, then, we desire to see an object clearly, we bring its image upon this spot and fixate it there. That point of the object to which the centre of the retinal area of clearest vision corresponds is called the "point of regard" (or "fixation-point"). In ordinary vision, then, the eye constantly changes its point of regard, and so brings successively upon its most sensitive area the images of the different points of its object.

The different changes of position in the point of regard are accomplished by the six muscles of the eyeball. This wandering of the point of regard over an object may be considered as due to rotating the eye upon a pivotal point, or "centre of rotation," by motions that have different axes of rotation. The centre of rotation is, however, only theoretically a point, but is really an inter-axial space. It has been variously located for normal eyes at about 13.45–13.73 mm. behind the cornea, and 1.24–1.77 mm. behind the middle of the optical axes. Of such axes of rotation, three are especially to be distinguished—an antero-posterior, a vertical, and a transverse. A line drawn from the centre of rotation to the point of regard is called the "line of regard"; since each eye has its own centre of rotation, there are, in vision with both eyes, two lines of regard. A plane passing through these two lines is called "the plane of regard" (or "plane of vision").[1] In the "primary position" the head is erect and the line of regard directed toward the distant horizon. The plane passing through the lines of regard of both eyes in this position is the "primary plane of vision." In this position for most eyes, however, the line of vision is inclined somewhat below the horizontal plane.

Starting from the primary position, one set of positions are successively assumed by moving the eye upon its transverse and vertical axes. When the eye rotates round the former, the line of regard is displaced either above or below; it thus makes a varying angle with the line corresponding to its first direction, and this is called the "angle of vertical displacement" (so Helmholtz), or the "ascensional angle." When it moves about the vertical axis, the line of regard is displaced from side to side, and forms with the median plane of the eye a varying angle called "the angle of lateral displacement." In passing from the primary position to the foregoing secondary position no rotation of the axis itself occurs. Another order of positions is assumed by an apparent rotation on the anteroposterior axis, combined with lateral or vertical displacements; this movement results in bringing the eye to an oblique position, and is really a *torsion* of the eye. The angle which the plane of regard makes with the transverse plane measures the amount of torsion, and is called the "angle of torsion."

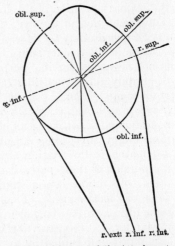

Fig. 122.—Diagram of the Attachments of the Muscles of the Eye, and Their Axes of Rotation—the latter being shown by dotted lines. The axis of rotation of the rectus externus, and internus, being perpendicular to the plane of the paper, cannot be shown.

§ 9. The law which seems to govern the eye's movements of torsion—or combined movements sideways, and either up or down—was conjectured by Listing, whose name it bears, and elaborated by Helmholtz. Listing's law is stated by Helmholtz[2] in the fol-

---

[1] For the detailed theory of the movements of the eye, see Hering, in Hermann's *Handb. d. Physiol.*, III, i, chaps. IX–XI; Helmholtz, *Physiolog. Optik*, § 27; Wundt, *Physiolog. Psychologie* (6th ed.), II, 548; and Zoth in Nagel's *Handb. d. Physiol.* (1905), III, 282 ff.

[2] *Physiolog. Optik*, p. 466.

lowing terms: "When the line of regard passes from its primary position into any other position, the torsion of the eye (as measured by the angle of torsion) in the second position is the same as if the eye were turned about a fixed axis standing perpendicular to both the first and the second positions of the line of regard." The same principle is stated in different language by Wundt:[1] "All movements of the eye from its primary position take place about fixed axes, each of which at the point of rotation stands at right angles to the plane which is described by revolving the line of regard; and all of these axes lie in a single plane, at right angles to the primary position of the line of regard, at its point of rotation." The orientating of the eye, then, for every possible position of the line of regard, may be referred to a constant standard.

More detailed statement of the laws of the eye's motion in vision is not necessary for the purposes of physiological psychology. It needs only to be noted that *the construction of the field of monocular or binocular vision is a synthetic mental achievement dependent upon the varying sensations which result from the wandering of the point of regard over the outline of an object.* Starting from its primary position, the eye may come around, as it were, by a variety of circuitous paths, to the fixation of any particular point of its object. In the pursuit of these paths it develops various sensations which are fitted to combine into a spatial series of sensations that have the value of "local signs." Thus the field of vision necessarily has the same form as the surface over which the point of regard can be made to wander. Its construction is a progressive synthesis of the mind, stimulated and guided by means which consist in varying states of consciousness.

§ 10. Certain important consequences follow as to the relation between the lines of the extended and objective "thing" and the lines of the retinal image, as affording the mind data for the spatial ordering of the sensations that arise from stimulating the nervous elements of the eye. Only those objects which are seen by direct vision (their images lying in the line of regard when the eye is in its primary position) appear in their actual place; lines lying outside of the vertical and horizontal meridians of the retina, in order to be seen straight, must be really bent; and all really straight lines in such positions are seen bent. This fact may be proved in various ways. If a sheet of white paper, having a black dot in its centre

---

[1] *Physiolog. Psychologie* (2d ed.), II, pp. 79 f.   In the sixth edition, the form of statement is somewhat changed, so as to indicate that the various *positions* which the eye assumes are the same as they would be if reached by movements about the axes so defined.   The actual movements of the eye from the primary position often show considerable irregularity.

to serve as a point of regard, be held at right angles to the line of vision, with the eye in its primary position and constantly fixed upon this point, thin, straight slits of black paper outside of the two meridians will appear bent. Or if the after-images left on these meridians of the retina by light falling through narrow and straight slits be studied when torsion of the eye takes place, these after-images will themselves be found to suffer torsion.

Besides the help from sensations due to movements of the eye in fixing its point of regard, account must be taken of those which may possibly result from accommodation of the eye (for the mechanism of accommodation, see pp. 188f). According to Helmholtz:[1] "There can be no doubt that any one who has much observed his own changes of accommodation and knows the muscular feeling of the effort belonging to them is in a condition to tell whether, when he fixates an object or an optical image, he is accommodating for a great or small distance." There is scarcely greater doubt that the significance of these changes would not be realized as indicating a third dimension of space, were they not combined with sensations belonging to the use of both eyes in conjunction with the organs of touch. Even adult judgment of distance, by accommodation alone, is extremely imperfect. Wundt[2] experimented to determine the niceness of this judgment by regarding a black thread stretched vertically against a white background, with one eye through an aperture in a shield. He found that almost nothing could be told in this way as to the absolute distance of the thread. Its relative position, however, could be discriminated with considerable accuracy by changes in accommodation; and, as might be expected, with more accuracy when the apparatus was called into more active operation by approach of the object toward the eye. We return to this subject later.

§ 11. But all the achievements possible to a *single* eye, when open and in motion, would not avail to produce the presentations of sight as our ordinary experience is familiar with them. Strictly *monocular* vision is for the most part a fiction of science. What we can see with one eye, after experience in binocular vision, depends upon what we have been accustomed to see with both eyes. Indeed, what we see at any instant with one open eye depends, in part, upon the position, motion, and retinal condition of the other and closed eye. A theory of *binocular vision*, however, requires the consideration of two sets of data in addition to those already enumerated. These are the existence and relations of the two retinal images, and the relations and laws of the binocular movements of the two eyes.

[1] *Physiologische Optik*, 633.
[2] *Beiträge zur Theorie d. Sinneswahrnehmung*, pp. 105–118 (1862).

The fact that two eyes are ordinarily active, and that there are, therefore, two images of the object, is a fact of the first importance for the theory of visual perception. Each eye is in itself, indeed, a complete optical instrument; each has its own point, line, and plane of regard, and movements of rotation, torsion, and accommodation. The two eyes, however, act normally as one instrument; and yet they cannot be regarded as mere duplicates. The theory of binocular vision, then, considers the two eyes acting as one. For the purposes of such theory it is not important what shape the two retinas are regarded as having; they are usually taken as surfaces with the curvature of the inside of a sphere whose centre lies at a point where all the lines of direction intersect. It may be assumed, to begin with, that this point of intersection is the same for accommodation to all distances of the object. If the two retinas were perfectly symmetrical all the nervous elements which compose the mosaic of each one might be regarded as situated at points *identical* with those occupied by the nervous elements of the other. In other words, the surfaces of the two retinas might be regarded as capable of being perfectly superimposed. Upon such retinas, when the eyes were parallel, each single point of an object would have its image formed upon two "identical" points of the two retinas—upon points, that is, whose position would be mathematically the same with relation to the centre of each retina.

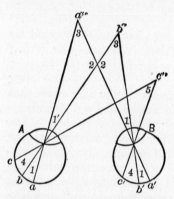

Fig. 123.—Diagram to illustrate the theory of corresponding retinal points. The images of objects at *a″* or *b″* or *c″* will fall on corresponding points of the retina—*a* and *a¹*, *b* and *b¹*, *c* and *c¹*—and be seen single.

But the retinas are not symmetrical, and the physiological centre is not the true mathematical centre; moreover, the eyes, to be of use, must act together in other positions than that called "primary." A distinction must then be made between *corresponding points* and identical points; the former are such as are found by experiment actually, as a rule, to act together and to combine their images when simultaneously stimulated. But, further, in certain cases the points of the retinas which customarily act together do not so act; points not exactly corresponding sometimes cover each other, and points usually corresponding sometimes fail to cover each other. Hence, a distinction may be made between corresponding points and "covering points"; the latter term being used for those points whose impressions, in each individual case of seeing, are actually referred to one and the same point of the object.[1] The two points of regard of the two eyes are in all cases *identical, corresponding,* and *covering.*

Scarcely more than a reference to previous elaborate attempts to determine the corresponding points of the two retinas is necessary for our purpose. Experiment shows that considerable reciprocal substitution takes place among the different points of both retinas. The eyes of most persons, if not of all, are both structurally and functionally incongruous. When the lines of regard lie parallel in the plane of the horizontal meridian of the two retinas, the vertical meridians do not correspond. A vertical meridian of the left eye, with its upper end inclined to the left, may be conjoined with a vertical meridian of the right eye that has its upper end inclined at about the same angle to the right. The image of a line which lies on these meridians thus inclined appears in the vertical horizon of the field of vision and divides it into a right and a left half.

§ 12. That objects are ordinarily seen as single when their images are formed on corresponding points of the retinas, and otherwise as double, may be shown by many familiar experiments. If we hold a finger before the eyes and look, not at it, but at the wall or the sky; or if we point it at some distant object, and keep our eyes steadily fixed on the object—two transparent images of the finger, rather than one solid finger, will be seen. Many persons may have difficulty in seeing the *two* images, but none will fail to notice their *transparent* character. Under these circumstances the wall, sky, or distant object may readily be seen through the finger. By experimental methods the images of a single object may be dissociated and what is really one be seen as two; on the other hand, images coming from two objects may be combined upon corresponding points, and thus what is really two be seen as one. It needs only a little skilful pressure upon one eyeball to create for us the double of each one of a group of friends, and to see one body partially through the transparent image of another. If two objects very similar—for example, the two forefingers—be held a little way apart at about a foot distant and against a clear sky, three like objects, one solid and two transparent, may be made to appear by combining the two middle images and dissociating the two on the outside. Two systems of regularly recurring similar objects—such as a regular small pattern of carpet or wall-paper, or the diamond-shaped spaces of a wire grating—may have all their images combined by slipping them, as it were, simultaneously to one side. There is, then, a double-seeing

---

[1] Wundt, *Physiolog. Psychologie* (6th ed.), II, 639.

of what is really single and a single-seeing of what is really double; but the latter is much rarer than the former, and usually occurs only when brought about for purposes of experiment.

§ 13. It is obvious that the relations of the two images of an object cannot remain unchanged when the eyes are moved from their primary position. When the eyes are converged upon an object, the images which are formed on the central spots of the two retinas by rays coming from the point of regard, are exactly identical and corresponding; the object in this case is therefore seen absolutely single. Points of the object lying near to the point of regard in any direction, and thus having their images formed close to the centres of the two retinas, are also seen single. For the points of the retinas on which the images are then formed, although not strictly identical, are corresponding; that is, they have habitually acted together in seeing objects single by binocular vision, and the slight incongruousness of the two sets of images is disregarded, as it were, by the mind. But all objects lying nearer or more remote than the point fixated by the eyes are liable to be seen double; for their images do not fall on corresponding points of the ret-

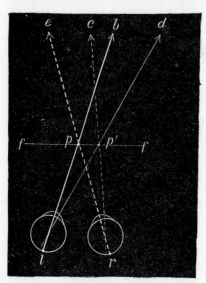

FIG. 124.—(From Hering).—*f f*, the sash of the window, and *p*, the black spot fixated. On the left line of vision *l b* lies a distant object, and on the right line *r e* another object. The images of *b* and *e*, as well as the image of *p*, fall on the place of direct vision and, therefore, on corresponding points of the two retinas.

inas. Objects lying below or above, or to one side or the other, of the point of regard, do not, as a rule, have their images formed on corresponding points; they may, therefore, also be seen double. Some of these points, however, which occupy positions below or above, to the one side or the other, of the point of regard, are seen single. The sum of all the points which are seen single while the point of regard remains the same is called the *horopter*.

§ 14. We must now advance to the consideration of the factors which enter into the construction of the field of so-called "three-dimensional space." Here the value, and even the necessity, of combining sensations due to movements of the organism with those more obscure local signs whose existence is required for the explanation of the retinal field, become obvious beyond all doubt.

The numerous factors which contribute to the perception of depth and relief may be grouped into three classes: (1) sensations of the position of the eyes; (2) parallax between the two eyes as due to movements of the head and body; and (3) associative aids, such as can be utilized to give an appearance of relief to a flat drawing or painting. We consider them briefly in the order just given: (1) Kinesthetic sensations. Since, in accommodating the lens of the eye for different distances, the ciliary muscle assumes various degrees of contraction, the sensory evidence of its contracted or relaxed condition may give an indication of the distance of the object for which the lens has been accommodated. This indication is hardly available, however, except for distances within a few feet of the eye. Kinesthetic impressions of the degree of convergence of the eyeballs, according to the distance of the object upon which they were converged, should be available for greater distances, perhaps even up to 100 feet. As has been said (p. 423), experiment shows[1] that, when other aids to accurate perception of depth are excluded, the judgments due to this means become very inaccurate. It will not, therefore, account for the accuracy ordinarily attainable.

(2) In considering the aids to perception of depth grouped under the head of "Parallax," we have to distinguish binocular parallax with unmoved eyes or head, from parallax (essentially monocular) as due to movements of the head or of the whole body. Since the eyes look from slightly different positions, they obtain, as has already been shown (p. 424), different views of the same (tridimensional) object. If the visual object is close to the face, the difference between the two views is great; but as the object retreats further and further, the view obtained by both eyes becomes more and more nearly the same. We should expect, then, that binocular parallax would be of importance in perceiving distance and relief when the objects are near at hand; and the actual importance of this factor is proved by means of the binocular stereoscope. If drawings or photographs are made of an object from two points of view that are separated by the distance between the two eyes, and if then the drawing from the more rightward point of view is placed before the right eye, and that from the more leftward before the left eye, and the two views combined by aid of the stereoscope, the appearance of depth is much intensified. For proving the importance of binocular parallax, the most important stereoscopic views

[1] Wundt, *Beiträge z. Theorie d. Sinneswahrnehmung*, 1862; Hillebrand, *Zeitschr. f. Psychol.*, 1894, VII, 97 ; Bourdon, *La perception visuelle de l'espace*, 1902; and others.

are those which consist of bare outline drawings of prisms, pyra
mids, dodecahedrons, etc., because in such views there is an absence of the associative factors which contribute to the perception
of depth. The small amount of line-perspective in these drawings
does not alone suffice to make the drawings appear solid, except
when they are binocularly combined.

The "pseudoscopic" effect also is important in this connection:
for if the views appropriate to the right and left eyes are interchanged,
then, in the absence of associative factors, the relief is reversed; and,
even if the associative factors are retained, as when the right and
left views of the landscape are interchanged on a stereoscope slide,
a certain degree of pseudoscopic effect is received. The appearance
of relief in the absence of associative factors, and even, to some degree, in opposition to these factors, is good evidence of the reality of binocular parallax as an important aid to the perception of
depth. On the other hand, the diminution of the pseudoscopic
effect when parallax has to contend with associative factors is evidence of the value of the latter.

A more exact conception of the "different views" of the same object which are obtained by the two eyes may be reached as follows.
Suppose two points to lie in the same line extending from the eye,
which may be called the line of sight. If the eyes are directed
on the nearer point, the farther one will be seen double; if the
eyes are fixed on the farther point, the nearer will be seen double.
The disparate images of the farther point, when the nearer is fixated, are called "homonymous," because the image which appears
to the right is that of the right eye; but when the farther point is
fixated, the double images of the nearer point are called "heteronymous," because the image which appears to the right is that of
the left eye. If, now, it can be assumed that the difference between
homonymous and heteronymous double images is a difference which
affects perception—though it is not a difference of which we are
consciously aware—then this difference would enable the observer
to know whether a doubly seen point were nearer or farther from
the eye than the point on which the eyes are fixed.

The accuracy of the perception of depth, by use of binocular
parallax, is very great for objects lying near the eye. Helmholtz[1]
measured the accuracy of this judgment of distance by a simple experiment, in which he fixed three pins upright in little blocks, and
endeavored to adjust them in a line at right angles to the line of
sight—screening the base of the pins and the table on which they
were manipulated, so as to exclude aids derived from perspective.
When the line of the pins was 340 millimetres distant from his eyes

[1] *Physiologische Optik*, p. 644.

and the pins 12 millimetres apart, he found that he never committed an error as great as $\frac{1}{4}$ millimetre. Bourdon[1] repeating Helmholtz's test, with the line of pins placed two metres away from the eyes, found the error (in judging whether the middle pin was at the same distance as the two end pins) to be always less than 2.5 millimetres, and seldom to exceed 1.5 millimetres. These judgments of distance are over 500 times as precise as can be made by use of convergence and accommodation alone.[2]

Parallax due to movements of the head has the advantage that the head can move through a greater lateral distance than that which separates the eyes; and thus can receive views of an object which differ more than do those of binocular parallax. There is an offsetting disadvantage, in that the two views are not received simultaneously, and so are not combined in that direct and probably instinctive manner which enables binocular parallax to convey an apparently immediate impression of the third dimension. But there is one way in which the parallax due to head movement is probably utilized—a way emphasized by Helmholtz,[3] and tested by Bourdon.[4] It is as follows: If we suppose the head moved to the right, with the eyes remaining fixed in their sockets, then all objects are displaced to the left in the field of view, and the nearer they lie to the eye the greater is their backward displacement. Since, however, the eyes do not remain fixed in their sockets during such a head movement, but instead remain fixated on some visible object, this object must remain at the centre of clear vision; while, on the contrary, objects nearer than it move backward in the field of view, and objects farther off than it move, in the field of view, in the direction of the head's movement. This motion of objects within the field of view is very easily and minutely perceptible, and is capable of giving a perfect indication of the relative distance of objects in the line of sight. The question is, how far this source of information is actually employed in ordinary perception. Bourdon finds that, in attempting to judge of distance with one eye, and without the aid of the associative factors, the observer does make involuntary sideward movements of the head, and that his judgment of distance is thus much improved.

(3) We now come to consider the so-called "associative" factors. Under this head belong the space in the field of vision which is occupied by an object of known size; the linear perspective; haze and other atmospheric effects; shadows and the covering of one object

[1] *Rev. philos.*, 1900, XXV, 74.
[2] See O. Zoth, in Nagel's *Handbuch der Physiologie*, 1905, III, 415.
[3] *Physiologische Optik*, p. 634.
[4] Op. cit., p. 286.

by another and nearer object; and the general make-up of the field
of view. In comparing the distances of objects, all of which are
over a mile or two away, we are dependent entirely on these associative factors. One-eyed individuals, also, must be dependent on
them, and on parallax due to movements of the head. Since one-
eyed individuals do not show a noticeable deficiency in the perception of distance under ordinary conditions, and since a person may
even become blind in one eye without being aware of the fact, it
is clear that very good indications of the third dimension are provided by the associative factors, in connection with movement-
parallax. It is probable enough that the factors here classed as
associative are of much influence even in normal binocular vision.
The significance and value of these associative factors will be further
illustrated—especially when we come to consider certain classes of
the errors, and illusions, that are so frequent in visual perception.
Since these factors bring into prominence the interpretative function
of the mind in all perception—that is, the presence, in the lowest and
earliest stages of the mental life, of the working of the so-called
faculties of attention, discrimination, association, etc.—such errors
and illusions have, hitherto, oftener than not, been laid to the fault
of "the judgment."

§ 15. A fact of profound and far-reaching psychological meaning
comes to the surface repeatedly in considering the factors on which
judgment of distance and relief is based. The fact is this: We are
often unaware of these factors, taken by themselves, and are even
unable to become aware of them directly, though their reality can
be demonstrated by their effects. We are unconscious, for example,
of the existence of two fields of view, one due to each eye; and, in
the case of double images, we are unable to tell by introspection
which belongs to the right eye and which to the left. It may even
happen that an object is visible only to one eye—as, for example,
when the fingers of both hands are held before the eyes in a sort of
lattice-work—and yet we cannot tell with which eye it is seen, or
whether it is seen with both. Notwithstanding this inability to
distinguish between the contributions of the two eyes, the facts of
stereoscopic and especially of pseudoscopic vision show that binocular perception of depth depends on some sort of (physiological)
distinction between the complex nervous impulses coming from the
two eyes. To this corresponds the distinction (psychological) o˝
the complexes of resulting sensations.

Again, perception of the distance of a familiar object and also
perception of the size of an unknown object, when its distance is
known, are both dependent on using the "visual size" of the object, or the angle subtended by it, as an indication of its real size

or of its actual distance; and yet direct judgment of this visual size is much less certain and accurate than judgment of the real size or actual distance. These paradoxes would amount to genuine impossibilities if the whole process of reaching a judgment of size or depth went on within the field of consciousness, and if every part of it were accessible to attentive observation.

Such experiences as these tend strongly—and, may we not say, conclusively?—to confirm our suspicion that innumerable complex "traces" of sensations due to native and acquired *motor* reactions are so fused with all the local signs of the retina, as to demand recognition in every satisfactory theory of the genesis and development of the entire class of visual perceptions. The infant does not even initiate, not to say achieve, the process of objective vision otherwise than through the use of a ceaselessly moving pair of eyes. And that our subsequent analysis, whether introspective or more purely experimental, cannot disentangle and reproduce in consciousness these fused, or synthesized, factors, no more proves that they did not formerly exist than does the similar inability of the accomplished violinist to reproduce all the sensations under the guidance of which he learned correct spacing and bowing for all the different "positions" of his instrument, and its most difficult and delicate work. Indeed, on the one hand, the player's violin is as much a seeming part of his own organism as is the seer's pair of eyes; and on the other hand, the complexity and depth below the threshold of consciousness, of the player's former sense-experience bears no resemblance to the complexity of the lost art of learning how to see with the average pair of eyes.

§ 16. And, indeed, as has already been indicated, the laws which control our estimates of visual magnitudes are psychological, and apply to all the action of the mind in constructing its sense-data into the presentations of sense. Yet more elaborate mental activities, such as take place when the distance, size, and contour of visual objects are deliberately estimated and expressed in terms of an accepted standard, of course imply more of dependence upon skill acquired through experience.

The degree of fineness with which differences of distance and magnitude can be seen, under the most favorable circumstances, is limited by the least observable differences in the members of the different spatial series of sensations which compose the visual objects. Of such series, those most capable of exceedingly fine differentiation are the local retinal signs and the sensations of position and motion accompanying convergence of the eyes for near distances. Different authorities assign different proportions to the different help which these series render in making the finest possible distinctions of visual magnitude. Hering[1] denies that any help is obtained from muscular sensations, or "feelings of innervation," in comparing the size of two minute objects near by, and assigns all the work of furnishing such data to the "spatial sense of the retina." Lotze,[2] who admitted the assistance of muscular sensations, nevertheless held that the fineness of the distinctions possible among them is not sufficient to support our ordinary judgments of the size, distance, and direction of objects. Wundt[3] and others claim that it is by gradations in the sensations of eye-movements that we make the most accurate of these estimates; they deny that any "spatial sense" (in Hering's meaning of the words) belongs to the retina. The evidence seems to favor the view that *both* classes of sensations furnish data for all nice discrimination of visual extension.

The particular degree of accuracy with which minute differences in the distance and magnitude of visual objects can be perceived varies greatly, according to different positions of the eyes and of the object, the amount of light, practice, etc.—and all these, as connected with individual peculiarities of structure and previous function of the organs of sense. That such estimates fall to some extent under Weber's law—in other words, that the least observable difference in the length of visual lines and surfaces is relative and not absolute—has already been shown (chap. III, § 23). Chodin found the relative value of the least observable difference, with a variation of the absolute vertical distance from 2.5 to 160 mm., to be as follows when the lines lie in the same direction:

Absolute distance..	2.5	5	10	20	40	80	160 mm.
Fraction of observable difference..	$\frac{1}{17}-\frac{1}{26}$	$\frac{1}{29}-\frac{1}{32}$	$\frac{1}{37}-\frac{1}{45}$	$\frac{1}{53}-\frac{1}{57}$	$\frac{1}{44}-\frac{1}{36}$	$\frac{1}{39}-\frac{1}{32}$	$\frac{1}{43}-\frac{1}{30}$

The fineness of ocular judgment is greater for horizontal distances.

The measuring power of the eye is much less accurate when the distances compared lie in different directions. In particular, points separated by a vertical distance of 20 mm. are estimated as equally far apart with those separated by a horizontal distance of 25 mm.[4] Most estimates of direction and distance are comparatively inaccurate when only one eye is used. A vertical line drawn at right angles to a horizontal appears bent to monocular vision; its apparent inclination is variable, and was found by Donders[5] to vary between 1° and 3° of the angle within a short time.

[1] Hermann's *Handb. d. Physiol.*, III, i, pp. 533 f.
[2] *Medicin. Psychologie*, 384 f.
[3] *Physiolog. Psychologie* (6th ed.), II, 574.
[4] So Wundt found, op. cit., II, 591.
[5] *Archiv f. Ophthalmologie*, XXI, iii. pp. 100 f.

§ 17. The data or *motifs* already described are the foundation, also, of our *perceptions of motion*, and of our estimates of its direction, speed, and extent. It need scarcely be said that all such perceptions and estimates are relative; they imply the existence of some point which may be regarded as fixed, and the application of a standard of measurement. For perceptions of motion by the eye, the point of regard when the organ is in the primary position furnishes the means of orientating ourselves and of placing the different things of vision in their right relations to us and to each other. Suppose the body and head to be erect, and the eyes motionless and looking into the distance with the lines of vision parallel; the perception of motion may then arise in either one of two ways. Of these, by far the most frequent is the change of relative position of an object in the field of vision which is occasioned by its movement. What is necessary, however, is simply the successive stimulation of continuous points or areas of the retina with images that are sufficiently similar to be perceived as one object. The perception of motion may also be produced by the successive stimulation of the same points or areas of the retina with images that are too dissimilar to be regarded as one object. One may thus see motion when neither the eyes nor any external objects are really moved, as is now so familiarly illustrated by the well-known performances of kinetoscope and kinematograph. It is in the latter way that the colored points of the images formed by the retina's own light, when the eyes are closed and motionless, seem to be in constant motion.

The direction and amount of motion perceived with the eyes is measured off upon the entire field of vision in accordance with previous experience and by means of the data already described. With the eyes at rest, the retinal local signs, or space-values belonging to the retinal elements, furnish the more important data; secondary helps, and associated sensations and ideas of position and motion, complete the perception.

It is assumed, in cases like the foregoing, that no sensations indicating motion of either the organ of vision, or the head, or the whole body, complicate the problem. But ordinary perceptions of motion are gained with the eyes in motion out of the primary position. When the eye and the object both move in such a way that the point of regard remains fixed on the object, our perceptions of motion, and estimates of its direction and magnitude, are dependent upon muscular and tactual sensations occasioned by the eye's changes of position. We know from experience what kinds and intensities of sensations are produced by keeping the point of regard fixed on an object which is moving about at a given rate in a given direction. If any of the links ordinarily belonging to this chain of conscious experiences drop out, our measuring instrument fails us either partially or completely. The head, too, is invariably turned when we are watching an object that is moving in any direction other than straight forward or away from us along the line of regard. The sensations originating in the action of the muscles and skin of the head and neck thus enter into our computation; they must have such a value in consciousness as to inform us about how far the head has gone from the position with which it started, in order to fixate the moving object. According to Helmholtz,[1] the ordinary movements of the head in vision follow the same principle as that followed by the eyes in movement; that is to say, the head turns from its primary position on an axis that is approximately parallel to the axis of the simultaneous rotation of the eyes. But Hering[2] asserts that a difference between the laws of the motion of head and eyes is of essential significance for our perception of space. However this may be, it is certain that the position and motion of the head, as known by its muscular and tactual sensations, must be taken account of in all ordinary visual perception of motion. The same thing is true of the position and motion of the entire body. Many of our errors of sense, or false perceptions of motion—its existence, direction, rate, and amount—are dependent upon the principles of judgment governing such data of sensations. We are peculiarly liable to error in all cases where the motions of our own bodily organs are passive; in such cases we do not have the ordinary *motifs*, or data, at our command.

Objects are perceived at rest, either when, our organs of vision being themselves at rest, the images of the objects do not change their position in the field of vision, or when sensations of motion occasioned by moving these organs are such and so great as we know by experience correspond to (or compensate for) the changes in the position of their images which are occasioned by their actually remaining at rest. But whenever we look with moving eyes upon a number of objects arranged in fixed position with relation to each other, a conflict between two sets of data really takes place. The result with respect to our perceptions of motion may depend upon which of the two is chiefly effective in arresting attention. When the eyes are brought from the parallel position, which they assume in vision of remote objects, to convergence upon some near object, the two fields of view belonging to the two eyes rotate in opposite directions, while the middle visual line maintains its position in the median plane.[3] Ordinarily we do not perceive this

[1] *Physiolog. Optik*, p. 486.
[2] In Hermann's *Handb. d. Physiol.*, III, i, p. 495.
[3] See Le Conte, *Sight*, p. 229.

rotary motion of the two fields of vision, but consider the field as one and stationary and ourselves as changing our point of regard in it. By attention, however, we may see that the external objects, although they really continue at rest, appear to move as the relations of their double images are changed. So, also, when the eye or head or body turns in either direction, in order that a new object may be brought under regard, it is possible either to perceive or not to perceive the entire field of objects sweeping by; and which of the two happens depends upon the direction in which attention is drawn. When strictly attending to the phenomena, we cannot well fail to regard everything as moving in the opposite direction from that in which we know the organ of vision to be turning.

§ 18. The principles already laid down also suffice to explain most of the ordinary "errors of sense," as well as certain extraordinary experiences of a somewhat different kind. The right to speak of errors of *sense* has been questioned. It has been claimed that such errors belong rather to judgment, and that sense pure and simple cannot err. The claim is based upon a misunderstanding of the nature of perception. A very obvious difference exists, indeed, between a mistaken estimate of the distance of a mountain through extraordinary clearness of atmosphere and the seeing of a square of white paper as green on a red ground, or as yellow on a blue ground. But the latter is surely an "error of *sense*," or sensation, in as pure form as such error is conceivable. That sense cannot err is true only in case we speak of unlocalized and unprojected sensation, regarded as not predicating anything beyond itself. In all presentations of sense a certain psychological judgment is involved; for all such presentations imply association of impressions discriminated as similar or dissimilar, and a mental synthesis which is dependent upon attention and the interpretation of certain *motifs* or *data* according to past experiences. *Clear vision is always mental interpretation.*

The attempt to assign the relative amount of blame to sense and to intellect, in cases where our presentations of sense do not represent objective relations of things, assumes an ability to make distinctions which we do not possess. Moreover, the distinction, when made as the objection would have it, will not hold. Innumerable experiences contradict the statement that immediate sense-perception cannot err. When one sees (with no power to *see* otherwise) a gigantic human form through the fog, or projected against the scenery of a stage, and yet *judges* that this form is only of usual size, the error is not one of judgment, but just the reverse. *Errors of sense* are only special instances where the mind makes its synthesis unfortunately, as it were, out of incomplete data, instantaneously and inevitably interpreting them in accordance with the laws which have regulated all its experience. As Lotze has remarked, "The whole of our apprehension of the world by the senses is one great and prolonged deception." Objects of sense are in no case exact copies of ready-made things which exist *extra-mentally* just as they are afterward perceived, and which get themselves copied off in the mind by making so-called impressions upon it; they are mental constructions. In the special case of sight we have seen that, in every particular—in its elements, its mode of construction, its laws of change—the field of vision is a subjective affair. The case is in no respect essentially different, whether our presentations of sense are so-called errors or true images of things. In both cases the same data and laws of the use of these data maintain themselves. Errors of sense, however, are distinguished from hallucinations, because the former result from the activity of an organism which is normal in structure and function, while the latter do not.

§ 19. The errors of visual perception are almost innumerable; they may be classified in part, however, according as they fall under some one or other of the before-mentioned principles. Such errors may be called "normal," because they are committed in accordance with principles which regulate the ordinary activity of the mind in making its synthesis by the help of the sense-data or *motifs* furnished to it through the excitement of the organism. Deceptions of this class really result, then, from the *fidelity* of both mind and nervous system. Certain errors of sense, for example, are special examples of the working of the laws which regulate the correspondence of the two images in binocular vision. Thus, near objects erroneously appear double when the eye is adjusted for distant vision, distant objects when it is adjusted for near vision; solid things are seen through other solid things; relations in space in general are perceived different from the reality; and all according to the law of the correspondence and non-correspondence of the two retinal images. Accordingly, the inquiry, Why is vision single when it is performed with two eyes? can demand and receive only one answer. An important condition of the single vision of solid objects is that they *shall be* seen with two eyes. Whether anything whatever is seen as two or one does not depend, primarily, upon its really being either two or one, or upon the existence of one or two retinal images of it (as though such images were directly perceived); it rather depends upon the appropriate data of sensations being furnished to the mind for completing its mental synthesis of the object. The two eyes being simultaneously affected in a certain way, these data are supplied. What is one is seen as one, and what is two is seen as one, and what is one is seen as two—all in essentially the same way.

§ 20. Under the head of *geometrical optical illusions* are grouped a large number of curious errors in the perception of lines and angles. Of the numerous figures which have been found to give rise to such illusions, only a small selection can be presented here; but it may be stated as a general principle, that scarcely any geometrical figure is free from illusory effects; or, in other words, that the apparent length and direction of a line is likely to be affected by all its visual environment.

Among the principal illusions of this general type are such as the following: (1) Specific illusions. Vertical distances are perceived as greater than mathematically equal horizontal distances.[1] This can be seen in Figs. 125, *a* and *b;* but the reader can best

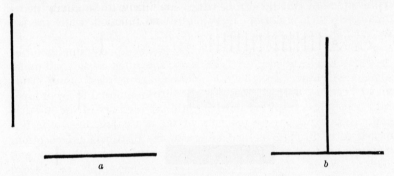

a   b

FIG. 125.

convince himself of the fact by marking off a vertical distance between two points, and then—keeping the original two points steadily in the vertical meridian of the field of view—locating a third point at what seems to be the same distance to the right or left of one of the original points. The error will then be apparent on measuring the two distances, or on turning the figure so as to interchange horizontal and vertical.

By a similar test the upper half of a vertical line can be shown to appear slightly longer than the lower half;[2] and in general, when one of two equal figures lies directly above the other, the upper appears somewhat larger than the lower. The upper and lower halves of a letter "S" or a figure "8" appear of nearly the same size; but when they are inverted ("S" and "8"), the actual difference between

[1] See J. Oppel, Über geometrisch optische Täuschungen, *Jahresbericht d. physikal. Vereins zu Frankfurt*, 1854–55, p. 37.

[2] Delboeuf, *Bulletin de l'acad. roy. de Belgique.*, 2 Sér., XIX, 2, 195.

the two halves becomes magnified. There is a somewhat similar illusion in dividing a horizontal line in halves,[1] when only one eye is used, and attention is directed to the middle of the line; the outer

FIG. 126.

half needs to be larger than the inner or nasal half in order that the line may appear equally divided. Not all individuals, however, are subject to this illusion, and it is always slight in amount.

(2) One-dimensional illusions. In distinction from the illusions already mentioned, which seem to be specifically connected with certain parts of the retina or of the field of view, there is a large class of more general errors which are likely to be committed in

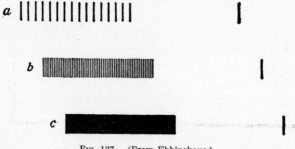

FIG. 127. (From Ebbinghaus.)

the judgment of lengths. They may be classed as one-dimensional illusions, since they occur within a single straight line, and are not due to the influence of figures in other parts of the field of view.

The best-known of these one-dimensional illusions is commonly expressed by saying that filled or divided space appears greater than empty or undivided space. This rule, however, is subject to certain qualifications. It is, first, rather the filled or empty ap-

FIG. 128.

pearance which counts, than the amount of light received from the spaces in question; for a black line on a white sheet appears longer than an equal distance laid off between two points (Fig. 126), though, objectively, it is the black line which is empty. In the same

[1] Kundt, Poggendorf's *Annalen*, 1863, CXX, 118.

way, it is not the most finely divided space which seems greatest, but the space of which the division is most obtrusive (Fig. 127). These facts indicate that the illusion is dependent on the figure which we are led to see rather than on the mere distribution of retinal stimulation. There are further qualifications, in detail, to the rule that divided space appears greater than undivided; for example, a single division of a line at its middle, or a division into three parts, of which the middle one is much larger than that at either end, causes, if anything, the opposite illusion (Fig. 128).

When subdivision of a line causes it to appear longer, the parts into which it is divided (or some of them) themselves appear shorter

FIG. 129.

than isolated lines of the same length.[1] If, on the contrary, the division is such as to make the whole line appear shorter, the parts then appear long in comparison with isolated lines of the same length. For example, if a line is divided into a large central piece and two small end-pieces, the whole line appears shortened, and the middle part lengthened; and this illusion is intensified by leaving the middle part blank, as in Fig. 129, in which, by a combination of these effects, the whole of the shorter line appears shorter than the vacant middle part of the longer line.[2] If, however, the middle part is relatively small, it appears shorter than an equal isolated line, while the whole line appears too long. By cutting out equal distances from the middles of short and of long lines, as in Fig. 130, an effect of contrast is produced.[3]

[1] Ebbinghaus, *Grundzüge der Psychologie*, 1908, II, 59.
[2] Compare the very similar illusions investigated by H. J. Pearce, *Psychol. Rev.*, 1904, XI, 143.
[3] Müller-Lyer, *Archiv f. Physiol.*, 1889, Suppl., p. 263; *Zeitschrift f. Psychol.*, 1896, IX, 1.

Very similar to these one-dimensional illusions of visual perception are some which occur in the comparison of distances by touch, when lines are applied to the skin, or by touch and the muscle-sense, when the finger is drawn along a line, the divisions being made in such a way as to be appreciated by touch.[1] And much the same illusions occur in the comparison of short intervals of time, when these are marked out by sounds. It appears quite probable, therefore, that these one-dimensional illusions are not specifically dependent on the processes of vision, nor even on the processes of space-perception. One may say that the process of comparison is affected, in all these cases, with the same sort of difficulty and source of confusion; or one may say that the same sort of configura-

FIG. 130.

tion is introduced into the percept in all these cases, and that the illusions are incidental to the configuration.

No fully satisfactory theory has yet been worked out to cover and explain all the facts. The illusions which have been mentioned in visual perception of lines are rather slight, and even inconstant from one individual to another; but they are made more striking, and harder to escape, by adding to the one-dimensional figure other lines and angles.

[1] Compare Robertson, *Psychol. Rev.*, 1902, IX, 549; Pearce, *Archiv f. d. ges Psychol.*, 1903, I, 31; *Psychol. Rev.*, 1904, XI, 143.

It should not be understood, however, that the same illusions occur in all cases in touch as in vision. Of the illusions to be mentioned on succeeding pages, that of Müller-Lyer holds of touch, but that of Poggendorf is reversed (Robertson). In an extended study of the illusion of filled and empty space in touch (*Arch. f. d. ges. Psychol.*, 1910, XVI, 418), Cook finds (1) that when adjacent areas of the skin are simultaneously excited, a filled space is overestimated by comparison with an empty, but (2) that when the stimuli are applied successively to the same area, the opposite illusion results; and (3) that when the stimuli are applied successively to different areas, no illusion occurs in the comparison of filled and empty space. Analysis of the total impression, or isolated attention to the particular elements to be compared, is favored, in the case of touch, by successive presentation. In general, it would seem that touch is rather more subject to illusions of this sort than is vision; for analysis is easier in vision.

(3) The Müller-Lyer illusion. The most striking illusion in length of lines is that first announced by Müller-Lyer in 1889, and called by him a "confluxion" effect, in opposition to "contrast."

FIG. 131.—The Müller-Lyer Illusion.

Fig. 131 presents the "confluxion" illusion in a common form, but there are numerous variants. A continuous series of transitional forms can be constructed, leading from this arrow-head

FIG. 132.—Modified Müller-Lyer Figure.

figure to the one-dimensional illusion of Fig. 129: thus, the horizontal line may be omitted, and only the arrow-heads left—the distances between the points of the arrows being the object of com-

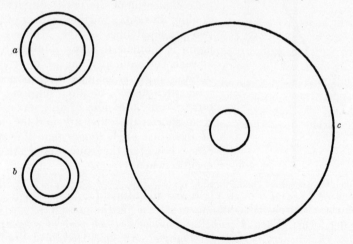

FIG. 133.—Confluxion and Contrast.

parison; the angle of the arrow-heads may then be diminished to zero, so giving the one-dimensional figure. Another transitional series can be made by substituting for the arrow-heads rectangles (with or without one side open), and then narrowing the rectangle

FIG. 134.—Reversible Müller-Lyer Illusion.

to the width of the "line" in the one-dimensional figure (Fig. 132). From the continuity of these series, there can be little doubt that the same principle enters into both extremes of the series; on the other hand, the introduction of figures in two dimensions certainly intensifies the illusory effect.

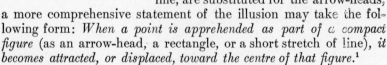

The Müller-Lyer figure, like the one-dimensional figure, and even more, produces a compound or reduplicated illusion. One of the two lines to be compared seems shorter than it is, and the other longer than it is, and therefore the comparison of the two is subject to a double illusion. Further, either of the two principal lines of the Müller-Lyer figure is influenced by two oblique lines at each end, and any one of these four oblique lines is enough to produce a moderate degree of the illusion. In other words, the sides of an acute angle seem shorter than they are, and the sides of an obtuse angle longer than they are. Since, however, the same sort of illusion occurs when rectangular figures, or curves, or even parts of a single straight line, are substituted for the arrow-heads,

FIG. 135.—The Angle Illusion.

a more comprehensive statement of the illusion may take the following form: *When a point is apprehended as part of a compact figure* (as an arrow-head, a rectangle, or a short stretch of line), *it becomes attracted, or displaced, toward the centre of that figure.*[1]

---

[1] Compare the similar formulations by Judd, *Psychol. Rev.*, 1899, VI, 241; by Pearce, *Psychol. Rev.*, 1904, XI, 143; by Benussi, in Meinong's *Untersuchungen zur Gegenstandstheorie und Psychologie*, 1904, p. 303; and by Smith and Sowton, *Brit. Journ. of Psychol.*, 1907, II, 196.

§ 21. A few words of explanation are needed with reference to the formula just given. Neither "figure" nor "centre" is to be understood in a strict geometrical sense. By "figure" is meant any part

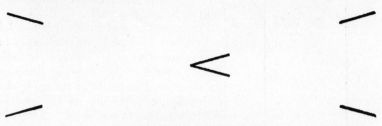

FIG. 136.—Modified Angle Illusion.

of the total presentation (whether this be visual, tactile, or auditory) which, usually because of its compactness, is apprehended as possessing a certain degree of unity and isolation. By "centre of the figure" is to be understood something analogous to the centre of gravity, but it is a *subjective* centre of gravity, depending rather on the figure as apprehended than on the exact geometrical relations within the stimulus. For example, when the inner circle in *a*, Fig. 133, is compared with the outer circle in *b*, an illusion occurs which is probably a reduplication of the one-dimensional illusion of Fig. 129; diameters drawn through the circles would give the one-dimensional figure. Both *a* and *b* are most readily apprehended as rings, and the centre of attraction lies within the ring and not at the geometrical centre of the circles. In *c* of the same figure, on the other hand, the ring is not compact, and the inner circle is apprehended as an independent figure; its centre of attraction lies at its geometrical centre, and the circumference is drawn inward; and thus comparison of the inner rings of *b* and *c* leads to

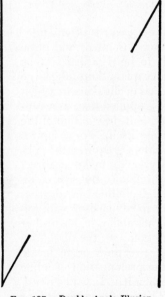

FIG. 137.—Double Angle Illusion.

a "contrast" illusion similar to that in the one-dimensional Fig. 130. It appears, therefore, that both the "contrast" and the

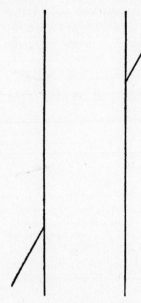

FIG. 138.—Poggendorf Figure.

"confluxion" illusions are covered by the comprehensive formula of the preceding paragraph. Which of the two effects shall result depends on the subjective grouping of parts.

The importance of some such mental or "central" factor as *apprehension* in the causation of these illusions is indicated by the fact that opposite illusions can sometimes be got from the same objective figure, according to the way in which its parts are combined. Thus, in Fig. 134, a given objective distance appears now longer and again shorter than another objectively equal distance, according as attention is fixed on the figures in black or on the figures in white.

§ 22. (4) Illusions of angles and the direction of lines. The apparent direction of a line is easily influenced by the presence of other lines in its neighborhood. The general rule applying to these cases is often stated in the following form: Acute angles are over-estimated, and obtuse angles under-estimated. This formula is to be regarded less as an explanation of the large class of illusions to which it is applied than as a convenient designation of the class itself. These figures seldom require the observer to make a direct estimate of the size of an angle, either in degrees or in comparison with another angle; he has rather to compare the directions of two lines or to locate the prolongation of a line when it is interrupted. The error committed is as it would be if the acute angles of the figure were over-estimated; but the over-estimation of the angle is not a directly observed fact. Indeed, when a direct comparison of angles

FIG. 139.—Zöllner Figure.

is required, under conditions which make comparison difficult—
such as omission of the vertex, or unequal length of the sides of
the angles—then quite other sorts of errors appear.[1] This makes it
appear doubtful whether the over-estimation of acute angles is,

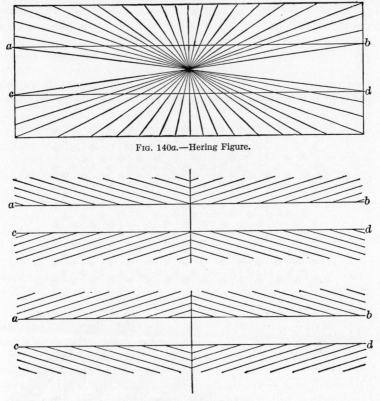

FIG. 140a.—Hering Figure.

FIG. 140b.—Hering Figure.

in reality, a universal principle which can be freely invoked for the
explanation of these illusions.

In the "angle illusion" (Fig. 135), the acute angle at the vertex
is said to be over-estimated, because the true prolongation of one
side falls within the apparent divergence of the sides. The illusion
appears to depend in part on the disparity in length of the two lines
which form the angle; if both are treated alike, as in Fig. 136, the
effect is reduced, made uncertain, and may even be reversed.

[1] Judd, op. cit., A. H. Pierce, *Studies in Auditory and Visual Space Perception*
(New York, 1901), p. 271.

Reduplication of the angle illusion gives such effects as are seen in Fig. 137, or, in more pronounced form, in Fig. 138, which last presents the long-famous Poggendorf illusion.   Various degrees of this illusion are produced by dissecting the figure and presenting its parts separately; thus the illusion is, if anything, strengthened by leaving only the exterior obtuse angles between the interrupted oblique line and the parallels, while it is much diminished or even reversed by leaving only the acute angles.[1]

By multiplication of the same elements, the figures of Zöllner (139) and of Hering (140 *a* and *b*), and other variants, are produced.   The same errors in the apparent prolongation of the oblique lines can be observed here, but, in addition, the parallels are

Fig. 141.—The Twisted Cord Illusion (Fraser).

affected in their apparent direction, and straight lines may even appear bent.   These illusions are interpreted in the following way, as coming under the rule of over-estimation of acute angles: If the angles between the parallels and the intersecting oblique lines are exaggerated, and if the resulting illusion affects chiefly the parallels, then these will appear swung around toward right angles with the obliques, and so the Zöllner illusion will result.   Further, since the over-estimation of the angles is greater, the smaller the angles, the parallels will appear bent when the angle of the intersecting lines varies; and thus the other figures are provided for.

It is a curious fact that when the oblique lines in the Zöllner figure are made exceedingly oblique, while at the same time the principal lines are indistinct, an illusion opposite to that of Zöllner is produced.   This may be called the "twisted cord illusion," since the figure (No. 141) produced is similar to the drawing of a cord

---

[1] Jastrow, *Amer. Journ. of Psychol.*, 1892, IV, 381; A. H. Pierce, *Studies in Auditory and Visual Space Perception* (New York), 1901, p. 257.

made by twisting together a black and a white strand.[1] The illusion is strengthened by placing the "cord" on a checkered background in such a position that each of the obliques is augmented at each of its ends by parts of the squares of the background. By varied application of this principle, Fraser has produced very striking illusions. Since the deflection of the "cord" is in the direction of the oblique lines, the illusion may be called one of "conflux-ion," and in distinction to it, the Zöllner illusion may be called one of contrast.

§ 23 (5) Illusions of area. The judgment of area, like that of angles and directions, is, introspectively, less direct and confident than the judgment of length. If the areas of the several surfaces in Fig. 142 are compared (without the aid of calculation), much uncertainty is likely to be felt; but the figures will probably appear unequal, though all have very nearly the same area. In general, compactness of form seems to diminish the apparent area of the

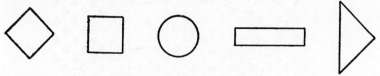

FIG. 142.—Comparison of Areas.

surface. Another cause must be sought for the illusion of Fig. 143. Here the judgment of area is perhaps confused by the obtrusive inequality of the adjacent sides, or by the evident tendency of the lower figure, if continued upward, to enclose the upper figure.

§ 24. The field of geometrical illusions has proved exceedingly fertile in theories, but rather barren of scientific agreement. A twofold division may be made into theories which appeal to peripheral factors and those which appeal to central factors. The chief peripheral factors are those which relate either to the retina or to the eye movements. On the one hand, it is impossible to found any comprehensive theory *purely* on peculiarities of the retina. On the other hand, the eye-movement theory has been applied to these illusions with much detail and much apparent success. The general conception underlying this theory is that the eye measures lengths, angles, etc., by moving over them, and that movements of greater extent or energy, or those which involve more effort, lead to the appearance of greater magnitude. Since, for example, vertical movements of the eyes require more effort than horizontal

[1] Fraser, *Brit. Journ. of Psychol.*, 1908, II, 307.

movements, vertical lines seem longer than equal horizontals; divided space impedes the movement of the eye over it, and so appears the greater; acute angles call for abrupt changes in movement, and so are felt as large in comparison with obtuse angles, which require but a slight deviation in the eye's direction. In the Müller-Lyer figure, the readiest explanation is that the eye is led to err in its fixations, and so comes to measure, not the distances between the points, as required, but rather the distances between the figures adjacent to the points.

Actual photographic records of the eye's movements during examination of the Müller-Lyer figure do not, however, as will be

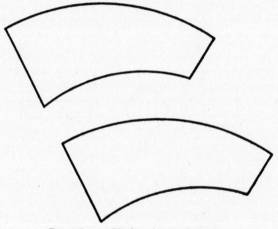

Fig. 143.—An Illusion of Area (Jastrow).

seen later in the chapter, always substantiate this interpretation. They are more favorable to the statement that the figure with inward-turned obliques impedes the eye's movement, making it "slow and hesitating," whereas the figure with outward-pointing obliques allows the eye free play for "extensive and energetic" movement.[1] Unfortunately, hesitating and impeded movements are required by the theory also for explaining the over-estimation of divided space; so that the two explanations are inconsistent.

Supporters of the eye-movement theory have often brought forward the observation that steady fixation diminishes the illusions, whereas free and rapid roaming of the eyes over the figures favors the illusory effect. On the other hand, opponents of the theory have reported that a momentary exposure of the figures—too brief to

[1] Wundt, *Physiol. Psychol.*, 6th ed., 1910, II, 583.

permit the eyes to move from one point to another—does not destroy the illusions but rather favors them. These two observations, in appearance contradictory, are in reality much the same thing; for, as will be set forth more fully in later paragraphs on this subject, rapid movement of the eyes over a figure amounts to obtaining a series of brief exposures—the figure being invisible during the movements, and being seen only during the brief fixations of the eye which intervene between the movements. It would seem, then, that the *absence* of the sensory effects which result from the eyes in motion is one of the factors most directly responsible for such geometrical illusions. Nor is it by any means fair to disregard the sensations of position and tendencies to movement, or memory images of past movements, which may exist in the absence of actual movement. From this point of view, the question of the relation of eye movements to these illusions is lost in the general problem of the visual perception of space.

§ 25. Of "central" theories of the source of these illusions, the most comprehensive are the perspective theory, the dynamic theory, and what may perhaps be called the "confusion" theory.

The perspective theory starts from the undoubted facts that even simple line drawings readily suggest objects in three dimensions; and that the introduction by suggestion of the third dimension must lead to changes in the apparent length and direction of the lines composing the figures. The application of this principle to some of the figures is readily made. Thus, vertical lines in the field of view very often represent lines extending away from the observer and foreshortened by perspective; such lines are interpreted in accordance with their objective length, and therefore as longer than equal horizontal lines of the field of view, which are not subject to foreshortening. In accordance with this tendency, vertical lines in these simple figures appear longer than equal horizontal lines. The application of the principle of perspective to many of the illusions,[1] however, is much less direct, and finds little support in introspection.

§ 26. The dynamic theory is the work of Lipps,[2] and is, without doubt, the most interesting and even fascinating of all. Lipps urges that account must be taken of the inner activity of the observing subject, even though this activity may not come to consciousness as anything separate from the figures, but may rather be pro-

---

[1] For the application of this theory to many other illusions, see Thiéry, in Wundt's *Philos. Studien*, 1895, XI, 307, 603; 1896, XII, 67; and Filehne, *Zeitschr. f. Psychol.*, 1898, XVII, 15.

[2] *Raumesthetik und geometrische Täuschungen*, 1897; *Zeitschrift f. Psychol.*, 1898, XVIII, 405; 1905, XXXVIII, 241.

jected into the figures, or "felt in" them. Always there is present, in the apprehension of a figure, an "expansion" of the mental grasp to include all of the figure, and an opposed bounding or limiting activity, by which the figure is distinguished from surrounding space. These activities are felt as belonging to the figure, and their balance determines the apparent length of a line. But the presence of other lines, as in the Müller-Lyer figure, leads to expansions and limitations which are appropriate enough as applied to the whole figure, but not as applied to the particular lines which are to be compared. In many cases, besides these expanding and limiting tendencies, other tendencies, drawn from the dynamics of nature, are felt in the figures. Thus, a vertical line suggests a struggle

FIG. 144.—A Test of the Dynamic Theory.

against gravity, and the gravity-feeling in it affects its apparent length. The same conceptions are applied by Lipps to the æsthetics of simple forms, and to architecture.

A difficulty with the dynamic theory is that it tends to run to fanciful explanations. It explains too easily and too much; it could often be just as well applied if the illusions were the opposite of what they are; for the dynamics of these figures is usually quite ambiguous. For example, a vertical line may be thought of as standing upright or as hanging downward; its relations to gravity are opposite in the two cases; if gravity tends to compress it in the first case, it tends to stretch it in the second, and therefore opposite illusions ought to result from the two ways of looking at it. In Fig. 144, therefore, there should appear quite a strong illusion as between the two vertical lines, and this should be reversed on reversing the figure.

§ 27. The "confusion theory" might also be called the attention theory. It takes its start from the evident fact that the illusion figures are so constructed as to make difficult the isolation of the particular feature which is to be judged. It is difficult to fix attention on this one feature, thrusting aside all complicating features.

If this difficulty is only partially overcome, judgment will be based on a partial confusion of complicating features with the feature which is ostensibly judged. Thus, in attempting to compare the areas of variously shaped surfaces (Figs. 142 and 143), one feels the difficulty of isolating the bare feature of area from the more obtrusive feature of compactness; and the errors committed go to show that the isolation has not been fully carried out. In the Müller-Lyer and other "confluxion" illusions, it is much easier to take arrow-heads, etc., as units, and judge the distance between *them*, than to isolate the exact points which mark the ends of the distances to be compared; and the errors committed seem to show that the isolation is not fully carried out. The nature of the "confusion" in the cases of "contrast" illusions is not so readily pointed out; and in the vertical-horizontal and other specific illusions, special causes would probably have to be invoked. Nor is it entirely easy to apply this conception to the illusions of angle and direction, though the judgment of these matters must be admitted to be rather indirect and indefinite, and such, therefore, as might probably be subject to confusion. The confusion theory has at least this advantage, that it almost certainly affords the true explanation of some of the illusions;—and this is more than can be said of the other central theories. But reference to confusion takes us only a little way, and, beyond that, leaves various possibilities of explanation open in each particular case. What is needed is to point out the nature of the confusion in each class of illusions; and this cannot yet be done with any certainty.

Rather in favor of the confusion theory, further, is the fact that practice in making the required judgments, in such cases as the Müller-Lyer and Poggendorf figures, produces a gradual decrease and ultimate disappearance of the illusion; and this result follows, even though the observer does not know the nature of his errors.[1] The probable explanation of this practice effect is that the observer is conscious of the difficulty of isolating the feature to be judged, and therefore devotes himself to this isolation. The skill which he thus acquires in thrusting aside complicating features of the figures is in part a specific aptitude in dealing with a particular figure, and may not be transferred promptly to another figure or even to a changed position of the same figure, yet facility in dealing similarly with another figure is more easily acquired because of the previous practice. That the practice effect truly consists in the acquiring of skill in isolation is indicated by the observation of Benussi[2]— namely, that the illusion is much more quickly overcome when prac-

[1] Judd, *Psychol. Rev.*, 1902, IX, 27; Lewis, *Brit. Journ. of Psychol.*, 1908, II, 294.
[2] *Op. cit.*

tice is governed from the outset by a clearly formulated intention to isolate a certain feature of the figure; while, on the contrary, practice with the definite intention of always grasping the figure as a whole leads not to the usual decrease, but to an actual increase of the illusion. In concluding the whole matter, we may confidently assert that the geometrical illusions, or most of them, are chiefly due to central rather than peripheral factors; and that these central factors are intimately bound up with the tendency to apprehend figures, and compact parts of figures, as wholes. It is, in most cases, if not in all, as wholes, or units of "apperception," that we have been accustomed to regard them. And this tendency may, therefore, well enough be the chief cause of the illusion.

§ 28. The necessity of appealing to certain obscure, but effective central factors, as mingled with, or even dominating the peripheral factors, is felt in trying to account for those errors of sense which occur in connection with the strife and prevalence of contours, and the binocular mixing and contrast of colors. If a well-defined image of some contour, such as a sharp-marked limit between two differently colored surfaces, be formed on one retina, and on the corresponding points of the other the image of a uniform-colored background, then only the former will be visible. This is called the "prevalence of contours." But if the contours of the images of two differently colored objects run on the retina so as to cross only in one place, then sometimes one color and sometimes the other will prevail and get itself perceived at that place. This is called "the strife of contours." If two squares of red paper and two of blue, all of equal size and brightness and without any distinguishing marks, be laid side by side at equal distances, and their images then combined, the color of the middle one of the binocular images will at first be sometimes redder and sometimes bluer than that of the two side images, but in no case exactly like either of them. By steadily looking it is said to be possible to mix the colors of the two objects in a binocular image which is reddish blue (or violet).[1] This is called "the binocular mixing of colors." If such a deception can be secured, and made subject to the more or less voluntary direction of attention, it is manifest that the mixing of colors on which it depends must be largely central, and not wholly dependent upon the retinas of the two eyes. If a white stripe be placed upon a black surface and divided into two images, the right one of which is formed by looking at one half through blue glass, the left by looking through gray glass, then the right image will be seen blue, but the left will be seen yellow. This is called "binocular contrast of colors."

[1] So Hering asserts, "Physiolog. Optik," in Hermann's *Handb. d. Physiol.*, III, i, p. 592. Binocular mixing of colors has been denied by some authorities.

The peculiar perception of lustre is due to a struggle between the two fields of vision which results, not in combining the black images of one field with the white images of the other so as to produce an equal tint of gray, but in a rapid alternation of the two. Very smooth bodies, when they reflect the light perfectly, do not appear lustrous. But when the surface of such bodies—as, for example, the surface of a sheet of water—becomes ruffled by ripples, it becomes lustrous. The perception of lustre may be produced by combining two stereoscopic pictures of an object which are alike in contour, but one of which is black with white lines where the other is white with black lines. Two such pictures not combining to produce an equal tint of gray over the whole surface, the images of the separate points on the two retinas enter into a struggle with each other; and the rapid alternation of the prevalence, first of one and then of the other, gives rise to the appearance of lustre.

Similar conclusions seem forced upon us by our experience with certain of the most common and persistent optical illusions of motion. The fact that a steady succession of images (as in the case of watching a fall of water), passing over a particular region of the retina for a long time, sometimes ceases to be perceived as a motion, and that the image of a stationary body on the same retinal region may appear to be moving in the opposite direction, has been explained by "Thomson's law." This law refers the phenomena to the principle of fatigue. Recent investigations, however, seem to show that the explanation is incorrect. They bring out the remarkable result that the same elements of the retina, when stimulated simultaneously, may give rise to impressions both of motion and of rest. For this result some unknown law of cerebral action would seem to afford the only possible explanation.[1]

§ 29. The fact that things are seen upright and in correct relations horizontally, by means of data furnished through inverted retinal images, as well as all illusions and errors that are connected with this normal fact, implies yet more maturity of experience. Why do we see the upper part of the object by means of the lower part of the retinal image, and *vice versa*? and why do we see the right side of the object by means of the left side of the retinal image, and *vice versa*? Such questions have often been propounded as psychological puzzles of special difficulty. The only answer possible follows, obviously, from the foregoing principles. Strictly speaking, we neither see the external object nor the retinal image; the field of vision is a subjective affair, and is like neither of these two. The presentation of visual sense is normally dependent upon the retinal

[1] See Bowditch and Hall, *Journal of Physiology*, III, pp. 299 f

image for the data from which it is constructed; the image is dependent upon the external object for its formation by rays of light reflected from the object and converged upon the nervous elements of the retina. The different parts of the object as seen are primarily localized simply with reference to each other by means of local retinal signs and of complex sensations produced by motion of the eyes. But as yet the field of vision has no *locality* in objective space; no part of it can be said to be either up or down, either right or left. The use of such terms of position implies an association of localized sensations of sight with those of touch and of the muscular sense, in giving us a picture of the relation of the different parts of the body to each other, and of the entire body to the ground, the sky, and the various parts of surrounding objects. When the eyes are moved downward, the lower parts of the body and objects situated on the ground successively come into the field of vision; when the eyes are moved upward, the near ground and lower parts of objects successively disappear from the field of vision, and remoter or higher objects come to view. Seeing objects to the right or to the left is accomplished by motion of the eyes in the corresponding direction. Right *is* the direction in which the right hand is placed from the middle of the body; left *is* the direction in which the left hand is found. The massive feelings of touch and muscular sensation keep us informed of the general relation of our bodies to the earth and to objects on its surface. The head is the upper part, or part farthest away from the ground; the feet are the lower part, or members of the body in contact with the ground. Thus we come to use terms for localized sensations of sight which, in this use of them, have no primary reference whatever to the field of vision in itself considered.

§ 30. The above view of the relation of erect vision to the inverted retinal image is substantiated by the experience of one looking through a microscope. Since the ordinary microscope itself gives an inverted image of the object, the second inversion by the eye gives an image on the retina which is erect with respect to the object, though inverted with respect to the usual retinal image of an object. There is, however, no distortion or internal change (except magnification) in the spatial relations within the image. Nor is there any change in the eye movements necessary to bring any part of the image to the area of clear vision; for these movements all involve a movement of the fovea toward a point of the optical image on the retina, and the latter movement remains the same no matter what inversions, or even distortions, the rays of light may have undergone on their way to the retina. In other words, the *eye-movement value*, as it may be called, of the various retinal points is unaltered by changes in the rays of light on their way to the retina. Therefore, the observer, looking through the microscope, obtains an internally correct view of the object, and experiences no difficulty in directing his eyes to any point of it. His difficulty begins, however, when he attempts to move the object under the microscope, so as to bring into view a fresh part of it; for now the long-standing connection between the retina and the movements of the hand plays him false; and he is sure to move the object to the left when he should move it to the right, and up when he should move it down.   No long experience with the microscope, however, is needed to overcome this difficulty by establishing a new association between retinal directions and appropriate hand movements.   This new association is operative only within the special situation of looking through a microscope; it gives way at once to the usual association on removing the eye from the instrument.   Much the same effect of practice is noted in handling objects while viewing them through a mirror; though here the inversion is not complete.

An interesting experiment, along the line of these observations, was performed by Stratton.[1] While covering one eye, he placed before the other an optical instrument which, like the microscope, gave an inverted image of objects, and so an upright image on the retina.   No light was allowed to enter the eye except through this inverting instrument, and this instrument was worn continuously in the daytime, both eyes being covered when the instrument was removed for sleep. The experiment was continued for a week, with the result that movements of the hands and body, which on the first day suffered great confusion, became rapidly associated with the novel visual relations, so that before the end of the week all bodily movements were correctly and promptly executed under the direction of the eye; and, whereas at first everything had appeared upside down, this appearance also gave place to a normal appearance after a few days.   When the instrument was removed at the end of the week, a new period of confusion, false movements, and inverted appearance supervened before the old association was re-established. This experiment, as well as the experiences with the microscope and mirror, are interesting as revealing a remarkable looseness or flexibility in the association between the spatial perceptions of different senses.

§ 31. In concluding this brief survey of the very fruitful field afforded by so-called "errors of sense," as bearing upon any attempt to frame an adequate theory of visual perception, we mention the following inferences as those—it seems to us—which are most amply

[1] "Vision without Inversion of the Retinal Image," *Psychol. Rev.*, 1897, IV, 341, 463.

supported.   It should be said, in a preliminary way, that the great variety of special and, too often, exclusive and partisan theories adopted by different observers, is what, under the circumstances, might be expected.   For explanation in general is, for this sort of phenomena, an extremely intricate affair.   And this is true, even when the phenomena themselves seem to be of the utmost simplicity in character.   A variety of theories, therefore, may well enough appeal to certain facts of experience, or rather, to certain aspects of common facts, to sustain their special contentions.   Perhaps, too, they are all needed; or at least, they may all be said to contain certain of the elements indispensable to a complete explanation.   The difficulty with nearly all of them, however, is that they fail to take sufficient account of the equally important facts on which other rival theories are based.   Moreover, it must not be forgotten that essentially the same errors of sense may in differing individual cases, or under slightly differing circumstances, require a somewhat different set of explanations.   The nervous mechanism engaged, and the mental development acquired, in the growth of perception through the use of the eyes, and the associations of this growth with the senses of touch and hearing, are variable to a certain extent which cannot be determined *a priori*.   It is a well-known fact that the mental pictures and conceptions of spatial extensions and of the relations of objects in space, are not by any means the same with all adults.   The claim has even been made that they are, in general, somewhat markedly different with the two sexes.   And certainly, in this regard, the accomplished geometrician, or microscopist, or astronomer, is at a world-wide remove from the savage or the newly-born infant.

§ 32. At the same time we repeat, with increased confidence, that the most recent investigations in this line tend to confirm, in its essential features, the theory of visual perception, especially on the side of the apprehension of spatial qualities and spatial relations, which has been advocated in the preceding sections; and which may—at least, for most of its more important connections—be associated with the great names of Lotze, Helmholtz, and Wundt. Its essential features, as we are inclined to adopt it, while confessing the many obscurities and difficulties which still accompany any attempt at completing it, are the following:

First: The data, or factors, on the basis of which, so to say, the construction of visual space proceeds, have all the characteristics required by the so-called "local signs" (compare p. 386).   They have these characteristics in the highest degree.   They are series of sensations, which, as series, are of like quality; which admit of easy, rapid, and frequent repetition in a varying order of arrangement; and which, by the very nature of the organism and the conditions of mental development, are adapted to combine with other series of like characteristics.   Of such series the most important are (1) the retinal signs, and (2) the entire complex of tangled and obscure sensations which accompany and follow the attaining and holding of any position, by movement of the eyes.

Second: As to the retinal signs, they may most properly be spoken of as "native"—at least, in the sense that their existence and *discriminable* character must be assumed as "given" (*datum*) in any attempt to explain the initial steps of visual perception.   There is scarcely less doubt that the motor reactions which, of necessity, evoke the first complex sensations of position (even of eye-strain) and of motion, are native, in the sense that they are innate powers and are not learned by the infant.   Indeed, it is by no means certain that the resulting sensations may not have from the first a certain value as local signs, comparable in a way to that of the associated local signs of the retina.

In this connection, attention should be called to the fact that the "centre of clear vision" is not a point, but an area within which many points can be distinguished; this makes it difficult to accept any theory which regards visual space as organized about a single point.   The analogy of latitude and longitude in geography, or of co-ordinate geometry, is tempting to the psychologist but is rather misleading.   The organization is indeed partly of this sort, as is shown by the fact that an object seen in indirect vision attracts the eye to make a movement toward it; and that this movement is about sufficient in extent to bring the object to the centre of clear vision.   To regard visual space as a system of "polar co-ordinates," the position of every point in the field of view being determined by its direction from the "origin," or centre of clear vision, and by its distance from that origin, is not, however, an adequate account of visual space.   The "origin" is here not really a point; and the subdivision of the field is much finer than can be accounted for in this way.   Neighboring and probably also distant points in the field must be *related directly to one another*, and not simply to the centre of clear vision.   The actual organization of visual space is, in general, from a mathematical point of view, much less simple and cleancut than a system of polar co-ordinates.[1]

Third: As between nativistic and empiristic theories, the balance of evidence seems to favor the former.   Certainly both types of eye movement are innate powers, and not learned by the infant. Their native character does not, perhaps, prove that spatial *con-*

[1] See Dodge, *Psychol. Rev.*, Monograph Suppl. XXXV (1907), p. 64.

sciousness is innate, but it does show that the spatial organization of the retina and of its nervous connections is partly innate. Biologically, it would be difficult to believe that a fixed form of organization, such as that of visual space, should be newly acquired by every individual. This consideration applies with most force to two-dimensional space, but also with some probability to the third dimension. In so far as distance from the eye is definitely related to binocular parallax, the reactions of the eyes and limbs to the distance of objects might well be, in a measure, instinctive. They certainly are instinctive in some animals; thus the chick, on emerging from the egg, correctly gauges the distance of a grain at which he pecks; and human infants, in spite of what has sometimes been alleged to the contrary, show little tendency to reach for the moon or for anything that is definitely beyond their reach.

Fourth: The incalculable, but enormous influence on sense-experience which lies back of all the phenomena obtained for scientific treatment, whether from the physiological, the psycho-experimental, or the purely introspective point of view, must never be lost out of account. Indeed, these *residua* of past experiences, if we may so call them, are doubtless in many cases the determining causes of the character of the new experience. They consist of obscure and scarcely recognized sensations, images of previous sensations, motor tendencies and impressions, fusions of unanalyzable elements, flighty and flitting syntheses that have scarcely the quality of even an instinctively formed judgment; and—perhaps, above all,—workings of the organism which do not result in any effect that rises "above the threshold" of consciousness. But it is just such unrecognized, and largely unanalyzable, factors as these, which chiefly determine, not only our conduct under the direction of sight, but also our seemingly most logical conceptions and deliberate judgments concerning visual objects.

Fifth: To deny the influence of "central" factors, and the necessity of a theory of perception which gives them their full value, would be to controvert everything which we know about the nature of the nervous mechanism and its relations to the awakening and development of mental life. We have already said that only *psychical* factors can be fused, or united, or consciously judged together in any sort of relation, in a mental product. Of this declaration, the physiological correlate is, of course, the recognition of the influence of the cerebral mechanism in every sort, and every individual experience, of sense-perception. And we only return once more to the psychological point of view when we recognize anew the abundant evidence that attention, active discrimination, varied forms of conscious feeling other than sensation, and innumerable forms of association, all enter into our experience of objects as known by the organism employed in vision.

§ 33. In all the older discussions there was little exact knowledge of the actual movements made by the eyes in their mastery of the details of spatial perception. Even the laws summarized under the name of Listing were based upon a study of the positions reached by movement rather than of the movements themselves. Recently, several observers have obtained actual registration of these move= ments; and the results must, assuredly, be harmonized with any theory of visual space-perception.

The simple experiment of comparing the observations of the movements of the eyes, as seen by another observer, with those which our consciousness seems to assure us are made, is sufficient to show how uncertain is the latter kind of evidence in support of the facts. In reading a line of print, for example, one may seem to one's self to be moving the eyes smoothly along the line, while objective observation shows that the actual movements are a series of jerks, separated by brief periods of rest. The jerky character of this movement is difficult, or impossible to correct; whereas, in following a moving object the eyes themselves move in a fairly steady way and at a speed regulated by the speed of the object.

§ 34. The needed method of obtaining an accurate graphic record of the eye movements was first successfully applied by Delabarre,[1] and was also employed with success by Huey.[2] These experimenters obtained a record by attaching a light disk to the surface of the eyeball; and from the disk a thread ran to a light lever which wrote upon a moving surface. This method had the disadvantage of weighting the eye and so producing possible distortions in its movements.

A much improved device for photographing the eye while in motion has more recently been accomplished by several observers.[3] This method consists in general of obtaining a photographic record of the movements of a beam of light reflected from the cornea itself, or from some object attached to the cornea. Among the important facts established by this method are one or two relating to the fixation of the eye. When the eye "rests upon an object," the fovea, or centre of clear vision, has a diameter of one or two degrees, and what falls outside of this area is seen with diminishing clearness as

---

[1] *American Journal of Psychology* (1898), IX, 572.

[2] Ibid., p. 575; and (1900) XIII, 282.

[3] For a more detailed account of the methods and results of these experiments, see Dodge and Cline, *Psychol. Rev.* (1901), VIII, 145; Stratton, *Phil. Stud.* (1902), XX, 336, and *Psychol. Rev.* (1906), XIII, 82; and Judd, *Psychol. Rev.*, Monograph Supplement XXIX (1905).

we move toward the periphery of the visual field.   In other words,
the fovea is not a mathematical point; and, consequently, fixation
of the eye is itself not a perfectly precise and rigid affair.   Within
this area there is a constant slow (exploring?) movement of the eye;
and if the eye is momentarily turned away from any point in the
area, on bringing it back to examine the same point its new position is not usually the same as the old.[1]

§ 35.   In regard to speed, the movements of the eye fall into two
main classes.[2]   Of the first type are the movements by which an
object, first seen in indirect vision, is brought to the centre of clear
vision.   This is the simple reactive movement of the eye to peripheral stimulation, with its psychological accompaniment of a transference of attention.   Its speed depends upon the extent of the movement, being more rapid for longer than for shorter movements; it
varies from .029 seconds for movements of 5 degrees to .100 for
movements of 40 degrees.[3]   In reading, however, the extent of this
movement is often less than 5 degrees, and, in time, not more than
one-fiftieth of a second.   The speed is not readily, or at all, subjected to voluntary control.   The function of this first type of eye
movement is simply that of carrying the eye from one point of
fixation to another, with the least possible loss of time.   No clear
vision results from the stimulation of the retina during these jumps
of the eye—nothing, in ordinary circumstances, but a brief and
featureless blur, which has no value for purposes of visual perception, and which is usually unobserved.[4]

The second main type of movement is the "pursuit" movement,
which occurs when a moving object is followed by the eye.   This
is determined by the speed of the object, but neither very swiftly,
nor very slowly, can moving objects be followed by the eye.   This

---

[1] McAllister, *Psycholog. Rev.*, Monograph Supplement XXIX (1905), p. 17.
The reader can readily satisfy himself of the truth of these statements by what is
called the "after-image method" of studying eye movements—a method long
in use, and in many respects valuable.   An after-image resulting from fixation
of a bright object moves with the eye and represents a fixed point of reference
in the retina.   If a sharp after-image is first secured, and then the attempt is
made to look steadily at a point on the wall, the after-image will seem to move
about over the wall, indicating the unsteadiness of fixation (see Dodge, *Psychol.
Rev.*, Monograph Supplement 35, 1907).   A variation of this experiment shows
that in repeatedly looking at the same object, there is a certain latitude in the
fixations of the eye.   If a bright light, such as the rising or setting sun, is looked
at repeatedly for a second or two, the eye being turned to some other object between the fixations, quite a group of after-images of the sun will accumulate;
and the extent of the group will show the variability of repeated fixations.

[2] Dodge, *Amer. Journ. of Physiol.*, VIII, 301.

[3] See the table given by Dodge and Cline, op. cit., 145.

[4] Dodge, *Psychol. Rev.*, 1900, VII, 454.

second type of movements of the eye differs from the first type, not only in speed, but also in function. Pursuit movements cannot be executed at will; they occur only in the presence of a moving object. Without them, however, clear vision of moving objects is impossible; as can easily be shown by casting a shadow on a page of print, steadily fixating the shadow, and then either moving the page from side to side before the fixed eye, or causing the shadow to move back and forth over the page and allowing the eye to follow it. In either case, the print becomes unreadable through blur-ring. The same effect is produced when the eye passes rapidly from one to another of a few bright spots standing out against a dark background. From these and similar expe-riences, we reach the conclusion that, in read-ing, we obtain fairly clear retinal impressions only during the fixation pauses of the eye, and that the practical valuelessness of the periods of blurring leads to the neglect of them. The same kind of jerky movement

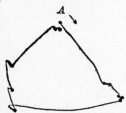

Fig. 145. — Photographic Record of the Eye's Movement in Tracing the Outline of a Circle. (Stratton.)

of the eyes, with periods of fixation between periods of blurring, occurs when we seem to ourselves to be sweeping our eyes slowly over any geometrical figure, or over any scene. This process has been carefully worked out in the case of one reading a printed page.[1] The eye moves across the line of a newspaper with a series of jumps, fixating from 3 to 8 points in a line, and with a speed de-pending on the mentality of the reader.[2] The accompanying fig-ure (No. 145), taken from Stratton,[3] shows how the eye "moves around" a circle which has been placed before it.

§ 36. In general, it must be noted that the power of making spatial distinctions greatly exceeds the accuracy with which dis-tances can be measured by the moving eye. A circle of an inch in diameter, placed five feet from the eye, is practically a unit to fixa-tion, although it contains a multitude of distinguishable points, and a variety of perceptible lines, angles, and figures. Spatial dis-tinctions in indirect vision are finer than the adjustment of eye move-ments to points in indirect vision. The eye can measure the dis-tance between two points much more exactly than it can jump from one to another.[4] It can distinguish forms much more accurately than it can follow them by its movements.

[1] Compare Huey, *American Jour. of Psychol.* (1900), XIII, 283; and Dearborn, *The Psychology of Reading* (New York, 1906).

[2] Ruediger, *The Field of Clear Vision* (New York, 1907).

[3] *Philos. Studien* (1902), XX, 336, and *Psychol. Rev.* (1906), XIII, 82.

[4] McAllister, op. cit., p. 17; Dearborn, *Psychol. Rev.*, 1904, XI, 297.

These experiments also show that we can no longer appeal, as Helmholtz and Wundt formerly did, to the supposed orderly procession of adjacent points of the field of view through the area of clear vision as the eye is moved. There is no such procession; and nothing objective passes in such review. As a specific instance of the difficulty connected with this same view, let us consider a problem which is fundamental in the perception of two-dimensional space. Such a space is characterized, as Helmholtz pointed out,[1] by the circumstance that, given any two points in it, A and B, it is possible to enclose A by a circle or any other closed line, so that passage from A to B can only occur by crossing the line. Now Helmholtz endeavors to show that experience could teach us this peculiarity of the visual field, since, whenever we turn the eye from A to B, we always observe the fixation point to cross the separating line. As a matter of fact, no such observation could ordinarily be made, for the separating line would simply disappear, in a brief unobservable blur, when the eye jumped from A to B. If the experience taught anything, it would apparently be that movement from A to B did not take the eye across the line encircling A. So elementary a spatial relation as that of a point or line lying *between* two other points could not be observed in the course of eye movements of the common jump type; for the eye would not show us the middle point in the course of its movement between the extremes. The eye might, of course, fixate first one of the outer points, next the middle point, and finally the other extreme; but it might also pass directly from one extreme to the other, and then to the middle. No fixed ordering of the points in the field of view could result from such experiences. To be sure, when objects move about within the field, the eye may follow them, and during such relatively slow movements observe the sequence of stationary objects over which the moving object passes; but the moving object may take any course, and the experience so gained would seem unfitted to give rise to a definite arrangement of points in the visual field, and so to a well-ordered field of space. All such experiences, in conjunction with others of the most varied kind, doubtless contribute to our knowledge of the spatial relations of objects; but the point is that the quasi-mathematical correspondence which Helmholtz conceived to exist between eye movements and visual space breaks down utterly before the fact that the jump of the eye—the only type of eye movement which shows any approach to the mathematical precision required by the theory—is too rapid to admit of perception during its execution, and amounts simply to a sudden shift of clear vision from one object to another.

[1] *Physiolog. Optik*, pp. 533 ff.

§ 37. Once again, then, in estimating the bearing of the recent experiments to determine more exactly the movements of the eyes, upon our theory of sense-perception, is it necessary to return to the original point of view from which all theories must take their start. *Only psychical factors can be built into mental products.* Objective measurements of visual movements are, therefore, of little value for theoretical purposes, except as they give sure indication of the present, or past, value of the quantitative and qualitative changes in the psychical factors that are correlated with these movements. A closer examination of these very experiments shows that, on the whole, they do not destroy, or even greatly depreciate, our estimate of this value. We have seen, for example, that when the eyes seem to us to be at complete rest while regarding attentively the field covered by the area of clear vision, they are really going through a succession of exceedingly minute and slow movements, as though ceaselessly "exploring" this field. Something similar may be brought—at least vaguely—into consciousness, by closing the eyes and watching the behavior of the retinal field as correlated with the changing complex of sensations. Neither the field itself, nor any of the minutest subdivisions of it—try as hard as one will to fixate it rigidly—can be kept from ceaseless motions; and by directing attention to the psychical accompaniments of these motions, they can themselves be regularly *felt*. Still further, the jerky and discontinuous character of the movements of the eyes, with the intervening pauses for momentary fixation, when reading print or surveying a geometrical figure, or a landscape, corresponds precisely with the correlated mental experience. Neither in reading print (nor in hearing speech), nor in looking at any object whatever, do we become consciously aware of more than a percentage of what, objectively considered, passes through the field of vision. Our mental apprehension is as jerky, as imperfect and full of blurred or blind spots, as are the movements of the eyes. As we have just seen, even the area of clearest vision requires to be diligently explored with slowly moving eyes, in order to become the more thoroughly apprehended.

Still further, it needs again to be insisted, that we are examining by relatively simple and coarse methods, the swift and complex processes of nature, where most of what there is to be examined has long ago fallen below the threshold of consciousness, and has become quite impossible to revive in anything approaching its original form. To employ again an illustration already used once before: By aid of delicate tactual and muscular sensations, which he once followed comparatively slowly and on the watch, as it were, to reproduce them, the accomplished violinist has acquired the art of spacing and bowing on the violin. But he cannot recall or describe those sensations; and the very effort to do so in any particular instance would paralyze his art. Neither can the experimenter determine their original quality as local signs, or specific value, by measuring the movements of the fingers and wrist of the left arm, or the sweep and the pressure of the right arm. But let paralysis impair the sensations of the skin and muscles of either of these members, and the art of the violinist instantly disappears. Although, however, the accomplished player can determine almost exactly the number of thousands of vibrations of his string, by moving his finger a minute fraction of an inch, his art is simple and coarse compared with that with which Nature endows the commonest pair of eyes.

§ 38. The nature of the "sense-data" which the mind has at its disposal for constructing its presentations of sense, and the psychophysical laws which are followed in the process of construction, have been explained in such detail that little need be added concerning the *development of visual perception*.[1] Visual space presents itself to us as a coherent complex of sensations of light and color systematically arranged. The arrangement implies certain native activities of the mind in connection with and dependence upon the action of the nervous organism; but it also implies an immense influence from experience. It is extremely difficult, if not wholly impossible, to distinguish with confidence the limits which must be drawn between what is native and what is learned. The seeing of colors is undoubtedly a far more simple and primary act than the seeing of colored objects as situated in relation to each other in objective space. A colored surface, or a system of color-sensations related to each other as side by side in space-form, results in experience from the weaving together of several spatial series of sensations. Such a surface may theoretically be conceived of as presented to the mind through the activity of the nervous elements belonging to the retina of a single motionless eye. The *motifs* or data which the mind would have for constructing such a surface must be found in the series of sensations of light and color as varying in intensity and quality according to the locally distinct nervous elements which are simultaneously excited. The evidence seems, on the whole, favorable to the assumption that some indefinite picture of visual space might be gained wholly through the excitation of a motionless nervous mosaic (like the retina) sensitive to light.

But visual space, as experience makes it known to us, requires

[1] On this subject, compare Ladd, *Psychology, Descriptive and Explanatory*, pp. 321–375; 487–495; and *A Theory of Reality*, chap. IX.

binocular vision with moving eyes. The firm spatial connection of all the parts requires that a system of lines of direction should be fixed, prescribing the objective points at which the sensations produced by exciting together the different pairs of the covering points of the retina must appear in visual space. To establish such spatial connection, both eyes must move in their conjoined action as a single organ of vision. By this action the field of binocular vision is built up in an order of experience which, on the whole, consists in the successive mastery of more and more complex problems. For the process of learning to localize, the one centre—the point of starting and the goal of return—is the area of clearest vision of the retina (the yellow-spot), to which the point of regard in the object corresponds. With the point of regard fixed in the primary position of the eye, the first and most essential means is gained for orientating objects in the field of vision. The meridians, horizontal and vertical, and the locations of different points in the surface of the field of vision thus presented to the mind, afford the comparatively simple problems furnished by the primary position. In this way a central area, determining lines, and finally a continuous surface are fixed, to which may be referred all the directions and locations of the binocular points and lines of regard in the secondary positions of the eye.

In constructing the field of binocular vision with moving eyes, the general principle seems to be observed that *by motion the relative space-values of the retinal elements are not changed; but their absolute values*—that is, the complex which is formed by combining all these muscular and tactual sensations with the local signs of the retina—*are changed in equal sense and measure.* What moving the eyes does for the retinal images, moving the head and body does for the presentations of sense as constructed in binocular vision; it alters the absolute values of the complex of sensation as related to objective space, while keeping the relative values belonging to the different positions of the eyes unchanged.

The visual perception of depth involves a later and more complex training from experience than the perception of two-dimensioned extension. To solve at all adequately the problem of depth, binocular vision with moving eyes, and its resulting combination and separation of the double images of objects, seems necessary. The existence and assistance of those secondary helps, which are so important in perceiving the solidity and distance of objects, imply a further development of experience. In all these advances, however, the course of acquisition is not in separate straight lines that run parallel or converge, as it were. More complex experience, when obtained, modifies what is really more simple and primary.

What we see in monocular vision with an open eye, and even what we see with both eyes closed and motionless, depends upon what we have learned to see with both eyes in varied movement and availing themselves of all possible secondary helps. It also depends upon what we have learned to know of the nature and probable position and shape of manifold objects of which the eye has already attained the mastery. How simple the visual data which the mind may have learned to interpret into terms of complicated visual objects, placed in definite spatial relations, is amply proved by every illustrated lecture, and by the phenomena of visual dreams.[1] Not infrequently—indeed, habitually—what the eyes present in the form of visual images, strictly so called, are the barest schemata of what the mind sees by way of interpreting these images.

§ 39. Finally, brief mention must be made of the connections which are constituted, in the development of our perception of objects as having the qualities and relations of space-form, by the joint action and mutual assistance of eye and hand. With the sense-presentations of one of these senses the images of objects as known by the other become most intimately related. It is a misuse of terms, however, and involves the entire subject in confusion, to speak of this joint product as a "sense-perception." It is rather to be spoken of as a mental image or concept. The visual presentation of an object—as, for example, a ball, a pen, a table—may recall its tactual presentation. We readily interpret one into terms of the other—sight into terms of touch, and touch into terms of sight. But all the perceptions, as such, of spatial properties and relations, whether gained by eye or hand, are kept quite distinct and separable in the mind. No such synthesis takes place between the spatial series of the one sense and the spatial series of the other sense as takes place between the spatial series of the same sense. And all the properties and relations of bodies as known in space-form are given by each of these senses. The view which makes the sense of sight dependent upon the sense of touch and the muscular sense for the construction of its spatial objects is erroneous. While feeling the pen, we can image how it would look; when seeing it, how it would feel. We can image how much exertion would be required to reach a mountain which appears to the eye so far away, or how a mountain would look at a distance of so many miles as measured by the exertion required to walk there. But the true presentations of the visual objects and tactual objects do not mix in one combined *perception*. They unite only in one image or idea of the object.

---

[1] On the latter subject compare Ladd, *Mind*, New Series, I, p. 299.

§ 40. Interesting experiments have been conducted to determine the *degree of accuracy* with which perceptions of distance by sight can be translated, as it were, into terms of the tactual and muscular sense. Some of these experiments show the amount of harmony which can be obtained between optical localizing and localizing with the finger. Helmholtz[1] made use of a vertical thread which he tried to locate, as seen in monocular vision, by hitting it with a pencil's point; Donders,[2] of a very small induction-spark, which was to be touched with the index-finger. The result of 50 experiments, made for distances along the same line of regard varying between 60 and 610 mm., when only the spark itself was seen in perfectly dark surroundings, showed that the distance was over-estimated 34 times, under-estimated 12, estimated right 4 times. The greatest errors were +35 and —34 mm.; the mean error 10.6 mm. When the surroundings were visible and the electrodes seen with open eyes, the eyes then closed, and the finger reached to the estimated distance, the greatest errors were +30 and —12 mm., and the mean variable error 9.8 mm., for distances from 80 to 630 mm. The exact localizing of the point of regard in terms of touch is more difficult the farther the object is removed and the less assistance is had from secondary helps. Localizing in the same way when the object lies out of the line of regard is still more inaccurate. In 29 experiments, where the spark to be localized was flashed at a distance of 210–600 mm. to one side of this line, the greatest errors were +120 and —68 mm., with a mean error of about 34 mm.

The problem of comparing the judgments of linear extension made by the eye, the hand, and the arm, and of determining their relative accuracy, has more recently been examined, experimentally, at considerable length by Jastrow.[3] His method was to present a definite length, varying from 5 mm. to 120 mm., to the retina, the skin (by application of a pair of points, or by motion of a single point), to the forefinger and thumb (by being held between the two), or to the arm when in free movement and guiding a pencil to express its estimate. The subject of experiment was required to get a clear perception of the given distance by one of these organs (called, in such case, the "receiving sense"), and then either simultaneously or successively express this perception through the same or some other one of these organs (the "expressing sense"). In this manner it was discovered that, if the eye is both receiving

[1] *Physiolog. Optik*, p. 650.

[2] *Archiv f. Ophthalmologie*, XVII, ii, p. 55.

[3] Article on "The Perception of Space by Disparate Senses," in *Mind*, October, 1886, pp. 539–554.

and expressing sense, small lengths will be under-estimated and large lengths exaggerated, the point where no error is made being at about 38 mm.; whereas, if the hand is both receiving and expressing, small lengths will be exaggerated and large lengths under-estimated, the "indifference-point" being at about 50 mm.; but the arm exaggerates all lengths within the limits of the experiments. When, however, the eye expresses and the other organs receive the impression, all lengths are greatly under-estimated; but if the hand is the expressing sense, all lengths are greatly exaggerated. The arm as expressing sense exaggerates all lengths received by the eye, and under-estimates all received by the hand.

The relative accuracy of the three senses, whether receiving or expressing, or both, stands in the order of eye, hand, arm—the hand being only slightly better than the arm. The degree of confidence felt in the estimate made is naturally greatest where the accuracy is greatest. Inasmuch as "the expressing sense gives the characteristic properties to the curve of error,"[1] the question arises whether all the phenomena cannot be accounted for by a special application of the law of habit in connection with the normal action of the sensory apparatus. Each sense, when expressing the estimate, tends to approximate it in size toward those dimensions which it is most accustomed to judge accurately.

All the foregoing results show plainly that the interpretation of visual distance in terms of the tactual and muscular sense is a matter of complex experience, and is not usually more than very imperfectly attained. It bears little comparison with the nicety of the spatial perceptions belonging to each one of the two senses concerned when interpreting its own specific data in corresponding terms, as it were.

§ 41. In closing this subject, the one psychological truth of pre-eminent value which has been most obviously demonstrated should be stated again. *Perception is the result of an extremely complex activity of the psychical subject, Mind; it involves the synthesis of a number of sense-data according to laws that are not deducible from the nature of the external objects, or of the physiological action of the end-organs and central organs of sense.* An analysis of these data themselves is not sufficient to explain perception. The descriptions of Physiological Psychology can do no more than enumerate these data, show their dependence on external stimuli, and the value which they have as *motifs* for the perceiving subject; and then understand the laws of this synthesis as the permanent modes of the behavior of the psychical subject. The object of sense-perception, the presentation of sense, is not an *extra*-mental

[1] Ibid., p. 549.

entity made up outside of the mind and borne into or impressed upon it through the avenues of sense.   It is a mental construction. The field of vision is a subjective affair, and so is the field of touch. The same psychical subject which reacts upon the stimulation of the nervous organs of sense in the form of sensations, by its activity in synthesizing these sensations, constructs the objects of sense. The fundamental fact is the presence and activity of the subject, known as *Mind*.

CHAPTER VI

TIME–RELATIONS OF MENTAL PHENOMENA

§ 1. So-called "presentations of sense" appear in consciousness, not only as having spatial qualities and relations, but also as occurring either simultaneously or successively as respects Time-form. The clearest experience of the manner in which our sensations are located in this framework of time, as it were, is gained by attention to the successive tones of a melody, or to the rhythm of visual or muscular impressions which accompanies a regularly recurrent motion of some member of the body. What is true of the presentations of sense is also true of all mental phenomena, such as the reproduced images of sense, the pure creations of fancy, and the thoughts. All these have that form of occurrence and relation which we call "Time."

Physiological Psychology, however, can no more give an ultimate explanation of this *time-form* which belongs to all mental phenomena than of the space-form which objects of sense acquire as the result of a mental synthesis. Experimental science cannot explain "time." Nothing is accomplished toward comprehending the origin of the mental representation of time by indicating the speed, number, and order of the various series of conscious experiences. Successive presentations of sense or successive ideas do not of themselves constitute a mental presentation or idea of succession. The idea that a follows or precedes b is not the idea of a nor the idea of b; neither is it the idea of $a + b$ or of $a - b$. Experimental science can explain the *order* of succession; but in doing this it implies the *idea* of succession, and this idea is not itself a succession, or an order of succession, or a compound of successive ideas.[1]

Many thousands of experiments have been made (since the work of Donders in 1868), with the use of the most complicated and delicate machinery, in order to fix the amount of time required for the various processes, both nervous and mental, which are the conditions of our conscious life. These experiments have succeeded in bringing many interesting facts to light. But the laws thus established beyond all reasonable question are remarkably few; more-

[1] Compare Volkmann von Volkmar, *Lehrb. d. Psychologie* (3d ed.), II, pp. 11 f.

over, they are nearly all merely restatements in more definite form of already familiar generalizations. That a kind of sluggishness or inertia, which the stimulus must overcome, belongs to all the senses and that they often continue to act, when once roused, after the exciting cause is withdrawn; that different sensations following each other too quickly tend to confuse or destroy each other; that no one can see or think more than about so rapidly, but that this rate varies with different individuals and with the same individual at different times; that it takes more time to perceive or think where the objects are complex, and are either too small or too large or too closely alike; that it takes time to will or choose, less time to act when we know what to expect, and more time to move, in response to a particular sensation, some part of the body which we are not accustomed to connect with that sensation; that practice increases the speed of our mental and bodily action, and that fatigue and certain drugs diminish it—all these statements were matters of common observation long before experimental psychology began its use of scientific methods.

§ 2. It is not necessary to describe the construction of the machines[1] which have been used in experimenting upon the time-relations of mental phenomena, or the methods of using them employed and commended by different observers. The general problem is in all cases essentially the same—namely, to produce certain definite impressions upon the organs of sense, to secure a definite result in the form of motion of some part of the body as a sign that the impressions have been received (and, perhaps, interpreted and mentally combined), and to measure with extreme accuracy the interval between peripheral stimulation and resulting motion.

The electrical current is ordinarily used to mark both the instant when the external sense-stimulus acts on the organ and that when the resulting motion occurs. The stimulus may consist in the flash or crackle of an electric spark, the appearance of one or more colors or figures, or letters or words, the sounding of a bell or a falling ball, etc.; the motion may be with the finger pressing a key, or the foot or hand closing or breaking a circuit, or the vocal organs calling into a tube, etc. The one difficult matter which marks the success or the comparative failure of any series of observations is the arrangement of the experiments and their tabulated results so as to analyze the different elements of the complex process involved. Such experiments need to be repeated many times upon the same individual, so as to eliminate the vari-

[1] For an excellent account of these machines, see Titchener, *Experimental Psychology, Quantitative* (1905), chap. III; and for the nervous mechanisms involved, nearly every chapter of part I of this book may be consulted anew.

able factors of bodily condition, attention or distraction of mind, practice, etc.; they need also to be repeated with many individuals, so as to calculate accurately the so-called personal equation.

§ 3. The interval between the instant when the external stimulus begins to act upon the end-organ of sense and the resulting movement of some member of the body has been called "physiological time" by Hirsch and others, and "reaction-time" by Exner. The latter term is preferable. "Reflex time" is a similar conception; but this term refers to the time of organized reflexes, whereas reaction-time refers to reactions which are not instinctively connected with the stimuli used. The reflex time varies greatly, as has already been stated (p. 167), in different reflexes; in some it is shorter than the quickest reaction-time, but in others not.

Reaction-time is "simple" when all the elements which tend to complicate the processes involved in the reaction, and so to lengthen the time required by it, have been as far as possible eliminated. Reaction obtained in response to a single sensation of known quality, the instant of whose appearance is expected, by executing a single natural and easy motion, best fulfils the conditions of simplicity. It is therefore requisite, for all experiments of this sort, that the average *simple reaction-time* of each individual experimented upon shall be determined; and also the effect of practice, exhaustion, and other influences upon this interval. But even the simplest reaction-time is, of course, a very complex affair.

Donders[1] distinguished no less than twelve different processes as entering into "physiological time" (or simple reaction-time)— and this without interpolating any purely psychical elements, as occupying separate periods, into the entire interval. The analysis of Exner[2] is more pertinent to our purpose. Exner finds seven elements in all reaction-time: (1) An action of the stimulus on the end-organ of sense preparatory to excitation of the sensory nerve; (2) centripetal conduction in this nerve; (3) centripetal conduction in the spinal cord or lower parts of the brain; (4) transformation of the sensory into the motor impulse; (5) centrifugal conduction of the impulse in the spinal cord; (6) centrifugal conduction in the motor nerve; (7) setting-free of the muscular movement. Of these seven factors, however, the fourth is most interesting to psychology. It may properly be called "psycho-physical" as distinguished from more purely physiological time. The other six elements (with the exception of the first, on account of difficulties inherent in the experiments) have been determined with some degree of definiteness. It is, then, *theoretically* possible to ascertain

[1] *Archiv f. Anat., Physiol.*, etc., 1868, p. 664.
[2] See Hermann's *Handb. d. Physiol.*, II, ii, p. 271.

the amount of these six and subtract them from the entire reaction-time; the remainder would be the interval occupied by the central cerebral processes (that is, by No. 4). Thus Exner assumed 62 metres per second as the probable rate of conduction[1] in both sensory and motor nerves; and in the spinal cord, 8 for the sensory and 11–12 for the motor process. In this way he calculated that about 0.0828 sec. is the "reduced reaction-time," or interval occupied within the cerebral centres in transforming the sensory into motor impulses—in the special case of reaction from hand to hand, where the whole reaction-time is 0.1337 sec. The uncertainties of all such calculation, however, occasion the demand for other methods of determining the strictly "psycho-physical" portion of reaction-time.

§ 4. As bearing on the foregoing problem of analysis, it must be remembered that any psycho-physical theory of the time relations of mental phenomena requires that account be taken of the *inertia* of the nervous system. As composed of moving molecules, it necessarily requires *some* time to be started by the action of a given stimulus, then reach its maximum of activity in a particular direction, then subside into a negative condition with respect to this direction (called "Anklingen" and "Abklingen" of the nervous excitement, by the German investigators). This statement follows as a necessary assumption from the physical nature of the nerve-fibres and nerve-cells, since inertia is a property of every material mechanism. It is difficult, however, to justify the assumption experimentally, or to fix the exact amount of time consumed by the inertia of different parts of the nervous system. Experiment demonstrates no stadium of latent excitation for the motor nerve, such as is about $\frac{1}{100}$ sec. for the muscle when electricity is used. The case is different, however, with the end-organs of sense. They do exhibit a certain sluggishness, and this is one reason why only so many sensations in a given unit of time can be produced by their successive irritation.

The result of the inertia of the end-organs, as determining the number of separate excitations of which they are capable in a second, varies for the different senses. The nerve-endings of touch probably exceed all others in the promptness with which they respond to stimulus and then return to a relative equilibrium. But the number of separate sensations of this sense which can be produced during a given interval depends in a remarkable way upon the quality and intensity of the stimulus, the place where it is applied, etc. The results of different experimenters therefore differ

---

[1] Compare p. 132. Recently, by improved methods, Piper (Pflüger's *Archiv*, 1908, CXXIV, 591) has obtained 120 metres per second in human nerves.

widely.   Preyer thought that 27.6–36.8 stimulations (per second) of the skin fused into one continuous sensation; but Valentin put the limit at 480–640, and von Wittich[1] succeeded in observing a vibrating or discontinuous sensation corresponding to about 1,000 separate excitations in this unit of time.   Hearing can receive nearly as many separate sensations in a second as can touch. The noise of the electric spark has been heard with one ear only, as separate sensations, at intervals of 0.00205 sec.; but hardly or not at all at intervals of 0.00198 sec.   The number of possible sensations of sound may then be placed at about 500 per second.   E. H. Weber noticed that we can tell whether two watches are ticking exactly together much better when both are held near the same ear than when one is held at each ear.

The smallest interval for sensations of sight, when the two stimuli act on the same place of the retina, is still greater.   In ordinary daylight, rotating disks whose surface is part white and part black become gray (that is, the sensations fuse) when they attain a motion of about 24 per second.   It can be told which of two images of electric sparks that are 0.011 mm. apart on the retina occurs first, if the difference in the time of their occurrence is 0.044 sec.   If the two sparks are seen as one with an apparent motion, its direction can be distinguished when the two ends of the line of motion are only 0.014–0.015 sec. apart.   But if one stimulus strikes the *fovea centralis* and the other a point of the retina 6 mm. off, the smallest interval for distinct perception is increased to 0.076 sec.[2]   Within certain limits these intervals are independent of the intensity of the light, when it falls on the retina near its centre; but (compare p. 333) the intensity and quality of the sensations are connected with the time during which the stimulus acts.   The law for the "time-course" of such retinal excitations has been stated and defended by Fick,[3] as known by the name of "Talbot's principle": If any place of the retina is periodically excited with light of given intensity, for a certain time a, and then left unexcited for a time b, and if the time $a + b$ is less than about 0.04 sec.,[4] then the sensation becomes

continuous, with a strength corresponding to the excitation $\dfrac{a}{a + b}.$

[1] For his remarks on Preyer's experiments, see the article in Pflüger's *Archiv*, II, pp. 329 ff.

[2] Compare Exner, in Hermann's *Handb. d. Physiol.*, II, ii, pp. 256 f.; and *Sitzgsber. d. Wiener Acad.*, LXXII, pp. 156 f.

[3] *Archiv f. Anat., Physiol.*, 1863, pp. 739 f.; and Hermann's *Handb. d. Physiol.*, III, i, pp. 212 f.

[4] This time, called the "action time of light," is the time during which the stimulus must act in order to produce its maximum effect, in point of apparent intensity.   Talbot's principle may be restated by saying that the apparent

The measurement of the smallest interval for sensations of smell and taste cannot be made with satisfactory exactness on account of the nature of the stimuli of these senses. Little is known which goes beyond ordinary experience concerning after-tastes analogous to the after-images of the eye. One experimenter (Bidder) thought that the sensation continued after the tongue had been so carefully dried off that no particles of the tastable substance were left remaining; but of this we can scarcely be sure. It may be that certain substances leave their after-taste because their tastable particles are dissolved later; or because their effect, being weaker, is at first suppressed by particles of stronger quality.[1]

§ 5. When the successive sensations are of different senses, the "smallest interval" between them, and so the number possible in a second, varies still more. The following table[2] exhibits the results obtained by several different observers:

Sec.

Between two sensations of sound (electrical sparks)	0.002
Between two sensations of light (direct electrical excitation of same retinal spot)	0.017
Between two sensations of touch (impact on finger—Mach)	0.0277
Between two sensations of light (at *jovea centralis*, by optical images) .	0.044
Between two sensations of light (at periphery of retina, by optical images)	0.049
Between sensation of sight and sensation of touch (sight following) . .	0.05
Between sensation of sight and sensation of hearing (sight following) .	0.06
Between two sensations of noises (each heard by one ear)	0.064
Between sensation of sight and sensation of touch (sight preceding) .	0.071
Between two sensations of light, one at the periphery and the other at the centre of retina	0.076
Between sensation of sight and sensation of hearing (sight preceding) .	0.16

§ 6. The point of starting for determining experimentally all the problems which concern the durations and relations in time of

intensity of a light which acts on the retina for less than its action time, is directly proportional to the time during which it acts. The action time varies, however, with the intensity of the stimulus, being, according to McDougall (*British Journal of Psychology*, 1904, I, 151), as long as one-fifth of a second when the stimulus is so weak as to be barely perceptible, and decreasing to 0.03 sec. when the intensity of the stimulus is sufficiently increased. According to Kunkel (Pflüger's *Archiv*, IX, 206), the action time varies for light of different colors. The action time for sound varies with the intensity, and apparently also with the pitch. With intense stimuli, the maximum subjective intensity was reached, in Sander's work (*Psycholog. Studien*, 1910, VI, 34), between 0.6 and 1.0 sec.; with weak stimuli, Kafka (ibid., 1906, II, 292) found that the maximum effect might not be reached under 1.5 sec. The subjective intensity rises at first rapidly, then more slowly, till the maximum is reached. The rise is more rapid for high than for low tones.

[1] Compare von Vintschgau, in Hermann's *Handb. d. Physiol.*, III, ii, p. 221.
[2] By Exner, in Hermann's *Handb. d. Physiol.*, II, ii, p. 262.

mental phenomena is, therefore, gained by fixing the so-called "simple reaction-time." In its very simplest form the question may now be stated as follows: How long an interval will elapse, under the most favorable circumstances, between the instant when some end-organ of sense is stimulated and the instant when motion follows as the result of recognizing the fact, in consciousness, that such stimulation has taken place? As has already been indicated: To shorten the reaction-time as much as possible, the subject must know what place of the sensory organism is to be hit by the stimulus, and about when to expect it; he must also be called upon to react, in one and the same easy and natural way, in all cases, as soon as he knows that he is hit at all.

Under the foregoing conditions the simple reaction-time varies usually within only rather narrow limits. It does vary, however, from one moment to another in the same individual, so that a series of reactions must be taken, and the average and variability computed. It varies also from one individual to another. Besides these variations, the reaction-time shows many interesting differences according to the exact conditions surrounding the experiment; such are the character of the stimulus, the nature of the reacting movement, the "central" or mental conditions, etc.

§ 7. Reaction-time varies, first, with the sense-organ which is stimulated. Some of the determinations of the older observers, which have been, in general, confirmed by later work, are brought together in the following table:[1]

Observer.	Optical stimulus. Sec.	Acoustic stimulus. Sec.	Stimulus of touch. Sec.
Hirsch	0.200	0.149	0.182 (hand).
Hankel	0.225	0.151	0.155
Donders	0.188	0.180	0.154 (neck).
Von Wittich . . .	0.194	0.182	0.130 (forehead).
Wundt	0.175	0.128	0.188
Exner	0.1506	0.1360	0.1276 (hand).
Auerbach	0.191	0.122	0.146
Von Kries	0.193	0.120	0.117

We conclude, then, that under the most favorable circumstances the reaction-time can scarcely be reduced to $\frac{1}{10}$ of a second, while it rarely rises much above $\frac{2}{10}$ of a second. Reaction to sound and to touch differ, on the average, but little, whereas reaction to light is distinctly slower.

[1] Taken from the article of Kries and Auerbach, *Archiv f. Anat. u. Physiol.*, Physiol. Abth. (1877), pp. 359 f.

Stimuli to the other senses have been less employed in reaction-time experiments; and, accordingly, the times are less well established. For warmth and cold, the times are somewhat longer than for touch, and longer for warmth than for cold. An approximate figure for reaction to cold is 0.15 sec. and to warmth 0.18 sec.[1] It should be noted that temperature stimuli cannot be so directly applied to the end-organs as can light, sound, and pressure on the skin; the temperature of the skin must first be changed. Hence the reaction-time to warmth and cold varies widely according to the mode of application of the stimulus. The times given above were obtained by bringing a warm or cold piece of metal in contact with the skin. If radiant heat is applied by bringing a candle close to the skin, then, though the final impression may be almost painful, its development is so slow that the reaction-time rises to half a second.[2] The fact that reaction to warmth is slower than to cold is believed to indicate that the warmth-receptors lie deeper in the skin than the cold-receptors (see p. 181).

Reaction to painful stimuli is especially slow. The fact that the sensation of cutaneous pain is slow in developing can be readily observed introspectively; a painful stimulus, if not applied precisely to a pain spot, is apt to evoke first a sensation of touch, and then, after an appreciable interval, a sensation of pain. If a pain spot is directly excited, by a strong stimulus, two sensations of pain are felt, though at an appreciable interval. The reason for this probably is that the strong stimulus excites the nerve-fibres directly, as well as the slow-acting end-organs of pain. A weak stimulus apparently excites only the end-organs; accordingly Thunberg finds[3] that pain-reaction requires over a second when the stimulus is weak, but drops abruptly, at a certain strength of stimulus, to 0.40 sec.

The reaction to taste is slow, and varies with the part of the tongue to which the stimulus is applied, and with the particular taste aroused. The following figures are given by Kiesow,[4] the stimuli being applied to the tip of the tongue:

To salt . . . . 0.307 sec.
To sweet . . . . 0.446 sec.
To acid . . . . 0.536 sec.
To bitter . . . . 1.082 sec.

[1] Goldscheider, *Archiv f. (Anat. u.) Physiol.* (1887), p. 469; Von Vintschgau and Steinach, Pflüger's *Archiv* (1888), XLIII, 152.

[2] Tanzi, cited from Sherrington in Schäfer's *Textbook of Physiology*, 1900, II, 963.

[3] Nagel's *Handbuch der Physiologie*, 1905, III, 710.

[4] *Zeitschrift f. Psychol.*, 1903, XXXIII, 453.

The reaction to bitter is prompter when the back of the tongue is stimulated. The slowness of reaction to taste may probably be due, in part, to the impossibility of applying the stimulus directly upon the taste-buds. Sensations of taste, as Kiesow notes, are slow and gradual in their development, and the reaction to the first appearance of the specific sensation is a reaction to very faint stimuli, and "sensorial" (see p. 485) in character, and therefore slow.

The reaction to smell is still slower, though how far this is due to the relative inaccessibility of the end-organs is uncertain. Times of 0.2 to 0.8 sec. have been obtained.[1]

The reaction-time to cutaneous stimuli varies with the part of the skin excited. This would be expected, on account of the unequal distances of different parts from the brain, and the consequent unequal times which must be consumed in transmission by the nerve.[2] However, the observed differences are not all accounted for by this difference in distance. Reaction to a stimulus applied to the forehead is more delayed than to a stimulus applied to the hand (Exner). Dolley and Cattell[3] measured the time of reaction to stimuli applied to various parts of the skin, and found many differences which could not be accounted for by the lengths of nerve traversed, but only by differences in the closeness of cerebral connection between sensory and motor nerves. Thus, the reaction of the right hand to a stimulus applied to that hand is quicker than to a stimulus applied to the left hand; and the foot, though it always gives slower reactions than the hand, is relatively quick when the stimulus is applied to the foot or leg. In general, it appears that the cerebral path from the skin of a given member to the muscles of that same member is either especially short, or especially open.

§ 8. It has been argued that the apparent difference in the reaction-times of different senses is due to difference in the intensity of the stimuli applied. Increasing the strength of the stimulus decreases the reaction-time in all the senses; but we have no very good means of measuring stimuli of one sense in terms of another sense. It has been proposed (by Wundt) to reduce them to a common standard by referring the sensations to the point where they barely reach the "threshold of excitation" (*Reizschwelle*); that is, where they are just perceptible in consciousness. In this way the mean result for sound (0.337), light (0.331), and touch (0.327) are found to be almost exactly the same. It has further been argued

---

[1] Moldenhauer, Wundt's *Philosoph. Studien* (1883), I, 606; Buccola, *Arch. ital. de Biologie*, 1884, V, 279; Beaunis, *Compt. rend. Acad. de Sciences* (Paris, 1883), XCVI, 387.

[2] See Kiesow, *Zeitschr. f. Psychol.* (1903), XXXIII, 444.

[3] *National Academy of Sciences*, 1893, VII, 393; *Psychol. Rev.*, 1894, I, 159.

that the speed of perception and the duration of psycho-physical time are the same for all the senses. On the contrary, there seems good reason to suppose that the reaction-time of sight is necessarily longer than that of hearing or touch, on account of the photo-chemical nature of its more immediate stimulus. One observer (von Wittich) has even gone so far as to conjecture that the speed of conduction in the optic nerve is less than that of the other nerves of sense; it is rather to be concluded, however, that the latent time of the sensory end-apparatus, and of the cerebral processes by which sensory impulses pass over into motor impulses, is different. But if equality of reaction-times in the different senses is to be taken as indicating equally intense stimuli, then a decidedly bright light must be regarded as having no more intensity than a very moderate noise or pressure.

Another suggestion[1] is that the reaction time is very largely consumed in the passage of the nerve-impulse across synapses (see p. 110); and that the path from the rods and cones to the brain has more synapses than the path from the organ of Corti. On the whole, the suggestion which probably is most generally entertained, and which seems certainly applicable to many of the differences above noted, is that already adopted by us—namely, that the inertia or latent time of different sense-organs differs.

§ 9. The fact that *increasing the intensity* of the stimulus diminishes the reaction-time has been incidentally mentioned above, in the cases of pain and temperature. The subject has been quantitatively examined by several authors; as by Exner in the case of light, by Wundt in the case of sound, by Berger and Cattell in light, sound, and touch, and by a few others. There is nearly universal agreement that the reaction becomes quicker as the intensity of the stimulus increases, though the change is not great, when once the range of very feeble intensities is passed. The most exact determinations on this point are those of Froeberg.[2] The stimulus used by this experimenter was light reflected from white, gray, and "black" paper; its relative intensity is stated in the upper line of the following table, the lower line showing the reaction-time of one individual in seconds:

100	56	25	16	10	7	3	2	0.7
.191	.194	.197	.202	.208	.210	.215	.220	.226

A second individual gave shorter times, but the changes in intensity varied to about the same extent. The result is summarized ap-

[1] Schäfer, *Textbook of Physiology*, 1900, II, 611.
[2] *The Relation between the Magnitude of Stimulus and the Time of Reaction* (New York, 1907).

proximately by saying that doubling the intensity of the stimulus decreases the reaction-time by 0.003–0.004 sec.; or, in other words, that the reaction-time decreases in arithmetical progression as the stimulus increases in geometrical progression. The analogy of this result to Fechner's law will at once be noticed. Froeberg obtained a similar result for varying intensities of an acoustic stimulus; and for variations in the area and (within the limits of the "action-time") duration of a photic stimulus.

§ 10. The character of the *reacting movement* influences the time of reaction. Reactions by the hand or a finger are usually quicker than those of any other member. A member unpracticed in quick reactions gives slower responses in these experiments than a member which is much used in similar performances; this difference decreases with practice in the unfamiliar movement.[1] When the reaction consists in pressing down a telegraph key, against the force of a spring, the time of reaction increases with the force of the spring.[2] This effect is probably purely muscular, as more time is required by the muscles to attain a strong than a weak contraction. The movement more customary in reaction-time experiments, a movement in which the key is kept closed by the finger till the stimulus is received, and then released, does not show a similar effect from the force of the spring; and hence is a better device for general use in these experiments.

The movement executed by the finger in such reactions has been subjected to analysis by several authors[3] and found to be by no means simple in all individuals. In the preliminary period of expectancy, an oscillation between greater and less tension in the finger has been observed in a considerable minority of the individuals tested. At the moment when the stimulus is received, there is in some persons a preliminary increase of the downward pressure on the key, antagonistic to the release movement which then follows immediately; but the downward movement consumes time and slows the reaction. When the required movement is itself a downward pressure on the key, the force exerted is, in unpracticed subjects, quite in excess of the amount needed to close the key; but with practice, this excess diminishes, and is accompanied by improvement in the speed of reaction.[4] In general, unpracticed subjects are apt, in these re-

---

[1] See the summary of these and many other results by Jastrow, in his *Time-Relations of Mental Phenomena* (New York, 1890).

[2] Breitwieser, *Psychol. Rev.*, 1909, XVI, 352.

[3] W. G. Smith, *Mind*, 1903, N. S., XII, 47; Judd, McAllister and Steele, *Psychol. Rev.*, Monograph Supplement XXIX (1905), p. 141; Titchener, *Exper. Psychol., Quantitative*, part II (1905), p. 351.

[4] Breitwieser, op. cit.

actions as in many other performances (compare p. 549), to make larger and more forceful movements than are required, and improvement in speed of reaction is attended by a more precise limitation of the movement. The speed of the reacting movement is, in practiced subjects, nearly uniform and does not follow the variations of the reaction-time; conditions which affect the speed of the reaction do not necessarily affect the speed of the reacting movement.[1]

§ 11. The "central" or mental conditions which influence the reaction-time are naturally of special interest to the student of psychology; but they are also specially intricate and difficult of exact determination. No doubt central factors are interwoven with all the sensory and motor influences which have already been mentioned. That changes in the general condition of the brain, dependent on disease, fatigue, the action of drugs, etc., influence the time employed by all our bodily movements need scarcely be mentioned. Less obvious are influences dependent on the particular manner in which the experiment is arranged.

In the usual method of conducting an experiment in reaction-times, the "subject," or reagent, is first made acquainted with a certain stimulus to which he is to react by a prescribed movement (usually a movement of the forefinger). There is no ready-formed connection—instinctive or habitual—between this particular stimulus and this particular movement; and the movement would not, in general, be made in response to the stimulus except for the instructions of the experimenter. The subject assumes a position of readiness—placing his finger on a key by means of which his reaction is to be recorded, and perhaps also directing his eyes toward the place where the stimulus (if visual) is to appear. He is usually warned a few seconds in advance to be "ready" for the stimulus. This preliminary signal is an important part of the procedure. If it is omitted, the time of reaction is increased. Wundt[2] found an increase from 0.076 sec. to 0.253 sec. in reacting to a loud noise (a ball falling 25 cm.); and an increase from 0.175 to 0.266 in reacting to a weak sound (a ball falling 5 cm.);—these increases being the result of omitting the "Ready!" signal. If the stimulus follows the signal at an irregular interval, the reaction-time is not so short as when the procedure is regular. If, indeed, the procedure is so regular that the moment of the stimulus can be exactly anticipated, the movement may be made to coincide in time with the stimulus, and the whole character of the experiment be thus changed. This

---

[1] T. V. Moore, *Psychol. Rev.*, Monograph Supplement, No. XXIV (1904).

[2] *Physiol. Psychologie*, 3d edition, 1887, II, 287. The increase is not always so great; see Wundt's 5th edition, 1903, III, 434.

result is avoided by varying the preliminary interval within narrow limits. The most favorable interval between the ready signal and the stimulus is one or two seconds; a shorter time does not allow the subject to prepare himself fully for the stimulus, while a longer period than two seconds allows more time than is needed and so affords a chance for wandering of the attention.

The preparation for reaction is clearly an essential part of the process; without some degree of preparation the reaction would not occur at all, and the more perfect the preparation, the more prompt the reaction. The preparation may be said to include an adjustment to the stimulus, and an adjustment for the movement to be made —the total adjustment including and connecting these two. The more precisely the character of the stimulus is foreknown, the more complete is the adjustment to it, and the more rapid the reaction. Thus, if the intensity of the stimulus varies so that it cannot be exactly anticipated, the reaction-time is increased. The increase is the greater if the alternation of intensities is very irregular. This fact is exhibited in the following table:[1]

I. Uniform change of intensity		II. Irregular change of intensity	
	Sec.		Sec.
Loud sound	0.116	Loud sound	0.189
Feeble sound	0.127	Feeble sound	0.298

By suddenly intercalating a feeble sound in a series of loud noises the reaction-time may be prolonged to 0.4 or 0.5 sec. Accordingly, the speed of reaction affords a measure of the precision of the preliminary adjustment.

§ 12. In attempting a psychological analysis of the nervous and psychical factors involved in such reaction-time experiments, it is important, then, to recognize that the whole process begins with the warning signal (if not, indeed, still earlier), and that it can properly be divided into three periods[2]: (1) the period of preparation; (2) the period of reaction; and (3) the period immediately following the reaction. These are sometimes named, respectively, the fore-period, the main-period, and the after-period.

The preparatory period is reckoned as beginning with the "Ready" signal; the reaction period with the stimulus; and the after-period with the reacting movement. These three correspond, in a way, to the cocking of a gun, the discharge, and the smoke.

---

[1] Wundt, *Physiol. Psychologie*, 5th edition, 1903, III, 440.
[2] See Ach, *Über die Willenstätigkeit und das Denken* (Göttingen, 1905).

During the preparatory period the reacting mechanism is adjusted or set for a certain form of action; then the stimulus comes and causes the predetermined action to take place; and then after-effects, such as feelings of satisfaction or of relief, may occur. When the adjustment is complex, and more than one response has to be made to the stimulus, some parts of the response may occur in the after-period, and are therefore not to be included in the time which is measured, for only those events which occur in the main or reaction period are timed by the experiment.

The importance of the above division into three periods is made clear by comparing it with the most famous of attempts to analyze the mental or central process entering into a reaction. The analysis of Wundt[1] divided the central or psycho-physical part of the reaction (No. 4 of Exner's seven processes, p. 472) into three psycho-physical processes: (1) entrance into the field of consciousness, or simple perception; (2) entrance into the point of clear consciousness, or apperception (attentive or discerning perception); (3) the excitation of the will, which sets free in the central organ the motor impulse to the reacting muscles. Obviously, the mental processes are here all conceived of after the analogy of sight. Consciousness is regarded as a field of vision; objects enter it and are at first only obscurely and indefinitely perceived, as are those visual objects whose images enter the field of the eye at the sides of the retina. Time is required for the objects to arrive at the spot of clear vision—the *fovea centralis* of consciousness (*Blickpunkt*)—where discerning attention is bestowed upon them and they are *apperceived*. When they are apperceived, further time is required to get up the corresponding molecular motion in the motor areas of the brain. All three foregoing processes are psycho-physical—that is, they comprise physiological processes in the central organs and simultaneous corresponding changes of consciousness occurring in time-form. There is no good reason to suppose that the mind occupies time for its own processes which is separate from and—as it were—thrown in between the physiological processes. Indeed, all the evidence is contrary to such an hypothesis.

Wundt has made an elaborate defence of his positions with regard to the nature of psycho-physical time. He and his pupils have attempted more definitely to characterize the cerebral changes which correspond to each of the mental elements of (1) perception, (2) apperception, and (3) will; and to determine what part of the total reaction-time must be assigned to each. His figure of speech, which likens all changes of conscious states to those produced by moving an image over the retina to the spot of clear vision, may be

[1] *Physiol. Psychologie*, 5th edition, 1903, III, 384.

accepted as helpful to the imagination; it must not be forgotten, however, that it is still a figure of speech. The fact of which it takes account is, that all changes of consciousness require time in order to define themselves with their maximum of clearness and intensity.

§ 13. Let us now suppose that Wundt's analysis be accepted as a true account of the mental process in a voluntary reaction, as distinguished from a reflex or from an habitual and automatic response; and let us also grant that the movement of the forefinger in response to a prearranged stimulus is not a purely reflex or automatic response; the subject's will, indeed, may be strongly excited to react as quickly as possible. Still it does not follow that all of the processes which Wundt recognizes as included in a voluntary reaction occur during the reaction period of the experiment and so enter separately into the time which is measured. Several of the leading students of reaction-times (Exner, Cattell, Lange, Ach, and others) have observed that no detectable act of will intervenes between the stimulus and the reacting movement, at least in most cases. The will may be exerted in the preparatory period, in setting up the adjustment for reaction; but, when once this adjustment is established, the stimulus calls out the response without any further act of will. In such cases, accordingly, "will-time" does not usually enter into the time which is measured. Somewhat the same thing is true regarding perception-time. Since the stimulus is anticipated and adjusted for, it does not need to win its way to the focus of attention, but its way is, as it were, "cleared" before it by the preparatory adjustment. No time is consumed, during the reaction period, in turning the attention upon the stimulus, for the attention is directed toward the stimulus before it arrives.[1]

As to "apperception-time," this is partly covered by the preceding remarks on perception-time; however, the full apperception of a stimulus involves a progressive apprehension of its exact character; it may first be apprehended simply as a change in the situation, and then as a particular color or sound; and so on. The full process of apperception may take considerable time, but it is not ordinarily necessary for this process to be complete before the reactive movement is initiated. Unless the reaction is required to occur only when the stimulus has a particular character which must be recognized before reacting, the movement may occur at any stage in the development of the apperception.[2] Part of the apperceptive process thus occurs in the after-period, and is not included in the measured time.

---

[1] See Ach, op. cit., p. 116.

[2] See Cattell, Wundt's *Philos. Stud.*, 1886, III, 452; and *National Acad. of Sciences*, 1893, VII, 393; Ach, op. cit., p. 117.

How much of apperception occurs within the measured time cannot easily be told; the amount is variable, and introspection can scarcely be trusted to indicate at what stage in a rapidly developing process a motor impulse leaves the brain.

The outcome of this discussion is that Wundt's analysis of a complete reaction cannot be regarded as applying accurately to the process which occurs between the application of the stimulus and the accomplishment of the movement. Experiment does not, therefore, generally afford a measure of the duration (nor the latent period) of the processes of perception, apperception, and will; the amount of conscious process included in the measured time may be very small. What is measured is rather the time needed to set in action a previously prepared adjustment; and the more perfectly the adjustment is prepared, the shorter will be its latent time. If we try to think in neural terms, we shall probably not be far wrong in supposing that the preparatory adjustment consists in some sort of making-ready (perhaps a partial arousal or sub-excitation) of the cortical areas which are to receive the sensory impulse and send out the motor impulse, and of the connections between these two areas; thus the incoming impulse, on reaching the cortex, finds a particular pathway wide open to it, and makes a quick passage to the connected motor nerves. Probably the time consumed in the brain depends partly on the relative directness or circuitousness of the pathway, and partly on the degree to which it is prepared or sub-excited. How much consciousness, therefore, should attend such a nervous impulse in its passage through the brain cannot be judged from the neurological conception. It seems certain, however, that our experiences of apperception and of willing are associated with the activity of longer and more complicated pathways than are traversed by the nerve-impulse in a prepared reaction. When viewed from the more purely psychological point of view, the entire process seems to involve the same substitution of the more speedy automatic elements for the slower but more distinctly conscious operations, with which our theory of the growth of experience by learning makes us abundantly familiar.

§ 14. The speed of any reaction, as can be judged from the preceding considerations, differs according to the particular adjustment which is prepared; that is to say, according to the particular requirements of the experiment. Variations in the reaction-time experiment are suited to discover the different speed with which different adjustments can be set in action. We shall now consider two classes of such variations of the experiment. The first variation falls under the head of the simple reaction-time, and refers to the distinction between "sensorial" and "muscular" (or "sensory" and "motor") reactions; while the second class includes the many varieties of "complex reaction-times."

The distinction of sensory and motor reactions was made by Lange in 1888,[1] and has aroused a great amount of observation and discussion. Lange found that when the subject directed his attention to the expected stimulus, the reaction-time was longer than when he directed it toward the movement which he was about to make. The difference in time between these two modes of reaction was considerable—the sensorial type being about 0.100 sec. slower than the muscular. Thus, Lange's figure for the muscular reaction to sound was 0.123, and for sensorial reaction to the same stimulus, 0.227. Most subsequent observers have obtained results which show a much smaller difference, varying all the way down to zero; and some subjects even give quicker reactions when they attempt to take the sensorial attitude.[2] It seems probable, therefore, that some individuals more readily and naturally adopt the sensorial attitude, and others the muscular attitude; but it is also probable that the instructions are differently understood by different individuals, so that what has passed for the same attitude, by being called by the same name, has in reality varied much in the different cases.

From more recent work[3] it appears that the names "sensorial" and "muscular" are not well fitted to indicate the difference in attitude of different subjects; and also that the object to which the attention is directed is not the determining factor in causing the differences in reaction-time. In the sensorial attitude, the subject prepares, not only to react, but also to observe the stimulus; but in the muscular reaction, he does not prepare to *observe* the movement. Rather, he prepares to *make* the movement, and to make it as promptly as possible on receiving the stimulus. This preparation for a speedy reaction is always more or less involved in reaction-time experiments; but concentrating the expectant attention on the movement seems to emphasize the matter of speed, by excluding every other consideration besides that of barely reacting. Sensations of tension or of tingling are apt to be felt from the muscles in the preparatory period of a muscular reaction; and premature reactions frequently occur, indicating that the "sub-excitation" of the motor apparatus has gone a little too far. In terms of the neurological conception sketched above we may say that the cere-

[1] *Philosoph. Studien*, IV, **479**.

[2] Münsterberg, *Beiträge zur exp. Psychol.*, I, 74; Baldwin, *Psychol. Rev.*, 1895, II, 259; Angell and Moore, *Psychol. Rev*,. 1896, III, 245; Flournoy, *Observations sur quelques types de réaction simple* (Geneva, 1896).

[3] Ach, op. cit.; Breitwieser, *Attention and Movement in Reaction Time* (New York, 1911).

bral pathway, in a muscular reaction, is as short and uncomplicated as possible, and as highly prepared as is possible without actual
movement.   In this way the greater speed of this type of reaction
would be explained.

Moreover, a *"pure* muscular" reaction is an extreme case, the
opposite extreme of which would be an attitude so purely sensorial
—so exclusively directed toward the apprehension of the stimulus
—that the preparation to move would not be completed till the
stimulus had been fully "apperceived."   Such reactions as this
seldom occur under experimental conditions; for the mere holding
of the finger on the key involves some degree of readiness to make
a particular movement.   Reactions which seem, introspectively,
to conform to the above definition of the pure sensorial type occupy a longer time than the usual sensorial reactions (0.3 to 0.8
sec., according to Ach); but also an exceedingly variable time.   The
usual "sensorial" reaction is, therefore, an intermediate type, in
which the adjustment to react is more or less, but not completely,
suppressed by the simultaneous preparation to observe the stimulus.
The reacting movement usually occurs during the process of observation, but not always at the same stage of this process.   According
to this conception, therefore, the longer reaction-time with "sensorial" preparation might be due either to a relatively long central
pathway—a pathway including parts corresponding to factors in
the process of apperception; or it might also be due to a relatively
low degree of sub-excitation of the motor part of the pathway and
of its connections with the sensory part.   Both of these causes
probably operate to produce great variations in the so-called sensorial reaction.

§ 15. "Complex reactions" are those in which several mental
factors intervene between the stimulus and the motor response.
The sensorial type of "simple reaction" belongs here, in all cases
where the reaction is actually held back till a degree of apperception of the stimulus has occurred.   Scarcely different from these are
reactions in which a variety of stimuli are used, but only a single
movement is required—the instructions being to react only when the
stimulus is recognized.   Such instructions uniformly lead to variable reaction-times; because they afford no guarantee against a short-
circuit in the brain, through which the reaction may be a direct response to the mere reception of the stimulus, and the mental process
of recognition occur in the after-period.

A more rigorous procedure requires different movements in response to different stimuli—as, for example, to react with the right
hand to one of two stimuli, and with the left hand to the other; or
to make no movement except in response to a specified one of the

stimuli; or to give a vocal response by naming the stimulus. With
such procedure, the reaction, to be correct, must be held back till
the stimulus is recognized and discriminated from other stimuli.
It was formerly assumed that the discrimination of the stimulus
must be followed by an act of "choice," by which the proper movement is selected; but this natural assumption, like many others
which have been made in regard to the mental process in reactions,
is not borne out by introspection.[1]   Unpracticed subjects, indeed,
in their first few reactions, may think of the movement after recognizing the stimulus, and before executing the movement; but with
a little practice, even this slight trace of choice disappears, and the
movement follows directly on the recognition of the stimulus.   In
other words, each movement becomes so firmly associated with its
appropriate stimulus as to follow it immediately.   It should be
noted that discriminative, or, as Jastrow[2] has called them, "adaptive reactions," are exceedingly common in ordinary behavior, as
in reading and naming objects, in obeying commands, and in making appropriate responses to the numerous stimuli which affect the
senses.   When the appropriate responses have been frequently associated with the stimuli, as in the case of reading, no consciousness
of a volitional character intervenes between the stimulus and the
response; volition has no opportunity to appear except when the
reaction is hesitating and uncertain.   Choice-time is therefore not
included in the measured period of a discriminative reaction; for
an act of will occurs only during the phase of preparation.   Discrimination certainly occurs in the practical sense that the reaction
differs according to the stimulus which is presented; but we are not
warranted in framing too formal a notion of such discrimination,
nor in thinking of it as a well-defined act intervening between the
reception of the stimulus and the response.   There is usually little
trace of a conscious comparison of the actual stimulus with other
possible stimuli; but, the rather, there is a simple apprehension of
the actual stimulus, followed by movement; and the apprehension,
as in the simple reaction, is prepared beforehand, and also need
not be completed till after the movement.   It must, however, be
so far completed as to determine the right movement.

§ 16. The time occupied by a "reaction with discrimination"
varies greatly according to the conditions.   Speed is favored by
a "natural," i. e., previously well-trained, association between each
stimulus and the movement which is assigned to it as its reaction.
The speed of reaction increases with practice in associating a given
movement with a given stimulus.   But the discrimination reaction

[1] See especially Ach, op. cit., pp. 129, 146.
[2] *The Time Relations of Mental Phenomena* (New York, 1890), p. 26.

never becomes so prompt as the muscular form of the simple re-action, though it may become as prompt as the sensorial reaction. This is what we should expect; because the preparation to move cannot be so complete when there is uncertainty, in the period of preparation, as to which of two movements is to be made; and besides, the perceptive process must be allowed to go further before the movement is initiated, than is the case in the more purely muscular reaction. The quickest discriminative reactions reported are about .180 sec., when two movements have to be held in readiness and each executed in response to one of two stimuli; when only one movement is held in readiness, and this is to be made in response to only one of two stimuli, the time may sink to .170 or even .160 sec.

The preceding remarks suggest, what has been found to be true in fact, that the time of a discriminative reaction increases with the number of movements that are held in readiness, to be executed, each in response to an assigned stimulus. Of the several authors who have investigated this matter, the results of Merkel[1] may be cited. He used as stimuli the numerals 1, 2, 3, 4, 5, and I, II, III, IV, V, by assigning them in a natural way to the ten fingers. He thus obtained the following reaction-times, as the average of ten individuals:

One movement (simple reaction) . . . . .188 sec.
Two movements, with two stimuli . . . . . .276 "
Three movements, three stimuli . . . . . . .330 "
Four movements, four stimuli . . . . .394 "
Five movements, five stimuli . . . . .445 "
Six movements, six stimuli . . . . .489 "
Seven movements, seven stimuli . . . . . . .526 "
Eight movements, eight stimuli . . . . . . .562 "
Nine movements, nine stimuli . . . . .581 "
Ten movements, ten stimuli . . . . .588 "

The discriminative reaction is lengthened not only when, as above, the preparation of the movements becomes more complex and uncertain, but also when the preliminary adjustment for the stimulus becomes less definite. Thus Cattell found[2] that it required slightly longer to react to one only out of ten possible colors than to react to one out of two possible.

§ 17. It appears from the preceding paragraphs that discriminative reaction is in part, like the simple reaction, *a measure of the perfection of the preparation to react to a stimulus*. In part, however, it is also a measure of the difficulty of the discrimination involved. The more difficult the discrimination, i. e., the more nearly alike the stimuli which must be held apart in reaction, the slower is the

---

[1] Wundt's *Philos. Studien*, 1885, II, 73.
[2] Wundt's *Philos. Stud.*, 1886, III, 460.

reaction.   On this point we may cite the results of Henmon.[1]   The
method employed by this experimenter, when the stimuli to be discriminated were visual, was the following: Both stimuli were presented simultaneously and side by side, and both hands were made
ready to react, each resting on a telegraph key.   The subject was
directed to react to a prescribed one of the two possible stimuli,
reacting with that hand which was on the side of the prescribed
stimulus.   For example, if red and green were the two stimuli employed in a series of reactions, the red was presented lying sometimes
to the right of the green and sometimes to the left, and the subject
reacted with the right hand when the red appeared on the right and
with the left hand when the red appeared on the left.   This form
of association between stimulus and movement was found to be especially easy, and so to give short and regular reaction times.

Experimenting in this manner, Henmon obtained the following
times for discriminative reactions between various colors:

White and black	.197 sec.
Red and green	.203 "
Red and blue	.212 "
Red and yellow	.217 "
Red and orange	.246 "
Red and orange mixed with 25 per cent. red	.252 "
Red and orange mixed with 50 per cent. red	.260 "
Red and orange mixed with 75 per cent. red	.271 "

All of these differences in the stimuli are well above the threshold
of color discrimination (compare p. 360), and yet they do not all
require the same time for discrimination, but the time increases as
the difference decreases.

Similar results were obtained in the times of reaction to differences
of pitch, as can be seen in the following table:

Difference of pitch in vibrations	16	12	8	4
Time of the reaction	.290	.299	.311	.334

Again, when the subject was required to react to the shorter of
two lines, exposed side by side, the following times were obtained:[2]

In discriminating lines of 10 and 13	mm.	. . .	296 sec.
" " "	10 " 12.5 "	. . . .	298 "
" " "	10 " 12 "	. . . .	305 "
" " "	10 " 11.5 "	. . . .	313 "
" " "	10 " 11 "	. . . .	324 "
" " "	10 " 10.5 "	. . . .	345 "

[1] *The Time of Perception as a Measure of Differences in Sensations* (New York,
1906).

[2] The times cited are those of the quicker of two subjects; the relations of the
times of the slower subject were approximately the same.

In general, then, diminishing the difference between two stimuli increases the discriminative reaction-time; and, further, diminishing the objective difference successively by equal amounts causes a greater and greater increase in the reaction-time, as the threshold of discriminable difference is approached. If we interpret this result in the light of our former discussions, we may probably conclude that the process of apprehension of the stimulus has to proceed further, before the initiation of the movement, when the difference to be reacted to is small than when the difference is large; and also that the preliminary adjustment of the movement is less complete when greater difficulty of discrimination is anticipated. In other words, *the smaller the difference between the simuli, the more the discriminative reaction approaches the pnre type of sensorial or apperceptive reaction.*

§ 18. It should now be made clear that the study of discriminative reactions is capable of giving information regarding the comparative ease or difficulty of different processes of discrimination, provided only that all the conditions of the experiment remain the same, so that the only factor influencing the reaction-time is the difference between the stimuli. In this respect, results like those quoted below from von Kries and Auerbach[1] are of interest. The numbers given in this table are obtained by subtracting the simple reaction-time from the time of the discriminative reaction, and need to be increased by .150–.200 sec. to make them comparable with the reaction-times previously given. Such comparison cannot, however, be properly made, because of individual differences. The validity of the method of "elimination by subtraction," employed by these authors to determine the pure time of discrimination, will be discussed later; meanwhile, the differences which appear in the table may be taken as indicative of differences in the difficulty of discrimination.

	Auerbach	Von Kries
	Sec.	Sec.
Discernment of the direction of light	0.011	0.017
Discernment between two colors	0.012	0.034
Localization of sound (minimum)	0.015	0.032
Discernment of tone when higher	0.019	0.049
Localization of sensations of touch	0.021	0.036
Localization of distance by sight	0.022	0.030
Discernment between tone and noise	0.022	0.046
Judgment of intensity of sensations of touch (strong) .	0.023	0.061
Discernment of tone when lower	0.034	0.054
Judgment of intensity of sensations of touch (weak) .	0.053	0.105
Localization of sound (maximum)	0.062	0.077

[1] *Archiv f. (Anat. u.) Physiol.* (1877), p. 298.

§ 19. Various interesting discoveries were made during the course of the experiments which resulted in preparing the foregoing table. For example, it was found that the simple reaction-time for A. (Auerbach), when stimulus was applied to the middle finger or back of the hand, was 0.146–0.147 sec.; and for K. (Kries), 0.117–0.119 sec. But, as the table shows, when discernment was required of the two observers, the reaction-time of K. was relatively so much increased as to make his discernment time greater than that of A. The result of practice in discernment was found to hold good for other areas of the skin than those in experimenting upon which the practice was gained. For discernment among three *places* (middle finger, back of hand, and middle of lower arm), the order being unknown and only one to be reacted on—the mean interval required was for A. 0.028 sec., and for K. 0.050 sec.; further practice, however, reduced this interval to about the same as that required for two places.

Discernment between two *intensities* of the sensation of touch was found to be very uncertain and difficult. Many more false reactions followed the attempt to tell whether the dorsal side of the last of the phalanges of the middle finger was being hit with the weaker or the stronger of two stimuli than occurred in the attempts to localize tactile sensations. The discernment time, when reaction followed the stronger stimulus, was 0.016–0.034 sec. for A., and 0.05–0.07 for K.; when reaction followed the weaker stimulus, the discernment time was 0.035–0.069 sec. for A., and 0.089–0.114 for K. The character of our judgments of intensity is, perhaps, dependent on the steepness, as it were, with which the curve rises in consciousness; but, however this may be, it appears that we discern how and where we are affected with a sensation more promptly than about how much we are affected.

When discernment between two simple tones of different pitch is required, the reaction follows the one of higher pitch more promptly. Thus the discernment time, under such circumstances, was for A., 0.015–0.044 sec., and for K., 0.043–0.11; but, if reaction followed the tone of lower pitch, the discernment time for A. was 0.03–0.059 sec., and for K. 0.045–0.092. To discern *tone from noise*, when reaction followed the tone, A. required 0.015–0.023 sec., and K. 0.036–0.055; when reaction followed the noise, A.'s discernment time was 0.017–0.025 sec., and K.'s, 0.045–0.047. The reaction-time diminishes as the pitch rises; for very high notes it nearly reaches the limit required for hearing the noise of the electric spark.

The simple reaction-time for sensations of sound remains nearly the same for all changes in the angle by which the locality of the sound diverges from the median plane between the two ears. But the time required for discerning the locality of the sound varies greatly for the different sizes of this angle. Thus the discernment time for locality, as to right or left, varied for Auerbach and Kries as follows:

	Angle 120°–35°	Angle 35°–26°	Angle 26°–11°
Auerbach	0.020 sec.	0.033 sec.	0.120 sec.
Kries	0.013 "	0.122 "	0.153 "

The discernment time required for localizing the direction of a spark by direct vision varied for A. from 0.005 to 0.025 sec., and for K. from 0.006 to 0.029 sec.; by indirect vision, for A. from 0.008 to 0.028 sec., and for K. from 0.007 to 0.028 sec. For localizing distance, A. required 0.019 to 0.027 sec. of discernment time, when the object arose in front of the fixation-point, and K. 0.027 to 0.035 sec.; but A. required 0.019 to 0.029 sec., and K. 0.021 to 0.036 sec., when the object arose behind this point.

§ 20. From the discriminative reaction we pass now to the associative. It is true that a certain amount of association is already involved in the discriminative reaction, since definite movements are associated, for the purposes of the experiment, with definite stimuli. But the stimuli and movements employed, and the associations between them, are few in such cases; and the subject knows, within a narrow range, what stimulus to expect and for what movement to prepare. In the typical experiment in association time, also, the subject knows, indeed, the general type of stimulus which he is to receive and the general type of movement which he is to make; but neither the exact stimulus nor the exact reaction need have been previously mentioned in the course of the experiments. He may be told, for example, that he will be shown some number, and that he is to react by calling out the number next larger; or that he is to be shown a word, and is to react by calling out another word, the first that is suggested by the presented word. The association between stimulus and response is here one of long standing, instead of being, as in the discriminative reaction, specially formed for the purposes of the experiment. The long-standing of the association favors quick response; but, on the other hand, the immediate preparation for the stimulus and for the movement cannot be so complete here as in the discriminative reaction; so that, on the whole, the associative reaction takes the longer time, and often a very much longer time. There is in fact no upper limit to the time which may be occupied by such a reaction; at its quickest, it occupies about half a second or a little less.

In the simple and discriminative reactions, we recognized two factors as determining the speed of the performance—namely, (1) the perfection of the preliminary adjustment or preparation; and (2) the degree to which the perceptual process must be carried before the impulse to movement could be initiated.   In the associative reaction, these two factors are joined by a third—namely, the degree of closeness of the previously formed association between the stimulus and the response.   We may profitably examine the influence of each of these factors on the association time, beginning with the last as the most obvious.

§ 21. That familiar associations operate more quickly than unfamiliar is too trite a fact to require elaboration.   It is obvious, for example, that one who is familiar with the multiplication table will call out the product of two presented numbers more promptly than one who is ill trained in multiplication; or that it will take less time to name objects in one's native language than in an unfamiliar language.   What is more worthy of note is that the association time reveals differences in the firmness of associations which are not evident to less precise modes of observation.   Thus one may have lived for some years in a foreign country and have learned to use its language fluently, and still require more time to name an object in that language than in one's own.[1]   Cattell found that it took much less time (0.345 and 0.389 sec., respectively, for two subjects), to name the month following a given month, than it took (0.763 and 0.832 sec.) to name the month preceding a given month.   Similarly, more time was required to name the letter preceding, in the alphabet, a given letter than to name the letter following; or to respond to a given number by the number next smaller than by the number next larger.   In all such familiar series, association is much quicker in the direction of the series than in the reverse direction.   Less obvious is the reason for the fact[2] that it ordinarily takes less time, on the average, to pass from a part to the whole (i. e., to give the name of the whole object when the name of a part is presented as the stimulus), than to pass from the whole to a part; and less to pass from a special class to a more general (e. g., "dog—animal") than from the more general to the more special.   These differences in speed of reaction are probably to be attributed, in part at least, to differences in the previous training of the associations.   Within the same category of associations, some are immensely more familiar and quick-acting than others; and even among those which seem, all alike, thoroughly familiar, some are

[1] Cattell, Wundt's *Philos. Stud.*, 1888, IV, 241; and *Mind*, XII, 68.

[2] Cattell, op. cit.; Trautscholdt, Wundt's *Philos. Studien*, I, 213; Watt, *Archiv f. d. ges. Psychol.*, 1905, IV, 289.

shown by experiment to give quicker reactions than others. Thus, if the requirement is to respond by a word having the opposite meaning to that of the stimulus word, about twice as much time is consumed in reacting to "smooth" or to "broad," as in reacting to "good" or "long." In this way, the study of association times reveals facts regarding the experience and training of an individual or of a social group which would otherwise be only vaguely suspected.

§ 22. The time of an associative reaction is not, however, an unequivocal measure of the firmness with which an association has been established by past experience; the speed of reaction depends in part on the perfection of the momentary preparation and in part on the complexity of the mental process which intervenes between the stimulus and the reaction. Introspective studies[1] have revealed some interesting facts regarding both the period of preparation and the principal or reaction period. The preparation may be more or less precise, according to the character of the experiment. Thus it has become customary to distinguish between "free" and "controlled" or "constrained" association: in the former case, the subject is simply directed to respond by the first word suggested by the stimulus word; in the latter, he is required to respond by a word which stands in some assigned relation to the stimulus word—as, for example, a word of opposite meaning, or the name of a class of objects within which the object named in the stimulus word is included. The constraint may be more or less complete; since in some cases there is only one right answer, while in others any one of a greater or smaller number of answers is correct. Free association is intended to be wholly unconstrained; but this ideal cannot be reached in practice, since the subject has at least to make a verbal response, and since, also, in many cases, he involuntarily sets himself a more definite task.

One seemingly strange result from these experiments is that free association often requires more time than constrained. The reason probably is that the constraint, by limiting beforehand the field of operations, permits of a more perfect preparation to react. The reality and efficiency of the preparation, in general, is shown by the promptness with which a correct response is given in constrained association; as well as by the fact that changing the preparation—for example, from an adjustment to multiply to an adjustment to add two presented numbers—leads to an entirely different set of responses to the same stimuli. Watt found that, at the commencement of a series of associative reactions of the same type, the task or problem (naming a higher class, etc.) was at first consciously

See especially Watt, op. cit.

represented in the preparation for each single reaction; but that this consciousness of the task decreased as the series of similar reactions progressed, till there might be nothing present to indicate the prepared condition except an unspecialized feeling of readiness. The adjustment for the reaction remained in force, however; and it even improved as the consciousness of it waned.

On changing from one task to another, the subject is likely to become more specifically conscious of the new problem; he is also likely to be slower in his reactions, even though the "new" problem may have been made familiar by previous experiments. This also goes to indicate the reality of some central adjustment by which the pathway of each fresh stimulus through the brain is made ready beforehand.

§ 23. The amount of conscious process which intervenes between the stimulus and an associative reaction varies enormously in different cases. When the preparation is perfect, and the association of response to stimulus is familiar, the time of reaction is brief, and there is little introspective evidence of the process, which seems to have become automatic. This is especially apt to be the case when there is only one correct response. When two or more responses are correct, and about equally familiar, the time is apt to be longer,[1] apparently because of an interference between the tendencies toward the two responses. Introspectively, this interference may be in evidence as an experienced need of selection between two consciously suggested responses. At other times, interference results from the occurrence of a conscious tendency to some false reaction; even if such a tendency is checked in time to prevent an incorrect motor response, it slows the reaction. Time may also be required in searching for a correct response. This searching, in not too difficult cases, is introspectively a waiting for the correct response to be suggested. Sometimes the correct response seems to come gradually, so that its coming can be observed; at other times it appears suddenly, or jumps into consciousness.

The interference of one associative tendency with another can also be strengthened by requiring a response other than the one which is likely to be suggested. Thus Ach,[2] after first forming by repetition strong associations between pairs of nonsense syllables, then presented these syllables with the requirement that the response to each should be, contrary to the formed associations, a syllable rhyming with it. Under these conditions, the first response suggested was almost sure to be the familiar but now incorrect syllable. If this wrong response was not checked in time, the false reaction led

[1] Compare Cattell, op. cit.

[2] *Über den Willensakt und das Temperament* (Leipzig, 1910).

to a strong determination to react correctly, and the effectiveness of this strong determination, which formed part of the preparation for the succeeding reactions, was often visible in a successful checking of the wrong response in the next trial. When the wrong response was checked in time, the thought of it was followed by a consciousness of the task to be accomplished (such consciousness not ordinarily being present between the stimulus and the response); and, next, by a period of searching for a correct response.

§ 24. It is clear that the amount of the entire mental process intervening between the stimulus and the associative reaction differs greatly in different cases. The time of such a reaction is not always the time of the same processes; because the total associative mechanism which may be called into play is vast and complicated, and subject to many varying influences, so that it cannot always be perfectly controlled. The time of an associative reaction, therefore, is a measure partly of the perfection and strength of the preliminary adjustment, partly of the strength of the particular associative tendency which leads to the response, and partly of the amount of interference between different associative tendencies.

§ 25. The object of the study of reaction-times, as it presented itself to the minds of the founders of this study, was that of determining the duration of definite mental operations, such as sensation, perception, apperception, discrimination, association, choice. Certain of these processes they recognized as involved in the simple reaction, and these they labored to isolate by variations of the experiment. Others of these processes they supposed to be added when the simple reaction was changed to the discriminative form, or this to the associative. Accordingly, they argued that the time occupied by these added operations could be obtained by subtracting the time of the simple reaction from the discriminative or associative reaction-time; and great ingenuity was displayed in so varying the conditions and requirements of the reaction as to permit of this "elimination by subtraction." More recent studies have shown, as described above, that the total actual process which is timed does not correspond, introspectively, with the analyses drawn up for it; and probably, also, it does not correspond physiologically. These supposed constituent processes—perception, apperception, discrimination, choice—were discovered by logical analysis of the result or outcome, and not by a direct study of the process itself. The process gone through in a discriminative reaction is not that of a simple reaction with a process of discrimination interpolated into it; but the whole performance is different, beginning with the preliminary adjustment. It follows, therefore, that the procedure of

elimination by subtraction is invalid,[1] and that the times occupied
by the supposed elementary processes are not revealed by the work
on reaction-times.   Yet the results obtained are of value, and the
method of reaction-times promises to prove of still further value—
when taken in connection with introspective analysis of the process
and with other indications of the nature of the brain's action—in
elucidating the dynamics of mental operations.

§ 26. One further remark should be made regarding reaction-
times.   In these experiments, the aim is to isolate as far as possible a single factor, so as to determine its speed and the process by
which it is accomplished.   From the very nature of the case, however, it is probable that this aim can never be accomplished perfectly.   In ordinary life, while reactions essentially like the simple
discriminative and associative reactions of the experimenters are
common enough, they do not occur in isolation, but as parts, usually, of continued performances.   Hence the importance of Cattell's attempt [2] to study the speed of such reactions under conditions approaching those of ordinary application.   When a whole
page of words or letters was placed before the subject, and he was
directed to read or name these consecutively and as rapidly as possible, the time consumed per letter was .188 sec. and per word .200
sec.   In the isolated reactions, however, the time for a word or
letter was .320 to .360 sec.   Two important facts appear in these
figures.   The first is that scarcely more time is required to name a
(short) word than to name a single letter; it is clear, therefore, that
the reaction to a word does not consist of a sum of reactions to the
letters composing it.   The reaction is by *larger units*.   The other fact
to be noted is that considerably less time is required to react to each
one of a series of letters or words when all are visible at once
than when it is required to react to a single isolated letter or word.
There is evidence here of an *overlapping* of the successive reactions.
While one word is being pronounced, the next is already in process
of apprehension.   The overlapping, in fact, extends beyond the
adjoining unit; by a special experiment, Cattell determined that it
extended, in the case of separate letters, over four or five of them.
(We note in passing that this corresponds to what we should expect to follow from the facts already brought out in the study of
visual perception.   See pp. 461f.)   Both overlapping and reaction
to large units enter into such skilled performances as those of a
typewriter writing from copy or of a musician playing from score.
These performances consist of a series of discriminative reactions;

---

[1] This procedure has been searchingly criticised by several of the authors cited
above, and also by Aliotta, *La Misura in Psicologia Sperimentale* (Firenze, 1905).

[2] Wundt's *Philos. Studien*, 1885, II, 635.

and yet their speed may be such that only an eighth or a tenth of a second is occupied by each movement—much less than the time of a discriminative reaction.   The high speed is due partly to apprehending and reacting to phrases rather than to single notes, words, or letters; and partly to carrying on processes of apprehension and movement simultaneously.   In both these processes, "practice makes perfect" by the expedient of dropping out of consciousness many of its procedures which, although originally necessary, have now become, under the laws of association and habit, quite dispensable without impairing, but rather with improving, the speed and certainty with which the desired result is secured.   Nor can there be any reasonable doubt that a corresponding "short-circuiting" takes place in the nervous mechanism, especially in the cerebral processes.   Thus skill is acquired.   To the same question as to how such skill is acquired, we shall have occasion to recur in a later chapter on "learning."   We close this discussion by referring again to the truth that both the reactions of the nervous mechanism and the correlated mental activities are immensely complicated; while at the same time, the factors which can be either definitely isolated or reasonably suspected are bound together, in both cases, into a marvellous unity.

CHAPTER VII

FEELING, EMOTION, AND EXPRESSIVE MOVEMENTS

§ 1. We have already had repeated occasion to remark upon the extreme difficulty of recognizing either by purely introspective or by experimental analysis the absolutely elementary factors of our complex mental states. As a matter of course, when such factors are successfully analyzed, they are found to be incapable of identification with one another; or of being substituted for one another, without changing the entire mental complex of which they form a part. All the difficulties connected with, or consequent upon, this fundamental fact of our experience, accompany in an exaggerated manner every attempt to form a satisfactory psychological doctrine of the nature and conditions of the feelings and emotions. And, indeed, as to the essential nature of feeling, no satisfactory definition can be given; since *to feel* is as simple and fundamental an operation of mind as it is to know. Feeling can never be stated in terms of knowledge. Inasmuch, then, as all definition is only the expression of an elaborate and complex form of knowledge, the nature of feeling is not capable of being defined; it must be *felt*. When, then, this nature is defined as consisting in some relation to physical sensation or to mental images, it is deprived of the very characteristic which makes it to be *feeling* rather than sensation or idea. Various theories, however, have succeeded in stating certain conditions or antecedents of the reaction of mind in the way of feeling.

§ 2. To this indefiniteness in the experience, the indefiniteness in the language which attempts to describe the experience bears witness. The term, "feeling," has, in popular speech, a wide and varied usage. Sometimes applied to the sense of touch, it is also used to indicate any and every emotional experience, whether dependent chiefly upon certain characteristic sensations, or chiefly upon conditions of an ideal or intellectual sort. An example of this last usage is seen in the expression, "I feel that there is some mistake in the argument, though I cannot tell just where the mistake lies." Psychologists have abandoned the first of these usages, but are not yet agreed as to the limits to be drawn within the broad field indicated by the second and third usages. Some would prefer to retain *feeling* as a vague term, applicable to any condition of consciousness which is lacking in clear definition. Others would narrowly limit the term to the feelings of pleasantness and unpleasantness, regarding which no doubt exists that they should be thus named.

The question is not entirely one of scientific terminology; for, from the point of view of the analysis of consciousness, many of these vague states must be regarded as composite; whereas pleasantness and unpleasantness are apparently not susceptible of further analysis, but seem themselves to be of an elementary character. From this point of view, therefore, the question arises as to what elements of consciousness, different from sensation, and analogous to these paradigms, pleasantness and unpleasantness, can be discovered. Even on this question, however, competent opinion is still widely divergent, since some authorities would limit the elementary feelings to the two mentioned, while others would increase the number to four or six, and still others hold to a very large and indefinite number. One writer,[1] for example, presents a long list, including feelings of interest, of reality and unreality, of belief and doubt, of clearness, confusion, effort, ease, eagerness, hesitation, pride, humility, admiration, scorn, reasonableness, etc. In the opinion of many psychologists, most of these, as well as the numerous other emotions which might be mentioned, are certainly complexes of many elements.

The dual conception of feeling, which would reduce all feelings to pleasantness and unpleasantness (in combination with a variety of intellectual elements), is the traditional view, and has usually been in favor with the analytic school of psychologists. Recently, however, Wundt[2] and Royce[3] have made the novel suggestion that there are, in addition to this one dimension of feeling, other dimensions. The latter proposes to regard feeling as a two-dimensional *continuum*, like a plane; he would, therefore, add to the traditional pleasantness-unpleasantness dimension that of restlessness-quiescence. This is to say that any state of feeling may differ from any other state in being more or less pleasant and also in being more or less restless. Wundt proposes to regard feeling as a three-dimensional *continuum*, and adds to the dimension of pleasantness and unpleasantness that of excitement and calm or depression (in which connection *depression* is to be taken as a simple opposite of *excitement* and is not to include any notion of unpleasantness), and that of tension and relief. Those who, in opposition to these suggestions,

[1] Baldwin: *Handbook of Psychology, Feeling and Will*, 1894, p. 242.

[2] *Grundriss d. Psychologie*, 1896, p. 98; *Grundzüge d. physiol. Psychol.*, 6th ed., 1910, II, 294.

[3] *Outlines of Psychology*, 1903.

continue to uphold the one-dimensional theory,[1] believe that the excitement, tension, etc., incident to certain states of feeling, are not elementary, but are compounds of bodily sensations.

§ 3. In criticism of the foregoing views, we remark that the reality of feelings of excitement and depression, of tension and relief, cannot be doubted, but only their elementary character; and this has not yet been established. Among the sensations, some classes are indeed characterized chiefly with a tone of either pleasantness or unpleasantness; here belong tastes, odors, and sensations of temperature. Visual and auditory stimuli do not usually arouse such intense feelings of pleasantness or unpleasantness; unless they have become associated with certain meanings, as in pictures, landscapes, and speech. Visual sensations, more than auditory, are likely to be relatively free from pleasantness and unpleasantness. There is much greater unanimity among individuals as to which is the most exciting color than as to which is the most agreeable; the latter judgment seems to depend largely on the associations of the various colors, while the exciting or calming effect of a color seems to be more intrinsic. Feelings of tension and relief are especially connected with auditory sensations, perhaps because the temporal sequence of this class of sensations is particularly prominent. In listening to a series of metronome beats—to take Wundt's example—one can detect a feeling of tension in anticipation of each beat, which gives way to a temporary relaxation or relief on the actual occurrence of the beat. So, also, in listening to, or in reading, a sentence which has a periodic structure, a feeling of tension can be observed which gives way to relief on the completion of the sentence. Tension is thus closely associated with expectancy, and relief with the fulfilment of expectation. Along with the expectancy there may be present, according to the circumstances, either pleasantness or unpleasantness; and the relief may also be accompanied with either of these feelings, according as the event is agreeable or the opposite.

As we have already seen, according to the theory of Wundt, the qualities of simple feeling have three dimensions, and no more. But it is very doubtful whether this view gives an adequate account of our feeling experience. Certainly there are many feelings which do not readily fit into these grooves, and which, though we may suspect them to be composite, do not as yet admit of being analyzed. Among these may be mentioned a class of feelings connected with memory and judgment. When one is trying to recall a name, the feeling of "being near," or "on the right track," often arises. If an-

[1] See Titchener, *Lectures on the Elementary Psychology of Feeling and Attention*, 1908; Ebbinghaus, *Grundzüge der Psychologie*, 1905, p. 567.

other than the right name occurs to the mind, it is usually attended with a feeling of its incorrectness, but when the right name occurs, it is *felt* to be right. Such affective experiences are accepted as the warrants of correct or incorrect recollection; they cannot be defended; they cannot be analyzed; they are distinctly subjective, and not referable to anything beyond the self; in all ways they answer to the conception of feeling rather than of any form of sensation or knowledge. The same can be said of the feeling of familiarity with a face or an odor which is not completely recognized, but is *felt* to be known as distinguished from "knowing it to be known." Then, too, there is the feeling of conviction which obtains when we pass from the former into the latter state of consciousness. Experiments on reaction time and association time have also brought to light feelings of readiness or unreadiness, of clearness or confusion, which have resisted analysis. Most of the feelings mentioned in this paragraph may be attended with pleasantness or unpleasantness, but they are *not simply* pleasant or unpleasant. On the contrary, they have, each one, a specific character. This character is not identical with the character of the name, for example, which is being recalled, for the same feeling may attach to any name under the circumstances of its being recalled after difficulty. The feeling seems, the rather, to be appropriate to a certain sort of mental performance. To resolve it into a complex of bodily sensations is at least premature; though it might, conceivably, be so composed, it might equally well, for all we can now see, be the specific accompaniment of a special sort of brain action. As the case stands at present, therefore, psychological analysis does not permit us to limit the number of elementary feelings to two, or to six, or to any specified number.

§ 4. We recur, then, to our previous statement with added confidence. About that aspect of our experience which we call our feelings, or our emotions—their nature, origin, relation to a physical basis and to sensations and ideas—we know remarkably little The reason for this fact is not difficult to discover. By their very nature, the phenomena are obscure, indefinite, and yet extremely variable and multiform. They are also connected with our sensations and ideas in such a way as to make all separation in fact quite impossible. The psychology of the feelings, as studied from the introspective point of view, has therefore always been peculiarly unproductive of assured results. The fact that their physiological conditions are laid so largely in obscure, rapid, and infinitely varied changes within the central organs, such as cannot be either directly observed or indirectly subjected to experimentation, increases the difficulties of the subject. What is the nature of feeling? How do the different feelings differ, and what elements have they in common? Under what conditions do we have sensuous feelings; and under what conditions are these feelings pleasant or unpleasant? Is feeling ever perfectly indifferent? is there a zero-point of feeling? How are the feelings related to the quality and intensity of physical stimuli? What is the physiological basis (if any exist) of the higher æsthetic, moral, and religious feelings? These and other similar questions may be asked of psycho-physical science with little satisfactory result. The attempt unduly to simplify, instead of increasing our scientific clearness in dealing with the subject, adds to its confusion.

§ 5. The experimental study of feeling in some of its aspects has developed two methods of investigation, called "the method of impression" and "the method of expression." Both are alike in that they bring to bear on the subject certain known stimuli, in order to determine their effect in exciting the feelings. The stimuli range, in different experiments, from simple colors, tones, odors, or tastes, to complex presentations, such as pictures or witticisms or musical and literary compositions. The two methods differ in the means by which the feeling of the subject is made known. In the method of impression, the person on whom the stimuli are made to act has simply to take note of the resulting changes in his affective tone, and to indicate the result of his observation in words. The method of expression is based on the fact that bodily reactions often appear in connection with changes of feeling—such as reactions of the organs of circulation, respiration, secretion, digestion, and involuntary movements and tensions of the muscles. The method of expression, acting on the assumption that these bodily reactions are the signs of inner feeling, seeks to record these signs themselves. The two methods are often joined, in that the subject is asked to report his feelings in words, and the correlation of the feelings, as introspectively observed, with the bodily expressive reactions, is made the main purpose of the experiment.

In the use of the method of impression, the most approved procedure is to present stimuli in pairs, and then to require a judgment on each pair, as to which of the two is the more agreeable, etc. A variation of this method consists in presenting a whole series of stimuli at once, and requiring that they be arranged in the order of their agreeableness or other value. The use of the method of impression has occurred, largely, in the field of æsthetics, into which Fechner[1] was the first to introduce the experimental method.

§ 6. Since it is the special purpose of this Treatise to investigate the phenomena of man's mental life in their relations to the functions of the nervous mechanism, some attempt at a physiological theory of the feelings and emotions would seem to be our appropri-

[1] *Vorschule der Æsthetik*, 1876.

ate task.   This method of approach, and the field of conjecture to which it leads, has proved particularly attractive to most theorists. But, unfortunately, far the greater number of such theorists have made no effort to take into consideration, much less to deal adequately with, the complex and intricate forms of nervous functioning, concerned in any comprehensive theory.   It is true, as Bain[1] declares, that "a very considerable number of the facts may be brought under the following principle—namely, that *states of pleasure are connected with an increase, and states of pain with an abatement, of some, or all, of the vital functions."*   But other facts in no small number cannot be brought under this principle.   It is not a difficult task for the physician to abate all the vital functions of the patient, even down to or beyond the line of danger, with the immediate result of producing pleasure rather than pain.   After objecting to Bain's statement as being "too vague," etc., Grant Allen[2] declares the true principle of connection to be the following: "Pleasure is the concomitant of the healthy action of any or all of the organs or members supplied with afferent cerebro-spinal nerves, to an extent not exceeding the ordinary powers of reparation possessed by the system."   Æsthetic pleasure he provisionally defines as "the subjective concomitant of the normal amount of activity, not directly connected with life-serving function, in the peripheral end-organs of the cerebro-spinal nervous system."   Now, that pleasure is the reflex of healthy and unimpeded activity is an old psychological truism; and that we are dependent upon impulses propagated in the sensory nerves of the cerebro-spinal system for sensations, pleasurable or painful, of muscular, organic, or more special sort, scarcely needs statement as a newly discovered law of "physiological æsthetics."   Nothing, however, could well be more "vague" than the limit fixed by the words "to an extent not exceeding the ordinary powers of reparation possessed by the system."

Even to undertake the study of the bodily expressions of feeling, it is necessary to have a knowledge of the physiology of circulation, respiration, secretion, reflex action, etc.   The movements of breathing, for instance, are, indeed, responsive to mental conditions—laughing, sobbing, and sighing are striking examples of this responsiveness—but they are also responsive to many other influences, such as the need of the muscles for oxygen.   Any sensory stimulus is likely to exert an influence on the breathing, and that even in a condition of unconsciousness through anæsthesia.   The rate and strength of the heart-beat is likewise subject to many reflex influences, as well as to influences proceeding downward from the cerebrum; and it is further influenced by the respiration.   The

[1] *The Senses and the Intellect,* pp. 281 f.
[2] *Physiological Æsthetics,* 1877, pp. 21–34.

circulation through any organ is influenced not only by the rate and force of the heart-beat, but also by the constriction or dilatation of the arteries leading to the organ, and to other organs as well. Even the activity of the voluntary muscles is certainly subjected to reflex influences, as well as to the influence of the cerebrum. It thus becomes a difficult matter to observe the effects of simple states of feeling, because of the complication of these with other effects.

The principal kinds of the observation of bodily functions in connection with the feelings have been the following: The movements of the chest and perhaps also of the abdomen in breathing have been recorded, by aid of pneumographs; and the relation of different feelings to changes in the rate and depth of respiration has been studied in the graphic records. The pulse has been recorded by sphygmographs applied to various arteries, among which the radial is the most accessible, though the carotid, since it supplies the brain, has appeared to many investigators as the most important for psychological purposes. Changes in the volume of the arm, or of a finger—changes which are due to the varying amount of blood contained in the member, and which depend partly on the output of the heart and partly on the vasomotor condition of the member and of other parts—have been deemed specially important by many authorities, and have been recorded by means of plethysmographs. Similar instruments can even be applied to the brain itself, in cases where part of it has been exposed through removal of a portion of the skull. One or two other methods of study will be briefly referred to below.

§ 7. We may begin by bringing forward the most ambitious attempt to reduce the results of the method of expression to the form of a law. Wundt, in whose laboratory several experimenters have studied the pulse and respiration during moments of pleasant feeling, etc., summarizes the results in the following scheme:[1]

Feeling	Pulse		Breathing	
	Strength	Speed	Strength	Speed
Tension	—	—	—	—
Calm	—	=	—	—
Unpleasantness	—	+	+	—
Pleasantness	+	—	—	+
Excitation	+	=	+	+
Relief	+	+	+	+

[1] *Physiol. Psychol.*, 6th ed., 1910, II, 310. The arrangement of the scheme is here somewhat modified from that given by Wundt. + indicates an increase in strength or rapidity; —, a decrease; =, no change.

In commenting on this scheme of results, it should be noted, first, that not all the results fit well into the scheme. This is even true of some of the work done in Wundt's laboratory, so that his scheme has undergone certain modifications from its earlier form, in consequence of later results which seemed more trustworthy. In the earlier scheme, the positions of excitation and relief are, approximately, interchanged; and the same is true of calm and tension. Moreover, the results obtained by other experimenters are often at variance with those of Wundt's laboratory. In analyzing the results of the table with a view to determine what they probably mean, the manner of conducting the experiments must first be understood. The subject, being taken in as nearly as possible a neutral state of feeling, is presented with certain sensory stimuli; or is required to perform some brief mental operation, such as multiplying together two numbers. The effects of these interruptions of the neutral state are noted in the records of pulse and respiration, and are then compared with the subject's own testimony as to the change of feeling induced. Interruptions inducing feelings of tension are, particularly, those which arouse attentive and expectant observation on the part of the subject, or those which require him to perform some brief mental operation; while relief is experienced at the successful accomplishment of any such task. That, under these circumstances, the breathing becomes weaker and shallower is a fact observed by practically all experimenters; it may be taken, in connection with the correlative fact that the opposite effect occurs at the close of the mental operation, as the best-established result of this entire line of study. At times, indeed, respiration may be entirely suspended during a brief attentive act.

Other movements besides the respiratory show similar changes. When, for example, an audience is restless, the speaker may succeed, for a moment, in checking the slight movements of numerous individuals which go to make up this restlessness, by showing them a picture, pointing to some object, posing a question, or otherwise arousing the mental activity of the audience. When the activity so aroused has reached its goal, there is likely to be a general shifting of position throughout the audience, and a return to other uneasy movements. It seems clear, then, that brief and attentive mental acts inhibit bodily movement, and that respiration participates in this inhibition. The subsequent reverse effect is doubtless due, in the case of breathing, to the need of air, i. e., to a slight dyspnœa produced by insufficient respiration during the brief period of mental activity. It would perhaps be better to think of the inhibited respiration during such periods of mental activity as a symptom of the activity (or of "attention") rather than of the feeling of tension which goes with the activity. It is claimed by those who refuse to admit tension and relief into the category of elementary feelings, that the feeling of tension is itself composed of sensations of shallow breathing and of the immobile and often strained position of the limbs; and that the feeling of relief is composed of sensations of deeper breathing (sometimes amounting to a sigh), and of the relaxation of the limbs from their fixed positions.

It should be noted that the statements made above regarding the effects of mental activity (or of "attention") on pulse and respiration hold good mainly of *brief* periods of activity. When mental work is long continued, the principal effect observed[1] is a quickening of the heart-beat.

As to excitement and its opposite, there is also little doubt that the above table corresponds pretty closely to the facts, and that excitement is usually accompanied by an increase in breathing, and calm by a decrease. It is difficult to attain the feeling of calm immediately after vigorous muscular exercise, when pulse and respiration are strong and rapid. In explaining the fact that the symptoms of tension so closely resemble those of calm, and those of relief so closely resemble those of excitement, it must be remembered that tension corresponds to a repression of bodily activity, and that relief brings a compensatory rebound from this repression.

§ 8. If we now turn to the accompaniments of pleasantness and unpleasantness, we shall find it hard to reach any satisfactory conclusion. For one thing, it is almost impossible, in an experiment, to keep these feelings free from tension and relief; that is, from the effects of observant attention and its satisfaction. Some stimulus must be used to arouse the pleasant or unpleasant feeling, and this stimulus arouses also the subject's attention. Thus Lehmann,[2] one of those who have most devoted themselves to this line of study, reports that colors and tones are unsuited for testing the effects of pleasantness and unpleasantness, since the only effects obtained by their use are those of attention; only olfactory stimuli seemed to him suited for the purpose; and even with these, the changes in the pulse were not constant, but sometimes consisted in a slowing and sometimes in a hastening. In general, the circulatory and respiratory symptoms of these feelings are inconstant, and, according to many observers, there is no clear difference between the accompaniments of pleasantness and of unpleasantness.

The same thing is even true of the cerebral circulation, as observed in cases where a portion of the brain has been exposed by the

---

[1] See E. Gley, *Études de psychologie physiologique et pathologique*, 1903, p. 29; Billings and Shepard, *Psychol. Rev.*, 1910, XVII, 217.

[2] *Die körperliche Äusserungen psychischer Zustände*, 1905, III, 481–482.

removal of part of the skull in a surgical operation. The brain can then be observed to expand and contract according to the amount of blood in it; and its volume changes according to the activity of the brain. But whether it expands or contracts, specifically, in conditions of pleasantness and unpleasantness, is a question to which the observations so far reported give divergent answers.[1]

The more intense and, as they are considered, more complex, states of feeling known as emotions, are also far from uniform in their respiratory symptoms. On the whole, therefore, the evidence from this line of study would seem distinctly opposed to analyzing the feelings into combinations of sensations with only a varying feeling-tone of pleasantness and unpleasantness.

§ 9. Of late years, a new symptom of the condition of feeling has come into prominence. The instrument used for the observation of this symptom is the galvanometer, and the bodily change noted is electrical. Féré[2] and Tarchanoff, independently, discovered that an electrical current, or a change of potential, could be observed by connecting a delicate galvanometer to two points of the skin, and then subjecting the person under observation to stimuli which influenced the state of feeling. Such a stimulus as tickling caused a current to appear in the galvanometer; as did also any emotion or the thought of an emotion. Mental activity of a non-affective sort produces comparatively slight currents.[4] But muscular activity produces deflections of the galvanometer. Veraguth[5] found that if a story were read to the subject while his skin was connected with the galvanometer, deflections occurred when emotional passages were read. Jung[6] turned the experiment to practical account, by showing that ideas having for an individual an emotional import could be detected by reading him a list of words, and observing which words caused an electrical response. The detection of such ideas, or "complexes" of ideas, which have a strong emotional tone for an individual, is often of value in treating hysteria and other neuroses.

The source of the electricity which is revealed by the galvanometer in these experiments is not yet certainly known. We know that activity of any organ is attended by the production of electric cur-

---

[1] See H. Berger, *Über die körperliche Äusserungen psychischer Zustände*, 1904 and 1907; E. Weber, *Der Einfluss psychischer Vorgänge auf den Körper*, 1910; and also short articles by these same authors in *Zeitschr. f. Psychol.*, 1910, LVI, 299, 305.

[2] *C. R. Soc. de Biologie*, 1888, p. 217.

[3] Pflüger's *Arch. f. d. ges. Physiol.*, 1890, XLVI, 46.

[4] Starch, *Psychol. Rev.*, 1910, XVII, 19.

[5] *Arch. de Psychol.*, 1906, VI, 162.

[6] See Peterson and Jung, *Brain*, 1907, XXX, 153.

rents. The sweat-glands in the skin, it may be, are excited, through their nerves, by brain activity, and so give rise to the current. Sidis and Nelson,[1] experimenting on animals, used electrodes which penetrated through the skin, and still obtained currents; they therefore concluded that it is the muscles which produce the electric currents—the muscles being involuntarily excited by the activity of the brain.

Though these electric phenomena are delicate indicators of emotional states, they do not, apparently, differ with the particular quality of the emotion. They do not furnish, therefore, a differential symptom of pleasantness and of unpleasantness. It is difficult, indeed, to discover such a symptom in the bodily accompaniments of feeling. To judge by the method of expression, we should be brought to the unexpected conclusion that pleasant and unpleasant states of mind resemble each other more than either of them resembles indifference. In other words, they are all alike *states of excited feeling*.

§ 10. To recur to a subject to which reference has already been made: It is impossible to make any final statement, or even to offer any weighty evidence, regarding the brain activities which correspond to pleasant and unpleasant feelings. The general biological interpretation of the feelings connects pleasure with beneficial stimuli and a good condition of the organism, and unpleasantness with injurious stimuli and bad bodily conditions—a rule to which, however, there are evident exceptions. But this conception does not yet indicate in what manner the feelings are generated. Is feeling a sensation[2] originating in the excitation of sensory nerveends—and, if so, are there specific nerves and sense-organs for feeling, or can many or all afferent nerves convey to the brain impulses which are capable of arousing these forms of consciousness;—or, on the contrary, do pleasantness and unpleasantness arise from conditions of the brain itself? The latter class of explanations has several representatives. Meynert[3] suggested that feeling is an indication of the nutritive condition of the brain, especially as dependent on the blood supply.

Lehmann's "dynamic theory" of feeling[4] regards pleasantness as

---

[1] *Psychol. Rev.*, 1910, XVII, 98.

[2] Stumpf, *Zeitschr. f. Psychol.*, 1906, XLIV, 1; Titchener, *Textbook of Psychology*, 1909, p. 261.

[3] *Psychiatrie*, p. 171, cited after Ebbinghaus, *Grundzüge der Psychologie*, 1905, p. 577.

[4] *Die körperliche Äusserungen psychischer Zustände*, 1901, II, 291; 1905, III, 403; other interesting conceptions of the physiology of feeling have been entertained by Marshall in his *Pain, Pleasure and Æsthetics*, 1894, and by M. Meyer, *Psychol. Rev.*, 1908, XV, 201.

the index of a proper balance between the supply and the expenditure of energy by the nerve-cells of the brain; while unpleasantness results from an excess of expenditure over supply; and therefore every very intense sensory stimulus is unpleasant, because it overworks some of the brain-cells, causing their expenditure to exceed the supply brought to them by the blood stream.

The Herbartian doctrine (see just below) of pleasantness as the measure of harmonious co-operation of ideas, and of unpleas- antness as the measure of conflict between ideas, might be translated into the neural terms of facilitation and inhibition, a facilitated reaction being pleasurable and an inhibited or obstructed response being unpleasurable. Somewhat similar is the theory of Ziehen,[1] that the ready discharge of an excited portion of the cortex along paths of projection or of association is pleasurable; whereas the obstruction of such discharge constitutes unpleasantness. Where pertinent facts are so meagre, an attempt at selecting the best of these hypotheses is scarcely worth while.

§ 11. On account of the nature of our work, only a brief reference is necessary to one of the most elaborate, and in many respects successful, of all the theories which derive the phenomena of the feelings and emotions, in general, from other and different mental factors. We refer to that best known as connected with the name of the great German psychologist, Herbart. This theory makes feeling dependent upon the relations of the ideas as furthering or checking each other. It cannot be admitted, to begin with, that feeling is a secondary or derived form of consciousness. No form of mental activity is more primitive and unanalyzable than feeling; none is earlier in the development of mental life.[2] Before the infant has localized the different sensations, and combined them into percepts of the different parts of its own organism, the consciousness of being affected in a given way, either pleasurable or not, must predominate. Other forms of feeling—of desire, uneasiness, comfort, etc.—are inseparably connected with its first states of consciousness; they belong to its inherited impulses and instincts, and are only later definitely related to the appropriate ideas. The primary formation of self-consciousness is quite as truly connected with *self-feeling*, pleasurable or painful, as with the process of ideation in constructing the concept of "me" and "not- me." Volkmann von Volkmar, in his great work,[3] considers feeling

---

[1] *Physiologische Psychologie der Gefühle und Affekte*, 1902.

[2] The same view of the feelings is maintained by Horwicz, and developed at length, polemically, by Lotze (Horwicz, *Psychologische Analysen*, i, pp. 168 f.; Lotze, *Medicin. Psychologie*, pp. 235 f.).

[3] *Lehrbuch d. Psychologie*, 1884, II, pp. 298 ff.

as the consciousness of the process of ideation itself as distinguished from consciousness of this or that idea, and it is conditioned upon some resistance being offered to the process. Feeling is, then, no one proper idea, to be placed in conjunction or classed with others. It is rather a becoming conscious of the degree of tension, as it were, which characterizes the process of ideation at each particular moment. The condition of the origin of a feeling is, then, the existence of two simultaneous opposed ideas. Their coexistence occasions a state of tension ("*Spannung*"), as it were, and this state gives way as one idea triumphs over the other. The type of simple feeling may be illustrated by the condition in which the mind finds itself when listening to harmonious or discordant musical sounds.

As has already been said (p. 511), this theory closely approaches one of the more prominent of the purely physiological theories.

But, although we are to distinguish sensation from feeling, we must regard the feeling which inseparably accompanies sensation as *feeling*, strictly speaking, and not as *tone of sensation;* or, in other words, the tone of every sensation, as either pleasurable or painful, is given to it by the feeling which accompanies and blends with it. The sensation, as having a certain quality, quantity, and locality, is capable of being built into a "Thing" which the mind perceives as not itself. But the feeling, the pleasurable or painful tone of the sensation, is always recognized as purely and simply a way in which the mind is affected. To refuse to speak of sensations and emotions, with all their complicated physical basis, as belonging at all in the realm of "feeling," is to restrict the use of the word unwarrantably. The Herbartian theory commits in this matter the mistake which it is guilty of committing repeatedly; it regards the "ideas" as realities that have in some sort a substantial existence, and can do something by way of furthering or hindering each other. But ideas are themselves nothing more than mental products that exist only when and so long as the mind acts with a definite degree and kind of energy. In determining the kind and degree of this ideating energy, the previous action and habit of the mind by way of feeling is quite as influential upon the mode of feeling as the manner of its ideating energy. Finally, this theory wrecks itself upon the denial of all that which the physiological theory maintains and establishes. The two theories, then, supplement and correct each other; but *even when combined they only tell us in part what are the physical and mental conditions under which feeling arises.*

§ 12. As a logical consequence of the very nature of all kinds and degrees of feeling, a strict classification of our affective and emotional states is impossible. The difficulty is even greater than that which was found to be encountered by every attempt to classify the sensations of smell, as such. In both cases—that of certain sensations and that of all feelings—the popular language is significant of this fact of universal experience. Sensations of color are either red, green, blue, etc.; but agreeable sensations of smell are either of a rose, or of a violet; and disagreeable odors are either of asafœtida, or of mercaptan, etc. In somewhat the same way, judgments are fitly classified as either positive or negative, universal or particular or distributive, etc.; but all these classes of judgments may, when considered in their affective or emotional aspect, be distinguished as characterized by feelings *of* doubt, or *of* certainty, and accompanied by feelings *of* sadness, or *of* joy, or *of* mixed pleasure and pain.

It is obvious, then, that any attempt at classifying the feelings is likely to be most practically successful, even if it must surrender the attempt at scientific accuracy, when it takes some one of the points of view from which the subject may be best seen in indirect vision, as it were. Among the classification schemes derived in this way, that is perhaps most convenient which emphasizes those other forms of mental activity on which the various kinds of feeling are chiefly dependent. In this way, we may recognize three, or four, great classes of human experiences, when looked upon as characterized by their affective, or emotional, aspect. These would be (1) the *sensuous* feelings, or those which are dependently related to, and in consciousness blended with, the different qualities and intensities of the sensations of the special senses or the more general organic functions; (2) the *intellectual* feelings, or those which precede, accompany, or follow the various activities of discrimination, association, judgment, reasoning, and, indeed, all the forms of functioning of the "mind" in the narrower meaning of the latter word; (3) *æsthetic* feelings, or those which belong to the perception and appreciation of what we call "the beautiful" (in its various forms), or its opposite; and (4) the *moral* feelings, or those affective experiences which appertain to the good and the bad, in human conduct. To these might be added a fifth class, to be called the religious feelings, were it not for the fact that the latter may be satisfactorily treated as special forms of the combination of the intellectual, æsthetic, and moral feelings.[1]

In adopting this, or any similar classification, it must be remembered, as a matter of course, that senses, intellect, and will enter into all the activities connected with every form of complex and highly developed emotion; and such are all the emotional states of our

[1] A similar classification is that proposed by Horwicz: *Psychologische Analysen*, ii, pp. 82 f.

adult experience. For this reason also, no hard and fixed line can be drawn about the different so-called classes of feelings. The æsthetic feelings cannot be separated from the sensuous; for example, the feeling which accompanies the sensation of a musical chord, or of the color purple, may be classed under either head. Nor can the intellectual feelings be separated from the æsthetic; the perception of harmony of colors and sound is inseparably connected with æsthetic and sensuous feeling, and the latter is intensified or otherwise modified under the intellectual laws of contrast, change, habit, and higher association. Even the feelings which we call "moral" on account of their connection with will and desire, often have an indefinite part of them so combined with feelings located in the bodily organism, or so dependent on its functions for their quantity and quality, that a strict separation becomes impossible. Love is seldom or never so purely ideal as not plainly to involve in itself feeling of sensuous and æsthetic sort; hate not mixed with anger, and so supported on some elements of that physical basis which underlies the latter, is hard to discover in real life.

§ 13. All feelings are characterized by tone, strength, rhythm, and content. Their *content* is determined by the ideating activity with which they are directly connected, or to which they are related; and this content may be comparatively simple, as is the case with the feeling connected with the presentation of a colored surface (for example, purple or green), or obviously complex, as is the case with the sentiments of patriotism, loyalty, and religious devotion.

Feelings, like all other mental phenomena, occur under *time-form;* they are, in general, rhythmic in character, and change in respect to content, tone, and intensity, with a movement marked more or less distinctly by the quality of periodicity. Their rhythm, with respect to content, is, of course, determined by the recurrence of changes in the ideating activity as dependent especially upon attention and the laws of association. Feelings of sadness or joy, comfort or discomfort, may come around again in consciousness, as it were, according to the rhythmic movement of the sensations which occasion them. Sometimes an alternation of tone takes place, which carries the mind back and forth by the point of indifference (or hypothetical zero-point of feeling) between agreeable and disagreeable sensations, or ideas of the same kind. Thus we are sometimes forced to say that we do not know whether a certain combination of colors, or quality of taste or smell, is pleasing to us or not; in such a case feeling seems to move rhythmically back and forth between a slightly pronounced tone of pleasure and a slightly pronounced tone of pain.

The *intensity,* too, of feelings rises and falls alternately in dependence upon the rhythmic movement of the nervous processes and of the train of ideas. No feeling is kept at a long continuous level with respect to its vigor and pitch of strength. The law of quickly alternating exhaustion and repair of the nervous elements underlies, to a large extent, this rhythmic movement of the intensity of the feelings. This is one of many proofs which go to show that the conditions of the end-organs and of the central organs are determinative of the tone and strength of feeling. Even when we are strictly attending to our painful feeling, the toothache is not a perfectly uniform and steady strain; even when we are doing our best to abstract attention from the pain, we succeed only intermittently. But the course of the ideas must also be taken into account as influencing the rhythm of feeling. As our sensations or mental images become more clear and vivid, the feelings attached to them gather strength; as the former become more obscure and feeble, the feelings also die away in consciousness.

§ 14. It has been said (p. 501) that some psychologists would divide all our affective states into two classes of feelings—viz., pleasantness and unpleasantness. But we have seen that this classification is entirely unsatisfactory; primarily because it fails to take account of the almost infinite variety of, not only our complex feelings, emotions, and sentiments, but also of those affective experiences whose analysis has hitherto resisted all our most ingenious methods, both introspective and experimental. We have, therefore, preferred to regard pleasantness and unpleasantness as the "tone" of feeling. This is to recognize the fact that, not only can we speak appropriately of the feelings of pleasantness and of unpleasantness, but that, with even greater propriety, we speak of nearly, or quite, all our feelings, of every class, as being themselves either pleasant or unpleasant. And, indeed, the feeling of pleasure and pain is probably the most general, most simple, and earliest psychical process. That almost all feelings are characterized by some positive tone—or, in other words, are not absolutely indifferent to us— there can be no question. Is it agreeable or disagreeable, at least in some slight degree and in some more or less indefinite manner? is an inquiry which we can pretty readily answer with respect to nearly all our sensations and ideas. The question has for a long time been debated, however, whether this is necessarily true of all our feelings. Is there any such thing as completely *"neutral"* feeling, or feeling that is in no respect or degree either agreeable or disagreeable to us? Neutral or indifferent feelings were recognized by Reid, but disputed by Hamilton.[1] Bain[2] asserted it as un-

---

[1] Hamilton's *Works of Thomas Reid*, p. 311 (Edinburgh, 1854).
[2] *The Emotions and the Will*, 3d ed., p. 13.

doubted that "we may feel, and yet be neither pleased nor pained," and that "almost every pleasurable and painful sensation and emotion passes through a stage or moment of indifference." Wundt[1] argued, on theoretical grounds, that pleasure and pain, as tones of feeling having a variable intensity, are conditions which may be regarded as on different sides of a zero-point, or point of indifference lying between them. It does not follow, however, that, because the mind passes in time from feeling of one positive tone (pleasure) to feeling of the opposite tone (pain), it must, therefore, at some instant be in a state of feeling that has no tone and lies between the two. The curve plotted to represent the rise and fall of feeling is a material line; it cannot be at one time below, and at another above, the abscissa-line, without at some single point (the zero-point) coinciding with it. But it does not follow that, because such a curve is a picture of the phenomena of feeling in one respect, it is so in all other respects. The question whether there is any zero-point to the tone of feeling can only be answered by an appeal to consciousness; and this answer, like all others given to similar appeals, is likely to contain dubious and conflicting elements. It is quite certain that one can pass from a high state of pleasure to one of intense pain without any consciously interpolated neutral feeling. For example, if while one is viewing a beautiful landscape one is stung by hornets, the condition of quiet massive pleasure may be converted into one of great physical suffering without any intervening feeling of indifference.

§ 15. As to the nervous apparatus and physiological processes concerned in the imparting of pleasant or unpleasant tone to the various kinds of feelings, two principal views have been current hitherto. As bearing upon the pleasure-pain tone of the sensations, one view holds that the same apparatus of end-organs, conducting nerve-tracts, and central areas, which on moderate excitement produces the simple sensations of pressure or of temperature, or the more complex sensations of tickling, shuddering, etc., produces the feeling of pain when irritated with increased intensity. Such a view would apparently have also to hold that muscular sensations have the same physical apparatus as do feelings of muscular weariness or exhaustion; and, perhaps, that cardialgia and hunger are due to modifications of the action of the same nerves of the stomach. But from the introspective point of view it is as certain that sensations of pressure or mere temperature are unlike the feeling of pleasure produced by gentle rubbing or by comfortable warmth, or the pain that comes from heavy pressure or burning, as it is that sensations of light are unlike those of musical tone.

[1] *Physiolog. Psychologie*, 2d ed., I, pp. 465 f.

It is now known, however, that there are, for the skin at least, end-organs at the "pain points" (see p. 345.) It becomes a reasonable conjecture that the pain which follows the excessive stimulation of the other end-organs of sense, such as the eye or ear, is due to the excitement of specific "pain nerves" connected with those organs. There are other physiological reasons for doubting the complete identity of the nervous apparatus of pleasurable and painful feeling with that of the sensations with which the feeling is allied. The facts upon which Schiff and others supported the view that nervous impulses resulting in pain travel by more or less distinct paths along the spinal cord have already been stated. More recent experiments seem to show that the end-organs of temperature, pressure, and pain are locally separable in the different minute areas of the skin. Pathological results indicating the same separation of the nervous elements of feeling also deserve a brief mention. In certain cases the sensibility of the skin to pain is lost, while its sensibility to touch is not weakened or is even increased. The reverse condition also sometimes occurs. "Analgia," as occasioned by pathological states of the spinal cord due to lead-poisoning, was noticed in many cases by Beau. This loss of sensibility to pain can hardly be explained by any change in the activity of certain end-organs *common* both to touch and to painful feeling. What impairment of function could possibly result in destroying the sensitiveness to strong mechanical and thermic excitations, such as ordinarily occasion great pain, while the response by way of sensations of touch to much feebler excitations remains undiminished?

The same argument would appear decisive against identifying, locally, the central nervous processes which result in sensation with those which result in feeling. In certain stages of narcosis, produced by ether or chloroform, the patient is able to perceive the slightest contact with the skin, but feels no pain even when the same area is treated severely. Moreover, in some cases of *tabes dorsalis*, a constant difference seems to exist in the time at which the sensations of pressure and the feelings of pain, simultaneously excited at the end-organ, arise in the mind. If the patient is pricked with a needle, he will instantly feel the contact, and the pain only one to two seconds later.[1] The case of the eye, which responds with sensations of light and color when the optic nerve is moderately excited, and with the painful feeling of being blinded when the stimulus is increased, is not perfectly clear; for cases of amaurosis are on record where the painful feeling persisted after the eye had lost all

---

[1] See Funke, in Hermann's *Handb. d. Physiol.*, III, ii, pp. 297 f.; such phenomena have been especially discussed by Osthoff, *Die Verlangsamung d. Schmerzempfindung bei Tabes dorsalis*, 1874.

power to distinguish light. It may well be, therefore, that while the specific sensations of light and color are due to the irritation of the optic nerve, the excitement of feeling indicates a simultaneous irritation of part of the trigeminus.

We are compelled, then, to confess that the localizing of the nervous apparatus, and the nature of the physiological processes which give the tone of painful and pleasurable feeling to our sensations, require further investigation. The tendency of the evidence, however, is toward a theory which assigns to feeling a more or less separate mechanism of end-organs, conducting nerve-tracts, and central areas (or at least of nervous elements in the central areas).

§ 16. Certain mixtures of vaguely localized sensations, with feelings of a more or less pleasant or unpleasant tone, have acquired the name of *sensus communis*, or "common feeling." Such feeling may have more or less of content of one kind or another, according to the state of perception and ideation with which it is combined. Nervous impulses of indefinite variety and the most manifold peripheral origin are constantly pouring in, as it were, upon the cerebral centres—each one contributing some element to the characteristic tone of consciousness. The resulting feelings are *modes of our being affected* which are not converted into definite presentations of sense, or referred to a particular part of our own bodies. The effect of changes in the minute blood-vessels and other capillaries about the nerve-endings, the presence of impurities in the blood, the condition of the lower cerebral centres, the action of the heart and lungs and other internal organs, and the connection of the sympathetic with the cerebro-spinal nervous system, are all felt in this way. Moreover, inasmuch as few (if any) sensations are without some tone of feeling, while many sensations are exceedingly heterogeneous in their elements, and not clearly referred to the place of their origin, a *mélange*, as it were, of obscure bodily affections is readily formed.

Sensations in themselves heterogeneous may also be brought into a temporary relation by the partial identity of their source of excitation, and of the nervous connections in the central organs. It is also always a very important question, how the more obscure and mixed bodily feelings stand related to the mind's course of ideation, to attention, association, etc. This relation often determines whether such obscure impressions shall be definitely objectified or not; whether they shall not rather run together in the dark stream of common feeling. Let any one suspend for an instant a train of interesting thought, which has up to the moment been interrupted only by certain obscure feelings of uneasiness, and such a one will be able instantly to select and localize in the cramped

chest, or oppressed limbs, or tired organs of special sense, most of
the sensations whose painful tone has thus colored the stream of
common feeling. Separation from localized sensations is, then, the
chief negative characteristic of common feeling. Under its different principal forms we may distinguish different total results, according to the general relation in which the being aware merely
that we are affected in an agreeable or disagreeable manner stands
to the being aware of *what* affects us in this manner. Thus we
sometimes feel well or ill, elevated or depressed, without ability to
assign these feelings at all definitely to the physical organism, either
as perceived or imaged, or to any reason in the train of ideas. At
other times the general impression of being in the body, for some
greater or less amount of either weal or woe, is emphatic; we feel
ill all over, or seem to enjoy the coursing of the blood through every
artery and vein, as though mentally present in the extended tissues.

This *mélange* of sensations and feelings, the so-called *sensus
communis*, is connected in an important way with the higher forms
of self-consciousness, and with our entire sense of personality.
Temporary and relatively unimportant disturbances of its more
essential characteristics may result in our "feeling queer," or "feeling not exactly like ourselves." More important and permanent
disturbances take the form of those illusions which are characteristic of certain forms of insanity, such as that some part of the body
is made of glass, or that wheels are whirling inside the head, etc.
Upon the introspective basis of such experiences of "common
feeling" a whole system of perverted judgments may be based,
and essential changes in the conduct of life brought about. This
is what would be expected as a consequence of the fundamental
psychological truth that our feelings are the factors, and the aspects,
of our total experience which we attribute most directly and essentially to our very "own self," as distinguished from other selves.
Functional disturbances of the nervous mechanism, both peripheral
and central, chiefly concerned with the feeling aspect of our experience, alter in the most important way our conception of the Self.

§ 17. The question whether every sensation has some feeling
must be distinguished from the question whether every feeling is
of either painful or pleasurable tone. The tone of the feeling of
sensations is the agreeable or disagreeable affection of consciousness which they often carry, as inseparably connected with them.
The particular tone belonging to any sensation is, to a large extent, dependent on its intensity. Sensations of moderate intensity—that is, of intensity below the point at which the minimum of
painful feeling begins—are usually pleasurable. The feeling of
pain rises in intensity, from the point where it begins, as the in-

tensity of the stimulus increases; but the curves which represent the increase of feeling and the increase of sensation by no means completely correspond. The amount of pleasurable feeling is also dependent on the element of time. It has been thought to reach a maximum at about the point where the strength of sensation is the most favorable for accurate discernment of the objective stimulus.

As to the dependence of the tone of feeling belonging to a sensation upon the quality of the latter, it has been held that no sensation is *absolutely* pleasant or unpleasant irrespective of its intensity. Even then, however, it would have to be admitted that qualitatively different sensations differ greatly in the amount which is consistent with an agreeable tone of feeling. It is, of course, with regard to the organic sensations, and the special sensations of touch, smell, and taste, that the relation between tone of feeling and the quality of sensation is most apparent. Doubtless large allowance must be made in all cases for individual peculiarities of organism, association, etc. The disagreeable tone of feeling which almost universally attaches itself to certain qualities of sensation, however moderate or unobtrusive their intensity, may be largely explicable on the principle of heredity. But, taking matters as they stand in present experience, it is impossible to maintain that the tone of feeling is not, in certain cases, directly dependent on the quality of sensation. This is a question upon which only consciousness can pronounce. All degrees of some tastes and smells are disagreeable to most persons. Bitter is a distinctive species of the quality of gustatory sensations; but the pleasure which some persons have in greater or less degrees of it is, as a rule, acquired. It is true that some substances, whose odor in large quantity is disagreeable, become tolerable, or even pleasant, when the smell from them is faint. But this faint smell is not the same, but a distinctly different quality; oftentimes it could not be immediately recognized as coming from the same substance as that which emitted the strong odor. Discordant sounds are, in all degrees of intensity, naturally unpleasant; and so most witnesses would pronounce certain complex sensations of the skin (as of creeping, prickling, etc.).

§ 18. The character of the disagreeable or painful feeling belonging to different classes of sensations also differs with respect to the nature of its attachment to a recognized physical basis. Inharmonious colors produce in us a feeling of mild dissatisfaction, which appears as almost wholly of a spiritual kind. Discordant tones cause more of physical suffering; and disagreeable smells or tastes create a wide-spread sense of organic discomfort. Pains in the skin and interior organs, however, may take a character of intense bodily anguish, which is distinctive of no other qualities of sensation, and which is capable of submerging all sensation, as such, in a flood of painful feeling.

The tone of sensuous feeling is also dependent upon the total condition of consciousness as determined by attention, mental habit, association of the feelings among themselves and with the ideas, control of the will, etc. Such feeling is, therefore, largely a secondary element of experience, which arises through certain acquired effects of the sensations as connected with previous activities of the mind. But concerning the physical basis of the feelings, in this aspect of them, we have scanty scientific knowledge; and the subject is not as yet one with which physiological psychology can very successfully deal.

§ 19. Characteristic mixtures of feeling—some of them scarcely describable—seem to be attached inseparably to different kinds of sensations. This is obvious when we consider the marked difference in the way we are affected by major and minor chords, by successive tones having different musical intervals (for example, the diminished third, etc.), and by the characteristic clangs of different musical instruments. Writers upon this part of musical theory may disagree as to the precise significance of the violin, clarinet, cornet, or hautboy, with respect to the tone of feeling belonging to each; but they can scarcely deny the fact of a marked difference. Goethe[1] called attention to the change in spiritual tone, as it were, which harmonizes with what the eye sees when looking upon the world through different-colored glasses. Here, again, the precise equivalent, or value, in terms of feeling, which the different color-tones possess, may be a matter of dispute; but the fact that the tones of feeling change with the color-tones is beyond dispute. That feelings of soberness or gloom go with black, of excitement with red, of cheerfulness with light green, of cool quiet with dark blue, of intense sensuous pleasure with saturated purple, would probably be admitted by most persons. Fewer would agree to describing the tone of feeling belonging to dark yellow or spectral orange as one of "suppressed excitement," or to brown as one of "perfectly neutral mood."

§ 20. Nearly, if not quite, all the various forms of feeling, when they become stronger and the disturbances of their organic basis, so to say, more powerfully show themselves in consciousness, partake of certain common characteristics which lead to their being classified as "emotions." But, again, they are subdivided in an indefinite way, according to the relation they sustain to their objects, or to the actions which they tend to induce or to influence. In

[1] *Farbenlehre*, § 763.

this way, such different words as "affection," "passion," "impulse," and "desire" (the former two emphasizing rather the passive, and the latter two, the active aspect of the affective condition) may be applied to essentially the same class of feelings. A sufficient increase in their intensity, and a resulting increase of the "somatic resonance," may even convert the higher, and usually milder, intellectual, æsthetic, and moral feelings into an emotional experience. In truth, essentially the same mental state, so far as distinctions of affective quality are concerned, may be called simply a feeling, or an emotion, or a passion, or a sentiment. For example, love, whether sexual or so-called Platonic, or that distinctive of any of the various social relations, may on different occasions merit the distinctions involved in any of these terms. Owing to this general fact, the physiology of the various more complex forms of emotion may be studied from the same points of view.

§ 21. All emotional forms of feeling are accompanied by abrupt and marked changes in the character and time-course of the mental train. Such changes may be regarded as standing in the relation both of cause and of effect to these feelings. Some impression with which strong feeling has become associated is made upon the mind; the result is a transitory interruption of the mental equipoise. This constitutes in part the justification for the saying that from mere feeling to affection is a "leap." [1] As a rule, the effect of any sudden and surprising impression—perception of some object of sense, or remembered image—is to start the flow of emotion. Thus anger, fear, desire, avarice, take men "off their guard"; the feelings of such kind that are started by a given mental impression themselves produce a confusion of the mental train. But, on the other hand, this very disturbance of the mental train is itself productive of a new phase of feeling, such as is associated with the particular ideas that in confused and hurried throngs rush into consciousness, as well as with the general state of consciousness considered as one of haste and confusion. The physical basis of this state is laid in the extraordinary condition of excitation that exists within the central organs—the ideo- and sensory-motor centres of the cerebral hemispheres.

A not unreasonable conjecture as to the central conditions on which the excitement of the more complex forms of emotion are dependent, would state the case in somewhat the following way: It is a well-known fact that different individuals differ more widely and incalculably as to the particular feelings evoked, on different particular occasions, than as to the sensations and ideas occasioned by changes in the amounts, kinds, and time-rates of the

[1] Compare Nahlowsky, *Das Gefühlsleben*, etc., *Einleitung*.

stimuli which act upon the peripheral nervous system. This fact suggests that our feelings are determined by the changeable relations of the neural processes to the constitution, previous habits and temporary mood of the nervous system, and by the relations of each neural process to all the others within the central system, in a more irregular way than are our sensations and our knowledge. Those conditions of the nervous processes which depend immediately upon the quality, intensity, and time-rate of the stimuli that act upon the end-organs of sense, are in general conformable to law; they are regular and—as it were—to be depended upon. In correspondence with them are the regularity and the dependableness of our sensations and of our knowledge by the senses. But over and above the more uniformly recurrent similar elements in all the peripherally originated nervous processes, there is more or less of "semi-chaotic surplus" of nervous action occasioned in the brain centres. In this semi-chaotic surplus—the general character of which depends upon what the whole nervous system was, and is, and has recently been doing, and upon how the various new stimulations, running in to the brain centres, fit in with all this and with one another—may we find the physiological conditions of the emotions. No wonder, then, that these conditions are so indeterminate for different individuals, and so changeable in the same individual. At any particular moment the kind and amount of feeling experienced has for its physiological condition the total complex relation in which all the subordinate neural processes, set up by the stimuli of that moment, stand to one another and to the set, or direction, of pre-existing related neural processes.[1]

§ 22. Besides the physiological changes of central origin, which accompany or follow certain perceptions and trains of ideas, the wonderful, characteristic effect which these forms of feeling produce upon certain of the vital organs is the most noteworthy peculiarity of all affections, emotions, and passions. Upon this point science has far less than we could wish of information reaching beyond the observations of ordinary experience. Of such information, perhaps the most important concerns the influence exerted through many groups of muscles, from the central organs, upon the vaso-motor system. The effect of shame, fear, or anger, for example, upon the circulation of the blood is matter of common remark. But some grow pale and others red, when angry. As long ago as 1854, R. Wagner investigated the effect of fear upon the heart of a rabbit. A blow on the table near the animal was found to cause its heart to stand still a short time, and then resume beating

---

[1] See Ladd, *Psychology, Descriptive and Explanatory*, 1894, p. 173; and on the whole subject of feeling, ibid., chapters IX, X, XXIII, XXIV, and XXV.

with accelerated frequency of stroke. Subsequent investigations have made obvious the general effect of emotion upon the curve indicating the blood pressure. The effect produced upon the pulse of a dog by hearing the sudden cry of another dog depends for its character upon whether the vagus nerves are cut or not; but even after their severance a marked effect of this kind is still manifest.[1] The great influence of these forms of feeling upon all the action of the capillary vessels, upon the secretions, etc., and upon the respiration to retard, or accelerate, or make it irregular, is of the same order. That care and anxiety disturb nutrition, that pain and sorrow cause the tears to flow, that fear and love and anger act upon the abdominal organs, is generally recognized. The effect is sometimes seen in suddenly innervating, and sometimes in depressing, one or more of the bodily organs; or in both innervating and then depressing them, in certain well-recognized cases. On the basis of such facts, Kant suggested a division of the affections into "sthenic" and "asthenic." But many forms of feeling, as they run their course, become by turns sthenic and asthenic. Strong emotions or passions of all kinds tend to destroy the nervous mechanism; "the sthenic kill by apoplexy, the asthenic by laming the heart." Unusual tension or relaxation of certain groups of muscles characterizes all these forms of feeling.

§ 23. The marked effect which certain feelings have upon particular organs of the body is complemented by the fact that such organic effect has in turn a marked effect upon the feelings. The organic disturbances advance step by step to form the physical basis of a rising tide of emotion, and then fall off with equal pace as the tide of emotion subsides. The organic changes are not merely an expression of the mental; they are its material cause and support. Hence, from the physiological point of view every strong emotion must be regarded as involving certain factors of a peripheral origin; and from the introspective point of view, as including factors which should be analyzed into vaguely (or not at all) localized sensations having a somewhat marked tone of pleasant or unpleasant feeling. This general truth is well expressed by Sherrington[2] as follows: "Of points where physiology and psychology touch, the place of one lies at 'emotion.' Built upon sense-feeling much as cognition is built upon sense-perception, emotion may be regarded almost *as* a feeling—a feeling excited, not by a simple little-elaborated sensation, but by a group or train of ideas. To such compound ideas

---

[1] This subject has been investigated by Conty and Charpentier, by Cyon, Heidenhain, and others; compare Exner, in Hermann's *Handb. d. Physiol.*, II, ii, pp. 289 f.

[2] *The Integrative Action of the Nervous System*, 1906, p. 256.

it holds relation much as does feeling to certain species of simple sense-perceptions. It has a special physiological interest in that certain visceral reactions are peculiarly colligate with it. Heart, blood-vessels, respiratory muscles, and secretory glands take special and characteristic part in the various emotions. These viscera, though otherwise remote from the general play of psychical process, are affected vividly by the emotional." Some of these movements and secretions are visible from the outside; others, however, are hidden from view. Under the latter class may be mentioned the inhibition of the wave-like movements of the stomach in anger, as observed by Cannon,[1] by means of the Röntgen rays, in a cat. It is this "somatic reaction," or "bodily resonance;" which largely gives to all the various emotions their peculiar tinge, or characteristic coloring, as they arise in consciousness.[2]

The claim, however, that the emotions are *simply* the expressions, or outcome, in consciousness of peripherally initiated sensations, or organic reactions of a visceral or vaso-motor character, accompanied by the reduction of the cerebral and psychical processes to a secondary rôle, as this claim has been put forth, with minor differences, by Lange, James, and Sergi, contradicts all the evidence which we can at present bring to bear upon the case. It is opposed to the order of dependent sequence, so far as it can be determined by introspective analysis or followed by experiment; to the general theory of brain action in its relations to mental life; and it seems to have been distinctly discredited by experimentation upon the lower animals.[3] The latter kind of evidence leads Sherrington to pronounce "untenable" the vaso-motor theory of the production of emotion, and as well the view that visceral sensations or presentations are *necessary* to emotion.

On the other hand, there is evidence that some of the expressive movements are as independent of the cerebrum on the one side as they are of the viscera on the other; for, as already mentioned (p. 158), movements "expressive" of pain, fear and anger can be elicited from a decerebrate animal, and belong therefore to the class of

---

[1] *Amer. Journ. of Medical Sci.*, 1909, CXXXVII, 480.

[2] For an analysis of the more prominent of the emotions, both on the physiological and on the introspective side, and some more specific account of the kinds of this "bodily resonance," see Ladd, *Psychology, Descriptive and Explanatory*, pp. 538 ff.

[3] Sherrington, by "appropriate spinal and vagal transection," removed from dogs, completely, all the sensations of the viscera and of the skin and muscles behind the shoulder. In the case of an animal, "selected because of markedly emotional temperament," the almost complete reduction of the field of sensation "produced no obvious diminution of her emotional character." Ibid., pp. 260 f.; *Proceedings of the Royal Society of London*, 1900, LXVI, 390.

sub-cortical reflexes. Expressions of pleasure, such as purring and wagging the tail, are not observed in a decerebrate animal. A few cases of *visceral* anæsthesia, of which the best is that of d'Allonnes,[1] show, as we should expect, a loss of the affective tone of certain emotions, in which, in the normal conditions, the visceral sensations play a prominent part. The woman whose case is reported by d'Allonnes, though previously affectionate and emotional, given to worry, etc., became indifferent to her beloved family, and sought admission to the hospital to be cured of this lack of power to feel emotions. She still retained her former habits and principles, and even preferences, but these, she said, no longer had any feeling connected with them. Yet her external expressive movements were retained; in particular, she wept, but without inner grief, and she showed the signs of anger, shame, disgust, etc., while protesting that she felt no emotion. Similar indefinite results have, however, been reported as sequent upon injuries to various portions of the cerebrum, where the peripheral organic functions remained practically normal.

Among the many and often conflicting investigations in this really difficult field may be mentioned a very careful piece of work by Shepard,[2] in which the previous results are reviewed. Shepard made a comparative study of circulatory changes in the brain (in a patient whose brain was exposed) and in the arm, and found that, "in general, all agreeable or disagreeable stimuli, all sensory attention or attention to arithmetical problems, all agreeably exciting light or music," gave a decrease in the volume of the hand and an increase in the volume of the brain. He concludes from these results, and from the studies of circulation and breathing during affective conditions in other cases, that a classification of the feelings cannot be made on the basis of their bodily accompaniments; that there is no opposition between the accompaniments of pleasantness and unpleasantness, nor any evidence for Wundt's three dimensions of feeling. "In short, all moderate nervous activity tends to constrict the peripheral vessels and to increase the volume and size of pulse in the brain. All moderate nervous activity likewise increases the heart-rate." Strong stimuli, such as arouse fear, etc., induce a more complex circulatory reaction, beginning, in the brain, with an increase in volume, passing thence to a decrease, and finally rising to a large increase, which gradually passes away. The mechanism of these changes in the blood supplied to the brain is probably to be sought, largely, in the vaso-motor control of the great abdominal veins. These investigations, there-

[1] *Revue philos.*, 1905, LX, 592.
[2] *Amer. Journ. of Psychol.*, 1906, XVII, 522.

fore, strongly support the central theory of feeling which we have been advocating.

§ 24. The *teleological* value of many of the emotions, especially such as man shares with all the higher animals, needs scarcely more than mention in order to be recognized. It is amply illustrated by the observations, both of biology and of psychology, when studied from the comparative and evolutionary points of view. In general these two principles apply to a large class of the emotions: (1) The motor reactions called forth as a part of the bodily resonance are adapted for the defence and preservation of the individual; and (2) by the application of the principles of imitation and sympathy, these same or other reactions operate for the defence and preservation of the species. Evolutionary biology is, therefore, justified in considering "the bodily expressions of emotion as instinctive actions reminiscent of ancestral ways of life."

§ 25. That there is a considerable class of feelings which may be properly classified as "intellectual," no adequate analysis of the extremely complex form of mental activity which we call knowledge, or cognition, allows us for a moment to doubt. Indeed, it might also be said that the influence of feeling is as obvious, and almost if not quite as great, in determining all our acts of knowledge, whether so-called presentations of sense or self-consciousness, as are the activities of discrimination, comparison, association, etc. The *so-called faculties of intellect and feeling blend in all cognition, and the complex result—the* very object of knowledge—*is determined by both.*[1]

Without attempting the difficult, if not impossible, task of enumerating all the intellectual feelings, we may remind ourselves of the changing affective tone of consciousness when, on comparing two or more objects, as wholes, or qualities of objects, we pass from a condition of doubt and uncertainty, through varying shades of the recognition of similarities and differences, into the feeling of certainty and conviction which is both the accompaniment, and the test in a measure, of our arriving at a completed act of cognition. Indeed, this conviction itself involves a sort of "belief in reality," for which we seem compelled to find a place among our most fundamental forms of feeling.

What can be claimed, or credibly conjectured, as true with regard to the forms of the functioning of the nervous mechanism on which many of these so-called intellectual feelings depend, or with which they are connected, has in large measure been said while treating

---

[1] For an extended exposition and defence of this doctrine see Ladd, *Psychology, Descriptive and Explanatory*, chapter XXII; *Philosophy of Mind*, chapter III; and *Philosophy of Knowledge* (passim).

of the sensations, their combinations into presentations of sense, and the physiological basis of the simpler forms of feeling. Something will be added in the following chapters which deal with the physiological psychology of attention, association, memory, and judgment. In all this field, experimental psychology has not much of clearly ascertained scientific truth, which can be employed to reveal the concomitant, or otherwise connected, processes of the nervous system—especially of the cerebral areas. But it is not by any means a wholly unfounded conjecture that hesitancy, inhibition, confusion, opposition, facilitation, with varying degrees of speed and smoothness, fixed habit in "dynamical associations" within the brain, and a number of similar terms, describe with reasonable appropriateness those central nervous processes which are correlated with the mental processes that we are accustomed to describe in similar terms.

One other thing is worthy of notice in this connection. Some of the intellectual feelings, especially when they take on the emotional character, quite naturally lead to expressive motions, or tendencies to move, or to hold in place, the muscular system, in whole or in part. All our language—such as "standing firm," or "pat," "holding on" to one's belief, or opinion, etc., and the whole practice of gesticulating and expressive posturing—is significant of the close relations existing between certain intellectual feelings and the muscular apparatus. Here, too, we must look for important "somatic reactions."

§ 26. The *æsthetic feelings* arise and develop chiefly in connection with presentations of sense, or with the remembered or created mental images that represent objects of sense. In their elementary form, therefore, they plainly have a physiological side which admits of scientific treatment—although they have received such treatment far less than could be wished. Many interesting facts and certain partial generalizations—having most application to the lower classes of pleasurable feelings through the organs of smell, taste, and the skin, when viewed in the light of the hypothesis of evolution—have been alleged by various observers. But even the most elementary æsthetic feelings cannot be considered as on a par with the sensuous feelings, or as mere aggregates of such feelings. The tone of feeling which characterizes the sensations furnishes a material, as it were, for genuinely æsthetic feeling; but the latter always implies also the working of certain intellectual laws, and a union of the simple feelings of sensation under time-form and space-form. Æsthetic feelings, then, may be said to spring, in a measure, from the manner of the combination of sensuous feelings; time and space furnish the framework in which they are arranged. Hearing is

the principal sense for combining sensuous feelings so as to produce
æsthetic feelings under time-form, and sight under space-form.
The development of even the elementary but genuine *æsthetic* feelings by other senses than the eye and ear is extremely limited.
The agreeable and disagreeable feelings which come through sensations of smell, taste, and touch are for the most part sensuous,
rather than strictly æsthetic.

Hearing, as pre-eminently the time-sense, has two forms of æsthetic feeling—harmony and rhythm.   The nature of the complex
sensations which produce the feeling of consonance and dissonance
has already been discussed.   Harmony is determined by the coincidence of certain partial tones belonging to different clangs simultaneously sounded.   The feeling of harmony is colored by the
peculiar way in which the combination of the clangs occurs.   The
principal difference of this sort is that which obtains between major
chords and minor chords; in the former the different clangs are
perceived as firmly held together by the fundamental clang, while
in the latter the coincident overtone performs the same office less
obviously.   The one is productive of agreeable æsthetic feeling
satisfied; the other of such feeling left unsatisfied—a feeling of
longing.   When, then, the one form of feeling becomes very intense, it may involve the pain of over-excitement; the other, when
intensified, stirs a kind of agreeable pain of unrest.   In musical
time it is the periodic nature of the excitation, with a change in the
individual presentations of sense, which produces the pleasurable
æsthetic feeling.

Two or three regularly recurring impressions, having the same
or a different content of musical sound, are combined into a series;
certain members among the whole number are then accentuated,
in order to form the different series that constitute the various kinds
of musical time.   All musical time, fundamentally considered as
respects its rhythm, is either two-time or three-time.   The difference in the feelings which respond to these two classes of musical
rhythm is obvious in a pronounced form, in the funeral march, on
the one hand, and the waltz, on the other.   In general, it is the
harmony of music which gives direction to its feeling, and the
rhythm which determines the rise and fall of feeling.   Thus *waves*
of different kinds of feeling are made by music to pass over the
soul.

§ 27. Even less than is the case with the intellectual feelings,
does experimental psychology serve to reveal the exact nature of
those physiological processes which are connected with the more
complex æsthetic feelings that greet the art of music.   Where these
feelings rise to an emotional character, the effect of the "somatic

reactions," and the influence of the associated ideas and tendencies to action (as to dance, to fight, to embrace, to march) become more clearly distinctive and powerful. The feelings with which we appreciate—whether favorably or unfavorably—those peculiar successions of tones which are required by melodies written in the various keys, or the tone-color of the various instruments in an orchestra, are more subtle and as yet quite indeterminate as to their essential content, not to say their physiological correlates. Those feelings of right "relationship" which have come to set the laws of the succession of tones in the affectively best melodies of modern music are of special interest to the investigator. But beyond the mere fact that some successions excite feelings of pleasurable satisfaction, and "finality," or feelings of recognition of the series as a unity, while others do not, little is known at present about the psychology of musical melody. The cause of this feeling of finality has been described as a "balanced muscular resolution." [1]

The elementary æsthetic feelings which come through sight lead to the consideration of the æsthetic effect of visual form. Such effect can be considered only very imperfectly from the physiological point of view. In one important particular, however, pleasurable æsthetic feeling is directly dependent upon the combination of the sensations, with their accompanying tone of feeling, under the laws of the mechanism of vision with both eyes in motion. Beautiful form is determined by the course of the limiting lines; and limiting lines, in order to have the effect of arousing agreeable æsthetic feeling, must accommodate themselves to the physiological and psycho-physical necessities of the eye when in motion. These necessities thus determine both the direction and the extent of the limiting lines. Lines of slight curvature, not too far continued in one direction, best comply with such necessities. Lines of very sharp curvature, or lines continued too long in one direction, do not produce a pleasing æsthetic effect. So also must the main lines of a building lie in horizontal or vertical directions, preferably in the former direction. But long oblique lines—for example, from a lower right-hand to an upper left-hand corner of a building—are scarcely tolerable. The ease with which the eye moves, by jerks (see p. 459), along the lines, in order to make that synthesis of successive similar presentations of sense in which every perception of a line consists, is plainly a determining factor in all these cases.

The æsthetic effect of visual form is also determined by the way in which the form is constructed, through repeating similar or unlike simple shapes and combining them into a totality. By this

---

[1] *Studies in Melody*, by W. Van Dyke Bingham. Monograph Supplements of the *Psych. Rev.*, 1910, vol. XII, No. 3.

means a feeling of pleasure akin to the feeling of musical rhythm is excited by the successive impressions which occur periodically as the eye, with a nearly uniform movement, sweeps the entire field. In horizontal directions, the law for the arrangement of the parts is that of symmetry of the simple parts; in vertical, rather the law of asymmetry. Certain proportions between the connected parts, and between the whole and the parts, are favorable to the development of æsthetic feeling. Ease of the mental apprehension with which the relations in proportion of the different parts are presented is favorable to agreeable æsthetic feeling.

§ 28. It appears, then, that the varied æsthetic feelings, pleasant and unpleasant, which are dependent upon visual sensations and perceptions, are of all others most closely connected, in respect of their facts and laws, with the so-called "intellectual" side of our objective experience. Conditions which determine our apperception of space-relations, as well as the harmony and contrast of colors, varied and often obscure associations, and even hereditary factors, are prominent in the causation of the various shades of æsthetic feeling of visual objects.

In conclusion of this subject it is worth while to notice that the emotions aroused by the markedly different classes of beautiful objects differ in a marked way among themselves, in respect to their "somatic reactions" and to the resulting affective tone of consciousness. Thus, for example, our appreciation of what we consider sublime is distinctly unlike, and in some respects the *opposite* of, our appreciation of what is beautifully delicate, the handsome, or pretty, so called. So, too, the mingling of sensations and feelings and ideas with which we greet objects that have the beauty of order and proportion (a Greek temple, for example) is very different from that with which we appreciate the beauty of luxuriance and wildness (a tropical forest, for example). Introspective analysis of the elements of these complex æsthetic emotions is relatively easy as compared with the experimental analysis of the simpler forms of feeling, under whatever class we may be inclined to place them.[1]

§ 29. Not only do the emotions involve elements derived from the changes initiated in the musculature, but they all tend to express themselves in the muscles of the limbs and trunk, head, eyes, and vocal apparatus. We are probably safe in saying that strained attention is associated with a tense and rigid condition of the muscles, and that relief brings relaxation and freer movements. Excitement seems to be expressed by much muscular activity, and calm and depression by muscular inactivity.

[1] Compare Ladd, *Knowledge, Life, and Reality*, 1909, chaps. XVII–XIX.

In regard to pleasantness and unpleasantness, considerable interest has been aroused over the assertion[1] that pleasantness is associated with expansive movements of the organism, and unpleasantness with contractive movements. The probability is that there is no such clean-cut distinction between the expressive value of these two classes of muscles, in so highly organized and so specialized a motor apparatus as that of man. Both flexors and extensors co-operate in the production of movements which may be, as wholes, reactions to beneficial or harmful stimuli, and so expressive of pleasant or unpleasant feelings. Although, for example, the primary reaction to a painful stimulus is the "flexion reflex" (compare p. 153), this changes, when the stimulus is intense or prolonged, to a movement of flight, in which the extensors take the leading part. The rapid alternation, in most active movements, of extensions and flexions, also makes it difficult to believe that either is specifically related to a certain tone of feeling. On the whole, then, there is little evidence of a specific bodily expression for pleasantness or unpleasantness—one, that is, which is expressive alike of all conditions into which these feelings enter.

§ 30. There is, however, good evidence of an exciting or depressing effect on the bodily activities of many stimuli and of many states of mind. These effects have sometimes been called *dynamogenic*. They are related to the reinforcement and inhibition which are seen in reflex action. A good index of the excited or depressed condition of the reflex mechanisms of the nerve-centres, and especially of the spinal cord, is afforded by the knee jerk, or smart kick of the foot produced by the extensor muscle of the thigh, when its tendon, passing over the knee, is struck. Though this movement is entirely involuntary, it is by no means removed from the influence of mental conditions. For example, anxious attention to the knee and foot inhibits the reflex, so that the physician, to whom the knee jerk is often a symptom of importance, must needs distract the attention of his patient from the knee. This he usually does by requiring the patient to grip or pull vigorously with the hands at the moment when the blow on the tendon is to be struck; under these circumstances the knee jerk is especially strong. The explanation of this result in terms of distraction—as if the only reaction of mental activity to the reflex were one of inhibition, which must be put aside by distraction—is not complete. Lombard[2] found that reinforcement or inhibition of the knee jerk could result from many stimuli and mental influences, even though the subject, from long-continued familiarity with the experiment, required no distraction to direct his mind

[1] See Münsterberg, *Beiträge zur exp. Psychol.*, 1892, IV, 216.
[2] *Amer. Journ. of Psychol.*, 1887, I, 1.

away from his knee. Martial music increased the reflex, whereas quiet though interesting music had the opposite effect. An exciting noise, such as the cry of an infant, increased it, whereas commonplace and insignificant noises, such as the rattle of vehicles in the street, were without effect. In these last examples it is evidently not the mere sensory effect of the stimulus, but rather its meaning for the individual, which exercises the exciting or depressing effect on the spinal cord.

One salient fact regarding the relation of consciousness to movement is, accordingly, that some conscious processes exalt, while others depress, the activity of the reflex centres and through them of the muscles.

Similar effects were observed by Féré[1] in the case of voluntary movements. He required his subjects to exert their utmost force in squeezing a dynamometer in the hand, and found that this "utmost" could be increased by sensory stimuli, and that different stimuli possessed different degrees of this dynamogenic influence. Light reinforced the action of the hand muscles, darkness depressed it. The colors were still more powerful and all dynamogenic; but red had the strongest effect. Of tastes, bitter had a strong dynamogenic effect, and sweet a weak effect in the same direction; of odors, the sharp and penetrating reinforced the pressure of the hand, and the heavy odors had the opposite effect—and this without much regard to the pleasantness or unpleasantness of the odor. It should be said that these effects are not strongly marked except in suggestible subjects; the average, "normal" individual is scarcely influenced at all by colors, for example. But there are certain more complex and, as one may say, more mental influences which do have a strong influence on the motor power of the normal individual. Chief among such influences is perhaps that of competition between individuals who alternately squeeze the dynamometer, or who are running a race.[2]

In fact, the supposedly maximal voluntary effort is, to judge from its muscular effect, a variable quantity, subject to many involuntary influences; and the experiments quoted illustrate the complexity of the mental influences which exalt or depress muscular activity.

§ 31. The relation of consciousness to movement cannot be fully appraised without considering another class of facts. These relate to the so-called *automatic movements*, or movements which, in contrast to expressive and voluntary movements, go on without

[1] *Sensation et mouvement* (Paris, 1887; 2d ed., 1900); *Année psychologique*, 1900, VII, 69, 82, 143.

[2] Triplett, *Amer. Journ. of Psychol.*, 1898, IX, 507; Wright, *Psychol. Rev.*, 1906, XIII, 23.

consciousness, or at least without clear consciousness. A good example is afforded by any much-practised movement, which continues smoothly while the attention is on something else. Another example is found in instinctive movements, such as breathing, which pursue their way, on the whole, undirected by consciousness. In studying reflex action (p. 173), we noted the solidarity of the nervous system, and the mutual influence which was likely to be exerted by the activity of one part on the activities of any other part; but we also noticed that the activity of one part might, on occasion, be relatively independent of other parts, so that two or more non-interfering activities might be going on at the same time in different parts of the nerve-centres. Automatic movement is an illustration of this relative independence of different parts of the system. The regular movements of respiration go on without much reference to what is occurring in the conscious centres of the cerebrum, except in cases of excitement, strained attention, etc. In the same way, the activity of some well-trained part of the cerebrum, which presides over a certain familiar performance, may go on without interfering with the activity of some other part with which the attentive consciousness of the moment is connected, and without being interfered with by it. This independence of different parts is, however, only relative; interference is likely to occur, and when it does occur, we have an expressive as opposed to an automatic movement. Those parts of the motor apparatus which are, at any moment, much influenced by conscious processes give rise to expressive movements; those parts which are little influenced give rise to automatic movements. Expressive movements, in a word, illustrate the solidarity of the nervous system, while automatic movements reveal a certain degree of dissociation within it.

In a negative way, automatic movements may themselves be expressive; for they usually cease or are somehow interfered with as soon as the conscious process becomes very intense. Breathing, as has been said, is likely to be inhibited during a brief period of intense mental activity. A man who is automatically walking while immersed in thought may sometimes be observed to stand stock-still when some specially interesting idea strikes him. Lindley[1] found two classes of involuntary movements, which might be observed, for example in a school-room: one class of movements accompanied intense mental effort, and consisted in strained positions of the members; the other class appeared when the mind wandered, and consisted in rhythmical movements. The latter, automatic class, gives way to the former, expressive class, on passing from mind-wandering to mental effort. There are, however, considerable

[1] *Amer. Journ. of Psychol.*, 1895, VII, 491.

individual differences in regard to automatisms. Binet[1] observed such differences among children, and Stein[2] in young adults. The last author found some individuals in whom intense mental application favored instead of inhibited automatic movements. In that peculiarly unstable condition of the nervous system known as hysteria, the tendency to automatisms and dissociations is at its maximum, and some such individuals may carry on complex acts, such as writing a letter, while the attention is absorbed in something quite different.[3] The relation of consciousness to bodily movement is therefore partly expressed by saying that conscious processes exert general dynamogenic and depressive effects on the motor apparatus, and partly by calling attention to the limitations of these influences.

But besides these general influences, specific conscious processes have specific motor effects. Certain ideas lead to certain definite movements, with which they have become associated by past experience. They may do so either with or without the full consent of the subject. When an idea leads to its appropriate movement with the full consent of the subject, we call it voluntary movement; but when the idea leads to movement, as it always tends to, while the subject's attention and intention are elsewhere directed, the movement is often named *ideomotor*. Examples of the last are seen in involuntary whispering of what one reads or thinks, in involuntary gestures, and often, in rather an amusing way, in the movements of spectators at an athletic game or an acrobatic show, when they are much absorbed in the movements about to be executed by the performers. and unwittingly execute such movements themselves.

This specific relation between particular ideas and particular movements has often been so conceived as to connect directly only ideas of the movements themselves with those movements. In other words, it has been assumed that any other sort of idea, to issue in movement, must first arouse an idea of the movement, which in turn would arouse the movement. Introspective examination shows[4] that in adults, at least, this conception is wide of the mark, and that the most direct conscious antecedent is likely to be an idea of any sort; it is specially likely to be an idea of some end which is to be attained by the movement. There is no reason why the idea of the end should not become directly associated with the making of a movement leading to that end; and there is good reason for thinking that in children, as well as adults, attention is attracted

[1] *La suggestibilité* (Paris, 1900), p. 360.
[2] *Psychol. Rev.*, 1898, V, 295.
[3] See especially Janet, *L'Automatisme psychologique* (Paris, 1889), p. 223.
[4] Woodworth, "The Cause of a Voluntary Movement," in *Studies in Philosophy and Psychology*, pp. 351 f. (Boston, 1906).

mostly to the end, and that ideas of the movement, in a strict sense, have always but a small place in consciousness. Indeed, of our habitual movements it is, in general, difficult or impossible for us to form any clear idea, strictly so called.

§ 32. It remains to notice a certain mixture of sensations and feelings, usually attended by a rather strong tone of unpleasantness, which may be grouped under the term, "Fatigue." In ordinary usage, the word fatigue has a somewhat ill-defined meaning, inasmuch as it refers partly to a certain feeling or mass of sensations, and partly to a condition of actual inability to perform a certain act, as well before as after the onset of the feeling of fatigue. It is in the latter sense that the term is employed by physiologists, who be-

Fig. 146.—Fatigue Curve of a Frog's Muscle. Each vertical line records a contraction, aroused by an electrical stimulus, and lifting a weight.

gan their study of fatigue with an isolated frog's muscle. If this muscle was excited by an electric shock once every two seconds, while being protected from drying, the first effect of the repeated stimulation was found to be a slight increase in the force of muscular contraction—that is, a slight increase in the height to which the muscle raised the weight with which it was loaded. This "staircase effect," or period of "warming-up," soon gave way, with further stimulation, to a gradual decline in the force of contraction; and this decline might go on to the zero-point. The course of fatigue, as indicated in such an experiment, is called the "fatigue curve." If the muscle, instead of being entirely isolated, is left with its circulation intact, the period of gradual increase of force is more prolonged, and the subsequent decline is less rapid (Fig. 146). If the muscle, instead of being excited by shocks applied directly to its substance, is aroused by exciting its motor nerve, essentially the same fatigue curve is obtained. And the result is essentially the same if the muscle is excited reflexly, by stimuli applied to some suitable sensory nerve.

Mosso[1] devised the ergograph for obtaining a record of the fatigue of voluntary movement in man; and many later investigators have labored to add improvements to the technique of this experiment. In general, the curve of fatigue obtained from human muscle

[1] *Arch. f. (Anat. and) Physiol.*, 1890, p. 89; *Arch. italiennes de biol.*, 1890, XIII, 123.

under excitation by the will is similar to that above described in case of the isolated frog's muscle. The period of warming-up is usually in evidence, and then there is a gradual decline. There is, however, much more variability between the separate contractions than appears in the isolated muscles; for at times the attention given to the muscular work wanes, and the force of the contraction slightly declines, while at other times there is renewed effort resulting in a "spurt" or rise in the curve. Besides this, there are differences between individuals, some showing a very gradual onset of fatigue, whereas others maintain nearly the original strength for a considerable time, and then weaken suddenly. Under the best conditions, a well-trained muscle will show but a gradual decline in force, and may be able, after an hour or two of such work, lifting the weight as high as possible once every two seconds, to reach still 60 to 80 per cent. of its original performance.[1] In fact, after an initial period of decline, the performance approximates to a level, known as the "level of fatigue."

Sensory fatigue, apart from "adaptation," of which more will be said later, is known principally in the case of the eye; it consists partly of sensations of soreness and partly of fatigue of the muscles of the eye. An actual loss of the functional power of the eye may result from continued work.[2]

§ 33. Mental fatigue, pure and simple, is difficult of observation, because almost any mental task which can be measured and used as the basis of a test requires the use of the eyes, or of the muscles, and so is likely to involve muscular and sensory fatigue. In case, however, the demand on the eyes and muscles is as moderate as possible, the signs of fatigue—i. e., of real inability to perform work —are slow in appearing. Reaction-time work has been continued[3] for 15 to 20 hours, and memorizing[4] for four or five hours, with little loss of efficiency. On the other hand, continued adding of columns of figures has shown, in some individuals at least, a more pronounced loss. No doubt common experience would make us incline to believe in the reality of mental fatigue, and even in a rather rapid rate in its progress; but there is this to be said, that mental work is not ordinarily done under test conditions, which

---

[1] Treves, *Arch. ital. de biol.*, 1898, XXIX, 157, and XXX, 1; also in Pflüger's *Arch. f. d. ges. Physiol.*, 1899, LXXVIII, 163; Schenck, Pflüger's *Archiv.*, 1900, LXXXII, 390; Hough, *Amer. Journ. of Physiol.*, 1901, V, 240; Woodworth, *Le Mouvement* (Paris, 1903), p. 371, where a résumé of work on motor fatigue is given.

[2] Scripture and von Tobel, *Studies from the Yale Psychological Laboratory,* 1896, IV, 15; Moore, ibid., 1895, III, 87.

[3] Cattell, Wundt's *Philos. Studien*, 1886, III, 489.

[4] Thorndike, *Psychol. Rev.*, 1900, VII, 571.

would keep up the incentive to do one's utmost.   In ordinary conditions, we yield more readily than in an experiment to feelings of ennui and weariness which do not necessarily indicate actual decrease of power.[1]

§ 34. In considering the *causes of fatigue,* we may take our start again with the muscle. *A priori,* three causes might be possible: the structure of the muscle might be partially broken down; or the fuel from the oxidation of which the muscle derives its energy might be limited; or, finally, the waste products of this oxidation might poison the muscle.   There is little sign that the structure of the muscle is impaired in normal fatigue; there is considerable probability that the supply of fuel may run low; or at least, as suggested by Treves, that a store of fuel laid up in the muscle during its previous resting condition may become quickly used up, so that the muscle becomes dependent on the supply brought to it by the blood, and therefore does not obtain its fuel as rapidly as at first.   That the muscle produces in its activity "fatigue substances" which partially poison or depress it, is an established fact.   The muscle, by its activity, evolves carbon dioxide, lactic acid, and acid potassium phosphate.   Lee has shown[2] that two at least of these three substances, when injected into a fresh muscle, cause in it marked signs of fatigue almost from the beginning of its activity.   He has further shown[3] that the first effect of a moderate dose of the same substances is to produce the staircase effect; he therefore suggests that this effect may, in the activity of a muscle, be the result of the beginning accumulation of these substances.

§ 35. The fatigue of voluntary muscular activity, depending as this activity does on the brain as well as on the muscles, was ascribed by some of the early experimenters, on what seemed good grounds, to the brain in larger measure than to the muscle.   More recently, this view has been subjected to severe criticism.   By a method similar to that which was previously used (compare p. 136) in examining the fatigue of nerve-fibres, the reflex mechanisms of the spinal cord have been shown[4] to be highly resistant to fatigue. When a block is interposed between the spinal cord and a muscle, and a stimulus is applied to a sensory nerve which would, in the absence of the block, arouse a reflex contraction in the muscle

---

[1] Kraepelin and his pupils have devoted much study to the fatigue curve of mental work, or to the "work curve," and have attempted to analyze out the various factors which contribute to change the working efficiency from moment to moment.   See the successive issues of Kraepelin's *Psychologische Arbeiten.*

[2] *Amer. Journ. of Physiol.,* 1907, XX, 170.

[3] Ibid., 1907, XVIII, 267.

[4] Joteyko, *Contes rendues de la Soc. de Biol.,* 1899, p. 484.

every second or two, the muscle, here serving as an indicator of the condition of the cord, responds well after the removal of the block— thus showing that the cord was not much fatigued by a long succession of stimuli which had reached it and caused it to discharge down a motor nerve.

Tests[1] of the excitability of a muscle which had been employed in voluntary contractions to the point of fatigue showed that the muscle had lost some of its responsiveness, and was therefore actually fatigued. Further, the fact seems important that fatigue is little if any more speedy in its onset in voluntary muscular work than in the work of a muscle excited directly or through its nerve. If the nerve-centres fatigued rapidly, activity involving these centres should show more rapid fatigue than similar activity with the centres left out. The slow rate of fatigue in purely mental work should also be recalled in this connection.

§ 36. The nature of brain fatigue, in so far as it occurs, is still unexplained. In considering the matter, we are invited to distinguish several sorts of "fatigue" which may be concerned. There is first the metabolic fatigue, such as has been demonstrated in the case of the muscle. Some indications of a metabolic change in the brain after very prolonged and usually excessive activity have been obtained by histologists,[2] but this evidence would, on the whole, tend to show that the metabolism of the brain is slight in amount.

A second variety of fatigue may be named the "transferred metabolic." This results from the carrying of fatigue products by the blood from the muscle or other organ in which they are produced to some other organ which has been resting. The effect is the same as that shown by the experiment in transfusing fatigue products, mentioned above. There is little doubt of the reality of this form of brain fatigue, as is indicated by the drowsiness and inability to perform mental work which immediately follows severe muscular exercise.

A third variety consists of feelings and sensations of fatigue. This is to be distinguished from true fatigue, as urged above; but at the same time it must be accounted a genuine inhibiting influence acting to cause the cessation of work, especially of the particular work which has been going on. When a small group of muscles is repeatedly innervated, pain may develop in the muscles and their tendons, and the natural reaction to this sensation is, either to stop the work, or at least to substitute the action of some other group of

---

[1] Storey, *Amer. Journ. of Physiol.*, 1903, IX, 52.
[2] Hodge, *Amer. Journ. of Psychol.*, 1889, II, 376; Goldscheider and Flateau, *Fortschritte d. Med.*, 1897, XV, 241; Dejerine, *Soc. de Biol.*, 1897, p. 728; Ewing, *Arch. of Neurol. and Psychopathol.*, 1898, I, 157.

muscles. This tendency to change may be wellnigh irresistible; its urgency may be compared with that of the impulse to breathe after holding the breath for some time. In mental work, there may occur local fatigue pains, because of the cramped position in which the neck or other parts are sometimes held during strained attention; but besides these, there are more diffuse feelings of restlessness and ennui, the analysis of which is difficult, but the tendency of which is clearly toward a cessation of the activity in progress.

A fourth effect which is sometimes classed under the head of fatigue is sensory adaptation. In the case of the eye, fatigue was the explanation advanced by Helmholtz for after-images; but since there are histological changes in the retina on exposure to the dark or to light, which are certainly not akin to the forms of fatigue so far mentioned, but constitute, rather, a positively adaptive phenomenon, it is now customary to substitute "adaptation" for "fatigue" in speaking of such changes. Adaptation occurs in the other senses, but its mechanism is unknown; its effect is to cause a stimulus to be less fully sensed after it has been steadily acting for a time than at first; so far, then, the effect resembles that of fatigue. It is probable that adaptation occurs in the central organs as well as in the sense-organs; growing so accustomed to a stimulus as not to notice it (e. g., the ticking of a clock) is often not a purely peripheral phenomenon, since the stimulus can be perceived at any moment if occasion arises for noticing it.

A fifth variety of impairment of efficiency which bears a superficial resemblance to fatigue is interference, and is best known in the case of memory. When a series of dissimilar acts must be performed in quick succession, one of these is likely to interfere with another. Inasmuch as a short series is relatively free from inner interferences, whereas a long series involves many such chances, a short series is apt to be performed with better success than a long series. The appearance then is that fatigue has influenced the longer performance. But since even this longer performance need be only a few seconds in length, and since recovery from the condition is prompt, such fatigue can scarcely be identified with the progressive and metabolic type.

§ 37. The "refractory period" (compare p. 131) is also a phenomenon related, at least superficially, to fatigue, though in duration it lies at the other extreme from the progressive type. It seems to be of the nature of a back-swing from the condition of activity. There is, apparently, a radical difference between metabolic fatigue, which really lowers the power of an organ, and the inhibitions which result from the action of certain stimuli to the organ. It is probable that inhibitions or interferences give the key to most appearances of intellectual fatigue. Yet the question cannot be said to be wholly cleared up. In certain forms of mental work, such as performing calculations in the head, or certain complex forms of memory work,[1] there is sometimes a sudden drop from efficiency to complete inability to continue; in such cases, the key to the situation is lost. Introspectively, this condition appears as a diffusion of attention, or a tendency to relapse into sleep; but the exact cause is not made out.

Finally, there can be little doubt that such complex intellectual and æsthetic or moral feelings as loss of interest, ennui, the feeling of being bored, desire to do something else, distate, whether of a mild order or amounting to disgust, and moral disapprobation, have much to do with the onset of fatigue, in the psychological meaning of the word. That there is, in such cases, some corresponding "slowing-up" or positive inhibition of the central nervous processes required for doing the work in hand, without the *feeling of fatigue*, scarcely admits of doubt. There would seem, then, to be no reasonable objection to speaking of this correlated lowering of energy in the cerebral centres as a true case of brain fatigue. Work done under such mental friction or "loading" of the cerebral activities wastes the cerebral stores of energy.

[1] Compare C. S. Yoakum, *An Experimental Study of Fatigue*, Psychological Monographs, No. XLVI, 1909.

CHAPTER VIII

MEMORY AND THE PROCESS OF LEARNING

§ 1. One of the most distinguishing characteristics of the higher animals, and especially of man, is the capacity of learning from experience, or of acquiring modes of reaction adapted to the peculiar circumstances of individual life. It is chiefly this which produces the individual modifications of behavior, as distinguished from the so-called "instinctive" behavior, or behavior common to the species. Each individual contracts habits of his own, acquires skill, learns to know things and to react to them as known. In this way, above all other animals does man come to have the course of his thoughts as well as of his actions modified by previously formed associations. Physiological psychology, however, can throw no light upon the philosophical significance of recognitive memory;[1] it must content itself with studying the more obvious modifications of behavior and of thought by experience, and with basing upon this study certain conjectures concerning the part played in the process of learning by the nervous mechanism. The method required by this investigation will lead us to recite certain facts regarding both animal and human learning (the latter, in cases of acts of skill as well as in cases of memory of facts); and then to seek to discover any general tendencies, or laws of association, which may emerge from our wide though somewhat hasty survey.

§ 2. All memory involves two events, and a condition persisting between them. The first event is the impression, or formation of an association; the persisting condition is the preservation of the modification, or the retention of the association; the second event is the changed reaction upon the recurrence of the original situation or of something resembling it. In place of the single first event, there may be a number of events, all tending to impress the same modification. In a broad sense, we speak of the series of events which impresses the modification as *experience*. We speak of the same series as the act of *memorizing*, when there is a definite intention of recalling later what has been learned; and as *practice*, or *training*,

---

[1] For discussions of the philosophical aspects of memory, see Ladd, *Psychology, Descriptive and Explanatory*, pp. 397–407; and *Philosophy of Knowledge*, pp. 122 f.; 262 f.; 386 f.

when the object in view is the acquisition of some sort of skill. The preservation of the results of experience, or training, through an interval of time, may be called *retention*. What is retained, however, is not the newly learned fact or action; for the fact is not consciously present during the interval, nor is the act continuously performed. If we wish to avoid, for the time being, any physiological hypothesis as to the nature of retention, we may, with Stout,[1] speak of a *disposition* left behind by the modifying experience, ready to give rise, on suitable stimulation, to a reaction which shall show the influence of that experience.

The second event referred to above, or the reaction showing the effect of past experience, is perhaps better covered by the name *reproduction* than by any other single word. But its character may be so varied, as well as so complex, that no one word is really adequate to designate it. In the sphere of conscious memory, it is common to distinguish two component parts of this event, as the *recall* and the *recognition*—the recovery of something from past experience, and the conscious reference of it to past experience. These two are often indistinguishably blended in the remembering consciousness; but the distinction between them is justified by frequent instances in which either may occur without the other. Thus, recognition without recall occurs when, for example, a name refuses to come at our bidding, and yet is recognized at once if spoken by some one else. Recall without recognition occurs in the habitual use of familiar words, and in the practice of familiar acts (for these are not attended by a conscious reference to the past), as well as in the interesting cases of "unconscious plagiarism," where the person believes himself to be inventing or composing something new in literature or art, though he is really reproducing something previously read or seen.

§ 3. Under the four heads of impression, retention, recall, and recognition may be grouped the problems which memory presents for our consideration, and also the many investigations which have been conducted in the hope of solving these problems. We may study the process of forming an association or learning an act of skill, and the conditions which help or hinder this process; or we may study the permanence of acquired dispositions, and the causes which lead to forgetting; and, similarly, the processes of recall and recognition may be chosen as the subjects for examination. The results of these four studies cannot always be so easily disentangled; for neither the formation nor the retention of associations can be examined except through their effects as seen in recall and recognition; and recall and recognition cannot properly be studied without tak-

[1] *Analytic Psychology*, 1896, I, 21 ff.

ing account of the conditions under which the associations were originally formed and have been retained. Neither is it always possible to analyze the results of investigation, so as to assign its part to each of the processes involved in the memory cycle.

A sort of justification of the above four-fold division of memory is, however, seen in pathological conditions. Among the diseases of memory are some which affect the formation of associations, and others which affect each of the other components. In senility, for example, there is a loss of modifiability or plasticity, with the result that new associations cannot be formed. A similar result appears in the "polyneuritic psychosis"—often a sequel of alcoholism —in which recent events are promptly forgotten, because of their having, apparently, made no impression on memory. As losses of retention may be mentioned the aphasias and similar defects (compare pp. 252 ff.) when these are due to the destruction of some part of the brain substance which was modified in the learning of language, etc. Under the head of loss of recall may properly be counted the amnesias of hysteria; since here what seems to be forgotten is not wholly lost, but may later be recalled under hypnosis or other conditions. Some of the losses of memory resulting from shock also belong here; since as the shock passes away, memory may return. Finally, under the head of recognition may be classed pathological conditions of two kinds: in one, there is a feeling of strangeness, which deprives things that are really familiar, and that can be dealt with as such, of their air of familiarity; whereas in the condition of "false recognition," events which are really new are felt to have occurred in exactly the same way before.

§ 4. Without attempting to trace the phylogenetic development of the power of learning through the ascending scale of animals, we shall first examine modifications of behavior as they occur in the lowest animals; then in the higher animals, and, finally, in man.[1]

Among unicellular animals, Amœba, Paramecium, and Stentor are the forms which have been best studied in regard to their behavior.[2] Of these, the amœba is already familiar to us (see p. 14); the other two are somewhat more highly organized cells, being provided with special motor organs in the form of hairs or cilia for swimming. Only slight and uncertain evidence of modifiability has been attained by observation of Amœba, but clearer signs appear in the behavior of Stentor. This little animal is of a trumpet

---

[1] For a presentation of the development of modifiability in the animal series, see M. F. Washburn, The Animal Mind (New York, 1908); E. A. Kirkpatrick, Genetic Psychology (New York, 1909); H. Piéron, L'Évolution de la Mémoire (Paris, 1910). The first of these works contains a valuable bibliography.

[2] See especially Jennings, Behavior of the Lower Organisms (New York, 1906).

shape, and is usually to be found attached by its stalk to some solid object in the water.   If, while thus attached, it is affected by a harmless stimulus, such as a mild jet of water, it reacts at first by bending away from the jet; but if the same stimulus is repeated, the reaction is discontinued.   The animal has become "adapted" to the harmless stimulus.   If, however, the stimulus is somewhat harmful, as a jet of some weak chemical solution, the first reaction being the same as before, repetition of the stimulus leads to a more powerful reaction—namely, the contraction of the whole animal; and if the stimulus is still repeated, the stentor pulls loose from its attachment and moves away.   This is an instance of the principle of *varied reaction*, which Jennings rightly emphasizes as of fundamental importance in animal behavior.   The various possible reactions to the same stimulus are not blended and confused, but are tried in turn until they are proved to be not efficacious.

Similar behavior has been noticed[1] in *Paramecium*.   When one of these boat-shaped creatures was sucked up into a capillary tube, of a diameter less than the length of the animal, it would, as usual, swim till it encountered some obstacle.   This it found, under these conditions, in the surface between the water and the outside air, at either end of the capillary tube.   On encountering this obstacle, it at first performed its customary reaction, by backing away, making a slight turn, and then going forward again.   This manœuvre was repeated many times, but finally gave way to a quite different reaction, the creature doubling on itself in the tube, and swimming off toward the other end.   Here the same obstacle was encountered, and the same sequence of reactions made.   After several such experiences, however, the doubling reaction occurred more promptly, till finally, in some individuals, it became the first reaction to each fresh encounter with the surface of air.   Such a change of behavior can, perhaps, be explained by a heightened excitability of the animal due to the constantly recurring obstacles to locomotion.   Heightened excitability might favor the more extreme forms of reaction; just as, in much higher animals, a state of high excitability may lead to violent reactions to feeble and insignificant stimuli.   If this is the explanation, the modification of behavior would not be expected to hold over a period of rest; and, in fact, there is little evidence of the *retention* by protozoa of such modifications as have been detected in their behavior.

In higher animals, however, a true retention, lasting from one day to another, has frequently been demonstrated.   A spider, on which experiments were made by the Peckhams,[2] made its usual

---

[1] Stevenson Smith, *Journ. of Comp. Neurol. and Psychol.*, 1908, XVIII, 505.
[2] *Journal of Morphology*, 1887, I, 383.

defensive reaction of dropping from its web to the ground, when a tuning-fork was sounded near it, and after it had regained its web, it repeated the same reaction on the repetition of the same stimulus; but after several repetitions ceased to do so.   On the next day, it ¬eacted as at first; but after many days, it no longer made this reaction to this stimulus.   It had become permanently accustomed or "adapted" to the sound.

Other forms of modification may similarly be retained for long periods by the higher animals.   Yet, together with retention, or rather, as acting against it, can be seen a tendency to recover from a modification, if the stimulus which calls it forth is not frequently repeated. In the protozoa, recovery is prompt and complete, and there are no after-effects; whereas, in many metazoa, after-effects remain when the temporary effects of adaptation, fatigue, and heightened excitability have passed away.   But even these after-effects become weakened by time, provided the stimulus which produced them is not repeated.   This recovery and forgetting are clearly not without utility; for the original, unmodified behavior may be, in general, a better starting-point for meeting any novel situation.

Still another form of modification, sometimes dignified by the name of "associative memory," has been observed in some invertebrates.   It consists in connecting a particular reaction with a form of stimulus which would not in the first instance tend to evoke it.   Suppose, to illustrate, that a stimulus A naturally evokes a certain reaction, and that another stimulus B, to which the animal would not react at all, or to which, at least, it would not respond by the reaction in question, is presented time after time along with A: the result may be that B comes to evoke the reaction which was originally appropriate to A.   Thus Spaulding[1] found that the hermit crab, which commonly avoids the darker parts of the aquarium, could be attracted thither by the chemical stimulus of food.   If a wire screen was placed in the way, the crab learned to go around and behind it, when attracted by this chemical stimulus; and after many such experiences, the crab would go behind the screen whenever it was placed in the aquarium, even though the stimulus of food was absent.   The sight of the screen, from its frequent association with the chemical stimulus, had come to evoke the same reaction.

§ 5.   All orders of vertebrates, but especially birds and mammals, give abundant evidence of learning by experience.   The study of this subject has recently, and especially since the work of Thorndike,[2] taken on a more precise and scientific character than formerly.

[1] *Journ. of Comp. Neurol. and Psychol.*, 1904, XIV, 49.

[2] "Animal Intelligence," *Psychol. Rev.*, Monogr. Suppl. No. VIII, 1898.

Anecdotes and incidental observations have given way to experiments, in which the learning process is under observation from the beginning. A comparison of vertebrates with invertebrates, and of higher with lower vertebrates, shows little that is essentially new in kind in the learning of the higher animals; but it does reveal a great increase in fertility and readiness of modification. Reptiles, as represented by the turtle,[1] learn more quickly than amphibia, as represented by the frog,[2] or than fishes.[3] Birds[4] and mammals, on the whole, learn better than the lower classes of animals. Among mammals, monkeys[5] certainly learn more, and more rapidly, than do rats[6] and mice,[7] or dogs and cats,[8] while the raccoon[9] seems to stand, in this respect, intermediate between the cat and the monkey. The various orders, families, and genera differ in the time required for the formation of a habit, in the permanence of the habits acquired, in the complexity of performance, and in the variety and number of the performances which they are capable of acquiring.

One typical form of experiment, equally applicable, in principle, to all sorts of animals, requires that a path to a desirable object (such as food, the nest, mates, etc.) shall be learned. Only one path is left open, and sometimes this is complicated into a maze. On the first trial, the animal goes at random, but finally reaches the goal; and on repeated trials, if the maze is not too complicated, the number of wrong turns decreases, till finally a fixed and successful path is followed. Fishes, frogs, and turtles have in this way learned to thread very simple mazes, while quite intricate ones have been mastered by rats, birds, and monkeys. The learning process may be described, externally, by saying that a kind of natural selection takes place among the different reactions, the successful ones being kept and the unsuccessful eliminated.

A second form of experiment, instead of providing rewards for well-doing, provides only punishment for ill-doing. The training

[1] Yerkes, *Pop. Science Monthly*, 1901, LVIII, 519.

[2] Yerkes, *Harvard Psychological Studies*, 1903, I, 579.

[3] Thorndike, *Amer. Naturalist*, 1899, XXXIII, 923; Triplett, *Amer. Journ. of Psychol.*, 1901, XII, 354.

[4] Thorndike, *Psychol. Rev.*, 1899, VI, 282; Porter, *Amer. Journ. of Psychol.*, 1904, XV, 313 and 1906, XVII, 248.

[5] Thorndike, *Psychol. Rev.*, Monogr. Suppl. No. XV, 1901; Kinnaman, *Amer. Journ. of Psychol.*, 1902, XIII, 98, 173; Haggerty, *Journ. of Comp. Neurol. and Psychol.*, 1909, XIX, 337.

[6] Small, *Amer. Journ. of Psychol.*, 1899, XI, 133, and 1900, XII, 206; Watson, *Animal Education* (Chicago, 1903); and *Psychol. Rev.*, Monogr. Suppl. No. XXXIII, 1907.

[7] Yerkes, *The Dancing Mouse* (New York, 1907).

[8] Thorndike, *Psychol. Rev.*, Monogr. Suppl. No. VIII, 1898.

[9] Cole, *Journ. of Comp. Neurol. and Psychol.*, 1907, XVII, 211.

of domestic animals furnishes many rough experiments of this sort, and the results seem to show that punishment is an effective means of selection.   More precise experiments have yielded the same result.   The young chick, after once pecking at a bee, avoids bees in the future;[1] mice quickly learn to avoid a spot where they receive an electric shock,[2] and a pike[3] or perch,[4] which instinctively snaps at minnows, learns not to do so if he is separated from them by an

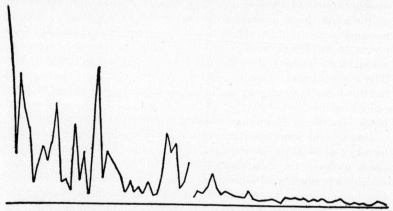

FIG. 147.—Curve of Learning (Thorndike).   The gradual descent of the line represents the decrease in time occupied by a cat to escape from a cage.   The association here learned (escaping by turning a button) was comparatively difficult for the cat.

invisible glass partition against which he bumps his nose at every attempt; after some weeks of this experience, the large fish can safely be allowed to swim freely among the little ones.

The third form of experiment which has been frequently employed is like the maze test in offering rewards, but differs from it in requiring not simply locomotion on the part of the animal, but the operation of some simple mechanical device.   In Thorndike's experiments, a cat was placed in a cage from which escape was possible by pulling a string, or turning a button, or pressing a lever, etc. To ensure an energetic attempt to escape, the cat was taken when hungry, and food was placed outside the cage and in plain sight of the animal.   Under these conditions, the animal attacked the sides of the cage vigorously, trying to squeeze between the bars, biting at them, clawing at anything loose, and, in the course of these instinctive acts, was pretty sure to turn the button or pull the string,

[1] Lloyd Morgan, *Habit and Instinct*, p. 53 (London, 1896).
[2] Yerkes, *The Dancing Mouse.*
[3] K. Möbius, *Die Bewegungen der Tiere und ihre psychischer Horizont*, 1873.
[4] Triplett, op. cit.

which opened the door and gave access to the food. On frequent repetition of this experiment, the useless movements gradually decreased in number, till finally all were eliminated, and only the one successful movement was continued.

In the experiment just narrated, the time taken by the animal to escape from the cage was noted, on each trial, and the decrease in this time indicated the progress of the animal in learning. An association is established in such cases between the situation of being in a cage while hungry and with food in sight outside, and a particular response which brings success. This successful response, to use Thorndike's terms, becomes gradually "stamped in," while the unsuccessful responses are "stamped out." The process of "stamping-in" and "stamping-out" is in some cases rapid, in others very gradual; while in still others, little or no progress is apparent in a long series of trials. The "curve of learning," obtained by plotting the times of the successive trials, gives a graphic view of the progress in formation of the association. The speed of

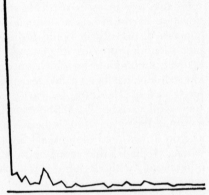

FIG. 148.—Curve of Learning (Thorndike). The same cat in a performance easier to learn. Here a loop attached to a string and hanging in the cage on the side toward the food was to be pulled. The act of pulling the string was, apparently, more a definite unit which would impress itself in connection with the resulting opening of the door; whereas the turning of the button was apt to occur in the midst of random clawing, and so to have little individuality.

this progress differs with the kind of animal, with the difficulty of the performance, and with the previous experience of the individual tested. A performance which is learned by a cat only in the course of many trials may be learned by a monkey in few trials; while a performance which requires the monkey many trials may be practically beyond the powers of the cat. The single door-button is slowly learned by a cat, but quickly by a monkey. A combination lock, first used by Kinnaman, in which four fastenings have to be undone in a certain order, was found too hard for cats, but was mastered by monkeys after many trials; an adult man usually masters it in from one to three trials. The influence of the previous experience of the individual animal is brought out by requiring the animal to master one puzzle after another. When the same sort of fastening is employed in two cages, but in different parts of the two, learning to operate it in the first cage often hastens the progress of learning to operate it in the second.   This means, therefore, that experience adds new (or more highly specialized) modes of reaction to the instinctive store with which the animal begins.

§ 6. Any attempt at interpreting the process of learning in animals must involve a consideration of some topics which are more germane to the next chapter than to the present.   For, as a matter of fact, the formation of associations cannot be understood without reference to processes of discrimination and attention. With the question of the limits of animal reason we are not here specially concerned, our object being rather that of understanding the simpler mental processes in general.   In the experiments already described, the method by which the animal learns to master a maze or a puzzle-box has been called learning by "trial and error."   We prefer to call it, "learning by varied reaction through selection of the successful variants."   Without variation of reaction, the cat would continue trying to squeeze between the bars toward the food, just as iron filings tend along fixed lines of force toward a magnet from which, perhaps, they are separated by a sheet of paper.   On the other hand, without some sort of selection from among the varied reactions, no progressive shortening of the whole time of reaction would occur.

The principal problems which arise in the interpretation of this sort of learning concern (1) the source of the varied reactions and the manner in which they are called into activity; and (2) the mechanism of selection.   In regard to the source of the variations, some are instinctive and others are derived from previous experience.   But not all of previous experience is utilized; and sometimes previously learned reactions which would fit the new situation admirably are not called into play at all.   The problem here is one which has passed under the name of the "transference" of the effects of training in one situation to another situation.   This problem again breaks up into two:—namely, (1) as to how far reactions learned in one situation can be *directly* applied to another; and (2) as to how reactions which might well be applied are *actually* recalled by the new situation.   In regard to the first point, we observe that there is often something specific about reactions learned in a given situation which unfits them for direct application in another situation, even though the two situations may seem, externally regarded, to be essentially the same.   The particular combination of movements, for example, which has become stereotyped in operating a fastening in one cage may need some modification to work well in another cage; and therefore the latter may need to be mastered afresh.   Granted, even, that a mode of reaction has been learned which is directly applicable to the new situation, it by no means follows that it will be called into play; for, since the new situation differs in some respects from the old, the proper reaction depends on the chance that the similar features of the two situations shall control the process of its recall. In every new situation, however, there are many features competing for prominence; so that the familiar feature has only a limited chance to become dominant.

The nature of the process of selection, by which the successful variants of reaction are strengthened from trial to trial, and the unsuccessful eliminated, is indicated to some extent by the curves of learning (see pp. 548 f.). Where the descent of these curves is gradual, the process of selection must itself be gradual; but where the curves show a sudden drop from a high to a low level, the process of selection must be correspondingly abrupt. These sudden drops, when (as in human learning) introspection comes to our aid in explaining them, are found to be due to a perception of certain facts about the situation, such as the uselessness of some reactions or the value of others. This perception is often a clearly defined event in the individual's experience, and its results are "stamped in" once for all. The absence of sudden drops in many curves of learning, even of those which describe graphically the attainment of a high degree of skill in manipulation, in man's case, is an evidence of the lack of moments of clear perception. In such cases, selection must be possible in some more gradual and mechanical way; but this gradual selection must be highly important and perhaps even fundamental in all learning. The following attempt at an interpretation of the process of selection in learning by trial and error should be regarded only as tentative, though combined of elements which are fairly sure to be genuine.

§ 7. In the first place, we must assume in the animal an *adjustment* or determination of the psycho-physical mechanism toward a certain end. The animal desires, as we like to say, to get out and to reach the food. Whatever be his consciousness, his behavior shows that he is, as an organism, set in that direction. This adjustment persists till the motor reaction is consummated; it is the driving force in the unremitting efforts of the animal to attain the desired end. His reactions are, therefore, the joint result of the adjustment and of stimuli from various features of the cage. Each single reaction tends to become *associated* with the adjustment. But the unsuccessful reactions are less strongly associated than the successful, because each one of the former is at some moment given up or inhibited; and this inhibition, too, being made under the influence of the adjustment, tends to become associated with it, and so to interfere with the association between the adjustment and the performance of this particular reaction. In the case of the successful reaction, however, the phase of inhibition does not occur, and the only association with the adjustment is of the positive sort. Thus the successful reactions must, in the long run, gain an advantage over the unsuccessful.

The preceding explanation, although satisfactory as far as it goes, is not fully adequate to account for all the facts. In particular, it does not take full account of the pleasure accompanying success, and of the often strong displeasure that attends baffled effort. Such pleasure and displeasure certainly occur in human learning, and seem present in the higher animals. Exactly how these emotions act to strengthen one association and to weaken or counteract another cannot readily be seen; but it is safe to assume that they correspond to some genuine dynamic process of great efficacy. The displeasure of failure and baffled effort, in particular, must be the indication of a stronger inhibitory process than is provided for in the preceding explanation.

§ 8. Where the curve of learning, instead of descending slowly, passes after the first few trials from long to short times—where, that is to say, the elimination of unsuccessful reactions occurs suddenly, and the right response is quickly associated with the situation— there, we may assume, something like a clear perception of the right reaction has intervened. But, in the case of the lower animals and even in man's case, too much meaning must not be read into the word "perception." The required mental act need not involve any insight into the reason why one reaction is successful and the other unsuccessful; there need not be any moment of reflective judgment, such as might be expressed in the words, "This is the way," or "That is not the way." All that is necessary is that some feature of the situation should prevail in consciousness, and that the reaction to it should have a certain separateness from the total series of changing reactions. This *distinctness of a certain feature* of the situation, and of the reaction to it, probably indicates a high intensity of the correlated neural process, and so a favorable condition for a strong association.

To illustrate this quick learning, and the lack of real insight that may accompany it, we will make brief mention of a hitherto unpublished experiment[1] on a chimpanzee—a species which, to judge by cerebral development, stands considerably higher than the smaller monkeys (compare p. 34). The specimen tested was a young female, about half grown, and corresponding in relative maturity, perhaps, to a child of the human species of ten or twelve years.

[1] The experiment was performed by R. S. Woodworth in 1902-03, in the laboratory of Professor Sherrington at Liverpool.

A box was prepared, having a slatted front with a door closed by a button, a turn of which through 90° released the door. The chimpanzee, on being placed in front of this box, in which a piece of banana had been placed before her eyes, quickly came to devote most of her efforts to the door (which allowed of some slight motion even with the button closed)—pulling it outward, pushing it inward, and shaking it. She soon, also, attacked the button, and alternated, for the most part, between this and the door. In this way, it was not long before she turned the button through 90°, then tried the door, and got in, thus securing the food. On a second trial, the chimpanzee worked almost entirely at the door and the button; and from the third trial on, her reaction was uniformly prompt and correct. After several more trials, a second button was added a few inches from the first, but much like the first in appearance, and operated in the same manner. The chimpanzee attacked the box as before, neglecting the second button. After once turning the first button, and pulling the door, which, of course, did not yield, she turned the first button again, so locking the door; then again tried the door, and continued in this way for a long time, before passing to the second button and dealing similarly with it. Entrance was finally secured by a chance placing of both buttons at once in the right position. In the course of several trials, no further progress was made. It seemed to be wholly a matter of chance whether both buttons should be put right at once or not. The experiment showed then a prompt narrowing down of the field of effort to the right feature of the situation; but this important factor in the process of learning seemed to be accompanied by a complete absence of insight into the mechanical principle involved.

In such experiments, one of the features of a situation which most readily becomes prominent is the *place* where the successful issue occurs. Often, after a few trials, effort will be concentrated at the right place, though many useless movements are made there.

§ 9. A contrast is usually drawn between learning by trial and error and learning by ideas,—the latter being clearly present in much human learning, but only doubtfully present in the learning of animals. "Ideas," if available, might be of service in several ways. First, an idea called up by some feature of a present situation might suggest some reaction which would not be directly suggested by the situation itself, and so might enlarge the range of the varied reactions, and afford greater opportunity for success. There is some evidence,[1] not wholly conclusive, that ideas may function in this way in some animals. Second, where a reaction has been previously tried and found unsuccessful, it might be mentally rehearsed

[1] Thorndike, Cole, op. cit.

without the actual motor performance. Such mental rehearsal of a reaction certainly occurs in human behavior, and possibly in the monkeys, which seem at times to inhibit movement as if in thought; but there is little evidence of it in dogs and cats, whose motor activity is perhaps too prompt and direct to permit of the necessary inhibition.[1] A third service of ideas might be the following: the successful reaction and its result might similarly be rehearsed, and thus practice in dealing with a situation might be obtained in the absence of the actual situation. This use of ideas occurs frequently in man, but in animals there is no clear evidence of it. Fourth, by a combination of the first with the second or third of the above uses of ideas, some feature of the present situation might suggest a reaction learned in previous experience; the consequences of this reaction might be mentally rehearsed, and its probable success or failure in the present situation judged without actual trial. This would be equivalent to "thinking out" the solution of a present difficulty without, or before, actually trying it. So complex a use of ideas, while perfectly within human capacity, occurs seldom even in man, in cases similar to the maze or puzzle-box experiments; for the prolonged suspension of motor reactions which it requires is disagreeable to most men—especially if the situation permits of immediate reaction.[2] Fifth, the ideas employed might have the character of general principles, from which the necessities of the present case could be deduced, and so the situation be thoroughly and surely mastered in advance of motor reaction. Such a use of ideas occurs in specially trained human individuals within the range of their specialty; but otherwise is probably rare, at least in any complete form.

§ 10. The differences between different animals, and between man and the animals, in the power of learning, are not fully accounted for by different degrees of the use of ideas. Greater fertility in association must also be allowed for in the human being. That discrimination favors association has been noted above, in saying that any feature of a situation or of the reaction to a situation, which stands out with a degree of separateness, has an especially good chance of becoming associated strongly with the adjustment to deal with the situation. That association favors discrimination has also been suggested by the fact that a previously familiar feature is likely to be singled out for present reaction. Now one of the differences between different species, and also between different

---

[1] But see Hamilton, "An Experimental Study of an Unusual Type of Reaction in a Dog," *Journ. of Comp. Neurol. and Psychol.*, 1907, XVII, 329.

[2] See Ruger, "The Psychology of Efficiency," *Archives of Psychology*, No. XV, 1910, p. 9.

human individuals, lies in their different powers of discrimination.
Greater power of analysis or discrimination belongs to man. The
terms, as here used, imply reacting to some feature of a situation
isolated from the total. Features which an animal cannot isolate
are easily isolated by man. For example, in dealing with Kinnaman's combination lock (p. 549), which requires several fastenings
to be undone in a fixed order, the cat seems wholly lost, and the
monkey succeeds only with difficulty, not because they cannot
master the separate fastenings, but because they do not take these
in proper sequence; but man quickly observes that a certain order
is necessary in dealing with the parts of a similar mechanism.
Whether he thinks of an interlocking of hidden parts, or does not
clearly formulate his conception in any way, that relation of parts
or of movements, which we have designated by the word "order,"
is a feature which his powers, dependent largely on his past experience, enable him to single out and make the basis of his reactions. Man, therefore, reacts to relations which the animal passes
by; and much of his superiority in learning to deal with complicated
situations is due to this power.

§ 11. Human behavior in situations resembling those employed
in experimenting on animals has been studied by several investigators. The solution of mechanical puzzles[1] is a task similar in
principle to that presented to the animal in a puzzle box, but of a
more difficult order. The behavior of a man on his first attempt
to solve such a puzzle often resembles closely that of the animals.
Under the influence of an adjustment to solve the puzzle, the man
usually begins promptly to manipulate, according as parts of the
device catch his eye and lead to instinctive or previously learned
reactions. This random procedure may continue till success is
accidentally reached; or, continued failure may lead to a period
of inhibition of movement, of closer examination of the puzzle and
a deliberate attempt to "think it out." This attempt is not always
successful, and random manipulation is again resorted to. In
the human being, however, the randomness of reaction is likely to
be limited by certain conceptions as to the probable line of successful effort; and though these conceptions are sometimes wrong and
a hindrance to prompt success, at other times they are of great value.
The first successful issue comes about, accordingly, in various ways,
sometimes by a pure accident which remains a mystery to the performer; sometimes by an accident which is nevertheless observed
and partially understood; sometimes as the outcome of consciously
trying whether a certain manipulation will succeed; and sometimes
as the result of clear insight into the necessities of the case. The

[1] Ruger, op. cit.

more there is of conscious prevision of the successful movement, the more certainly will the first success lead to prompt and correct reaction in all subsequent trials.

Suppose, now, that the solution of the same puzzle is undertaken time after time, with a constant effort to increase the speed. A curve of learning then appears, which may vary in form between extremes such as are represented in the two curves for animals shown above. In general, gradual improvement is visible in the midst of many oscillations. As soon as the main path to success is well known, new difficulties of manipulation emerge, and each of these becomes a problem, which is likely to be solved in any one of the variety of ways which appear in the main solution. Decrease in the total time of manipulation occurs sometimes gradually, from the increasing firmness of association between the parts of the performance, and sometimes suddenly, from the adoption of a "short-cut" or better form of manipulation. The steps in the manipulation, which in the early stages of practice are separate acts and require separate attention, come later to be combined into larger units. It thus becomes possible to keep the attention ahead of the hands, and to prepare mentally for each step before the time for it arrives. In this way time is saved in passing from one step to another, and the whole process gains in speed and smoothness.

§ 12. Much more complex than the solution of a mechanical puzzle are some of the performances which have been made the material for experiments on practice. Bryan and Harter[1] have studied the process of mastering telegraphy, and Book[2] the acquisition of skill in typewriting. In contrast with the maze or puzzle, which can sometimes be mastered in a hundred trials—though it offers a surprising amount of opportunity for continued improvement in matters of detail—telegraphy and typewriting require years of practice before the highest expert stage of skill is reached. Progress consists in the formation of numerous specific but interrelated habits, some of which are formed early in the process of training, and may be called habits of the lower order, whereas others are superimposed on these first, and may be called habits of the higher order. All in all, as Bryan and Harter state the case, mastery of such an art consists in the formation of a hierarchy of habits. In learning to telegraph, the first step is to acquire some familiarity with the alphabet of dots and dashes. The beginner, in sending a message, laboriously spells out each word letter by letter. He learns to make a particular combination of dots and

[1] *Psychol. Rev.*, 1897, IV, 27, and 1899, VI, 345.
[2] "The Psychology of Skill," *University of Montana Publications in Psychology*, 1908.

dashes in response to each letter of his "copy"; and the association so formed between the several letters and the appropriate finger movements constitutes his habits of the lowest order. Soon, however, he comes to run together the letters of familiar words, thinking rather of the rhythm of the whole word than of the patterns of the constituent letters. As his skill increases, he adds more and more word-units to his repertoire; and these word-units constitute his habits of the second order. He does not stop here, however, but

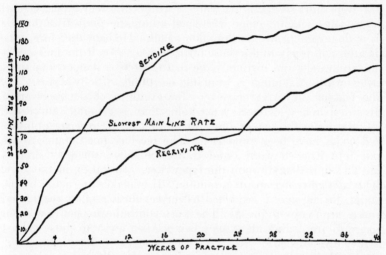

Fig. 149.—Curves Showing the Improvement in Sending and Receiving Telegraphic Messages (Bryan and Harter).

begins to train his fingers to the rhythm of phrases and other frequently recurring combinations of words. The progress of improvement in sending telegraphic messages is shown in the upper curve of Fig. 149, in which a rise indicates improvement. The main characteristic of the practice curve, as here illustrated, is the rapid rate of improvement at the beginning, and the gradual slackening of improvement as the practice continues, till the "physiological limit" for this particular performance is reached, and no further improvement is possible.

The curve of improvement in receiving messages over the wire is more complex, and the whole process of receiving is more interesting to study. At first, greater speed is possible in sending than in receiving, and this difference continues for a long period. In sending, the operator has matters in his own hands; he can adjust his rate to the difficulties of the copy, and he can see ahead. In receiving, he has none of these advantages. In spite of this early advantage of sending over receiving, in the long run the speed of receiving surpasses that of sending, so that an expert can receive faster than either he or any other man can move his fingers. Habits, or units of perception, of different orders are formed in learning to receive much as in learning to send. The beginner must attentively isolate the letters from the series of clicks which he hears; later he becomes able to catch the pattern of frequent combinations of letters and of common words; still later, he apprehends phrases and even short sentences as wholes; while "the real expert has all the details of the language with such automatic perfection that he gives them practically no attention at all. He can, therefore, give his attention freely to the sense of the passage; or, if the message is sent accurately and distinctly, he can transcribe it upon the typewriter while his mind is running on things wholly apart. . . . The feat of the expert receiver—for example, of the receiver of press despatches—is more remarkable than is generally supposed. . . . To bring the sender's rate up to that of the receiver abbreviated codes have been prepared. The receiver must translate the code into English words, and transcribe these, correctly capitalized and punctuated, upon the typewriter. He takes, in this way, eighty or eighty-five words a minute. If mistakes are made by the sender, the receiver is expected to correct them as they come, and send a clean copy to press. The work continues for hours without leisure for rereading, the pages being taken away to press as fast as they are finished."[1]

§ 13. For an understanding of the psycho-physical mechanism of learning, and so of the processes of association and discrimination involved in learning, it is important to attempt an analysis of such feats of skill as those described above. An essential feature of the performance of transcribing a telegraphic message, is that the skilled receiver keeps several words behind the message as he hears it. The expert learns not to guess ahead, or anticipate what is coming, for in this way false readings are sure to occur. Yet he does not by any means spell out the letters as they come. He seems rather to let the pattern of the clicks "soak in" for a time, gradually interpreting those that come earlier in the light of those which follow. For this purpose, the expert, in receiving a connected despatch, "prefers to keep from six to ten or twelve words behind the instrument." This gives an index of the size of the units in which he thinks.

The process of acquiring skill in typewriting has been even more minutely examined by Book, who employed in his study a combina-

[1] Bryan and Harter, *Psychol. Rev.*, 1899, VI, 352.

tion of objective records and introspective observations. The general course of practice is the same as in telegraphy, and the same sort of hierarchy of habits appears. Many habits are only temporarily formed and used, but are later supplanted by the development of other habits better adapted to a higher degree of skill in writing. Thus, when the beginner is learning by the "touch method," and the keyboard is concealed by a screen, the first associations formed are between the letters and their place on a plan of the keyboard, which may be held in mind as a visual image. Later, this image or plan disappears so completely that a skilful performer may be unable to tell the location of the letters on the keyboard without actually writing and finding out where his fingers automatically place themselves. In such cases the plan has already become unnecessary, because of the direct associations which have become established between the letters and the appropriate movements. When such associations are well learned, and even before they are perfected, frequently occurring sequences of letters begin to be associated with sequences of finger movements, so as to constitute those units of motor reaction to which reference has already been made. Prefixes and suffixes, short words, longer words, and even phrases of some length, become in this way reduced to specific motor habits, which stand ready to command.

Since, however, the possible sequences of words are much too numerous ever to be all reduced to automatic habits, the procedure of the finished expert does not consist simply in writing in large units, but rather in utilizing letter associations, word associations, and phrase associations, according to the exigencies of the copy. This the expert accomplishes while still maintaining a wholly unbroken series of finger movements at the maximum rate; no "units," higher or lower, can be detected in the rhythm of his motor reactions. The means by which this result is accomplished consists in keeping the eyes, on the copy, several words ahead of the fingers. What are the marvellous internal, or psycho-physical processes (mind and brain) which occur during the interval between the reading of the copy and the writing of it? An indication of the answer to this question is afforded by the fact[1] that when some special difficulty appears in the copy, the eyes are slackened in their advance, and the hands partially overtake them. One might have supposed that the hands would slacken, and the eyes get still farther ahead, but the contrary is the case; and, indeed, the hands do not need to slacken, for by the time they have reached the difficult spot, the way has been made ready for them by special attention devoted to the details of the coming movements. There occurs, then, in

[1] Book, op. cit., p. 44.

this important interval between the reading and the writing of a word, an organization of the coming reaction, in which such of the various ready-formed phrase associations, word associations, and, if need be, letter associations, are utilized as fit the requirements of the case. The entire procedure is an elaborate process of recall of many associations, and of appropriate combination of these associations.

§ 14. The foregoing studies of typewriting, telegraphy, and the manipulation of mechanical puzzles serve admirably to throw into relief the importance, for skilled and efficient action, of two principles which were found necessary to a satisfactory theory of perception, and which were mentioned in a previous chapter (p. 498): these are (1) the principle of higher units,[1] and (2) the principle of overlapping. Overlapping of different reactions is clearly in evidence when the reading of the copy precedes by several words the writing, or when the hearing of the telegraphic clicks precedes by several words the full interpretation and transcription of the message. Such overlapping is a result of practice; the "span of attention," it may be said, is lengthened by practice. But the increase in the attention span does not mean, mainly, that a large number of distinct items are held at once in consciousness; the meaning is, the rather, that these items are now grasped in larger units, such as words and phrases. In a sense it is true that the expert at the typewriter carries in mind twenty or thirty letters at once, and that the expert telegrapher, in receiving, carries in mind over two hundred clicks; for the total reaction in progress at any moment covers this large number of elements. But the letters or clicks do not remain separate in the performer's mind; they take the form of "units," consisting of words, phrases, etc. The lengthened span of attention, and the extensive overlapping of processes, are the result of the higher units in which the reaction is carried on.

§ 15. The rate at which improvement progresses with practice is seldom steady. Usually the curve of learning shows temporary descents in the midst of the general rise. Many brief relapses can be explained by poor bodily condition, or by distractions and failures of interest and effort. But in some of these curves there appear longer periods of no appreciable gain, which can scarcely be explained in this way. For weeks, it may be, the learner remains at

---

[1] A similar demonstration of the change from lower to higher units of reaction has been obtained by Leuba (*Psychol. Rev.*, 1905, VII, 351) in a much simpler performance, which consisted in transliterating German script into English script, and *vice versa*—a key of equivalents being at hand for consultation. At first the German letters were read and transliterated one by one, but later words were reacted to as units.

a standstill, and seems to have reached the limit of his capacity. And then, if he perseveres, a sudden advance may carry him to quite a new level of efficiency. He apparently begins a fresh ascending curve on the top of his old one. Such a compound curve is seen in Fig. 149 (the curve for receiving by telegraph). A period of no gain, followed by rapid improvement, has been named the *plateau,* and the study of the process of learning raises the question, whether this "plateau" is a universal and necessary feature of the practice curve. It can hardly be called universal, for it does not clearly appear in many curves; as, for example, in the sending curve in telegraphy, and in most of the animal curves. In practice with puzzles, however, the plateau is a frequent occurrence, and its external explanation is usually to be found in the adoption of some new and improved method, after a prolonged period of practice with inferior methods. In the case of the long-protracted plateaus which appear in typewriting and telegraphy, change of method is again the explanation of the rise from the plateau. The plateau occurs where further improvement is impossible without some change of method. In typewriting and telegraphy, the required change consists in the substitution of words and phrases for letters as the units of performance. In typewriting Book found two plateaus, one at the transition from letter-reactions to word-reactions, and another at the transition from word-reactions to phrase-reactions. But why should not these transitions occur promptly, without the long period of no apparent gain? Bryan and Harter believe that real gain is being made, below the surface, in the further perfection of the more elementary reactions; and, in support of this view, they are able to show, in the case of receiving telegraphic messages, that ability to receive isolated letters and detached words does slowly improve during the plateau. Until, therefore, these simpler forms of reaction have reached a high degree of facility and promptness, the higher reactions are impracticable. Swift,[1] who has investigated the process of learning in a variety of activities, including the learning of a language, subscribes in the main to this view of Bryan and Harter, but shows that the higher forms of reaction do not *all* wait till the end of the plateau, for some of them are present from an early stage. Book's observations lead him to a somewhat different conclusion. He found that the beginning of a plateau was marked, introspectively, by some loss of interest in the work, and by a tendency of the mind to wander. A little later, the learner becomes aware of his lack of progress, and may increase his efforts; but at this particular time his efforts are likely to be ill directed and result in no improvement. What he needs is attention to the details of work-

[1] *Mind in the Making,* p. 208 (New York, 1908).

manship; what he is apt to strive for is speed or higher methods which are at that time not wholly within his grasp and only dimly understood. The loss of interest which initiates the plateau is easily explained by the comparative facility which has been achieved in a certain lower form of reaction. Attention is set free from many of the details which have hitherto held it. What is needed then, from the introspective point of view, is to find new objects of attention, and new modes of reaction which shall nevertheless lie within the learner's powers at the stage which he has reached. Specially ingenious individuals may, as Book found,[1] come quickly upon such modes of reaction, and avoid the plateau altogether. Book concludes that the plateau is actually, as well as apparently, a period of no progress; but this conclusion does not take account of Bryan and Harter's demonstration of progress in the lower habits during this period, nor does it explain how the plateau is ever left behind. The probability is that continued practice does perfect elementary reactions to some extent, and that it thus becomes easier to enter upon the more inclusive reactions.

It seems to us, however, that all explanations of the process of learning, and, especially in such cases as we are now considering, of the occurrence of the so-called "plateau," which do not concentrate attention upon what is probably going on in the mechanism of the central nervous system, are surely destined to prove unsatisfactory. Perhaps it would express the truth better to say, that all explanations are satisfactory only in so far as they involve certain facts and laws of the central nervous mechanism. It is plain that as the overlapping of the psycho-physical processes proceeds, and the accompanying higher and higher psycho-physical units take place, more numerous and more locally distant cerebral elements are becoming involved. This fact implies, of necessity, more numerous chances of inhibitory processes, and also increased difficulty in effecting the required co-ordination of these elements; or—to speak figuratively—of establishing those coherent "dynamical associations" which are the psycho-physical basis of the higher unities. That cerebral associated activities of this complicated and locally diverse character, as respects the nervous elements taking part in them, should advance by "fits and starts" rather than always at a uniform pace, seems to us, therefore, to accord perfectly with the nature of the central nervous mechanism itself. Indeed, we might well venture to say, that such a way of development accords with the nature of all living substance. The chemico-physical changes in which the life of this substance consists seems to require this irregular manner of behavior.

[1] Op. cit., p. 20.

§ 16. The relation of consciousness to the process of learning is an important topic on which the conclusions of different investigators are still somewhat at variance. Several questions can be raised under this general head as to the participation of consciousness, first, in the origination of new methods; second, in the selection of one method and the rejection of others; and last, in the later stages of practice, when automatism has become the condition of the acquired skill.

In regard to the first question, as to how consciousness is concerned in the origination, invention, or "hitting-upon" of new methods, there is little doubt that this process is essentially the same as the "varied reaction" observed in animals. Each new method comes first as a spontaneous variation. But in human learning the variation may occur in the form of a recalled "idea," or in the form of a clear perception of some hitherto unnoticed feature of the situation. In other cases, however, the variation occurs first as a motor reaction. In which of these several forms it shall occur depends on the nature of the situation in relation to the past experience of the learner. Where the difficulties encountered are similar to those which have previously been met, there is likelihood that past experiences or ideas derived therefrom will be consciously recalled. But where the situation is very unusual, the contributions of past experience are vague and not suited for definite ideational recall. In such cases, the new variation has to be achieved in the thick of the fight, so to say. Then the individual finds himself acting in some new way, which he did not plan nor foresee, and which as yet he does not fully understand.

Unusual situations and difficulties are often created by the process of learning itself; for when once the learner has acquired a considerable degree of skill, the difficulties which next confront him are such as do not occur in an unskilled performance. Unusual precision of manipulation may be demanded, or overlapping and higher units of reaction may be necessary for further advance. Past experience is not likely to provide modes of reaction, or ideas, which are applicable to the case in hand. The learner may indeed have previously acquired high skill in some other performance, such as the use of language; but each new skilled performance must be precisely adapted to the particular material dealt with, and previous experience can only furnish vague hints for guidance. This vagueness of relation of the present to the past situation not only makes it difficult to apply past acquisitions, even if they are recalled, but it also renders the recall of them doubtful. Consequently the new variations which lead to the highest skill are likely to make their appearance in the midst of actual performance and without the foreknowledge of the learner. This fact has sometimes been rather ineptly expressed by saying that the new variations occur "unconsciously." By this, it is by no means intended that they occur in a condition of unconsciousness, or even of inattention; on the contrary, it is recognized that they are unlikely to occur at all except in a condition of "rapt attention" to the work in hand. Nor are they likely to occur in one part of the performance, when attention is directed to another part; but they occur where attention is keenest, and often where attention is striving to enlarge its span or to perfect its grasp. They occur, therefore, in the *very focus of consciousness*, but are "unconscious" in the loose sense that they are unpremeditated and not reflectively observed. They are not thought *about* at the moment when they first occur; consciousness is too much absorbed in *doing* the thing to classify it or speculate about it.

As to the second point—namely, the participation of consciousness in the selection and rejection of methods of reaction—here, too, no one general rule is applicable to all cases. Sometimes new variations of method, without being reflected on or definitely conceived, become habitual and automatic. In such cases, the learner never really *knows* how he has come to gain the skill. At other times, the variation catches the eye of reflection, is definitely made note of and perhaps formulated in words, and the learner can later tell by what means he has improved. At times this reflective attitude proves to be of value; for a definitely conceived and formulated reaction is more readily recalled under somewhat changed conditions.

As to the third point, there is no doubt that attention tends to desert a reaction which has become well-drilled and facile, and to pass to something else; in illustration of this, the feats of skilled performers on any instrument, while their minds are occupied with something else, are well known. But the very highest skill is never manifested except when the performance is fully occupying the attention. No matter how far the elementary reactions have become automatic, there are always higher units and combinations which demand the best efforts of the performer. Given, then, a constant degree of zeal in the learner, the progress of practice does not lead to a diminution of the consciousness attending the performance, but to *a change in the distribution of consciousness*. The expert finds within the work new objects of attention which lie entirely beyond the ken of the beginner.

The changes of feeling which occur in the course of practice are also noteworthy.[1] A new occupation, in which there is some degree of immediate success, is interesting and pleasurable; as the near-lying difficulties are overcome, a feeling of monotony and un-

[1] Book, op. cit., p. 71.

pleasantness ensues; but as the possibilities of higher forms of reaction open before the learner, the pleasure in the work returns, and the keenest pleasure of all may be felt by the expert, if only there is sufficient incentive to spur him to his best efforts.

§ 17. How far skill acquired in one performance can be "transferred" to another performance—how far success in dealing with one situation is an equipment for dealing with other situations—is a problem of evident importance, regarding which, however, great differences of opinion have appeared. Some remarks on this matter have been included in the preceding discussions (p. 550), and need not be repeated here. The history of the question begins with Volkmann[1] and Fechner,[2] who reported, in 1858, observations tending to show that training one function might result in the improvement of other closely related functions. In Volkmann's case, the function trained was the discrimination of two points applied to the skin (the "two-point threshold," compare p. 402) of the left arm, and the other function thus improved was the same discrimination when the points were applied to the right arm. Also, training applied to one finger improved the power of discrimination in the other fingers, but not in the arm. Fechner's observations showed that teaching a boy to write with his right hand might give him power to write with the left hand also. This special form of the transfer of acquired skill, between symmetrical parts of the body, received the name of "cross-education" from Scripture,[3] who, with his pupils,[4] demonstrated the reality of it in a variety of cases, such as speed, force, and accuracy of movement.

The probable explanation of cross-education lies in the fact (compare p. 263) that the same portion of the left hemisphere (in right-handed persons) is concerned in skilled movements of either hand, or in the skilled use of sensory data from either side. If an essential part of the neural mechanism for co-ordinating a skilled movement is the same, whether that movement is executed by the right or by the left hand, then, naturally, training of either hand should improve the other hand also. But since some of the neural connections are different for the two hands, training of one hand would still leave something to be accomplished by special training of the other;—and this deduction also corresponds to the facts, for the untrained hand does not at once show all the skill of the trained hand, but only some of it.

---

[1] *Berichte d.k.-sachs. Ges. d. Wissensch., math.-phys. Kl.*, 1858, X, 38.

[2] Ibid., 1858, X, 70.

[3] Scripture, Smith and Brown, *Studies from the Yale Psychol. Lab.*, 1894, II, 115.

[4] Davis, ibid., 1898, VI, 6; Scripture, *Psychol. Rev.*, 1899, VI, 165.

This relatively simple case may contain the germ of an explanation of other cases of transferred training. If the brain functioned as a whole, we should expect that training in any special performance would operate equally to produce the improvement of all other performances; if it functioned in compartments, corresponding to "memory," "discrimination," or to other so-called "faculties" or phrenological organs, then we should expect training of any special performance within the scope of a faculty to benefit alike all other performances included within that faculty. But since the evidence points to a highly detailed localization of cerebral functions, and since the neural mechanism employed in any performance cannot be wholly identical with that required for slightly different performances, though it may be partly the same, training in one performance would not be expected to improve another, except in so far as the neural mechanisms involved were in part identical —i. e., employed the same cells, fibres, and synapses. As applied to psychology, this would mean that, in order for a transference of skill to occur from one performance to another, there should be, between the two, not simply likeness in the abstract, but some concrete part-performance in common, as there is between boxing and fighting, or between saying "boot" and saying "book." In general, since the neural process in any reaction undoubtedly has more detail than appears either to introspection or to objective observation, it will not always be possible to point out the common features of two reactions; but that there should be features in common, if any transference of training is possible from one to the other, seems necessary from the physiological point of view.

§ 18. But leaving these speculations for the present, let us return to the investigations of fact. James[1] opened a new line of inquiry by seeking to determine whether training the memory for one kind of material increased the power of remembering other kinds. His method was to practise memorizing the poetry of one author, and to test beforehand and afterward the ability to retain another author. His results showed, on the whole, a lack of improvement of the memory, except for the material on which it was trained. The exceptions he believed could be explained by improved methods of memorizing; he, therefore, concluded that retentiveness, as such, was not susceptible of improvement by training.

The problem of memory training was taken up again with the same general method, by Ebert and Meumann,[2] who made more extensive experiments, but came to a somewhat different conclusion. These investigators trained their subjects in memorizing lists of

[1] *Principles of Psychology*, 1890, I, 666.
[2] *Archiv f. d. ges. Psychol.*, 1905, IV, 1.

nonsense syllables, and, before and after this course of training, took a "cross section" of the subjects' powers of memory by testing them with lists of letters, numbers, disconnected words, vocabularies, passages of prose and of poetry, and meaningless visual characters. In all these tests they found great improvement, but much more in some than in others. It seemed to them that the improvement was great in proportion as the new material resembled the nonsense syllables with which the subjects were trained; and they interpreted the results to mean that memory, trained by use of one sort of material, is thereby trained for other sorts; not however equally for all sorts, but most for those sorts which are closely related to the material used in the training. They, therefore, conceive of several special "memories" in place of the old faculty of memory, and within the scope of each of these sub-faculties they suppose that skill is readily transferred from one performance to another. This is all rather mysterious, and it is more to the point to note that many *improved methods of memorizing* were invented by the subjects during their training, and that some of these methods—such as giving a rhythmic form to a list—were readily applied to different sorts of material. Feelings of distaste, strain, and doubt gave way, with continued experience and success, to pleasure and confidence in the work. Distractions and useless reactions were better repressed; the proper direction of attention was better understood; and the subject came to know his own powers and limitations.

A similar line of experimentation, with similar but better-analyzed results, was undertaken by Fracker.[1] He trained his subjects in an unusual feat of memory, as follows: four sounds, differing in intensity, were presented in varying orders, and the subject had to notice the order of each presentation, and reproduce it, designating each sound by a number; but before he was allowed to reproduce one order, he was required to observe a second; and the second tended to interfere seriously with the first and cause confusion. In this novel situation, the subjects tried a variety of means to escape from the difficulty, and most of them hit upon some successful device. In some of the subsequent tests with other material, the device so learned was readily applicable and these tests profited by the transference of the device. But to other material, such as poetry, these devices were not applicable; and here the tests showed no improvement as the result of the special training in memorizing the order of sounds. The author's main conclusion is that effective memory-training consists in the development of methods of memorizing.

Most of the studies of transference of acquired skill have suffered

[1] *Psychol. Rev.*, Monogr. Suppl. No. XXXVIII, 1908, p. 56.

from an obvious defect of method, which lies in the fact that the performances which are supposed to receive no direct training must themselves nevertheless be tested, and so exercised. But even a little practice in a novel performance may cause considerable improvement, and therefore the amount of special training received by the "untrained" performances is by no means negligible. In fact, Dearborn,[1] on repeating the preliminary and final tests of Ebert and Meumann, without the intervening special training, found a considerable improvement, and thus showed that the results they obtained need to be considerably discounted.

§ 19. It was a much-needed addition to the methods of investigation when Bair[2] tried the plan of following up the training of one performance by the training of another, to see whether the curve of learning of the later-trained performance would show any effect from the previous training. In his experiments he made use of a typewriter, using only a part of the keys, which he covered with different colors, while his "copy" consisted of series of color stimuli, to which the subject reacted by striking the corresponding keys. After one particular series of colors had been copied time after time till great speed and accuracy were attained, the order of colors was changed and a new learning curve obtained. The new performance showed from the start the influence of the previous training; for though the new series was not at first written as rapidly as the old had come to be written, it was written more rapidly than the other had been at the start; moreover, it improved rapidly, soon passing the limit of efficiency reached in the first series. This result would indeed be expected, for the single reactions remained the same as before; the same key was struck in response to each color, and only the order of the colors was changed. The fact that there was *some* loss in passing from one order to another proves that the performance first learned consisted partly in a reaction to the order of the stimuli; and this was an untransferable feature of the performance. In this way, then, both the gain in general facility and the loss in special facility are accounted for.

Bair now interchanged the colors on the keys, so that a new reaction was required to each single stimulus, though the order of stimuli remained as it had been just previously. This change in the character of the single reactions proved to be more of a disturbance than the previous change in order; yet in this case, too, the new performance did not start back where the first had started, but showed from the beginning some of the skill acquired in the previous training. From the point at which it started, the new performance

---

[1] *Psychol. Bulletin*, 1909, VI, 44.
[2] *Psychol. Rev.*, Monogr. Suppl. No. XIX, 1902.

also made more rapid progress than the first had done—thus showing, beyond doubt, a transference of the previously acquired skill. What was transferred was probably, besides acquaintance with the order of the stimuli, an adjustment to the apparatus and general conditions of the experiment, which remained the same throughout.

The method of Bair has also been employed in the previously mentioned researches of Leuba, Book, and Ruger. The latter noted several kinds of transference: transference of special methods; transference of more "general" methods, such as transference of the habit or idea of analyzing each new situation, or of trying to induce variations instead of repeating an unsuccessful reaction time after time; transference of a confident and self-reliant attitude toward a new situation; transference of the habit or idea of keeping up active attention during the course of practice, and of looking for improved methods and higher units, instead of settling down to a mediocre performance. Transfer is readiest in the realm of ideas; and the more definitely a method of work, either special or general, has been conceived and formulated, the wider is the field of its probable usefulness. It may be remarked in passing that all *these admittedly possible forms of so-called "transference," when taken together, amount to a tolerably complete summary of the most essential factors in what is popularly included under the training, or culture, of the mind.*

The conception of a general transference or spreading of the effects of training was called in question by Thorndike and Woodworth,[1] who experimented, by a method similar to that of James, in performances involving observation, discrimination, estimation of magnitudes, etc., and found, in general, rather a small amount of transference from any specially trained performance to others which, superficially, appear quite similar to it. This led them to conclude that the mind works in great detail, adapting itself, of necessity, to the particular material with which it has to deal; and, therefore, that training in one performance could only help another when the two had elementary factors in common.[2] This is to say that what has been found to be transferred has always been some specific habit, or reaction, or idea, or attitude; although it need not always be a *motor* reaction.[3]

§ 20. Another line of evidence is available regarding the transfer of training in memory. It is not necessary that the *kind* of material

---

[1] *Psychol. Rev.*, 1901, VIII, 247, 384, 553.

[2] Compare also Coover and Angell, *Amer. Journ. of Psychol.*, 1907, XVIII, 328.

[3] For a discussion of the present state of the problem, and of its practical bearings, see a symposium between Professors Angell, Pillsbury, and Judd in the *Educational Review*, 1908, XXXVI, 1, and also the works of Meumann referred to on p. 571.

should be changed, in order to test for transference.   Does learning one list of twelve nonsense syllables make it easier to learn the next list, composed of other nonsense syllables?   Of this there is no doubt; the times needed for learning such series decrease rapidly with practice.   Now the particular associations formed in learning one series are different from those formed in learning another; and yet the learning of one set increases the power to learn other sets. This, it would seem, is as good evidence as could be desired of training one performance by practising another.   But there is another curious fact to be considered in connection with the foregoing. The learning of one such list may *interfere* greatly with the learning of another similar list, especially if little time intervenes between the two.   If, immediately after one list has been learned, another is begun, it will be found, later, that neither list is as well retained as if either one had been attempted alone.   Therefore it is not the particular associations of the one list which favor the associations of the other.   There is no spread of associative power from one association to another unrelated association; but there may be improvement, through practice, in the *process of memorizing*.

Let us consider the meaning of this experience.   When a person first takes part in a memory test, there are many unaccustomed features of the situation to which he must react.   He must adjust himself to the apparatus and procedure and to the peculiarities of the experimenter; he must master his own distaste for the monotonous work; he must exclude the distractions which are inherent in the circumstances and in himself; he must become negatively adapted to these, as one becomes adapted to the ticking of a clock. The material to be learned has some special but rather uniform character, and he readily becomes accustomed to that; some ways of trying to memorize it are good and others bad, and he has a chance to learn the most suitable method.   In a word, the situation to which he reacts is decidedly complex, and his total reaction is correspondingly complex.   What he learns is not merely the list of syllables; but he learns, or begins to learn, how to react to that particular complex situation; and when a similar list is later presented to him, a large share of the situation remains the same and can be reacted to as before.   Thus, by degrees, he comes to master *that type of situation;* and even if the situation is changed somewhat by the introduction of a new sort of material to be learned, many of his old partial reactions are still applicable to changes in the material.

It would seem, then, that the most practical sort of memory-training, for ordinary purposes, is probably to be obtained by connecting together things that belong together for some purpose in hand, and so building up a system of valuable associations.   The suggestion of Meumann[1] to the effect that a species of "formal discipline" of the memory might lead to good results, is not without force; since what he means by formal discipline is memory work under conditions resembling those of the experiments which have proved to lead to greatly improved technique in the memorizing of certain kinds of matter. Experimental conditions are stimulating, largely because one has a measure of one's success and progress; and the habit of checking up one's work can scarcely fail to prove of benefit wherever measures of success and failure are practicable.

§ 21. One other most important, and indeed essential, consideration must certainly be borne in mind, in every attempt to deal with the problems of memorizing and of the "transference" of acquired skill. In studying the development of sense-perception, we saw that, from the introspective point of view, attention and discrimination are involved in all human knowledge and in all forms of human learning. From the same point of view, these both appear as active forms of consciousness in all memorizing. But it is "I" that attend, and "I" that discriminate. What forms of cerebral conditions, or of cerebral changes, correspond to these conscious activities, we may be much at a loss to point out. But everything which we do know indicates that these conditions and changes must be of a general character to correspond with the general character of the mental aptitudes involved. It might be, then, quite appropriate to speak of training the "faculty" of attention, and the "faculty" of discrimination, so as to pass over the results of this training from one species of skilled reactions to another. In all such cases, the well-known distinction between the speed of the total motor reaction, or of the total act of committing to memory, and the factor consumed by the acts of attending and discriminating, must be taken into the account. For example, experiments conducted in the Yale Laboratory showed that while the reactions, under customary conditions, of the master of a fencing club were speedier than those of any of the members of the club, when discrimination was required by unusual conditions, his discrimination-time was slowest of all. And two Yale professors, one of whom had never used foils, while the other had not practised fencing for many years, excelled in the speed of their "discrimination-time" every member of the club with the single exception of a gentleman who was himself both a skilled fencer and highly educated. Indeed, to claim that trained

[1] *Vorlesungen zur Einführung in die experimentelle Pädagogik*, I, 200 (Leipzig, 1907); *Okonomie und Technik des Gedächtnisses*, p. 258 (Leipzig, 1908).

Improvement of memory with practice under experimental conditions, has also been found by Winch (*Brit. Journ. of Psychol.*, 1904, I, 127; 1906, II, 52; 1908, II, 284) to occur in school-children.

powers of attention and discrimination are not available for transference to unusual situations would contradict the whole round of
human experience.   At the same time, it must be admitted that a
high standard of specialized skill in certain lines may hinder, rather
than help, the rapid attainment of skill in other non-cognate lines,
through the large number of inhibitory processes which it may introduce, if in no other way.   *Concentration* of attention may also
be opposed to *nimbleness* of attention.   In a word: *It may be possible, by training, to increase the speed and improve the quality of
those general cerebral conditions and forms of functioning, to which
attention and discrimination correspond from the introspective point
of view.*

§ 22. We pass now to a study of that complex form of functioning which is called "memory," in a more special meaning of the
word.   Investigations of this subject have been numerous since
Ebbinghaus [1] showed that it afforded a fruitful field for experiment.
Ebbinghaus contributed, first of all, a method for measuring the
degrees of memory for all kinds of material; he further introduced
a new kind of material—namely, so-called "nonsense syllables," [2]
which possesses the advantage of being comparatively free from
ready-formed associations; and he applied both material and method
to the study of some fundamental problems of the formation and
retention of associations.   His method, which passes by the name
of the "learning method," consists in presenting a list of nonsense
syllables to be memorized, and in determining the time, or the number of readings, necessary before the list can be recited without error.   Care must be taken that the list is not "over-learned," i. e.,
that more study is not given to it than the bare amount necessary
to reach the standard of one perfect recitation immediately after the
study. [3]

The same method was ingeniously adapted to the study of retention: after a given list of nonsense syllables (or, for that matter,
any other material) had once been learned up to the above standard, further work on it was suspended for a certain interval, and then
it was relearned to the same standard, the time or number of readings
needed for *relearning* being determined as before.   Two important

---

[1] *Über das Gedächtnis* (Leipzig, 1885).

[2] A nonsense syllable, as used by Ebbinghaus and later investigators, consists of a vowel or diphthong between two consonants.

[3] Some investigators have indeed chosen a higher standard—namely, *two* successive recitations without error; and have found that considerable further
study is often needed to reach this higher standard.   See Radossawljewitsch,
*Das Behalten und Vergessen bei Kindern und Erwachsenen nach experimentellen
Untersuchungen* (Leipzig, 1907).

facts immediately came to light and served as the foundation for
further use of the method. First, when a list was learned barely
enough to permit of one perfect recitation immediately at the close
of the learning, an interval as brief as twenty minutes, or even five
minutes, made another perfect recitation of the list impossible; and
second, after a much longer interval, though the list might seem,
introspectively, to be altogether forgotten, the time necessary to
relearn it was less than the time needed to learn it at first. This
showed that the associations formed in the first learning had not been
entirely obliterated; there was a partial retention, and it could be
measured by the *saving* (in time or number of readings) apparent
in the process of relearning as compared with the first learning.
If, for example, the first learning of a list required 10 readings, and
relearning after a week required only 8 readings, the saving due
to partial retention was 2 readings, or 20 per cent. of the original
labor. As thus applied to the study of retention, the Ebbinghaus
method is called the "saving method."

The method of Ebbinghaus was improved in two respects by
Müller and Schumann.[1] They introduced rules for the preparation of lists of nonsense syllables which should be as nearly as possible equal in difficulty; and they provided an apparatus for exposing the syllables to the eye at a fixed speed, so making the entire
procedure more uniform.

A second method of experimentally studying memory was introduced by Miss Calkins,[2] and more fully formulated by Müller
and Pilzecker,[3] who named it the *"Treffermethode."* This name has
been roughly rendered into English as the "method of hits and
misses," or as the "scoring method." The method has also been
named,[4] and perhaps most suitably, the "method of paired associates"; since syllables, words, or other materials, are presented in
pairs, the effort of the learner being to associate the pairs. Later,
one member of each pair is presented and the subject responds, if
possible, with its associate. A score of the "hits," or right responses,
gives the measure of memory, and the association time for each response can also be determined. This method has certain advantages over the other, in requiring less time, and in permitting a more
detailed study of individual associations.[5]

[1] *Zeitschr. f. Psychol.*, 1894, VI, 81, 257.

[2] "Association," *Psychol. Rev.*, Monogr. Suppl. No. II, 1896.

[3] "Experimentelle Beiträge zur Lehre vom Gedächtniss," *Zeitschr. f. Psychol.*,
Ergänzungsband I, 1900; also Jost, *Zeitschr. f. Psychol.*, 1897, XIV, 436.

[4] Thorndike, *Psychol. Rev.*, 1908, XV, 122.

[5] For the latter purpose, Ebbinghaus (*Grundzüge der Psychologie*, 1905, I, 648)
has introduced a modification of the learning method, which may be called the
"prompting method," and according to which, after a few preliminary readings,
the subject attempts to reproduce the series of syllables, and is immediately

Two other simpler methods[1] are of use for some purposes; they may be called the "memory span method," and the "method of retained members." The latter, which might also be designated as a method of measuring the accuracy of recall, is the simplest in principle of all, and consists merely in measuring how much of a list of syllables, or of any other material, can be correctly reproduced. The "memory span" is the largest amount of any given material which can always be correctly reproduced immediately after one presentation. For example, in adults, about 5–7 nonsense syllables, 8–11 one-place numbers, and 15–25 words of easy connected prose, can be so reproduced. The span is determined by starting with a short series and passing to longer and longer series till errors begin to appear. The method is susceptible of various modifications.[2]

§ 23. The results of work by all these methods are well worthy of a much more extended analysis than space will here permit.[3] We may consider first the decline of retention with the passage of time. Ebbinghaus studied this matter by aid of his saving method, and, as the result of many experiments, in which, however, he alone was the subject, found that the loss of retention was rapid at first, and then slower and slower. If retention is measured by the percentage of the original time which is saved in relearning, the following table[4] shows the loss of retention after different intervals:

Interval since the original learning	Per cent. of saving, or of retention
20 min.	58
1 hour	44
8.8 hours	36
24 hours	34
2 days	28
6 days	25
31 days	21

prompted or corrected when he halts or errs. The number of promptings and corrections gives a measure of the degree to which the series is learned, and also shows which parts of it are learned. The process can be repeated till no more help is needed. See also Ephrussi, *Zeitschr. f. Psychol.*, 1904, XXXVII, 222.

[1] Jacobs, *Mind*, 1887, XIII, 75; Pohlmann, *Experimentelle Beiträge zur Lehre vom Gedächtnis* (Berlin, 1906).

[2] Ebert and Meumann, op. cit.; Kirkpatrick, "Studies in Development and Learning," *Archives of Psychology*, No. XII, 1909.

[3] Probably the best general treatment of the subject is that by Ebbinghaus in his *Grundzüge der Psychologie;* see also van Biervliet, *La mémoire* (Paris, 1902). A concise account of experimental results is given by Myers in his *Textbook of Experimental Psychology*, pp. 144–182 (London and New York, 1909). For bibliographies, see Burnham, *Amer. Journ. of Psychol.*, 1888–89, II, 39, 225, 431, 568; Kennedy, *Psychol. Rev.*, 1898, V, 477; Reuther, Wundt's *Psychol. Studien*, 1905, I, 93.

[4] *Über das Gedächtnis*, 1885, p. 103.

These results may be plotted into a "curve of forgetting" (or of retention), by making the distances along the horizontal axis proportional to the time elapsed, and the vertical distances proportional

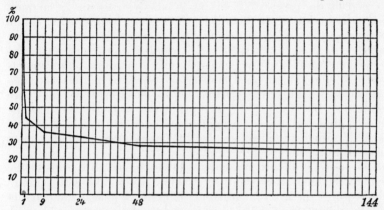

FIG. 150.—The Curve of Forgetting (Ebbinghaus). The numbers along the horizontal base line give the hours elapsed since the time of learning; the numbers along the vertical line give the percentage retained.

to the percentage of material retained. For comparison with this curve of forgetting, a typical curve of learning may be presented; in which case a certain similarity between the two is at once apparent, inasmuch as the rate of change in each is rapid at first and then

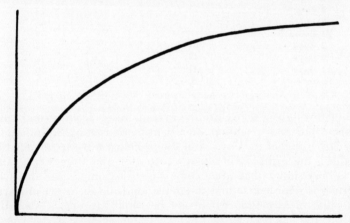

FIG. 151.—A Typical Curve of Learning. The curve is not typical in one respect, since it does not show the fluctuations of efficiency which always appear; but it is intended to show the general increase (rise) of efficiency with continued repetition of the performance. Horizontal distances denote the time spent in learning, and vertical distances the measure of efficiency.

slower and slower. On the other hand, if the two curves are thought of as combined, a certain discontinuity between the two is evident, inasmuch as the slow increase of the strength of association toward the end of the process of learning suddenly gives way to a rapid loss on cessation of the learning. But such a combination of the two is unjustified; for the learning which would give rise to such a curve, with slow gain at the end, is carried much further toward perfection than that from which the curve of forgetting takes its start. Ebbinghaus stopped learning as soon as he had reached such a proficiency that he could barely repeat the list of syllables once correctly; while the typical learning curve supposes the learning to be continued almost to the point of automatism. When the learning is thus long continued, subsequent forgetting goes on at a much slower rate. Ebbinghaus himself showed that increasing the number of readings of his nonsense syllables increased markedly the amount retained after twenty-four hours; and Radossawljewitsch,[1] who required the lists of nonsense syllables to be studied till two successive perfect recitations could be made (instead of one, as in Ebbinghaus's experiments), found the loss of retention to proceed still more slowly. He also found the retention of poetry to decline more slowly than that of nonsense syllables, as is shown in the following table:

Interval since the original learning	Per cent. of retention in nonsense syllables	Per cent. of retention in poetry
5 minutes	98	100
20 minutes	89	96
1 hour	71	78
8 hours	47	58
24 hours	68	79
2 days	61	67
6 days	49	42
14 days	41	30
30 days	20	24
120 days	3	?

The figures given above are the average result from several individuals. The poor retention after eight hours is assigned to fatigue in the latter part of the day. But the principal thing to be noted in the table is the slight loss of retention after five and after twenty minutes. This shows that after some "over-learning," the onset of forgetting is retarded, so that the transition from the curve of learning to that of forgetting would not be wholly abrupt. When the over-learning has been carried to a very high pitch, as in the experiments reported above with the typewriter—to so high a pitch that a very large share of the associations involved have been reduced

[1] Op. cit., p. 8].

to a condition of automatic efficiency—then the onset of forgetting is extremely slow. Book found,[1] after refraining for a full year from all use of the typewriter, that his speed had only decreased by 8 per cent., and this small loss was fully regained in forty minutes of fresh practice.

Material having "sense" is, as the last preceding table shows, better retained than nonsense syllables. Even after twenty-two years, Ebbinghaus found[2] a perceptible retention of stanzas of poetry learned only once to the point of one perfect recitation, and never since seen. Forgetting can, of course, be stayed by learning anew; and after each new learning the progress of forgetting is slower and slower, till finally recall after an interval is possible with no further study.[3]

§ 24. Regarding the process of memorizing, or the formation of associations, many interesting facts have been established, and some advance has been made toward their explanation. Some of the results of experiment appear rather obvious, from the fact that they are met with in ordinary experience, but they are none the less curious when attentively considered. Among such may be mentioned the ease with which a short list of words or syllables is memorized, and the rapid increase of difficulty which appears as the list is lengthened. A certain length of list, corresponding to the memory span, can be immediately reproduced after one reading; but if the list is lengthened beyond this point, several readings are usually required. Thus Ebbinghaus[4] could recite a list of seven nonsense syllables after one reading; but it took him 13 readings to fix a list of 10 syllables, 17 readings to fix a list of 12, 30 readings to fix a list of 16, 44 readings to fix a list of 24, and 55 readings to fix a list of 36. Binet[5] found that a list of 11 one-place numbers could be reproduced after 4 seconds of study, whereas, to learn a list of 13 numbers, 38 seconds were needed; and 75 seconds for a list of 14.

When a list is too long to be learned in a single reading, continued reading does not develop the mastery of all parts of it with equal speed; but some of it will be known long before the rest. Generally the first and last of a list are known long before the middle, which remains like a shapeless mass after the ends have taken shape in the mind.[6] More rapid organization of the middle of a list—and therefore more rapid learning of the whole list—is accomplished

---

[1] Op. cit., p. 75.
[2] *Grundzüge der Psychologie*, 1905, I, 681.
[3] Ebbinghaus, *Über das Gedächtnis*, p. 110.
[4] Op. cit., pp. 64, 67.
[5] *Psychologie des grands calculateurs*, 1894.
[6] W. G. Smith, *Psychol. Rev.*, 1896, III, 21.

by following the natural tendency to accent certain members of the list and thus impress on it a rhythmic form. It is not, indeed, an advantage to divide the list into parts and learn these separately, afterward putting them together; for this method is found to take more time than learning the whole list together by reading it through and through.[1] But dividing it into measures or feet, with regular pauses and accents, while still reading the list straight through, is found to be the most economical device for memorizing nonsense lists,[2] and still more for memorizing poetry. If, indeed, the material is not required to be recited as a whole, but in parts, as in the case of vocabularies, or, in general, in experiments by the method of paired associates, then division into parts, and prolonged attention to each part before passing to the next, is apt to give the best results. Again, where the members of a list are individually hard to grasp, it may be economy to repeat or linger on small parts of the list.[3] Similar considerations apply to the question as to the best rate of reading a list; a slow rate is more favorable for the formation of single associations between the pairs of which the list is composed, and a rapid rate of reading is relatively favorable for learning the list as a complete list.[4]

§ 25. A partial explanation of the peculiarities of the process of forming associations is afforded by the three following considerations.

(1) Associations are certainly formed, not only between the successive members of a list, but also between individual members and their positions in the series. The first member becomes strongly associated with the first place, and the last member with the last place; and when the list is rhythmically organized, the accented member of each measure is associated with its place in the rhythmic pattern. This association with position helps to explain not only the advantage of the rhythmic form, but also the disadvantage of learning a list in disjointed parts; for the latter method generates false associations of position, since the last term of each section becomes associated with a final position and a "full stop" which do not belong to it in the complete list. Any such false associations must, therefore, be broken up before the list is ready to be handled as a whole.

(2) "Higher units," similar to those which were assigned such importance in the learning of an act of skill, are present also in the

---

[1] Lottie Steffens, *Zeitschr. f. Psychol.*, 1900, XXII, 321; Pentschew, *Archiv f. d. ges. Psychol.*, 1903, I, 417.

[2] Müller and Schumann, Ebert and Meumann, op. cit.

[3] Ephrussi, *Zeitschr. f. Psychol.*, 1904, XXXVII, 161; Pentschew, op. cit.

[4] Ogden, *Archiv f. d. ges. Psychol.*, 1904, II, 93; Ephrussi, op. cit

process of memorizing, both when the material to be learned has meaning and when it is, as far as possible, void of meaning. Meaning organizes the words of connected speech into phrases and still larger groups, which are grasped as units, and thus it is that prose or verse can be memorized with enormously greater ease than an equal number of unconnected words. But even in learning a list of nonsense syllables, the formation of higher units can be detected. The syllable is itself entitled to rank as a higher unit, for it is found that many more letters can be learned in a given time when they are combined into nonsense syllables than when they are wholly uncombined. And further, the measures or feet, into which a list of nonsense syllables is almost inevitably broken up, and which greatly facilitate the memorizing of the list, also belong in the class of higher units. The dynamic unity, or "dynamical association,"[1] of the measure is shown by the facts[2] that relearning of a list is made more difficult by breaking up these measures, or even by altering the position of the accent within each measure; while, on the other hand, a list built up out of complete measures taken from different, previously learned lists, is comparatively easy to learn. If the measures are short, they are more readily joined into larger groups which have a certain unity.

The further fact that associations are formed between the constituent syllables and their positions in the list is evidence of some degree of unity in the grasp of the entire list. Associations are also formed between the single measures and their positions in the list. Still another evidence of the unitary grasp of large sections of the list, or even of the whole list, is afforded by the fact that each syllable has a tendency to call up, not only the immediately succeeding syllable, but also the syllable which comes next but one;—and, indeed, the syllable which comes next but two, next but three, etc. But the strength of these "remote associations" decreases with the number of intervening syllables.[3] Associations are even formed in the backward direction, so that the later members have some tendency to call up the earlier, at least within the same measure. Enough has been said to show that the learning of a list of nonsense syllables is very far from being simply the formation of a chain of serial associations. The process embodies great multiplicity, and at the same time much unity.

(3) Inhibition or interference is a factor to be reckoned with, both in memorizing and in recall. A distinction may be drawn be-

[1] For an explanation of this phrase, see Ladd, *Psychology, Descriptive and Explanatory*, pp. 242 f. and 384 f.

[2] Ebbinghaus, Müller and Schumann, op. cit.

[3] Ebbinghaus, Müller and Schumann, op. cit.

tween the two cases, by speaking of "associative inhibition" as that which occurs in the process of learning, and impedes *the formation* of associations; and "reproductive inhibition," or that which hampers the process of recall or *the operation* of associations. A clear instance of inhibition appears in the fact that lists of words or syllables, up to a certain length, can be recited after one reading, whereas adding one or two more members to the list makes many readings necessary. Perhaps an individual can recite, after one reading, a list of six syllables, but, on attempting a list of seven, is unable to give more than one or two of them, or even any at all. The seventh syllable has driven away the others, without becoming fixed in their place.

§ 26. The exact nature of the psycho-physical mechanism involved in these inhibitions is by no means easy to make out. The clearest case is, perhaps, that in which a given stimulus or antecedent, A, is already firmly associated with a certain response or consequent, B, and now the attempt is made to associate with A a new response, C. A leads so promptly to B that C does not have a chance, at least till after B has had its turn; and thus the learning of the sequence AC is impeded, while that of the sequence AB may be further strengthened. Even if the overt reaction B, or the conscious thought of B, should be repressed, A would still exert a tendency toward B, and might sub-excite it, or bring it into "readiness," and thus hinder the formation of the association AC, while being itself somewhat strengthened. If, however, AB is not very strong to start with, it is likely to yield to the pressure toward AC, though interfering somewhat with the formation of the latter association. The reality of such interferences has been shown by Müller and Pilzecker[1] in the case of learning pairs of nonsense syllables, and by Bergström[2] in the case of associating certain movements with certain stimuli. But the relations of interference to such factors as amount and recency of training in the opposing associations are very intricate and by no means fully worked out. It was shown by Münsterberg[3] and later by Bair,[4] that two opposed responses to the same stimulus might both be learned so well that either could be set into operation at will. They had ceased to interfere with each other to any perceptible degree.

It is quite possible that interferences between the manifold associations formed in reading over a list of nonsense syllables are the main cause of the difficulty of learning such lists, especially when the length of the lists is increased and the associative tendencies

[1] Op. cit., pp. 138 ff.
[2] *Amer. Journ. of Psychol.*, 1893, V, 356; 1894, VI, 433.
[3] *Beiträge z. exp. Psychol.*, 1892, IV, 69.   [4] Op. cit.

are thus made more numerous. Repeated reading strengthens the principal or serial associations more than the remote associations, till at last the interferences are unable to prevent the correct recitation of the list.

§ 27. On recurring to the discussion of the problem whether practice in learning, in one rather specialized line of performance, is available for the culture of the faculty of learning in general, we may gain additional light on the reasons for the negative results, from the facts just disclosed by the experiments on the conditions of successful memorizing. It was formerly shown that great skill in making certain motor reactions can be attained only at the risk of establishing increased chances of interferences and inhibitions, when the attempt is made to substitute a certain changed system of such reactions. And now the same thing appears to be true in the cultivation of skill in memorizing. It is a well-known fact, however, that there are certain natural or acquired aptitudes in the retentive and associative factors of conscious memory, as there are aptitudes, both natural and acquired, for performing highly specialized feats of skill in motor reactions. Only a detailed study of each particular instance of failure to pass from one kind of facility to another kind, could eliminate the influence of the inhibitory and interfering processes, which belong to the passage itself. An over-cultivated, and so implastic mind, or brain, in some special kind of learning—whether it be in the form of nearly automatic motor reactions, or of conscious attention, discrimination, and deliberate memorizing—might be a temporary hindrance to "transference" of the facility along other lines. But all this affords no satisfactory proof against the almost universal assumption that the power of discriminating, attending, memorizing, and learning in general, can be cultivated.

§ 28. Another class of interesting facts regarding the process of memorizing may now receive attention. It is found[1] that a list can be learned in fewer readings when these are spread over several days than when all are concentrated into a single learning period. Since a similar fact appears in muscular training, the explanation is probably to be sought in the effects of activity upon the nutrition of the organ exercised. Probably, also, the lapse of time allows the minor interfering associations to die out more than the principal associations, and thus favors the latter in the new impression. A similar dropping out of interferences, and consequent rapid improvement after an interruption of practice, has been noted by Book in typewriting, and by Ebert and Meumann in memorizing.

[1] Jost, op. cit. A similar result has been obtained in learning other performances by Leuba, op. cit., and by Kirkpatrick, op. cit.

Another fact, which has been brought out most definitely by Witasek,[1] is the superior value of active recitations of the matter to be memorized, as compared with the more passive reading of the presented lists. Long before a list can be recited entire, it is possible to recite parts of it, and if the learner does this, relying on himself as far as possible, but being prompted when he hesitates, the list is learned in fewer repetitions than otherwise. In partial explanation of this important result, it is a plausible conjecture that the passive or receptive attitude leaves the door open to incidental and interfering associations; while an active reproduction, so far as it succeeds, requires the suppression of interferences and the selection of those associations which contribute to success. From this point of view, there is a certain analogy between learning a list of nonsense syllables, and learning the successful response to a situation by the method of trial and error. This experience also illustrates the value in all learning of a cultivated power of giving attention, in general.

The same conclusions are further enforced by the fact that to achieve quick learning, it is necessary to arouse the "will to learn."[2] If a subject maintains a purely passive attitude toward the lists which are shown him, his learning is indeed slow. He may adopt a decidedly active attitude, but if this is rather that of observation of the members of the series than of associating them so as to be able to recite the list, repeated presentations may leave him without the power to recite it.[3] It is, therefore, clearly possible by an act of will to set up an adjustment specifically favorable for memorizing, though it is by no means clear, introspectively, in what this adjustment consists. There is even some evidence that the adjustment may be different, according as the list is to be retained for a long time, or only for a few moments.[4]

§ 29. If now we turn from the "first event," or impression, and pass over the intervening time, during which the disposition left behind by the impression is gradually dying out, we come finally to the "second event," the so-called "reproduction" or "recall." Neither of these terms is perfectly correct; for the original impression is not always, and perhaps never, fully and accurately reproduced. Few people can reinstate an impression in all its sensory fulness

---

[1] *Zeitschr. f. Psychol.*, 1907, XLIV, 161, 246.

[2] Ebert and Meumann, op. cit.; Meumann, *Ökonomie und Technik des Gedächtnisses*, 1908, pp. 24, 232.

[3] Müller and Schumann, op. cit., p. 291.

[4] Ohms, *Zeitschr. f. Psychol.*, 1910, LVI, 73; Henderson, "A Study of Memory for Connected Trains of Thought," *Psychol. Rev.*, Monogr. Suppl. No. XXIII, 1903, p. 53.

and vividness; many can accomplish this with moderate success; while others are quite incapable of seeing their breakfast table "in their mind's eye," as if it were actually before them, though they are fully capable of recollecting aspects of, or facts about, the original experience. This difference between individuals is spoken of as a difference in their powers of imagery.[1] Besides this deficiency in fulness and vividness, all reproduction, when tested carefully by comparison with the original experience, is apt to be found infected with certain erroneous factors.

It will be remembered that in considering the topic of "association times" (see above, p. 493) we found the stimulus A calling up the reaction B, although both stimulus and reaction were internal rather than sensory and motor. This was explained as due to a "disposition" left behind by the previous experience. Recall, then, may—at least sometimes—be considered as a certain type of reaction. And concretely, the condition would seem to be somewhat as follows: The individual, being in a given situation, and being adjusted or prepared, voluntarily or involuntarily, in a certain direction, and having within him a host of dispositions or reproductive tendencies of varying strength and manifold connections, is affected by a certain stimulus, and reacts to it. This reaction is his recall or reproduction, and it is determined by the stimulus, by the individual's present adjustment, and by his past experience as retained in reproductive tendencies.

§ 30. If we now ask what determines the reaction to a given stimulus—and if, for the present, we leave out of account the important factor of adjustment—our previous discussions have sufficiently shown that A is likely to recall B when it has been already associated with B; and that the likelihood of its recalling B is greater in some proportion to the frequency and recency of this association. If A has been previously associated with both B and C, then the likelihood of its calling up one rather than the other of these associates depends on the relative frequency and recency of the two associations, as also on the vividness or intensity of the associative events.[2]

Recall also depends on the degree of success or pleasure which has attended previous reactions to A by B or C (compare pp. 547, 552). The tendency of A to call up B is also strengthened, if A has been immediately followed by B, and if attention has been directed to connecting the two; but in a less degree, if A was preceded instead of followed by B, or if it was only indirectly followed by B, or if both A and B formed parts of a single group or "higher unit."

[1] Galton, *Inquiry into Human Faculty*, p. 83 (London, 1883).
[2] Calkins, op. cit.

In all these cases, we may speak of A and B as having been *contiguous* in past experience; and we may speak of the present recall as resulting from "association by contiguity" in experience.[1] Probably it is not so much a mere contiguity in "experience" that counts, as some definite contiguity in reaction. Perhaps we may express the general fact best by saying that the contiguity must effect a "dynamic association." When A and B have formed parts of a single unit of reaction—such a unit, for example, as one of the rhythmical measures in which a list of syllables is learned, or such as the noting of a relation between A and B—they become associated much more strongly than when they have simply been present to consciousness at the same time or in immediate succession.[2]

§ 31. The association between A and B may have, at a given time, any strength from zero to a maximum such that A will recall B with certainty and promptness. Below a certain strength, it cannot be utilized for purposes of recall. In other words, a reproductive tendency may lie below the "threshold of recall";[3] or, we may speak of some associations as being "*sub*-liminal." The existence of a subliminal association may be shown in several ways: sometimes by a partially correct recall, and sometimes by the feeling of "being near" a name which is vainly sought for in memory. Its activity may also be tested by the following experiment: Suppose the association AB has proved to be subliminal at a certain time; that is, A, being presented, has not been able to recall B. Now let B itself be presented, but not clearly; let it be shown for too brief an interval to allow of accurate reading, or let it be pronounced through a poor telephone, so that it cannot be distinctly heard; under such conditions, it has been found[4] that B is more likely to be rightly read or heard if it has just been put into a condition of "readiness" by the use of the subliminal association AB. In such a case the subliminal tendency from A toward B facilitates (compare p. 170) the arousal of B by another stimulus. It may also inhibit the tendency to some other response. Two associations,

---

[1] On the possibility of reducing the so-called laws of association to the principle of "contiguity in consciousness," see Ladd, *Psychology, Descriptive and Explanatory*, pp. 263 ff.

[2] "To be associated it is not enough that two impressions shall occur together or in immediate succession. B may follow upon A as a physical event till doomsday, but it is only as A and B are apperceived as in some sort one and connected," that A will afterward give rise to B. J. Ward, *Mind*, 1894, N. S., III, 509. This statement may perhaps need some qualification; but the experimental work on memory shows abundantly that no strong associations are formed by virtue of *mere temporal* contiguity in consciousness.

[3] Müller and Pilzecker, op. cit., p. 34.

[4] Ohms, *Zeitschr. f. Psychol.*, 1910, LVI, 1.

AB and *AC*, tending in different directions with slight and about equal strength, may inhibit each other so that neither *B* nor *C* is recalled.[1]

Reproductive interference between different associations is probably of great importance in explaining the difficulties of recall. Suppose, for example, that reproductive tendencies *AB* and *AC* exist in an individual at a given time, but that *AC* is the more readily excited; then the stimulus *A* may lead to the response *C*, though *B* may be the response desired. When an association has been very recently exercised, it is left in an excitable condition and is more quickly re-excited to full activity than an old and perhaps well-ingrained association which has not been recently active. In other words, the association time for recently active associations is especially short.[2] A recently active association is, therefore, likely to "get the start of" an older and perhaps better-established association, and thus govern the first response. By so doing it acquires even more of the advantage of recency, so that a renewed attempt to arouse the old association may simply lead to the recent one again. This occurs in trying to recall a piece of music which resembles a piece just heard; it is hard to drive one air out of the mind and give the other a chance. The same difficulty occurs in case of a slip in writing or spelling. One sometimes, after making a "slip of the pen," goes back to write the sentence correctly, and commits the same error again. In playing a musical instrument or in a highly skilled athletic performance, an error tends to be repeated and to put the performer "out of form" for the time being, or until the recent bad associative tendencies have time to "cool down." The same sort of trouble occurs at times in trying to recall a familiar name; unless the right response occurs at once, it appears to be short-circuited by the false responses which occur, and the best plan is often to abandon the search for a time, and allow the interferences to go to sleep. It would seem safe to say that, as a rule, an existing reproductive tendency *AB* must control the reaction to *A* except for the interference of other instinctive or associative tendencies set into activity by *A* or by some other stimulus acting at the same time.

§ 32. A very interesting conception of the interferences operative in preventing the recall of a familiar name, and in causing lapses and slips of various kinds, has been put forward by Freud.[3] Without attempting a lengthy exposition of this theory, we may get a glimpse at its character in the following way: Let us suppose that a name has several associates which tend to be recalled with it. It may be that these associated ideas are unpleasant, or that they have been un-

---

[1] Müller and Pilzecker, op. cit.   [2] Müller and Pilzecker, op. cit.
[3] *Zur Psychopathologie des Alltagslebens* (Berlin, 1904).

pleasant at some time in our past experience; or it may simply be that they are not welcome at the moment because they would distract attention from the present object of interest. In any of these cases, there is a tendency to repress or inhibit these undesired associates, even before they actually break into consciousness. But in repressing them, we may repress the name as well; or we may only partially suppress it, and so recall a name similar to it. Or, again, some of the associates may not be fully suppressed, but may be operative in recalling a substitute name. In other words, a forgotten name points to a repressed complex of ideas and emotions, and what is thus suppressed may be discovered by removing the suppression, and allowing a train of perfectly free association to take its start from the forgotten name when, later, it has been found. By this method of "psycho-analysis," Freud, and others following him, have been able to bring to the surface submerged "complexes," which, in nervous persons, are sometimes the source of much mental inefficiency. Freud is inclined to look especially for old emotional suppressions, often of a more or less sexual nature, as lying at the bottom of apparently trivial lapses of memory. It is highly improbable that all interference with recall possesses this highly elaborate and significant character; interference could hardly act in these complicated ways did it not also act—as has been abundantly shown that it does—in simple ways; but it may very well be that such inhibitory mechanisms as Freud conceives are sometimes operative.[1]

§ 33. What was said above of the liability of a recently active association to re-excitation leads to a further important consideration. In certain abnormal conditions of the nervous system, a tendency is visible to repeat an act time after time, when once it has been aroused by some appropriate stimulus. Or, in an association test, which calls for responses to one after another of a series of presented words, there may appear a tendency to give the same response to several words—a response which was evidently called up by association in the first instance, but which has no relevance to the later words. The response, once excited, persists or perseveres. This tendency to "perseveration" is not confined to abnormal conditions, but has been demonstrated by Müller and Pilzecker in normal subjects,

---

[1] An example may perhaps make this clearer. A certain author has frequently had difficulty in recalling the name "Wadelton." When he applies free association to this name, the first idea that occurs to him is that of waddling—a notion which does not in the least comport with the individual so named. Moreover, this cheap punning on names is a thing to be suppressed, and the author has been at some pains to suppress it. Now it may be—to speak in a figurative way—that recall, in reaching for the name, got hold also of these unsuitable associates, and, in trying to drop these, dropped the name with them, and so was unable to pull it up into consciousness.

when, in trying to recall nonsense syllables, they are operating with rather weak reproductive tendencies.   Perseveration may then appear in the repeated recall of the same syllable, as a response to syllables with which it has not previously been associated.

Perseveration is most apt to lead to the recall of recent experiences, and is most apt to appear when attention is relaxed, and the mind allowed to wander freely.   Instances of perseveration are found in the running of a tune in the head, soon after it has been heard; or in the flashing of a scene before the mind's eye soon after it has been actually seen; or in the reminiscences of the day which are apt to come to mind as one is dropping off to sleep.   In the case of visual dreams, these may be caused by the persistence of the after-images in the "fundus" of the eye.

The theoretical importance of such facts lies in the apparent absence of a stimulus to recall. B comes, it seems, not in response to any A, but entirely of itself.   It seems to spring up of its own elasticity, when the repressive force of other interests is removed.   Perseveration seems thus not to belong altogether under the head of association, and has accordingly been assigned an independent standing as a cause of recall.   We may conceive, perhaps, that the cerebral mechanism which takes care of B, after being strongly excited, does not at once lapse into quiet, but remains subliminally active; it may thus become the most active part of the brain by virtue of a decrease in the activity of other parts.   However, it is not necessary to adopt exactly this conception; for, if a mechanism, because of recent activity, simply is highly excitable, it might be thrown into activity through feeble associative links, of which, as the preceding pages have shown, many are formed between things which seem only remotely connected in consciousness.   Such a condition is especially emphasized when, either through the excitement of fever, or the relaxation of control over the train of ideas on account of exhaustion, or in sleep, a perfect hurly-burly of disconnected mental images takes possession of the conscious mind.   Whatever be the explanation, the facts indicated by the name perseveration are important in any sketch of the succession of thoughts which pass through the mind.

§ 34.   Perseveration is not the only apparent exception to the rule that recall proceeds along the lines of previously formed associations.   The law of association requires that A, in order to recall B, must have previously been associated with it.   But often A is new, and so never previously associated with B; or, though A and B may both be old, they may never have been present together in experience. The question is, then, whether, and how, A can recall B without having been previously associated with it.   The cases in which this seems to occur are chiefly of two kinds:[1] first, A may be similar to some stimulus which was previously associated with B; and second, A may be similar to B itself. The first case is exceedingly common, for a stimulus seldom recurs exactly as it was formerly received; its quality, intensity, or setting may vary, and yet the same reaction be evoked. The child, having learned the name "dog," for example, applies it readily to dogs of various sizes and colors, seen from various angles and in various attitudes; and even has little hesitation in applying the same name to a variety of other animals. The mastering of a new situation by aid of some act learned in response to a similar situation is an essential factor in learning. This form of recall thus takes us back to our previous discussion of the transference of a learned reaction from one situation to another; and our previous analysis of transference as dependent on the existence of something common to the old and new situations and responses is still applicable. The new stimulus need not be an exact copy of the old; neither does the new reaction need to be an exact copy of the old, for it is modified by the exigencies of the present situation; but both stimulus and response are partly old, and, therefore, connected by an old association.

Less common, but still common enough to be of constant and great importance in mental life, is the case in which A leads to a B which is similar to A itself. This is the famous case of "association by similarity." Although it differs, descriptively, from the preceding case, dynamically it is much the same. A stranger, for example, reminds us of an acquaintance, because of some resemblance between their faces. In this case, A is the sight of the stranger, and B the thought of the acquaintance, and A and B have never been associated in our past experience. If, now, the resemblance had been so great as to lead us to call the stranger by the name of the acquaintance, the response would clearly belong under the preceding case; it would be transference of a reaction rather than association by similarity. But if the resemblance is not strong enough to lead to a transferred motor reaction, it still exerts a tendency in that direction, and may give rise to an "idea" of our acquaintance. The two cases differ in the kind of reaction, but not in the mechanism of recall.

Let us further examine the question in an instance which has been experimentally worked out with some detail.[2] Suppose a collection of two-syllabled "nonsense words" to be made familiar by a moderate amount of study, and a few minutes later let similar non-

---

[1] Compare Ebbinghaus, *Grundzüge der Psychologie*, 1905, I, pp. 636, 642.

[2] Peters, "Über Ähnlichkeitsassociation," *Zeitschr. f. Psychol.*, 1910, LVI, 161.

sense words be presented—the similarity consisting in the general construction and in the possession of letters in common; then it is found that a word has considerable power to recall the similar word which has recently been made familiar. For instance, *tolaf*, being presented, recalls *golap*, recently studied. Now the common group of letters, *ola*, was an essential part of the stimulus which led to the percept *golaf;* and therefore tends to recall *golaf*, even when presented as part of another complex. If the association formed between *A* and *B* were exclusively concerned with *A* and *B* as totals, it would be difficult to conceive how anything similar to *A* could recall *B*, but since associations are formed connecting *parts* of *A* with *B*, the recall of *B* by partial recurrence of *A* presents no real exception to the law of association.

§ 35. The full importance in intellectual life of association by similarity does not, however, become evident till we consider that, though similarity may be analytically regarded as due to the possession of features in common, yet the detection of these common features is not always easy or even possible in concrete cases. It is not usually easy, for instance, to analyze the resemblance between two faces, so as to state exactly what they have in common; and yet one face may remind us of the other. Clearly, therefore, association by similarity does not depend on a *conscious* analysis of the stimulus, and a *conscious* discrimination of the features which have power to lead to the recall of some other complex. The recall of similars provides, the rather, an occasion for subsequent analysis. *A* recalls *B*, we do not see why, though we are vaguely aware of some resemblance between them. We may, next, become aware of the point of resemblance, and thus be led to an analysis of what would otherwise have remained unanalyzed. So, when a new situation arouses either a thought of some earlier situation, or a reaction which was made to it, the feature common to the two situations may become isolated in thought, and thus a more intelligent grasp of both old and new be promoted. Such seems to be the mechanism —at least in part—by which new insights and discoveries are often achieved. Thus transferred reactions and associations by similarity lead over from memory to productive imagination and thought.

§ 36. Thinking is, in very large measure, a process of recall, but it involves one factor which has not yet been fully considered. It has been shown that most cases of recall are of the nature of a reaction; and that, besides the stimulus, and the existing stock of reproductive tendencies, an important factor in the result is the mental adjustment present at the moment. Recall is seldom perfectly "free"; usually it is governed or directed by some present interest or state of mind. Reproductive tendencies, formed in past experience, are numerous, and make possible many reactions to a given stimulus; and which, in particular, of these reactions shall occur is dependent not only on the relative strength of the reproductive tendencies, but also on the present adjustment.   In reading, for instance, the context so "sets the mind" that the appropriate meaning of each word is at once recalled, though the word may have many meanings, and each of these may have been previously associated with the word.   In arithmetical work, the numbers "three and four" suggest "seven," if the adjustment is to add; but "twelve," if the adjustment is to multiply.   Mental work of any kind would be a hopeless tangle of associations, were it not for the directive power of preparatory adjustments.   This factor is a selective one; without increasing the stock of associations, it gives the preference to some and suppresses others.

The most important question regarding this "selective mechanism" is whether it acts before, or after, the reproductive tendencies have done their work.   Does such a word as "fair," for example, when occurring in context, first call up several of its familiar meanings, from among which, next, that which suits the context is selected; or does the selection so occur that only the appropriate meaning comes to consciousness?   If, in multiplying, we meet the numbers 7 and 9, do we recall both their sum and their product, and afterward select the product?   In such cases, introspection gives a clear answer: usually only the appropriate response appears; and in fact the reaction is objectively too prompt to allow of multiple recall and subsequent selection.   The preparatory adjustment here facilitates one reproductive tendency and inhibits the others from the very start of the total process.   Such, indeed, is the case in all smooth-running mental work.   On the other hand, there are not a few cases where the appropriate reproductive tendency is weak, and other reproductive tendencies are relatively strong; and in all cases there are limits to the power of the adjustment.[1]

§ 37. Recall is likely to be attended by feelings of familiarity, of recent occurrence, of correctness or incorrectness, of certainty or doubt; and these feelings are often the chief subjective constituent of what is termed "*recognition*."   A high value is attached to them by the individual, inasmuch as he is usually willing to assert that they indicate the truth.   He "feels sure" that he has seen this face before, or that he has recalled this name correctly, or that seven times nine is sixty-three, without further evidence than his immediate impression.   Without doubt, these feelings have a considerable degree of trustworthiness, especially when they are strong and posi-

[1] Experimental evidence in support of these conclusions has been presented in a previous chapter, pp. 495 ff.

tive. They are not, however, absolutely trustworthy; for cases are easily found, in experiment, in which a false recall is attended with the feeling of correctness and confidence, as well as cases in which a right recall is attended with a feeling of its incorrectness.[1] Testimony, whether in ordinary intercourse or in courts of justice, regarding events experienced shows similar cases; and in fact, where the testimony can be controlled by a full knowledge of the facts, a considerable proportion of false recalls, attended by a feeling of correctness, is ordinarily found.[2] A witness in court may even be willing to testify under oath, and in perfectly good faith, to the occurrence of an event or to the identity of a person, when his memory is really at fault.[3] Still, the feelings of recognition are on the whole worthy of confidence. In some persons they are highly trustworthy; in others much less so, according to the temperament; and, again, they are much more reliable as to certain classes of facts than as to other classes.

§ 38. No subjective guarantee of the correctness of memory is superior to these feelings of recognition. One may seek outside corroboration, or one may criticise one's recollections on the basis of probability; but in so far as one must rely on one's own memory, the feelings are ultimate, and there is no way of going behind them to justify or to discredit them. It has indeed been sometimes suggested that recognition consists in more recall, i. e., in the recall of the original setting of the particular fact recognized. This is so far true that recall of the setting of a fact often occurs, and permits of a more exact assignment of the fact to its place in past experience; and, besides, recall of the setting reassures us as to the correctness of the central fact. But what guarantees the correctness of the *recalled* setting? How do we recognize that? If a setting is all that is required, imagination is perfectly capable of conjuring one up about an imagined fact; only, such a setting will not *feel* genuine and familiar. The recognitive feeling must attach to the setting to give it subjective validity. Try as we will to justify memory by indirect evidence from within ourselves, we have always, in the last analysis, to rely upon a feeling of direct certainty—though the certainty may be so categorical as to occasion very little emotional tumult. Such rather neutral states of assurance are the rule where recognition is easy and unhesitating, as when a daily companion is seen, or a well-known date recalled. This feeling of unquestioning assurance, as distinguished from feelings of uncertainty, hesita-

[1] Müller and Pilzecker, op. cit.
[2] Cattell, *Science*, 1895, N.S. II, 760; Stern, *Zur Psychologie der Aussage* (Berlin, 1902).
[3] Urstein, *Zeitschr. f. Psychol.*, 1906, XLIII, 423.

tion, and doubt, is the correlate in consciousness of the uninhibited and smoothly running adjustment and unimpeded dynamic association of the cerebral mechanism.

That recognition does not consist essentially in the recall of a setting was asserted by Külpe,[1] who drew a distinction between the "mediate" or indirect and the "immediate" or direct types of recognition. In the mediate type, the setting is recalled and aids in the recognition; but in the immediate type, the recognition occurs before the setting is recalled, if indeed it is recalled at all. The immediate type occurs when recognition is prompt and sure. Experiments on the recognition of odors, undertaken by Gamble and Calkins,[2] showed instances in which an odor was recognized without recall of previous experiences of it, and other instances in which past experiences of the odor were recalled only after the odor had been recognized.

[1] *Grundriss der Psychologie*, 1893, pp. 177.
[2] *Zeitschr. f. Psychol.*, 1903, XXXII, 177, and XXXIII, 161.

CHAPTER IX

THE MECHANISM OF THOUGHT

§ 1. Logic treats of rational discourse as made up of syllogisms; of these in turn as composed of propositions; and of these, finally, as containing terms and a copula, or sign that the terms belong together. Or, starting from the terms, logic regards the proposition as resulting from comparison of the terms, and the syllogism as resulting from the comparison of propositions. Though this treatment is based on the analysis of the linguistic expression of thought rather than on the analysis of concrete mental processes, it may serve to indicate, in a provisional way, the topics suggested for study in the field of thought.

§ 2. The so-called "terms," or "ideas," of which a proposition or judgment is supposed to consist, are supplied either by perception or by recall. This fact makes desirable some further consideration of the nature of perception, although the topic has already been discussed (Chapters V and VI of Part II) in detail. It is clear, in the first place, that sense-perception commonly depends on past experience. In general, each thing is perceived as a familiar individual, or as belonging to a familiar class of things; or as like something already known; or as compounded of known elements. Perception thus involves recognition; and what has been said of recognition applies also to perception. In particular, the distinction between mediate and immediate recognition is applicable in the field of thought, and in the study of its mechanism. When an object appears in a new setting—and every setting is likely to differ somewhat from those in which the object previously occurred—the old setting may be recalled and apparently aid in recognizing the nature of the object. This is "mediate" perception; but it is far from being the common type, for usually an object of a familiar class is recognized in a new setting promptly and directly; and this is equally true if the present object differs from similar objects previously experienced, even as much as an outline drawing differs from an actual scene. The outline drawing is readily "understood," or recognized as a representation of *a certain sort* of object, without the recall of the colors or background which an actual object must have. When the same outline drawing can represent more than one object—as is the case in the "staircase figure"

593

and other ambiguous figures—the transition from one way of seeing the figure to another is not attended by the recall of a new setting.[1] The observer seems to see only the figure before him, but to see it now as this object and again as that. In perception generally, past experience is not overtly present in consciousness; one seems to live in and deal with the present, while all the time one is really utilizing previously learned reactions.

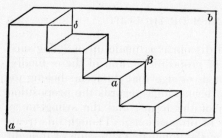

FIG. 152.—The Staircase Figure (from Wundt). *a* can be made to appear either nearer or farther off than *b*.

§ 3. A percept belongs without doubt to the class of reactions to stimuli, and usually to the class of reactions previously learned.[2] Yet introspection can seldom distinguish between the stimulus and the reaction in a perceptual act. It is impossible to lay aside habitual modes of perception, and to receive the stimulus as a "pure sensation"; it is also usually impossible to detect by introspection an interval between the reception of the stimulus, as such, and the recognition of it as some definite thing. Brain pathology, however (compare p. 252), affords reason to believe that the reception of the stimulus and the perception of it as some known object are *two* events; and even that an interval occurs between the beginning of the first event and the beginning of the second; but this interval is probably a small fraction of a second, and is not, moreover, an empty interval, but a period of *gradual change* in consciousness. Introspection, therefore, could not be expected to be aware of the interval, or to distinguish the earlier from the later stages of the total process.

In cases of difficult perception, however, it is often possible to observe the gradual development of a percept. A sudden and startling stimulus may call out an immediate motor response, attended by mental confusion, which then gradually gives way to a clear perception of the nature of the stimulus or of the object indicated by it. At other times, an unfamiliar stimulus, especially a curious sound, may give rise to a rapid succession of "trial percepts" which are promptly rejected, each for the next, till one is reached which satisfies the mind. A few seconds may see the whole series of tentative interpretations gone through with, and a satisfactory percept reached. In such cases, perception has definitely the character

[1] Woodworth, *Journal of Philos.*, 1907, IV, 169.
[2] Ward, *Mind*, 1893, N.S., II, 355.

of response by "trial and error"; varied reactions, provided by instinct and previous training, are tried in succession, till one is
reached which gives satisfaction.   On the other hand, the perception of a familiar object has the character of a well-learned reaction,
which is recalled swiftly and automatically by the stimulus.

More definite experimental analysis of the process of perception
has been obtained in case of complex visual stimuli, such as reading
matter or "nonsense drawings."   The method used in these studies
is that of exposing the object for too brief a time to permit of a complete and accurate perception, and then repeating the exposure
time after time, noting after each exposure how far the observer is
able to reproduce the object.   When reading matter is so presented,[1]
the observer is able, at the first presentation, to read a certain number of words with certainty; to distinguish the general shape of
another word or two; and to hazard a guess as to some vague character of the next word or two.   On the next exposure, his eyes being directed to words which were only partially grasped the first
time, he sees these distinctly and his area of indistinct vision is extended to new words further to the right.   It moreover appears certain that the indistinct perception of words is of value in the subsequent clear perception of them.   The indistinct perception renders
the clear perception more prompt.   In the case of nonsense figures,
composed of seven short lines and curves, Judd and Cowling[2] found,
with repeated exposures of ten seconds each, a gradual development
of mastery of the figure.   Some subjects got at first the general outline and later the details; while others neglected the general outline at first and mastered a few details, adding to them in later trials.
In all cases, there was a shifting of attention as the exposures were
repeated, so that now one part, and now another came into prominence.   Further, in this more deliberate process, as distinguished
from the rapid succession of trial percepts spoken of above, there
was not a strict following of the method of trial and error, but some
individuals adopted a definite plan of operation from the beginning;
and formulations in general terms of the way the figure was constructed were sometimes in evidence before the details were mastered.
On the whole, then, perception presents certain features essentially
the same as the processes involved in the reaching of a successful
motor reaction to a situation, as the latter were described in the preceding chapter.

§ 4. Logic shows the importance of general and abstract terms,
and it will therefore be worth while to consider how abstractions

[1] Hamilton, "The Perceptual Factors in Reading," *Archives of Psychol.*, No.
IX, 1907.

[2] *Psychol. Rev.*, Monogr. Suppl. XXXIV, 1907, p. 349.

are developed.   The prominent characteristic of an abstract conception is that it neglects many of the features of a concrete situation or thing, and considers only certain features.   A thing cannot
exist except in the concrete, and in a concrete setting; but the concrete setting and many of the concrete details of a particular thing
can be neglected for the purposes of thought, and so the thing be
treated as abstract.   Indeed, if the mind were incapable of this process of so-called abstraction, all the generalizations of science and
of practical life would be impossible.

Logic usually speaks of ideas or concepts only as being abstract;
but psychologically considered, a percept may be, and indeed must
be, abstract; since every percept isolates some feature of a thing or
situation, and for the moment neglects the other features.   A
motor reaction does the same, for it is never a reaction equally and
indiscriminately to the whole situation, with all its concrete features, but is predominantly a reaction to some particular feature.
Both motor reaction and perception treat a situation, therefore,
as the bearer of the feature to which response is made; and thus the
situation is generalized, while the feature perceived, or reacted to,
is abstracted, though it actually remains concrete.   *Every percept
is, therefore, a partial analysis of the situation, emphasizing one
feature to the neglect of others*.

This process of analysis or emphasis is often considered under
the name of *attention*; and some of the results of the study of attention are of importance in our present inquiry.[1]   Attention is closely
related to analysis and abstraction, since it is always directed to
some feature of a situation, others being neglected for the moment;
attention is, in other words, *selective*.   Yet attention should not be
identified completely with analysis; for analysis occurs without attention.   A motor response to some particular feature of a situation
may occur automatically, while attention is elsewhere directed; and
perception of particular features may also occur without attention
being especially directed to them.   While attention is directed upon
some visible object, sounds which occur may be perceived as voices,
footsteps, and the like; or, while attention is directed to some "internal" thought, the eyes, if open, are sure to be accurately directed upon some object, and this object is apprehended as an object (for example, as a word, when the eyes rest inattentively on the
page and the thoughts are wandering).   What is not especially attended to, therefore, by no means remains "pure sensation," or
wholly undifferentiated from the total situation.

Moreover, several motor or perceptual reactions may occur at the

---

[1] For a fuller treatment, see Pillsbury, *Attention* (London, 1908), and Wirth,
Die experimentelle Analyse der Bewusstseinsphänomene (Braunschweig, 1908).

same time, but attention is usually concerned, in any special way, with only one of these. These facts make it difficult, and at present impossible, to define attention as a special function, or in any terms except those of degree. The descriptive definition which is usually attempted takes a figurative form. Of all the contents of consciousness at any moment, some are said to have the quality of "clearness," and it is the clear contents which are spoken of, in other words, as the objects of attention. "Clearness" has here a special meaning, which can only be defined by referring back to attention. A vague or obscure impression may be clear in this sense, since it can be the object of attention. A definition in terms of degrees of consciousness is perhaps admissible. We are, at any moment, more conscious of some objects than of others, and it is the objects of which we are most conscious to which we are said to attend, or which are said to be "clear." Within the field of consciousness there are gradations, and the most conscious part of this broader field is the narrower "field of attention."[1]

§ 5. The attempt to fix the number of objects which can be attended to at once, or to measure the so-called "span of attention," has been made by determining how many small and discrete units can be grasped in one presentation. Cattell[2] found that four or five short lines could be apprehended correctly in a brief exposure; beyond this, perception was not clear and reliable, though approximate judgments were possible with considerably larger numbers. The span was about the same for disconnected letters; but when the letters were combined into short words, about four words could be perceived. Similar results have been obtained in other senses. It is not so much the span of attention as the span of apprehension that is measured in these experiments; that is, it is not so much the extent of the field of clear consciousness as the extent and kind of object which can be perceived as a unit, that determines the result. Training increases the "span," not, probably, by increasing the amount of clear consciousness, but by developing "higher units" of perception. After training has done its perfect work, apprehension may proceed by large spans, while attention is elsewhere occupied. The span of attention, therefore, measures, not so much the area of the field of attention, as the number of stimuli which can be taken care of in a brief perceptual reaction (compare p. 498).

---

[1] For a treatment of attention as one of the "most general forms of all mental life," and the condition and accompaniment of all consciousness, see Ladd, *Psychology, Descriptive and Explanatory*, chap. III.

[2] Wundt's *Philos. Studien*, 1886, III, 94, 121. This is one of the oldest experiments in psychology, having been performed, in a relatively crude way, by Bonnet and by Sir William Hamilton.

§ 6. The *shifting of attention* from one object to another is a fact of common observation, of which psychology supplies examples of great precision. The most instructive cases are those in which the objective situation does not change, and yet, from internal causes, now this feature and now that becomes prominent. A good example is afforded by the changes in appearance of the staircase and other similar figures, which have several times been mentioned. Perhaps a still better example is seen in McDougall's[1] "dot figure,"

FIG. 153.—The Dot Figure (McDougall).

the particular construction of which can be varied *ad libitum*. If this figure is steadily examined, ever new groups and arrangements appear within it; but it is practically impossible to hold any one for a long time. "Varied reaction" continually occurs in a pronounced degree. Changes of the fixation point of the eyes are also likely to favor change in the groupings; but the shifting of appearance is by no means fully explained by these changes of fixation. The main fact is that a complex stimulus, which can be apprehended in several ways, or out of which several features can be isolated—all equally easy and of equal significance—gives rise to a succession of different percepts.

A similar instance of the shifting of attention, or of perception, is found in "binocular rivalry."[2] Ordinarily, both eyes receive only slightly differing views of an object, and these views are combined or blended in a single percept (compare p. 425). But if, artificially, and most easily by aid of the stereoscope, very different views are brought before the two eyes, the conditions suitable for single vision are not fulfilled, and there is likely to be an oscillation, in consciousness, between the deliverance of one eye and that of the other. If a plain red field, for example, is held before one eye, and a plain green field before the other, we see red and green, not usually together, but alternately. When one of the fields is

[1] *Mind*, 1902, N. S., XI, 316.
[2] Compare Helmholtz, *Physiologische Optik*, p. 766.

plain, and the other contains a figure, the figure remains seen for most of the time, though the background may oscillate as in the cases of the other figures. Voluntary attention devoted to one field gives it some advantage over the other, by bringing it back more quickly and thus abridging each appearance of the other field. This is true to some extent even if both fields are plain; but voluntary attention has much more effect in holding a field which presents considerable detail and so allows of a succession of percepts.[1]

It is clear that binocular rivalry belongs in large measure to the level which we are apt to distinguish as "physiological," in contrast with the mental; but it is equally clear that the value of each of the two opposing stimuli is important in giving the advantage to one or the other of them. Binocular rivalry reminds us, on the one hand, of the oscillation of attention between two topics of interest; and, on the other hand, of the alternation of two reflexes when the stimuli for both are continuously acting (p. 173). Apparently, then, we may formulate a law of the shiftings of attention in almost the same terms as those of the law for the alternation of reflexes. When two stimuli act simultaneously, either of two results may happen: The two may facilitate each other's action—that is, in psychical terms, they may give rise to a combined or blended percept; or they may be incompatible with each other, in which case they will not give a resultant effect, but one or the other will get the "right of way" and inhibit all response to the other for the time being. This inhibition, however, is followed by a "back swing" which gives the advantage to the response that has just been inhibited; and so an alternation of two responses occurs. Accordingly, it would be better to substitute for "shifting of attention" some such term as "shifting of perceptual reaction"; since rivalry between the eyes, and between different appearances of an ambiguous figure as well, occurs even if attention is directed to something entirely apart.

§ 7. What have been called "fluctuations of attention" also occur, if the attempt is made to hold continuously under observation something which is just above the threshold of perceptibility, such as the ticking of a watch when the watch is held at a distance such as to be barely audible; or such as a small and barely perceptible speck of white, or a patch of gray just distinguishable in brightness from its background. In these cases, the watch is heard for a time, then becomes inaudible, and then is heard again; and similar alternations occur with the other stimuli. No one interpretation of these experiences is altogether satisfactory; for oscillations in the condition

---

[1] For these and several other facts regarding this important phenomenon, see Breese, *Psychol. Rev.*, Monogr. Suppl. No. XI, 1899; also Sherrington, *The Integrative Action of the Nervous System* (New York, 1906).

of the sense-organs may as well be the cause as oscillations in attention, or "perceptual reaction"; and the fluctuations in perception do correspond to some extent to oscillations in the blood pressure and in respiration.[1]

The tendency of attention to shift adds another factor to those spoken of in the preceding chapter as determining recall. It is not simply the stimulus, the stock of reproductive tendencies, with their varying strength, and the adjustment of the moment, which are effective in governing recall; but the tendency to change operates counter to perseveration and to the factor of recency, which, without it, would probably control the mental train so as to make mental development difficult or impossible.

§ 8. The direction of attention, or of analytic perception, is determined in part by dispositions left behind through past experience, as was said a few paragraphs back. It is not, however, entirely so determined; for certain classes of stimuli have a natural or instinctive hold on attention. Very intense stimuli compel attention, as do sudden stimuli, sudden changes in a stimulus, or moving objects in the field of view, or over the skin; sharp contours in the field of vision, and objects contrasting strongly with their background, have a similar attraction. These causes operate even in young children, independently of previous experience, and lead to some degree of analysis of a presented complex of stimuli. Each individual also possesses native interests, which make their appearance as he grows older, and which lead him to analyze out and react to certain features of situations to which other individuals may remain relatively inattentive. In proportion as these instinctive analyses are exercised and trained, they afford a basis for further analyses of a more varied and more specialized character, so that the adult's attention becomes directed very largely by his acquired tendencies.

§ 9. Psychology, as studied from the physiological and experimental points of view, can make at present only meagre contributions to a theory of the development of abstract concepts. But there is one more fact which should be mentioned in this connection. Though a percept involves abstraction, a recalled impression is likely to surpass its percept in this respect; since the setting is more fully neglected in recall than in perception. Recall of the full setting of an impression is seldom possible (compare p. 582); but recall of a feature which has previously been observed often occurs without recall of the setting. Among the features of a situation, which can

---

[1] Urbantschitsch, *Centralblatt f. d. med. Wissensch.*, 1877, p. 626; Lange, Wundt's *Philos. Stud.*, 1887, IV, 390; Lehmann, ibid., 1894, IX, 66; Slaughter, *Amer. Journ. of Psychol.*, 1901, XII, 313.

be relatively isolated in perception, are relations, forms, groupings, and meanings of the most varied character. Each of these factors is actually presented in some concrete setting; but it is partially analyzed out of the situation by the act of perception.[1] Now it appears that any such feature which has been observed can be recalled without its setting; or, the setting may be only vaguely recalled while the feature in question comes to clear consciousness.[2] Even so "abstract" a feature as the meaning of a proverb can be recalled and identified as equivalent to that of another proverb, while the words in which it first occurred are altogether forgotten.[3] This tendency is of importance in the development of abstract concepts.

§ 10. *Comparison*, or the judgment of likeness or difference, is, like simple perception, dependent on memory. There are exceptions to this rule, especially in the case of different colors or degrees of brightness when lying immediately side by side; for then an elementary apprehension of difference involves little more than the perception of the line separating the surfaces. But in most cases, the objects to be compared must be examined one after the other, so that memory of the first one examined is necessary. Such judgments have been frequently subjected to psychological experimentation, although attention has usually been directed to the accuracy of the comparison rather than to the process by which the judgment is reached.

A stock experiment in judgments of this sort consists in the comparison of two weights, first one and then the other being lifted, and the judgment being announced after the second lift. It would seem theoretically necessary that the experience of lifting the first weight should be recalled for comparison with the experience of lifting the second; but Schumann,[4] who had an intimate knowledge of this experiment, asserted that this is not the case, and that no recollection of the first weight need be present in consciousness when the second is lifted. Külpe[5] introduced here, as in the case of recognition, the distinction between mediate and immediate judgments, and experiment[6] has abundantly justified this distinction, in the comparison not only of weights but also of other successively presented

---

[1] Compare Ehrenfels, "Über Gestaltqualitäten," *Vierteljahrschr. f. wiss. Philos.*, 1890, XIV, 249; Grünbaum, *Arch. f. d. ges. Psychol.*, 1908, XII, 452.

[2] Compare Wundt, *Psychol. Studien*, 1907, III, 301; Titchener, *The Experimental Psychology of the Thought-Processes* (New York, 1909).

[3] Bühler, *Arch. f. d. ges. Psychol.*, 1908, XII, 24.

[4] *Zeitschr. f. Psychol.*, 1898, XVII, 119.

[5] *Grundriss der Psychologie*, 1893, p. 212.

[6] Bentley, *Amer. Journ. of Psychol.*, 1899, XI, 1; Whipple, ibid., 1901, XII, 409, and 1902, XIII, 219.

stimuli.   Martin and Müller,[1] who, more than other experimenters, have sought to dissect the process of comparison in the case of weights, also found that no clear recollection of the first weight need be present when the judgment was made.   Often introspection revealed nothing like a comparison of the two weights—if by "comparison" be meant some form of holding them together—but the judgment seemed to be based simply on the impression produced by the second weight.

If now we attempt an interpretation of what must seem at first rather a mysterious process, we can make use of conceptions which have become familiar in preceding discussions.   It is probable that the first weight arouses an adjustment or preparation for the second, such that the effect of the second will be different in dependence upon its being either heavier or lighter than the first.   The adjustment may consist in regulating the muscular force with which the second weight is lifted; if, for instance, the force is so gauged that it would lift the first weight with a moderate speed, and the second weight yields tardily to this force, then the second weight appears heavier than the first; but it appears lighter, if it yields with great promptness.   Repeated lifting of the same weight perfects the adjustment of muscular force to it; so that when this weight is compared with other weights a little heavier or lighter, in a long series of trials, the delicacy of adjustment to the central weight may be such that lifting one of the lighter weights will convey an "absolute impression" of lightness, etc., and upon this impression the judgment may be based.[2]   It is probable that this conception of the adjustment set up in comparing weights, which is founded on the theory of Müller and Schumann,[3] is not fully adequate; and certainly an adjustment of this motor type cannot easily be conceived as available in the comparison of pitch, brightness, and many other kinds of stimuli.   Some kind of cerebral adjustment is likely, however, to be set up in anticipation of any stimulus the character of which is approximately foreknown.   When the expectation is not fulfilled, a shock of surprise is experienced, but this surprise does not by any means imply that an image of the expected event is present in mind alongside of the actual event, but only that something happens for which we are not ready, i. e., not adjusted.   Innumerable examples of this truth may be derived from daily experiences, which show that the way the mind reacts to any new event requiring judg-

---

[1] *Zur Analyse der Unterschiedsempfindlichkeit*, 1899.

[2] Martin and Müller, op. cit.

[3] *Arch. f. d. ges. Physiol.*, 1889, XLV, 37.   Interesting examples of the reality of motor adjustment or "Einstellung" are given in this paper and in a supplementary study by Laura Steffens, *Zeitschr. f. Psychol.*, 1900, XXIII, 241.

ment depends upon a multiplicity of pre-existing conditions, many of which are barely above the threshold of consciousness or even wholly subliminal. Such experiences vary from the physical shock which we encounter on miscalculating the width or the height of the step of a stair, to the spiritual shock with which an insulting look, or an unpleasant memory, or an immoral thought, is greeted in consciousness.

Fine comparisons require a much more delicate adjustment than is present in many cases of expectation, but the inner process is probably of the same general character. Since these are generally made with more deliberation, and what may figuratively be called "weighing of evidence," we often find ourselves alternating between mental images that represent the more recent, and the more remote, of the sensuous impressions that are to be compared. But if the attempt is made to tell "just how much" the more recent experience differs from the earlier, a voluntary effort to recall more distinctly the memory image of the earlier is quite sure to follow. In all these cases of so-called "comparison," when considered from the introspective point of view, enough of recollection is involved to account for that recognition of the character, amount, and direction, of the change in the sensation elements of consciousness on which the judgment is based.

§ 11. The psychology of *reasoning* is even less understood than that of abstraction and comparison.[1] Little aid can be derived from logic for an understanding of the actual processes which go on, either in consciousness or below the threshold, in an act of reasoning. The formal character of the syllogism is undoubtedly a travesty, rather than a description, of most concrete instances of inference; and, in particular, the major premise, or general principle involved, is almost always implied rather than overtly expressed in the thinking process. But there is a more serious exception to be made. The syllogism treats inference as though it were a straight-ahead process; the premises are supposed to be given, and the conclusion is supposed to follow from them by "laws of thought" which are axiomatic and compelling. If this were a true account, rational thinking would be a much simpler and easier matter than it is. But reasoning is not, in fact, a straight-forward progress, and does not proceed by rule; neither are the premises customarily recognized as given. This is true, at least, in a large proportion of concrete cases of the discovery of causes and the drawing of inferences. It is comparatively unusual to ask: "What further use can be made of the knowledge which I possess?" The usual

[1] See Pillsbury, *The Psychology of Reasoning* (New York, 1910); Dewey, *How We Think* (Boston, 1910).

question is, "What do I know that will help me to solve this particular problem?" What is given is a problem. The solution of the problem corresponds to the conclusion of the syllogism; the minor premise corresponds to an insight into the problem, i. e., to the perception of some feature which is the key to the situation; the major premise consists of previously acquired acquaintance with, and knowledge about, this feature; but this knowledge may or may not have received a definite formulation.

As a hypothetical example, we may suppose the following thoughts to have passed through the mind of Ebbinghaus, as he considered the problem whether anything once learned was ever forgotten; or to what extent and at what rate it was forgotten. Clearly what was in his mind to start with was something more like the conclusion than like the premises of a chain of reasoning; he could formulate alternative conclusions from the beginning, but would not know which was true. As he considered the problem, it may have first occurred to him that learning produces some effect on the mind, or on the brain, and that a change once induced ought never to be entirely lost; and therefore what has been learned ought never to be entirely forgotten. In other words, he has isolated from the solution the feature, "Change produced in a substance," and has either recalled, or newly formulated, a general principle applicable to this feature. But he may also have had his attention directed to another feature—namely, that he has now to deal with a living creature, and that atrophy through disuse is characteristic of such creatures; and thus he may have come to doubt the validity of his first conclusion. He may then have been driven to abandon the attempt to solve the problem deductively, and have sought to approach it inductively, or by way of examining concrete instances. He may have thought of the first lines of the "Æneid," which he learned fifteen years before—possibly he can recall some of them now. This failing, he was not satisfied to conclude that they have been all forgotten, for it might be that, once started, he could continue these lines. He hunts up a Vergil, and allows himself to refresh his memory by seeing the first line; but on turning from the book, he is unable to continue. Still unsatisfied, for the first line had a tinge of familiarity which seemed to indicate some degree of memory of it, the thought may have occurred to him: "It might be easier to relearn these lines than to learn an equal number of lines from some other part which had never received special attention." He then tries this supposition, and finds it correct. But now subordinate problems sprout out of the main problem, bearing on the best methods of testing this matter of relearning; till finally the "saving method" and the use of nonsense syllables are decided on as suitable means for examining the degree of retention; the experiments are tried and the solution reached. Clearly the entire process in this case has been anything but straight-ahead; it has depended on "turning over in the mind" the situation of trying to recall something long forgotten, and being "struck by" this and that aspect of the situation in the light of previous experience. Translated into psycho-physical terms, it has been distinctly a process of "varied reaction"; and both the inductive and the deductive parts of the process are alike in this respect.

§ 12. In a word, reasoning involves hunting for premises, or for features which are significant; and for past knowledge of, or reactions to, these features. As in other processes of analysis and recall, the course of thought is determined in part by the present adjustment, or direction toward a certain problem; partly by reproductive tendencies of varying strength; partly by the concrete situation with its many incidental and often confusing features; and partly by the fundamental tendency to vary the reaction.

Though the above example is hypothetical, it follows along the lines of actual instances of rational response to a concrete problem, especially as these are presented in such trivial but easily observed processes as the solution of puzzles.[1] In many such cases, it is difficult to distinguish reasoning sharply from complex cases of "transferred reaction"; the reasoning process consists, in fact, of the transfer to a new situation of some mode of response previously acquired in different situations, and depends on some degree of isolation of features which are common to both the new situation and the old. The transference is regarded as more rational in proportion as it is conscious and deliberate; and in proportion, also, as the varied reactions are tried out mentally instead of being impulsively put to an immediate motor test. Though it is apparently impossible to lay down any straightforward procedure for approaching the solution of all problems, a few general maxims emerge from the examination of concrete processes of reasoning. A good supply of major premises—in the form of reproductive tendencies ready to be brought into play—is a fundamental desideratum. And the more clearly these premises have been thought out and generalized, the more likely they are to be recalled in a variety of situations. Further, the importance of keeping an open mind for features or possibilities which do not at first appear—i. e., the necessity of inventing and adopting varied reaction—is so great that it may well be used as a maxim for the practical guidance of reasoning. Finally, as an offset to the preceding maxim, another may be based on the value of dwelling on each feature long enough to afford an

[1] Compare the previous reference to the work of Ruger, pp. 555 f.

opportunity for any reproductive tendencies connected with it to be brought into play.

§ 13. Reasoning, like recognition, perception, and comparison, may be "immediate" as well as "mediate";[1] and some of the cleverest instances of reasoning are cases in which a new situation is seen to be an exemplification of some general principle, without conscious recall of the former situations in which the principle was learned, and even without conscious recall of the principle itself as independent of the case in hand. An abstract general principle, or a principle as exemplified in some former situation, needs always to be applied or adapted to the novel situation; but immediate reasoning short-circuits this process by seeing the principle, not as "in itself," so to say, but as adapted or exemplified. If we possessed an introspective history of moments of new insights and discoveries, we should probably find that the insight usually started with this immediate or implicit reasoning, which was followed by explicit statements such as are necessary to present an inference in language.

On glancing back over the preceding sketch of the psychology of thinking, meagre and disconnected as it must seem, one cannot fail to be impressed by the great similarity of the mental process as it appeared in all those forms of perception, analysis and abstraction, comparison and reasoning, as well as those of learning and recall, presented in the preceding chapter. All of these performances, even the most intellectual, though they differ greatly in content, preserve the method of procedure that was visible in learning by trial and error. In all cases of this procedure there appears the controlling influence of some problem or aim which so sets or adjusts the psycho-physical mechanism as to select the relevant associative tendencies and make them prevail above others which are irrelevant to the problem in hand. In all cases, too, the process of solution—with the exception of persons well drilled in very similar problems—is usually far from straightforward; it has rather the form of varied and tentative reaction; and in all, an essential fact is the dealing with parts or features of a situation by emphasizing each in turn to the temporary neglect of other features. Such thinking appears, in other words, as a species of observation with reaction; and the degrees of its intellectuality and practical success depend largely on what is observed, i. e., on the content or material of the process rather than on its form. It is a question of what features of a situation are isolated or analyzed out, and made the starting-point for recall and motor reaction. To note the fall of an apple is to analyze out a com-

---

[1] Störring, *Arch. f. d. ges. Psychol.*, 1908, XI, 1; Pillsbury, *The Psychology of Reasoning*, pp. 119–120.

paratively obvious feature; to distinguish falling as a feature of the moon's revolution about the earth is still analysis, proceeding in much the same manner, but dealing with more difficult material and working with much more refined and elaborate tools.

§ 14. During all the discussions of the last five chapters, and, indeed, throughout the entire Part II of the book, one truth of supreme importance has been both assumed and illustrated, even where it has not been made perfectly obvious. This truth has been embodied in the language which we have found ourselves forced to employ. The similarity of the terms, and even in many cases their identity, which were used in describing the histological structure and physiological functions of the nervous mechanism, when studied from the points of view afforded by kindred natural and physical sciences, with the terms used in describing the conditions and activities of the conscious mental life, when studied from the introspective point of view, can scarcely have escaped notice. This "parallelism" is undoubtedly of the highest significance. It is true that some of these terms are rather highly figurative, and constructed upon a basis of analogy rather than of observed facts; it is also true that many of them only imperfectly suggest what we are led to believe are the actual phenomena, and the laws of their interdependence. On the other hand, it cannot be doubted that they describe, on the whole faithfully, the real character of the facts. But this is to say that, *between the nervous mechanism and the phenomena of conscious mental life, as respects the constitution and the behavior of both, there is, in man's case also, an extensive and intricate system of "correlations."*

Among those correspondences of language which are significant of correlations in fact, the following are some of the more important. In describing the structure and functions of the nervous mechanism and, as well, the nature and development of mental life, it was found necessary to employ terms indicative of a great variety of highly differentiated elements combining in manifold intricate ways, and in different degrees of intensity, to bring about more and more complicated and purposeful results. We spoke of "stimuli" and "reactions" to stimuli, in the case both of mechanism and of mind. But the one is a physical, the other a psychical, sequence. We took note of "transferences" and "consequences"; of "facilitation" and "inhibition," or "interference"; of the acquirement of "habits of reaction" as shown in the recurrence of states or forms of action, essentially similar although modified in various details. There were tokens of the laws of "conservation" and of "perseveration" in both nervous mechanism and mental life. But especially was it significant to see how the development of both mechanism and mind was dependent upon the speedy and, so to say, accurate formation of "higher units" of reaction out of the more elementary factors; and how in the formation of such units the more elementary conditions and reactions were absorbed or lost out of sight. Indeed, if now all the facts and laws hitherto treated are passed in review as illumined by this thought of the actuality of the relations between mechanism and mind, as testified to in the very language employed to describe both—the one from the objective, and the other from the introspective point of view—the significance of the term "physiological psychology" will be enforced and illustrated anew.

§ 15. In closing this Part of our work, therefore, we may fitly attempt to summarize some of the results in the form of established correlations between the nervous mechanism and mental life, while leaving details to the further and renewed study of the same class of facts which have occupied our attention, and been made the basis of our theories, from the beginning of the book. The general problem with which we have been concerned may now be formulated anew in somewhat the following way: What conception can be formed of cerebral action, in the combined light of the facts of anatomy, physiology, and pathology, as these were set forth in the first Part of the book, and of the facts of psychology as set forth in its second Part? Without necessarily looking to cerebral action as the explanation of mental activity, one may be convinced that the brain is active in mental operations, and may seek to form scientific conceptions of the character of its activity. It is certainly to psychology that the neurologist must appeal, in large measure, for the facts of behavior on which his conceptions of such activity must be based. It will be admitted at once by the psychologist that the data supplied by him are deficient not only, for the time being, in range and quantity, but also in minuteness and definiteness of detail. As was shown in considering the subject of localization of cerebral function, the brain must work in much greater detail than is visible to the observation of the psychologist, whether his observation be of the introspective or of the objective type. From the latter point of view, he determines the reaction of the subject to stimuli, and obtains a rough dynamics of behavior; in introspection, he seems to have some insight into the process intervening between stimulus and reaction, and so to penetrate somewhat to the inside of behavior. But a reaction, as judged by its end-effect, is a mass action; and introspection shows little of the detail which must be present in all brain action. Hence there is no immediate prospect of obtaining from psychology a full and minute account of any single mental performance, or of reaching by this means anything like a detailed description of the cerebral process. The most that can be hoped is to gain some indications of the general character of cerebral action.

§ 16. Peculiar difficulties encompass the problem of determining what cerebral activities are the indispensable conditions of consciousness, in general. For, not only do we find what must appear to us as abundant signs of intelligent and purposeful activity in animals of a simple and low form of nervous organization, or of no strictly nervous mechanism whatever, but also in plant life, and even in the ova and protozoa, and in the individual cells which are aggregated to form both vegetable and animal tissues. As to a full explanation of consciousness in terms of brain activity, to propose the problem is to expose the absurdity of an attempt at its answer. But to inquire as to what are the cerebral conditions of consciousness in man's case, is a legitimate and interesting problem for physiological psychology. Alas! that the answer to the problem still remains so incomplete.

Consciousness may reasonably be taken as indicating brain activity; in other words, when there is consciousness, then the brain is active. And degrees of consciousness may probably be taken as indicative of degrees of brain activity. The field of attention may therefore be taken as an index of the field of greatest brain activity. Many parts of the cerebrum—many systems of nervous connections within it—are likely to be simultaneously active; it is, therefore, a reasonable supposition that the most conscious part of consciousness is an index of the most active part of the brain; so that, when sights and sounds are both simultaneously present in consciousness, but sights occupy the field of attention and sounds are relatively in the background, at such a time the visual area and its immediately connected areas are more active than the auditory area and its connections. Even this supposition, however, is not altogether free from difficulties.

§ 17. The more precise question now arises as to what is meant by the brain activity that is said to be indicated by the existence of consciousness. The mere transmission of nerve-currents along the numerous "association fibres" of the brain is not, probably, what is directly correlated with consciousness. The activity of the nerve-cells in the cortex would be a better guess. But on account of the great functional importance of the synapses, a still more likely supposition would regard the brain activity indicated by consciousness as occurring at these junctions between neurones; or, perhaps, both in the synapses and in the dendrites and nerve-cells. The activity of the brain resolves itself, accordingly, for the most part into the passage of nervous "currents" or "impulses" across the junctions between the terminations of axons and the dendrites with which they come into contact.

According to this view, consciousness serves as an index that nerve-currents are traversing synapses in the brain; and incidentally also, of course, passing along the nerve-fibres between one synapse and another. But now a difficulty arises from the fact that well-trained or habitual reactions occur with a minimum of consciousness. It even happens that strong sensory stimuli, if commonplace and of no momentary significance, are neglected by attention for much weaker sensory stimuli; and that fairly energetic motor reactions may be carried on while the centre of consciousness is fixed upon something quite different. "He that runneth *may* read," or otherwise direct his attention; though no doubt motor quiet would be a more favorable condition for such intellectual activity. On the other hand, there can be no doubt that if reading were originally learned while running, the act of running would *facilitate* the act of reading. The difficulty is, then, that performances which involve the cerebrum, and which seem to require a considerable activity in the parts of the cerebrum concerned with them, may yet be attended with but a low degree of consciousness. We may note at once, however, that, though intense sensory stimuli and energetic muscular action must require strong activity in the parts of the cerebrum which are concerned with them, this is no proof that other parts of the brain may not be simultaneously in even greater activity. To compete with a strong sensory stimulus, another object of attention must have much momentary attraction or significance; and this probably indicates that its system of cerebral pathways is in a condition of very high activity. The focus of activity need not always lie in the sensory or motor areas.

§ 18. Important, if not decisive, objections maintain themselves to each of two opposed theories: one of which[1] regards clear consciousness as indicating an open path for motor discharge; and the other of which[2] considers that the difficulty of free passage stimulates attention and so increases the degree of clear consciousness, or that consciousness itself is the product of a condition of tension at the synapses.[3] The former, the so-called "Action Theory," seems discredited by the general experience that well-trained reactions, which imply open motor-pathways, are almost uniformly only dimly repre-

---

[1] So Münsterberg, *Grundzüge d. Psychologie*, 1900, I, 525.

[2] Dewey, *Psychol. Rev.*, 1894, I, 553; 1895, II, 13; *Philos. Rev.*, 1897, VI, 43.

[3] Montague, "Consciousness a Form of Energy," *Essays Philosophical and Psychological in Honor of William James*, 1908, p. 103. Objections to Wundt's theory of a special centre for attention or "apperception" in the frontal lobes have already been brought forward (p. 274).

sented, if at all, in consciousness. The supposition that such pathways do not lie in the cerebral hemispheres, but only in the cord and brain-stem, is opposed to the phenomena of aphasia, apraxia, asymbolia, etc., which follow upon injury to these hemispheres.

The theory which emphasizes the difficulty of reaction as the cause of increased clearness of consciousness hardly seems to comport well with all that we know about the *preference* of objects, both in perception and recall—a matter which, except in the most extreme cases of selective attention, and largely even then—seems to be determined by influences that do not manifest themselves in consciousness at all. Nor can it be claimed that the "feeling," or other evidence, of tension is anything like a constant, not to say indispensable, precondition of clear consciousness.

§ 19. The shifting of attention, and "varied reaction" in general, next claim our notice. This problem has already met us in the sphere of reflex action (pp. 165, 173), in the form of that alternation of responses which sometimes results from a single stimulus. As in reflexes, so here in the shifting of perceptual reactions, the facts point to the existence of branching tracts in the nerve-centres, and so of alternative pathways open to a nerve-current, but unequally open. McDougall, who in his "Physiological Psychology"[1] has made one of the most serious of recent attempts to conceive the neural apparatus involved in mental action, offers a theory of the mode of action of these branching pathways. He makes use of two conceptions: of fatigue, and of the "drainage" of energy from all parts of a neurone into any synapse across which the current actually breaks its way. Suppose—to illustrate—that a nerve-current reaches a point where the paths branch; there is synaptic resistance to its passage into either of these paths; the nerve-current is, for an instant, dammed up against the entrance to each of them, and gathers tension at each. At whichever entrance the resistance is lower, there the gathering tension will soonest be sufficient to force a passage, and when once an outlet is thus secured, all the energy is drained off into it, so that none takes the alternative path. But now the synapse across which the current is moving suffers fatigue from this passage, and its resistance increases till further passage is blocked. The result of this blocking of the first outlet may be that the alternative outlet is forced, and so the current takes a new path and gives rise to a different reaction. Such a shifting from one outlet to the other may be repeated time after time. This interpretation, its author thinks, is readily applied to the alternation of percepts in viewing the staircase or dot figures, and probably to all cases of shifting of attention.

[1] London, 1905; see also *Mind*, 1906, N. S., XV, 329.

There are, however, what appear to us decisive objections to this ingenious hypothesis. In the first place, it does not explain the high excitability of a pathway which has just been inhibited.[1] Possibly a slight modification will enable the theory to succeed better at this point. The nerve-current which beats at the door of a pathway without gaining admission is, in fact, a "subliminal stimulus" at that point; and the fact of "summation of subliminal stimuli" shows that such a stimulus, though it does not arouse activity, induces a heightened excitability. Let us suppose, then, that a nerve-current, acting on a branched path, not only breaks through at one point and produces activity there, but raises the irritability of all synapses against which it impinges without being able to break through. It would therefore leave such synapses in a "condition of readiness" for any soon-following stimulus. Stated in this modified form, the conception is rather attractive; since it would apply not only to shifts of attention, but equally well to the condition of readiness observed in experiments on memory, when A, previously associated with B, does not now recall B, and yet makes it easier to reach B by some other way. In such a case, we may imagine that the nerve-current started by the presentation of A impinges, at some point in its passage through the brain, upon a synapse leading to the response B, but this synapse has a high resistance, and the current does not pass that way; yet it raises the excitability (or lowers the resistance) of this synapse, so that some other nerve-current, reaching the same synapse or nerve-cell by another route, enters and gives rise to the response B.

A further and more decisive objection to the conception of varied reaction as due to branching paths is this: unicellular animals, like Amœba and Paramecium, exhibit varied reactions, but, having no nervous systems, can hardly be credited with alternative paths. Their varied reactions are not executed by different effectors; but the whole cell seems to participate in different and often opposed movements. *Varied reaction is, therefore, much more primitive and fundamental than branching paths.* Indeed, were this not so, the very existence and development of animal life would seem impossible. Besides, fatigue is not admissible as an explanation of the shifting of response in these unicellular forms; since the same structures are active throughout the sequence of movements. Such behavior as that of Stentor, for example (p. 544), in response to a continued stimulus could not be explained in terms of fatigue; for if a cell is fatigued by its first gentle response, how could the same cell shift at once to a more vigorous response to the same stimulus? Some internal change certainly occurs in the cell, in consequence of

[1] Compare Sherrington, op. cit., p. 203.

the first stimulus and response, and by virtue of this change repetition of the stimulus gives rise to another response; but this change cannot be of the nature of fatigue.

§ 20. Although we have no certain knowledge as to its nature, we must at least accept the gross fact that some change occurs in the condition of the cell, such that the same stimulus, on being repeated, gives rise to a different response.   It is not, accordingly, a wholly unreasonable attempt to view the nervous system of man in the light of this behavior of unicellular animals.   If we suppose that each neurone has *the power of varied reaction,* we have a way out of some of our difficulties.   The neurone has hitherto been held to have only one form of reaction; but the facts of inhibition, refractory period, etc., seem to indicate that it has at least two opposed modes of reaction, and that these correspond, in a manner, to the two opposed reactions of the amœba.   Now the amœba sends out branches in response to some stimuli, and draws them back in response to others.   Some neurologists have believed that protraction and retraction of the dendrites occur, and have based explanations of sleep, etc., on these "amœboid movements" of the neurone.   The balance of evidence is against these movements, but inner changes of a chemical or electrical nature might have the same results. Protraction of the dendrites was supposed to give closer contact at the synapses and so to lower the resistance to passage of a nerve-current, and retraction to have the opposite effect.   Similar changes in resistance might, however, be the result of changes of surface tension in the dendrites, or of other changes not involving molar motion. Suppose, then, that each neurone retains so much as this of the primeval power of varied reaction; suppose that it has two opposite modes of response, positive and negative, corresponding to excitation and inhibition.   It may in this case give either response to a stimulus, according, perhaps, to the character of the stimulus, but more particularly according to its own condition as determined by preceding stimuli and responses.   Each positive response is followed by a negative phase, and each negative response by a back swing toward a positive phase.   Aside from this substitution of negative response for fatigue, the cerebral action in varied reactions could then be conceived as before, in terms of branching paths, drainage, and summation of stimuli.   The most recent researches seem to favor such a view of the "selective affinities" of the cells composing different structures of the animal body, and even of individual cells.

§ 21. On recurring to what was said concerning the known facts and laws of the Presentations of Sense, and the varying qualities and quantities of the sensations composing them, the correspondences between nervous mechanism and mental phenomena, as indicated by the language employed to describe each, will be found to pervade the entire treatment of the subject. It is, therefore, necessary to add only a few words of a more general character at this point. In the first place, the distinctive qualities of things as apprehended by the senses are undoubtedly significant of specifically different reactions of the brain to the various kinds of stimuli coming into it along the different paths from the different end-organs of sense. Qualitative distinctions, as observed by the conscious mind, imply specific differences of some sort in the correlated brain activities. Something definite as to special localities chiefly concerned in the cerebral activities connected with the different senses, and even as to histological differences within those centres, is already scientifically established. And we seem to be on the eve of knowing something, or at least of having some ground for conjecturing something, about the chemico-physical peculiarities of the different states and forms of cerebral functioning concerned with the different senses.

Further, the whole theory of "local signs," as justified from the introspective point of view, suggests a corresponding theory of the highly complex character of the brain reactions that result from the simultaneous discharge into the cerebral hemispheres of a great variety of weak stimuli from a correspondingly great variety of receptors. The quantitative relations between brain activities and the conscious estimate of the intensity of our sensations, and of the magnitude of the objects of sense, are too obviously in place here for more than a mere reference to chapter III to be necessary. The same thing is equally true of that sequence in mental events of which we are consciously aware and the objective time occupied by concurrent or sequent events in the areas of the cerebral hemispheres.

In all these cases, the correspondences of quality, quantity, and temporal relations are no simple and easily analyzable affair. Neither do they lend themselves readily to the discovery and confident announcement of so-called "laws," whether it is proposed to apply the term to the activities of the brain or to our conscious experience by way of sense-perception. Even less do they, up to the present time, enable us to enunciate a system of fixed and inflexible terms on which the brain and the mind shall, so to say, pay attention to each other. But as to this condition of general correspondence, and as to the abstract possibility of extending our knowledge of it more and more into details, the evidence from the study of the development of sense-perception in man's case is, of all the available evidence, quite the most conclusive.

§ 22. In studying the presentations of sense from this point of view, it must be borne in mind, that they can never be regarded as merely fortuitous, or most strictly necessitated, aggregations of sensations, qualitatively and quantitatively different. They all imply such activities as selective attention, more or less conscious discrimination, and mediate or immediate judgment and voluntary or involuntary recall. They are also creatures of habit, so to say. But attention, discrimination, judgment, and recall, as studied from the introspective point of view, of themselves invite and encourage the study of the corresponding brain activities. What can be made a matter of reasonable conjecture as to the conditions and functions of the cerebral hemispheres in connection with these conscious activities belongs, also, to our legitimate attempt to explain, or illustrate, the nature of sense-perception in the light of physiological psychology.

§ 23. A certain antagonism between the tendency to change and the tendency to persistence or "perseveration" of a response, has already been remarked. It is certainly a fact that a response just made is more readily evoked a second time. The effects of great "recency" in favoring recall are too clear to be doubted. The contradiction between this fact and the fact of shifting of response is only apparent. The refractory period, or negative after-effect, of response is of variable, but usually of very brief duration (compare p. 164), and gives way, in turn, to a condition of heightened excitability. This can easily be demonstrated in case of the heart muscle, in which both the refractory period and the increased excitability after response are present to a marked degree. Skeletal muscle also shows both effects, as do unicellular animals. It is then a legitimate supposition that a cerebral neurone, after recent activity, is in such condition that it is readily excited again; its synapses have a low resistance, and any nerve-current which impinges on its dendrites from any axon is likely to enter and give rise to a repetition of the recent reaction.

§ 24. In the last paragraph we have entered upon the attempt to conceive of the cerebral action in Memory and Learning. A response once made leaves behind a condition favorable to the repetition of the same response. But this after-effect is, in itself, only temporary, and appears in low organisms which show no sign of a permanent modification of behavior. Something must be added to our conceptions to account for true learning and for the formation of habit. The "law of habit" states that a response, once made, is more readily excited again, even after an interval of complete quiescence. Perseveration, "warming up," and the ready recall of very recent responses, are best understood as due to a persistence of activity. The structures concerned have not entirely cooled off, or gone to sleep. The recall of a response after a longer interval corresponds to the awakening of organs which have once been active but have since been asleep. This is quite another thing, and demands a quite different interpretation. Some comparatively permanent change of structure has been induced. Since the structures with which we are here concerned are living, the change can best be thought of as having a metabolic or nutritive character. We know that activity of a muscle enables it, in its subsequent rest, to take up nutriment from the blood, and so to increase in size. There is evidence (p. 58) that activity of the brain causes a growth in the fine branches of the axons and dendrites, which are the essential structures in forming connections. Besides this growth in size, a muscle shows, after exercise, an improvement in its inner condition; it shows this in the fact that its increased strength is often too great to be explained in terms of increased size. The exact nature of this inner change is unknown, but it may reasonably be supposed to be nutritive or metabolic. It is not unlikely that neurones also improve in their inner condition as the result of preceding activity. Both growth of the fine branches and improvement in internal condition are, probably, factors in the retention of a response. We may regard the combination of neurones which are concerned in carrying out any reaction as an organ, which grows and improves its condition as the result of exercise, and which is thus made more ready for work and more likely to be called into activity. *That an organ improves as the result of exercise is the fundamental physiological conception in the doctrine of habit and learning.* In connection with this must go the explanation of what we have called "dynamical associations."

§ 25. Several details of the process of retention, as revealed by psychological experiment, fit easily into the above conception. That retention dies out with the lapse of time seems but an instance of "atrophy through disuse," or—to speak in more general terms—of the tendency to recovery and "regulation." That repeated exercise gives continued improvement, in motor skill or in the mastery of a series of nonsense syllables or a poem, may be explained as due to the accumulation of the nutritive after-effects of a single period of activity. The advantage of periods of rest between the successive repetitions of an act to be learned, is what would be expected from the behavior of other organs, such as the muscles. No one would hope for great and permanent increase in the strength of a muscle from prolonged over-exercising it at one time; common experience teaches the advantage of spreading out the exercise over many days. A physiological explanation of this fact may be attempted as follows: the nutritive after-effect of exercise occurs largely in the subsequent period of rest. After a little exercise, rest improves the organ, which enters on the next period of activity more capable of deriving benefit from it.   It is, perhaps, a larger organ, and so able to absorb more nutriment in its next rest.   Massing all the exercise in one period of continued activity prevents, in large measure, the summation of nutritive after-effects.   But since, in all learning, it is not isolated but co-ordinated, and often widely locally separated activities of the brain which are involved, something of a more dynamic character is needed to account for the phenomenon of "associated" retention.

§ 26. While, then, the physiology of simple retention, as in the case of the muscles, falls readily into accepted biological terms, the physiology of the *formation* of associations meets with peculiar difficulties, such as might be expected from the fact that the capacity for initiating connection between stimuli and responses not hitherto connected with them is peculiar for the most part to the nervous system, and especially to the brain.   The problems chiefly suggested are the two following: (1) What is the physiology of learning by "trial and error," and of the selection of the successful response? (2) What is the physiology of the formation of an association between two presented stimuli?   In regard to the mechanism of selection from varied reactions, we have already expressed an opinion (pp. 551 ff.), though not in strictly physiological terms, and that matter need not be further rehearsed.   The second problem is one of so great importance, as to lead one author to declare: "If no solution can be found, physiological psychology is bankrupt."[1]

The problem of association by contiguity, as already stated, consists in the fact that A and B, between which an association is formed, do not stand from the outset in the relation of stimulus and response. A does not originally give rise to B, but each is independently supplied.   A difficulty therefore enters here which is not present in learning by trial and error.   The animal, striving to escape from a cage, makes a series of different responses to the situation; each response is actually called out by the situation acting as stimulus.   The nervous connections between the stimulus and response are traversed by nerve-currents, and therefore strengthened in accordance with the law of exercise; and the only question is to explain the advantage which accrues to the successful reaction. But in the case now before us, as when a person is presented and his name spoken, neither the name nor the face of the person comes as a response to the other.   The first sight of the person does not suggest his name, nor the first hearing of a name suggest the appearance of the person.   The two associates come independently, one by way of the eye, the other by way of the ear; and there seems no occasion

[1] McDougall, op. cit., p. 126.

for the activity of any neural connection between the parts of the brain thus independently aroused to action. And yet, later, the name recalls the face or the face the name—showing, in accordance with our general conceptions of the brain mechanism, that connections have been established between the parts concerned with face and name respectively. When and how have these connections been formed?

§ 27. Such is the problem of the physiology of association by contiguity. A solution has been attempted by James,[1] and elaborated by McDougall.[2] As the latter states the case, a certain part or system of neurones in the brain is thrown into activity by A, the sight of the person, and immediately afterward, another part or system is thrown into activity by the sound of the name, B. The centre of activity shifts from one part to another, as it does in other shifts of attention, and the second centre of activity attracts, and drains off, the energy of the first centre, so that there is really a transmission of nerve-currents from the first to the second. The path from one to the other is thrown into activity, as truly as if the sight of the person had actually called up the name, and thus receives the nutritive after-effect of activity and becomes a favored path, or path of low resistance.

This explanation probably proceeds in the right direction, so far, at least, as this : Nerve-currents do pass between different centres of activity in the brain; but the theory seems rather too elaborate and highly specialized to explain some cases of association by contiguity, while it is not elaborate enough to explain all cases. We have grave doubts about the concept of "drainage," which enters here in even a vaguer form than in the case of the alternation of reflexes or of percepts of an ambiguous stimulus. To test the matter, let us recall that, in looking at the staircase or the dot figure, the observer shifts completely from one appearance to the other; so that the drainage of the first-acting system by the second should be complete, as is required by the conception of drainage in the formula of McDougall. But there is, in fact, no such complete shifting in the instance of the face and the name; for the face does not disappear when the name is spoken. The drainage is not, then, complete in this case. In general, the fact that the field of consciousness is broader than the field of attention goes to show how more than one system of neurones may be simultaneously active in the brain; and how no one system exerts complete attraction on the energy of the other systems. Partial drainage, however, is a much less clean-cut conception than complete drainage, and since it has no special

[1] *Principles of Psychology*, 1890, II, 584.
[2] Op. cit., p. 126.

claim to acceptance in regard to the activity of the brain as a whole (though it may be accepted in regard to a single neurone), we may profitably seek some more satisfactory explanation.

In our search let us, first of all, assume that the neural connections which are formed in learning are not wholly formed at the moment of learning; for it would clearly be impossible to suppose association fibres to grow all the way from the visual to the auditory centre in the few moments needed to connect a face with a name. These fibres already exist in great numbers, and connections are already formed in the rough, and need but a few "finishing touches," so to say, to make them good conductors. Probably the finishing touches are applied to the synapses. Thus much any theory must assume, and it is entirely in accordance with neurological probability.[1] Now let two centres, thus loosely connected, be thrown into simultaneous or nearly simultaneous excitement. Each centre discharges mainly into some previously trained channel, giving rise to motor reactions, percepts, or associated ideas. But after each has thus discharged itself, its activity does not come to an abrupt end. Each probably continues active to a slight extent, and each is also in a condition of heightened excitability; therefore the conditions are favorable for the passage of currents across the imperfectly formed synapses between them. Each has something to give, and each is ready to take, and so an interchange takes place between them. The foregoing is intended only as a formulation of the minimum conditions of association. Memory experiments have shown the formation of "remote" associations, i. e., associations between non-contiguous members of a series of syllables, etc.; in such cases no shifting of attention occurs directly between the remote terms which become associated; and the conception of drainage does not appear applicable. The conception just offered would better suit the multiplicity of associations which experiment has shown to be formed between other than directly adjacent members of a series; it would allow, in fact, for the formation of associative paths between any two cerebral organs which might be thrown into activity at nearly the same time. Taken by itself, therefore, the drainage theory suffers from defect of explaining too much; since it allows for associations which are not demonstrably formed. It is by no means everything present in consciousness at the same or nearly the same time which becomes associated with everything else so present. But it fails to

---

[1] McDougall also makes this assumption (p. 127): "We may legitimately assume that all parts of the cerebral hemispheres are connected together in such a way that, under favorable conditions, the excitement of any sensory neurone may spread to any part, just as in the strychnine-poisoned animal the excitement of a sensory neurone may spread through all parts of the spinal cord."

explain the strong associations formed between successive members of a series which is memorized, and to show why the forward associations in such a series are so much stronger than those in the backward direction.

§ 28. It is to these strong serial associations that the drainage theory has been most applied and appears most applicable. But its applicability here is mostly an illusion. More careful analysis shows that this theory rests on two assumptions: (1) that, psychologically, serial associations are formed when attention shifts from each member of a series to the next; and (2) that, physiologically, shiftings of attention are always attended by a drainage from the centre first active into the centre next active, with consequent inhibition of the first centre. Neither of these suppositions is probably true for all cases; and the cases where one is true are the cases where the other is not true. In those cases where psychological facts point to something like drainage in the cerebral mechanisms—such as the often-mentioned cases of the staircase and dot figures, and numerous others like them—one percept vanishes as the other appears; that is, the activity of one centre is accompanied by inhibition of the other. But there is no evidence that such shifts of attention give rise to a serial association between the two percepts; the evidence is rather to the contrary. After experience with an ambiguous figure, one of its appearances does not seem to call up the other; the observer has still to wait for the process of varied reaction to cause the changes. He may obtain a certain degree of control over them, by learning the best fixation point to bring out either appearance; but this control does not establish an association between the two percepts. It is also true that the alternative views are apt to succeed each other more rapidly after experience with the figure; but this is sufficiently accounted for by the greater familiarity of each appearance, taken by itself as a response to the stimulus. The *relation between* the alternative percepts, however, remains essentially the same after experience of the shifting as before; and the *shifting* of percepts *itself* corresponds always to the type of varied reaction, and never to the type of serial association. Essentially the same things can be said of other cases which belong under the type of varied reaction. The result of learning by trial and error is not the formation of serial associations between the successive reactions; but the successful reactions become associated directly with the situation and with the "adjustment," while the other reactions tend, on the whole, to be dissociated. Once more, the shifting of attention that occurs with a sudden interruption to the course of thought does not result in a strong association between the thought interrupted and the interrupting stimulus. But this experience is pretty nearly equivalent to proving that cases which do correspond well with the drainage conception, are not cases of strong serial association.

On the other hand, the cases in which strong serial association does occur do not conform to the type required by the drainage conception. A case in point here is that of the two syllables which form a single measure in a memory series. The movement of attention from the first to the second syllable of such a measure differs in two important respects from the movement of attention in examining an ambiguous figure: (1) the first syllable does not pass entirely out of consciousness with the coming of the second; and (2) the second is anticipated while the first is being presented. The movement of attention is, therefore, continuous in such cases; whereas in viewing an ambiguous figure—or in other cases of varied reaction —it is discontinuous. The reactions to the two syllables are not opposed and mutually exclusive, but overlap and enter into a "higher unit" of reaction—namely, into the measure. Even in memorizing by rote we make use of such higher units; and the strongest associations are those between the parts of such units. But the drainage theory has no place for such higher units as extend over two or more successive acts; for it, each act is antagonistic and inhibitory to its predecessor. Any attempt to apply the drainage theory to the cases of learning typewriting and telegraphy—in which overlapping and higher units of reaction are so much in evidence—would reveal beyond doubt its utter inadequacy. This theory also has no room for adjustments which last for a while and control a series of acts; but the process of learning can hardly be interpreted without allowing for such adjustments.

§ 29. The foregoing considerations have increased enormously the complexity of the problem of explaining all kinds of mental association in terms of cerebral activities. Nothing so simple as the shifting of activity from one centre of the brain to another can satisfy the conditions set by experience of the facts. It is best, however, to pause before attacking the physiology of "higher units," in order to see if any case can be made out for purely serial associations, uncomplicated by such higher inclusive units. For it will soon appear that the concept of serial association is needed in explanation of more complex associations. Suppose, for instance, that attention moves from A to B, yet not by way of transition between mutually exclusive terms, but with a certain anticipation of what is to come, or condition of expectancy, and with a lingering of what has just gone. Now expectancy means a suspension of reaction till the expected has happened; that is, a reaction is partially prepared, but is not "discharged" until the coming stimulus shall have arrived. In physiological terms, expectancy probably indicates a damming-up of nervous energy till the new stimulus comes; then, the accumulated energy is set free, and very likely it is discharged into the centre aroused by the stimulus. If one says, for example, "Let me present Mr. A," the nervous energy aroused by the sight of the man is perhaps held in check till the name is spoken, and then discharged into the centre aroused by the auditory stimulus, which, on account of its being aroused by this stimulus, would the more attract other nerve-currents having a partially open path into it. Such a condition would account also for the special clearness with which an expected stimulus is perceived. In other words: *It is the movement of expectant attention, rather than the shifts between antagonistic reactions, that gives rise to strong serial reactions.* This movement of expectant attention is perfectly consistent with the persistence of adjustments, and with the simultaneous operation of higher units.

§ 30. To pass, now, to an attempt at conceiving the neural mechanism of "higher units." They may best be conceived of after the analogy of those co-ordinating mechanisms of which convincing evidence was found in studying the spinal cord. These mechanisms showed the existence of both collecting and distributing groups of neurones. Nerve-currents from different sources converge by means of collecting mechanisms, and diverge by means of distributing mechanisms. In the case of learned and mental performances, it is easier to conceive of the working of the distributing mechanisms, and of the development of the collecting mechanisms. Let us begin, therefore, with the distributing mechanisms, and take for illustration those which may be supposed to care for learned combinations of movement, or, in other words, for skilled performances. A succession of simple instinctive movements is performed as a single act; it is a veritable *unit*, in spite of the fact that it appears as a succession of movements which may enter into other combinations.

A distributing mechanism, in connection with serial associations between the component movements, thus seems adequate to explain the general fact of co-ordination. The distributing group of neurones calls into play the groups of cells in the motor area which preside directly over the spinal centres for the component movements. Serial association, however, seems necessary to account for these movements occurring in the proper order. The serial connections alone cannot, indeed, account for the co-ordination, since the same component movements enter, in different orders, into several skilled acts, and serial association would be liable to go astray, and lead off into the wrong series; but the distributing mechanism, by holding certain motor groups of cells in readiness, brings about a proper selection among the various possible serial orders. A good example of this is afforded by any word which, as spoken, is a series of articulatory movements. The word is a unit to consciousness and is also a unit in reaction. Yet it is composed of elementary movements which, in other words, enter into an enormous number of other combinations. A distributing unit, corresponding to the word and holding in readiness the proper groups of motor-cells, *plus* the established serial associations between the groups of motor-cells, seems to afford a partially satisfactory conception of the possible neural mechanism.

The explanation just given is not indeed wholly satisfactory, for it does not explain the differentiation between two words, such as "cat" and "tack," which are composed of the same movements in different orders. Of the two mechanisms postulated in this explanation, the distributing unit is supported by the best evidence, psychological as well as neurological; and if we could attribute to such a unit the power, not only of distributing its nerve-currents to selected groups of motor cells, but also of exciting them in a certain order, our explanation would be made more complete. This last is a difficult conception, however, and serial association seems to be indicated by certain forms of lapses, in which a word, a melody, or a series of manual movements, though rightly begun, runs off the track by switching to some other familiar series of movements.

§ 31. A conception of collecting mechanisms is specially needed for explaining the physiology of percepts. A number of items, once attended to singly (as the clicks in receiving a telegraphic message), come to be apprehended in groups; it would seem, therefore, that the nerve-currents set up by the individual items of stimulus must converge upon some unitary mechanism, which can discharge as a unit, and so give rise to unitary motor reactions, and other unitary sequels. This is not at all a difficult nor improbable conception; but some difficulty arises from the fact that we may pass easily from such wholes of apprehension to the items which arouse them; for such passage implies distribution, in addition to collection. In like manner, it is difficult to imagine how a distributing unit could acquire its special form of distribution, except on the supposition that the subsidiary units react upon it—which would make it a collector as well as a distributor. We conclude, therefore, that collecting and distributing mechanisms always exist in close relation one to the other.

§ 32. Can any notion of controlled association be formed in terms of physiological psychology? This would require an instrument of selection among the numerous paths leading out from a given starting-point. A word, taken in isolation, may suggest any one of many meanings; but in context it suggests only one. To put the fact in neural terms: many paths lead from the auditory centre for that word to many other groups of cells or systems of neurones; and all of these paths have become developed by previous exercise. Any one of them is a path of low resistance; but, under the given conditions, only one of them is traversed by the current starting from the auditory centre. Our question is, What cerebral mechanism corresponds to the context, and selects the proper path? It is not altogether impossible to reach a rough notion of such a mechanism. It would have the general character of a distributing mechanism, holding certain paths in readiness, and facilitating their action above those not so prepared. Some special cerebral activity is indicated by our awareness of the trend of the meaning of a passage; the parts thus active exert their influence, not promiscuously over all the neurones of the cortex, but *selectively*; that is, they favor certain responses to each new word as it comes. If one says "Add!" for example, an adjustment is set up which favors the paths developed in learning the addition table; and the nerve-currents started by hearing two numbers in this context take this favored path.

A certain amount of controlled association would thus reduce, physiologically, to compound or convergent association. It is probable that simple serial association is decidedly the exception, but compound association the rule, in all mental processes; and that, therefore, the cerebral activity indicated by mental processes is by no means a mere succession of currents passing from one system of neurones to another. All our attempts to picture the process in detail must be ludicrously inadequate before its real complexity. But from both the physiological and the psychological points of view, the mechanism involved in the formation of so-called "higher units" is the most important of all psycho-physical mechanisms to conceive of in a clear and definite manner.

§ 33. In considering the process involved in the isolation of a simple or complex feature from a still more complex situation, our previous studies have shown that such analysis is most apt to occur when the given feature has been previously experienced in other, somewhat different situations. How does it come about that a stimulus which acts now in one combination, and again in another, may come to arouse a reaction on its own account? We must suppose, here as always, that the cerebral process is much more detailed than consciousness would indicate, and that when a combination of stimuli acts on the organism, each component stimulus has some separate cerebral effect, though consciousness reveals but a blended total, and though motor reaction is also but a single joint response to the whole mass of stimuli. Notwithstanding this gross effect, the brain paths directly reached by the incoming sensory currents have the benefit of exercise, while other paths not so excited do not receive the same benefit. When, therefore, a new combination of stimuli occurs that contains some old components, the brain paths which receive these old components have an advantage over those not previously exercised, and a corresponding especial influence in determining the following reaction. They may even determine a new reaction, such as would not result from the equal balance of all the stimuli entering into the combination.

§ 34. In closing this part of our work it is scarcely necessary to confess anew the limitations within which the scientific studies of the order required by physiological psychology find themselves confined. Everywhere, the complexity and subtlety of nature's processes far surpass all the attempts, however successful, of human science to unravel and depict them. But such are the limitations of every form of science. That they are uncommonly restrictive in this field is, doubtless, in large measure due to the very character of the facts and of the relations which are to be examined.

Nor can it escape the insight of those accustomed to reflect upon all the phenomena displayed by the human mind in its higher stages of development, that many of the most important and distinctive classes of these phenomena have really not been treated, from the physiological point of view—have, indeed, scarcely been mentioned at all. Such are the phenomena of the higher degrees of selective attention, and of deliberative choice, of the more logical forms of judgment and of reasoning, of the thinking involved in the construction of scientific systems and philosophical conceptions, of the feelings of the more strictly ethical and æsthetical order, and of the ideals of art, duty, and religion. But all these so-called higher forms of functioning do seem to be involved, as it were, in a sensory-motor basis, to which they are responses of a secondary and derived order, and so require the assumption of the activity and development of that conscious subject of them all which we call the Soul or Mind.

PART THIRD

THE NATURE OF THE MIND

CHAPTER I

GENERAL RELATIONS OF BODY AND MIND

§ 1. Without entering in a definite and detailed way into the field of metaphysics proper, there are certain quasi-metaphysical problems to which psychology, when studied from the physiological and experimental points of view, can scarcely avoid making a constant reference; and, indeed, about the most plausible solution of which it cannot, in fidelity to its own completeness, fail to express some opinion. Such of these problems as we are now proposing briefly to discuss may be conveniently grouped under two heads. We ask, in the first place: In what terms shall we conceive of the most general relations between the Nervous Mechanism and the Subject of the psychical or mental phenomena? And in the second place: In what terms shall we conceive of the nature, or most essential and permanent characteristics, of this Subject itself? Or more popularly stated: How are Body and Mind essentially related, as respects their development and the forms of functioning assigned to each? and What may be affirmed as to the reality and unity of the so-called Soul or Mind? Both of these questions, however, are to be considered only so far as some indications leading to a correct answer seem to exist on scientific grounds.

At this point it is necessary to recall what was said at the beginning, and what has been amply illustrated and enforced by the facts and the conclusions of the entire treatise. Our problem concerns the very conception of physiological and experimental psychology. The express object of this science is to investigate the relations between the constitution and functions of a certain mechanism, the human Nervous System, at the various stages of its development and under the excitement of various forms of internal and external stimuli, and the changes effected in consciousness, whether of a temporary or more permanent character—in a word, the behavior and development of human Mental Life. Since these relations *appear*, at least, to maintain themselves in both directions, as it were; and since sometimes the physical phenomena are antecedent to, and sometimes consequent upon, the mental phenomena, they may be spoken of as "co-relations." By speaking of *co*-relations, how-

629

ever, we are only adopting a term which summarizes in a convenient way a working scientific hypothesis.

§ 2. The nature of this hypothesis needs further explanation. For this purpose a brief reference to two particulars is sufficient at present. In the first place, any piece of scientific research, no matter how much it may abjure all definite metaphysical theories, is compelled to make certain assumptions and to indulge certain beliefs, which are really of a metaphysical character. It is quite right, however, that these assumptions should be those which have a *prima facie* evidence for all human thought; and that these beliefs should be such as accord with the so-called "common sense" of mankind. Science, as long as it remains science, does not undertake to furnish a system of critical metaphysics; its metaphysics is naïve and popular, rather than the metaphysics of any of the schools of philosophy. It is this kind of metaphysical attitude which we purpose to adopt at the beginning of the discussion of both classes of the problems just proposed. And, for the most part, we intend to maintain this attitude throughout the entire discussion.

§ 3. Now there can be no doubt as to what "naïve metaphysics," which is the commonly and properly adopted attitude of science, has to say as to the general relations of body and mind. Its theory is what the expert in philosophy and its history would call "an uncritical dualism." Of course, everybody, from the most untutored savage to the most accomplished student of psycho-physics, whenever the subject is not taken as a purely scholastic question, believes, speaks, and acts as though there were two existences, a body *and* a mind; and as though each one of these two had much to do with the behavior, the welfare, and indeed, the very life of the other. In fact, the body—as respects both what it is and what it is doing— is always thought of as acting upon and influencing the mind; and in like manner, the mind is always yielding to or resisting the bodily influences. Moreover it habitually uses the bodily organs as though they were its ministers or tools. It is as an embodiment of this dualistic theory, which is commended both by common sense and by science as a working hypothesis, that we have adopted the term "correlations."

It must be said in the second place, that no one word can serve equally well to define, or even to describe, all those reciprocal influences which furnish conditions to man's complex life and development as an ensouled body or an embodied soul. It is not, however, at all strange that such should be the fact. For in their very nature, the relations between neural and mental phenomena are of all others about the most abstruse and complex; and in man's case, the beings between which they are assumed to maintain themselves are of all

physical and psychical existences, about the most complex and difficult of access.

Our course would, therefore, seem to be plainly marked out for
us, so far as the problems are concerned which fall more properly
under the titles of these chapters. However, at once we are met
by differences of method; and finally, by two rival and contrary
ways of replying to the general inquiry. One of these denies that,
in order to account for mental phenomena, we need assume the existence of any reality other than the material substance of the living
and active nervous system (especially, or wholly, of the brain). The
other, on the contrary, claims that no explanation of mental phenomena is possible without referring them to a non-material or spiritual entity as the real subject of them all. Both of these ways of
explanation admit of various modifications. A third view, which
regards both the so-called "brain" and the so-called "mind" as
merely phenomenal aspects of some one reality that *is* like neither,
but *manifests* itself in both, requires for its discussion so much of
subtle metaphysics, and is so foreign to all the scientific material
with which we have thus far been dealing, that it is for the present
passed by with a bare reference.

In the remaining part of our discussion we shall be chiefly occupied with considering which one of two theories best accords with
all the facts. These facts, which are to test the theory, are facts of
the nervous mechanism, and of the correlations between this mechanism and the phenomena of consciousness. The question before us
may then be stated in the following provisional form: Do the phenomena of consciousness require for their explanation nothing more
than a statement of those changes in the material mechanism with
which they are obviously correlated; or do they also require the assumption of one real and non-material being as the subject and
ground of them all?

§ 4. How, then, we now inquire, are body and mind related, as
respects their development and the forms of functioning assigned
to each? The two series of phenomena, as has already been
said, when looked at superficially, appear correlated—*reciprocally.*
What, however, is signified by these apparent or obvious facts as to
the *real* connection of the two?

Various attempts have been made, from different points of view,
to sum up in some single word the relations that maintain themselves
between the body and the mind. Thus, the body has frequently
been spoken of as the "seat" or "organ" of the mind. Looking at
these relations from the more strictly mechanical point of view, mental phenomena have been regarded as the "products" of the functional activity of the brain. More highly figurative terms even have

often enough been employed, especially in the supposed interests
of morals or religion. The body has then been called the "prison"
or "tenement" or "tabernacle" of the soul. Not seldom, also, has
the mind been represented as mastering and controlling, and even
"moulding" the body—somewhat as the rider subdues and guides
his horse, or the worker in clay and metal shapes the product of his
toil.   One form of the doctrine of "animism" has held that the mind
is identical with the vital principle, which is busy from the very im-
pregnation of the ovum in shaping its increasing molecules according to an unconscious or dimly conscious plan.   Much debate has
also been held as to whether the conception of "cause" is applicable to any of the relations in which body and mind stand to each
other—whether, indeed, it must not rather be held that what happens in one is only the "occasion" on which some underlying cause,
common to both, operates to produce a change in the other.

§ 5. The inquiry in what sense, if at all, the brain can be said to
be the "seat" of the mind is more easily answered in a negative
than a positive way.   Nothing but the crudest notions, both of the
nervous mechanism and of the mind, would be consistent with any
of the more literal and direct interpretations of this word.   No one
would seriously regard the mind as a special entity, whether constructed of ordinary material atoms or constituted in ethereal form,
that maintains a sitting or other posture amidst the cerebral masses.
Nor is it any more correctly conceived of as thinly diffused over the
entire mechanism of nerve-cells and nerve-fibres, or as wandering
about among the cerebral elements to find its temporary "seat"
where occasion seems to require its presence.   And, although some
of the two classes of phenomena perhaps admit very well of being
brought under the conception of an atom, acting and acted upon in
varying relations to other atoms of kinds different from itself, no
essential gain is made by the attempt to regard the mind as in reality anything of the sort.   In brief, there is no literal meaning of the
words in which we can speak of the mind as *seated* in the brain.

The phrase, the brain is the "seat" of the mind, is, however, very
well adapted to raise the whole question of the spatial qualities of
the mind, and of its alleged spatial relations to different portions of
the central nervous system.   We shall, then, briefly consider the
grounds for the use of this figurative term.   There can be no doubt
that science justifies ordinary language in speaking of the soul as
in the body, in some sense in which this term does not apply to any
other collection of material atoms.   The human soul *is* in the human
body as it *is not* in the bird, the tree, the house, the star.   Even that
way of regarding the mind's nature which does not hesitate to speak
as though it were a thinly diffused and half-spiritualized form of

matter, assents to the necessity of asserting a special relation in space between it and the body.   Hence some old-time philosophies represented the soul in perception as streaming out through the avenues of sense in order to get the sensuous object into its embrace; or else pictured some etherealized copy of this object as streaming into the soul by the same avenues.   Modern vagaries, in the form of theories of an "astral body," or of "spiritualistic materializations," are familiarizing us with such representations anew.   But even such a view of the nature and activities of the mind is based upon the claim that the body is, in some sort, the peculiar dwelling-place, or "seat," of the mind.

A correct account of the process by which the world of things becomes known also shows that all our experience is connected with the establishing and justifying of a similar claim.   There are no "things" known to experience except as our sensations, or modes of being affected, are both localized and projected *extra*-mentally.   Inducements and considerations, such as have already been treated in great detail, irresistibly urge on science to arrange all phenomena under two classes—phenomena which are qualities of outside things, and phenomena which are mere states of internal experience.   But the same inducements and considerations compel it to look upon certain phenomena of the first class as related to those of the second class in a peculiar way.   The world of things outside always (at least in ordinary experience) affects us—is perceived by us or modifies our consciousness—through the body.   The mind is, therefore, said to be *in the body*.

The conclusion from the foregoing general experience is confirmed by certain experiences of a special order.   The feelings of pleasure and pain, which have so immediate and incontestable a value for the life of consciousness, are all connected with sensations more or less definitely localized in the body.   So close is the connection between the localized sensations and the painful or pleasurable states of the mind, that the mind actually seems to be suffering *in* that part of the body where the sensations are localized.   When the localizing of sensations connected with feelings of strong "tone" is very indefinite, as it is in cases where the feelings arise from the condition of large areas of the internal organs, the soul seems to be suffering in, and throughout, almost the entire body.

Furthermore, both ordinary experience and scientific observation require us to regard the mind as standing under certain special relations to certain parts of the body.   The ancients located the soul in the heart or lower viscera, because of marked connections between conscious states and the condition of these organs.   But the obvious connection of the head with the more obtrusive sensations of the perceptive order tends to confirm the belief that the mind, as perceptive, has its "seat" in that region of the body. For reasons already given in detail modern scientific researches justify us in narrowing more precisely the local domain within which we can affirm the mind to have its seat. The mind is certainly *in* the nervous system, in a sense in which it is not in any other of the systems of the animal body. More precisely yet, it is pre-eminently in the brain; and, among all the complex groups of encephalic organs, the final and special claim of the cerebral cortex to be the "seat" of the mind is most easily maintained. Here, in this convoluted rind which forms the interlaced "projection-systems" of sensory and voluntary motor-impulses, here—if anywhere—must it be held that the subject of the states of consciousness has its peculiar dwelling-place and home. And yet, recent experiments in cerebral surgery upon human subjects have demonstrated the fact that the conscious mind, when the sensory areas of the brain are stimulated, itself localizes, or *seats*, its own sensations and feelings, not *in* the brain at all, but in the appropriate areas of the periphery.

§ 6. On the contrary, the results of modern scientific inquiry become unfavorable to the effort yet more precisely to designate a material "seat" for the mind. Is there any one mathematical point, or minute area, in the cerebral cortex that is most especially of all the dwelling-place of mind? If so, might it not be properly conceived of as ordinarily remaining at this point to receive the messages despatched to it from the various parts of the periphery; and as executing its will over those peripheral parts by sending back to them corresponding messages despatched from the same central point? The pineal gland has undoubtedly lost the significance which Descartes gave to it as the special seat of the soul. But can no substitute be found to take and hold so important a place? The answer of cerebral histology and physiology to the foregoing questions is, on the whole, a decided negative.

At this point it is customary to greet with peculiar satisfaction, as though we had found the solution of a puzzling metaphysical problem, the discoveries of cerebral localization, in recent times. Certain areas of the cerebral cortex do, indeed, appear to have a particular connection with the execution of certain functions of the mind. But the very phenomena on which reliance is placed for establishing this connection forbid us to regard the mind, in its special relations to the brain, as limited to any point or small area of the cerebral cortex. Both gross and microscopic anatomy show us that the cortical part of the brain, like all its other parts, is not constructed on the plan of having its uses for the mind concentrated in any one minute circumscribed spot. In any sense in which the mind can be said to have its "seat" in the brain at all, in that same sense, and with equal propriety, may the entire cerebral cortex, with its vast complexity of nerve-fibres and nerve-cells, be said to be entitled to something of the same distinction. Moreover, the combined testimony of physiology and surgery establishes the truth that the brain never localizes the mental products of perception within its own areas. The simple yet essentially mysterious truth is—as has just been pointed out—that when certain cerebral areas are properly stimulated, the mind localizes its own sensations, either in the corresponding peripheral parts of the body, or somewhere external to the body.

§ 7. And now the puzzling question recurs: What that is intelligible can be meant by designating the supreme central organs of man's nervous mechanism as the "seat" of his conscious mind?

The only solution for such a puzzle as the foregoing—if solution it can be called—must always consist in calling attention anew to the essential facts of the case. Certain particles of very highly organized chemical constitution, when grouped into nerve-fibres and nerve-cells, and when further associated into organs, may be acted upon by appropriate stimuli. These material particles are locally *in* the cranial cavity, and, more precisely, in this or that area or organ of the cranial contents. Moreover, a large and important part of the phenomena of consciousness consists in localized bodily sensations of a painful or pleasurable character. To these facts investigation adds the inference as based upon experiment and observation in the case of others, that the localized sensations are themselves ultimately dependent upon the behavior of the aforesaid material molecules in the brain. That is to say, we directly localize many of our mental affections in this or that part of the body; by remote processes of observation and argument we infer that the last material antecedent of them all is the behavior of certain invisible parts of the body within the brain. Therefore we say: The mind is in the brain; or the seat of the mind is in the brain. By this, nothing further can be meant of an assured or intelligible character than the emphatic repetition of the same principal facts: *the sensations which we localize at the periphery of the body, or project from the body in space, all have a* sui generis *connection with the condition and action of that portion of the same body which is contained in the cranial cavity.*

As to the possibility of such a *sui generis* relation between material elements which exist in space, and the localizing and other activities of a being not to be conceived of as, strictly speaking, in space, only experience is entitled to pronounce. Such a relation is an accomplished fact. The fact is, therefore, not to be disputed on any so-called *a priori* grounds. It does not follow, however, that the relation of the mind to the brain is any more essentially mysterious than that of the molecules of the brain to one another. Nor does it form an insuperable objection to the former relation that it is not, like the latter, a relation of changes of position in space. For who shall undertake to affirm that beings which are not extended and movable in space, because their very nature is of another order, cannot exist in relations of any kind to beings which are thus extended and movable? It is precisely in this way that the mind is actually related to the brain. To speak of the mind as having its "seat" in the brain is only a figurative way of affirming the reality of such relations.

§ 8. The term "organ" (or instrument) of the mind, as applied to the body, is particularly calculated to emphasize the relation of the ideas and volitions which arise in consciousness to the control of the muscular apparatus. But the same term may also be used, though with less propriety, to describe the relation of the brain to the mind in sensation and thought. Thus we may be said to feel or think *with* the brain, in some manner supposed to be analogous to that in which the workman accomplishes his task by availing himself of a particular tool or instrument. It is obvious, however, that the figure of speech suggested by these terms also will not admit of a literal interpretation. We cannot conceive of the mind as a peculiar kind of material entity which, when it desires or wills to move the bodily members in a certain way, lays a clutch—as it were—upon the nervous substance of the central organs, and so makes the body serve as an "organ" of the desire or volition. Even less are we to conceive of the brain as a complex tool or mechanism which the mind uses in thought and feeling, somewhat as senses and fingers avail themselves of a calculating machine or of a musical instrument.

In producing changes of shape and position in masses of matter outside of our own bodies, we ordinarily find it convenient to use some material medium between those masses and the various movable parts of our own bodies. We can, by means of complicated mechanisms, accomplish a great variety of changes which it would be quite impossible to accomplish without such aid. On the other hand, we sharpen, define, and multiply our sensations and percepts of things in similar manner. The deaf man hears *with* a trumpet or other acoustic contrivance; and the scientific observer contrives an instrument for observing the absolutely simple tones as analyzed out of the composite clang; and with a prism the optician beholds the colors of the spectrum.

It is characteristic of all the most skilful use of tools and instruments that they come to seem to the observer like a part of his own bodily mechanism. By feelings of "double contact" the workman comes to know, *with* the chisel, the wood or metal which he is carving—just as the blind man seems to extend his conscious life to the very end of the stick he is accustomed to carry. In these cases the mental picture before the practised mind is not that of the hand and the way it must be moved, but of the graving tool and the motion to be imparted to it—as though the instrument itself were immediately subject to volition.

The conception of an "organ" or instrument may, with a certain propriety, be extended so as to cover the relation which exists between the nervous system and the muscular, and between the central and peripheral parts of the nervous system. Thus it may be said that the spinal cord and brain move the limbs "with the use" of the afferent nerves, or that the cerebral hemispheres employ the lower ganglia of the brain in effecting certain co-ordinations of sensation and motion; it may even be said that the end-organs of sense communicate with the supreme central organs "by means of" the afferent nerve-tracts and the lower ganglia. All such language expresses, correctly enough for popular usage, the undoubted fact that, in the complicated relations of position and motion which are maintained among the different members of the nervous system, a certain order of action is constantly preserved. Changes originate in one part, and are propagated to other contiguous or more distant parts. In such propagation of the changes a regular tract of the advancing motions is assumed always to exist; and thus to science the parts that lie between the extremes may be looked upon as *means* or media—i. e., as instrumental to the completion of the process. To the uninformed person, however, the result seems to be an "immediate" effect of the will.

§ 9. It is obvious from the foregoing remarks that one part of the nervous mechanism can be said to be the "organ" or instrument of another part, in the meaning of the word which cannot properly apply to the relation of the brain and the mind. In a certain justifiable meaning of the word, all the rest of the body may be said to be the *organ* of the brain. That is to say, those changes in the molecules of the brain's substance which arise there—whether because of certain ideas and volitions of the mind, or because of changes in the character of the blood-supply, or of sensory impulses thrown in from the periphery or other lower nervous centres—get themselves expressed *through* the other members of the body. One part serves as an instrument or "organ" for another, because the changes in it effect changes elsewhere, not directly, but through contiguous and connected parts. If the necessary contiguous parts are

wanting or their relations disarranged, if the connection is interrupted or destroyed, then the work cannot be done; the "organ,"
"instrument," or "means," is lacking.

But, in truth, only a part of the real relations existing between
mind and brain can properly be described under such terms as
"organ," "instrument," etc. The brain, with its appropriate functions, is an indispensable medium between certain changes in the
peripheral parts of the body and corresponding changes in the states
of consciousness. As much as this is true of *all* the efferent tracts
which lead from the cerebral cortex through the lower portions of
the encephalon, along the spinal cord, and out to the particular
groups of muscles. Something more and special is, however, true
of the brain. It is the first of the indispensable physical links in
the whole chain; it stands nearest, as it were, to the mind. All
the other steps in the execution of the ideas and volitions of the
mind depend upon what takes place in the brain. In this sense,
at least, the brain is the particular organ of the mind; it is the most
intimate and indispensable means for the execution of all its ideas
or volitions of motion.

It does not appear that the foregoing statement by any means
exhausts the description of the experience, reflection upon which
induces us to regard the brain as the "organ" of the mind. For
the brain seems to serve as the special physical basis of the ideas
and volitions of motion themselves. Experiments with animals,
by extirpating the cortical areas, and observation of human pathological cases—especially, perhaps, in certain forms of aphasia—
seem clearly to show that a much more intimate "organic" relation
exists between the brain and the mind. With the destruction or
derangement of certain cerebral areas, the power even to form certain ideas and volitions, or to have certain feelings, seems to be impaired or lost. We cannot say, to be sure, that the mind has lost
a part of its general faculty to conceive, to feel, and to will. It has,
however, suffered in respect of its power to frame a certain set of
definite ideas and volitions for the purpose of controlling the motion of the peripheral members. This class of facts is certainly
calculated to emphasize strongly our conception of the brain as
being, in a special sense, the indispensable means through which the
states of consciousness are related to changes in the position of
molecules and masses of matter.

§ 10. There is another most important class of facts which may
be partially described under the same terms as the foregoing. The
brain is the indispensable means for furnishing the mind with its
sensations, and so with its presentations of sense or perceptions of
things. This statement is not to be understood as though the brain

could, of itself, construct the sensations and perceptions and hand them over ready-made, as it were, to the mind. Sensations are states of consciousness, not modes of the brain; and even when they are synthetically united, localized, and projected to the periphery of the body, or into surrounding space, they are brought under no essentially new relations to the nervous mechanism. Sensations are not nerve-commotions, "etherealized" by the optic thalami and cerebral convolutions, and then handed over to consciousness. Therefore the instrumental relation between brain and mind is not that of transmitting a peculiar kind of motion from one phase into another, or from one being to another. Nevertheless, no sensations will arise in the mind unless the brain be affected in a certain way. Looking at the chain of sequences as it runs from without inward, we might say: The brain is the organ, or instrument, through which the stimuli of the outside world, acting on the end-organs of sense, finally reach the mind. Or, to say the same thing in other terms: The brain is the last and most important physical antecedent to the mind's being affected with the different sensations.

§ 11. Still another class of attempts to generalize, and embody in a single term, the various essential relations of the brain to the mind leads to the inquiry after some one special "connection" or "bond" between the two. Here, again, any too literal answer to this inquiry leads at once to manifest absurdity. A material bond designed to unite mind and brain might perhaps be conceived of as connected with the latter, and yet as remaining material; but in order to make it connect with the former (the mind) it would have to become non-material, unless we are ready to concede that the material and the non-material can stand connected without any special bond. In case this concession is once made, however, we cease to feel the need of a special bond between the mind and the brain. But if it be at once admitted that no connection is to be sought, or can be found, between the mind and the brain, beyond the fact that their modes of behavior are mutually dependent, it will not be necessary to appeal to any special mystery. This is simply to admit that general fact of correlations upon which every form of science depends for its conclusions. What bond connects together the planets of the solar system so that each one moves invariably with reference to the position of all the others, and yet in a path peculiarly its own? We can only respond by talking of the force and laws of gravitation. These "laws," however, are only a mathematical statement of the uniform modes of the behavior of certain physical beings; this "force" is no entity existing between the individuals, as the rods of the orrery bind its parts to a common centre. Cohesion and chemical affinity are not special bonds; they, too,

are but expressions for the facts that the elements of material reality, under certain conditions and according to the kind to which
they belong, behave *as though* bound. That is, they are actually
correlated. The behavior of the so-called atoms, like that of the
stars, is, as a *simple matter of fact*, "relative," each to the others.

§ 12. It will scarcely be supposed that information of scientific
value concerning the nature of the real connection between the
body and the soul can be obtained from terms which are yet more
purely figurative and poetic than those which have already been
examined. The limited and defective nature of our sense-perceptions, the misery of much of life, the unrealized longings for knowledge and happiness, and the work of imagination in framing a picture of some state of existence in which the limitations are removed
and the longings realized, have led men in all ages to regard the
body as the "prison" of the soul. Because the senses are not more
in number than they really are, or more far-reaching and accurate
than their construction permits them to be, they are regarded as re-
straining the soul, rather than as bringing it information which has
the character of satisfying reality. The brevity and uncertainty of
life, and the speed with which accident and disease impair or dissolve the bodily functions, together with the persuasion that the
thinking principle will have a continued existence, suggest the reflection: the body is only the "tenement" or "tabernacle" of the
soul.

§ 13. It appears, then, that all the terms in popular use to convey
the impressions of a "dualistic" theory of the relations between the
body and the mind are well grounded in facts of experience. They
express the truth, although only in an incomplete and figurative
way, which we have tried to summarize under the word "correlations"; and by this term we understand series of changes occurring
in the physical mechanism that are dependently related, either as
antecedents or consequents, to series of phenomena occurring in
consciousness. So unlike in their most essential characteristics are
these two classes of phenomena that we are forced to assign them
to different species of beings—in this case, minds and bodies; and
yet so intimate and regular are at least some of the forms of this reciprocal dependence, that we are entitled to speak of the general
facts of relation as constituting so-called laws. All the researches
of physiological and experimental psychology, as thus far conducted,
do not contradict, but rather confirm, this popular and naïve dualism.

The same thing cannot be said, however, of certain other terms
which have been proposed in the name of psycho-physical science,
and for use by all its various subdivisions and branches, taking the
words in their widest possible application. For these terms at-

tempt in some manner, or to some degree which the popular impressions do not warrant, to *identify* the body and the mind. Now, although this particular word is seldom used, there are theories which have not a few defenders, and which have, indeed, not a few facts of experience in their favor, that would bring the correlations between the mechanism and the mental life under some such conception as that of "product," or other similar term. In their more customary form these theories regard the brain as in some sort the *producer* of the phenomena of the conscious mental life.

By the word "product" we ordinarily understand the result of some process of manufacture; or in the case of a living organism like the human body, the results of the secretory or metabolic processes of these organs are spoken of as their "products," after the analogy of the products of the field or of the loom. But to speak of mental states and processes as *products* of the brain, in any corresponding meaning of the words, involves us in the grossest absurdities. The peculiar secretory product of the brain is the fluid found in certain of its cavities; and its metabolic products are the worn-out materials which it discharges into the venous circulation, or the renewed elements of its own substance. In case it is preparing abnormal or diseased products, these take the form of abscesses or tumors, or of blood-vessels and nerve-cells that have gone wrong.

A more plausible use of the word product, as applying to certain correlations between the brain and the phenomena of consciousness, might assume the following form: The functional activity of the nervous centres might be regarded as the product of the matter constituting these centres. But after admitting the propriety of this manner of speech, the very same problem remains upon our hands; and it is no less difficult and mysterious than it was before. For the problem is: How shall we conceive of the correlations between the different forms of this very nervous activity and the antecedent, concomitant, or sequent changes in the conscious mental life? If our knowledge of these relations were indefinitely increased, and even if it became perfect, it is still impossible to see how the term "product," or any similar term, would fitly characterize *these* relations.

§ 14. The term "cause," or necessary precondition, seems of all much most appropriate to describe in general the nature of the correlations between the body and the mind. And, indeed, as we shall subsequently show, when properly understood, the essential nature of these relations may be described as causal. But here again, it is customary to give a too strictly mechanical and physical interpretation to the words employed, and to assume that this causal relation works in only one way.

Thus we are treated to a theory of the correlations between the body and the mind which renders the latter absolutely dependent upon the former, not only for the precise forms of its characteristic functioning, but also for its unity and claim to even a temporary existence. This theory assumes that *all* mental phenomena, whatever their varied characteristic shading, have their exact equivalents and necessary conditioning causes, only in specific forms of the nerve-commotion of the living human brain. We may give a more definite statement to this mechanical theory in the following way: With changes in the substance of the brain which may be designated A, B, C, D, etc., the mental processes called a, b, c, d, etc., are uniformly and necessarily joined; and with the combination of molecular changes which may be described by $A + B + C + D$, etc., the mental states $a + b + c + d$, are as uniformly and necessarily joined. When the same molecular changes recur in a fainter or modified form, as A', B', C', D', then there must be a recurrence of the corresponding mental states, only in fainter form, as a', b', c', d'. Finally, it is without exception true—so this theory holds—that nothing happens in the mental life, by way of conscious sensation, presentation of objects of sense, ideation, reproduction of mental images, and higher æsthetic feeling, or processes of reasoning, or choice, which does not find its only real explanation in the equivalent changing states of the nervous system. How stupendous are the assumptions involved in such a theory, and how far it outruns all our knowledge of the facts, has been made obvious by the entire course of our previous investigations. Besides, these investigations have abundantly shown that no one-sided view of the nature of the correlations between body and mind can lay claim to all the facts in its support.

§ 15. We have now to examine more carefully the propriety of applying terms which imply causation (such as "energy," "action," "force," "impulse," "effective agency," etc.) to the case of mind and brain. Everything which has been said has involved the inference that these terms may be so understood as to be really applicable. There would be no advantage to the mind in being "seated" in the brain—that is, in being under any special relations to a given extent of nervous matter—unless it were somehow influenced or acted upon by this nervous matter, and could in turn influence and act upon it. No "organ" or instrument is of any use whatever—that is, no thing can become an organ or instrument—unless it can be acted upon by that which employs it as an organ, and can in its turn act upon other things. Action of mind on brain is implied in calling the latter the organ of the mind's volitions; action of brain on mind is implied in calling it the organ of the mind's sensations.

In general, to act and to be acted upon is equivalent to standing in the relation of cause and effect.

It is not at present necessary to point out in detail how much of obscurity and contradiction are involved in all the more popular ways of mentally representing the foregoing relation. The transmission of energy (or force) is popularly spoken of as though such energy streamed off from one body and attached itself to another; and as though the quantity of energy thus given off were dependent upon the strength of the blow given by one body to another. Let it be supposed, however, that the application of the law of causation to the case of brain and mind is made in the most approved manner. It is simple matter of fact, as tested by thousands of observations and experiments, that changes in the condition and functional activity of the nervous centres are followed by changes in states of consciousness, in a regular way; and that, conversely, changes of the latter sort are followed by changes in the relations of the masses of the body, and of the functional activity of nervous centres and end-organs of sense. Now, unless we are ready to be satisfied with simply stating the facts, without making the attempt to find any rational account for them, we are obliged to consider these correlated changes under the terms of cause and effect; and in fact, were it not for the influence of prejudice derived from speculation upon certain philosophical, ethical, and religious questions, no one would think of hesitating to apply the terms of causation to the case of mind and brain.

How impossible, indeed, it is to avoid speaking of the connection of mind and brain, in terms of causation, may be illustrated by the relations between the condition of the intercranial blood-supply and the states of consciousness. A slight increase of this circulation, resulting from a small quantity of alcohol or other drugs, or from the hearing of interesting news, produces an increased speed in the mental train. Reaction-time is found to vary with changes in the circulation. In the delirium of fever the wild and quickly moving condition of the thoughts, fancies, and sensations is a direct expression of the kind of work which is going on, because of the accelerated heart-beat and the disordered character of the blood, within the cerebral arteries. Schroeder van der Kolk tells of a patient who, when his pulse was reduced by digitalis to 50 or 60 beats per minute, was mentally quiet and depressed; when it was allowed to rise again to 90 beats, his mind was in maniacal confusion. Cox narrates the case of a sick man who, at 40 pulsations in the minute, was "half-dead"; at 50, melancholic; at 70, quite "beside himself"; at 90, raving mad. The character of dreams is determined, to a considerable extent, by the position of the head and the way in which

this position affects the cranial circulation.   Hallucinations not infrequently are immediately made to cease when the person having
them assumes the standing posture, or has leeches applied to the
head.   Indeed, the phenomena which illustrate the causal influence of the nervous mechanism on the mental life constitute a large
part of the entire body of the science of psycho-physics and physiological psychology.

§ 16. On the other hand, phenomena which indicate that mind
operates as a true cause within the structure of the body are also innumerable.   They are quite as numerous, though perhaps not so
obvious and impressive, as those which indicate the reverse relation.   The chief reason why these phenomena are relatively little
regarded in psycho-physical researches is that the real causes are
in this case not readily made the objects of observation and measurement.   External stimuli constitute those causes of mental changes
which we can most easily observe and estimate.   Ideas, feelings,
and acts of will arising in consciousness, and considered as causes of
the resulting bodily changes, cannot be treated by the same methods
of experimental science as apply to physical stimuli.   But that the
mind acts on the body is one of the most familiar of experiences.
Such action penetrates and modifies all the life of the body.   Hence
the material mechanism of the animal structure can never be considered, with a view to explain what is going on within it, as though
it were disconnected from the consciousness of the animal.   The
most purely vegetative of the processes of the human body are
dependent for their character upon the states of the human mind.
The nutrition of the tissues, the circulation of the blood, the secretion of different kinds of fluids, the healthy or diseased nature of
the vital processes, are greatly influenced by conscious processes.
If abnormal digestion produces melancholy, it is equally true that
melancholy causes bad digestion.   In the case of the rise of strong
emotions, like anger or grief, the increasing affection of the mind
builds itself up upon a physical basis of increasing disturbance of
the organs; but it is equally obvious that the starting of the emotion in consciousness, and the letting of it slip from control, are
necessarily followed by gathering momentum to the organic disturbance.   Irregular action of the heart, caused by organic defect
or weakness, occasions a feeling of indescribable alarm in the soul;
fear is followed, through the action of the mind upon the nervous
centres, by functional incapacity of the heart.   The impure condition of the arterial blood which is characteristic of certain diseases
brings about a chronic state of mental lassitude or anxiety; care,
chagrin, and ennui poison the arterial blood.   The lesion of the
cortical substance produced by a growing abscess or broken blood-

vessel impairs the mind's powers of sensation and thought; excessive thought and over-excited feeling wear away the brain.

The entire class of phenomena which we are entitled to call "voluntary," in the widest sense of the word, might be appealed to in proof of the same principle. Whether they show that the mind is "free," in the highest ethical meaning of the word, or not (and upon this question psycho-physical science cannot pronounce), they certainly do show that the condition of the bodily organs is made dependent, through the nervous elements of the brain, upon the states of the mind. And here are, in point, the phenomena of the voluntary innervation of the organ by fixing the attention, of the dependence of reaction-time upon the exercise of the will through attention of the person reacting, of the abstraction of regard from the images of sense when occupied in reflective thought, as well as all the more marvellous instances of self-control in determining the results of disease, etc.

The elevation of the bodily activities to the most astonishing precision, under the influence of high and strong artistic feeling, or sense of duty, is also a noteworthy fact of the same order. The mind has not the power to constitute, in opposition to fixed chemical affinities, a single molecule, or to execute the slightest movement of a single muscle, without involving the nervous system in the expenditure of the requisite energy. Moreover, this energy must be started in the appropriate cortical area and descend along the allotted motor tracts. We cannot explain how it is that molecules of nervous matter can be acted upon in view of states of consciousness. But neither can we explain how one kind of atoms comes to act as it does in view of the presence and action of atoms of another kind. Nevertheless, we can just as little assume to explain away the fact of such obvious causal connection, because we cannot bring the measure of the connection under the same law as that which maintains itself among certain modes of physical motion.

§ 17. It would scarcely be worth while to consider seriously either the older or the more modern forms of the denial that any real causal relation exists between body and mind, were it not for the fact of their essential agreement upon a false conception of the nature of causal relations in general, and upon a false theory as to the particular case of the correlations of body and mind. Two remarks bearing upon all such theories are, therefore, necessary. The assumption that matter and mind are separated from each other "by the whole diameter of being," if it be held to mean that the two forms of being are so disparate in nature as to be unable to act on each other, is an unverifiable assumption. It even goes squarely in the face of many of the most important psycho-physical facts. We know nothing about what kind of beings can or cannot act on each other, except through our experience of what beings do actually act upon each other. The mystery involved in any one being acting on any other is equally deep and unfathomable, in whatever direction we attempt to explore it. Before experience with the facts, we should be quite at a loss to tell whether atoms of oxygen could act on atoms of hydrogen, under the laws of chemical affinity, or not; whether molecules of iron could act on other molecules of iron, under the laws of cohesion, or not, etc. How it is that material masses or molecules can "influence" each other, or what is the real nature of the force which binds them together, physical science is quite unable to say. So that even if we were entitled to regard matter as somewhat, the very essence of which it is to be spread out, and mind as somewhat, the very essence of which it is to be conscious and not to be spread out, we should still be quite without justification in asserting (*a priori*, as it were) that one cannot act upon the other. But—just the contrary—if we are to accept, unbiassed, the obvious witness of the facts, we are compelled to affirm: The phenomena of mind and the conditions of the brain are related so constantly and immediately under law, that we are warranted in believing in the action of each upon the other.

§ 18. But, in the second place, most of the modern objections to speaking of causal relations existing between the nervous mechanism and the processes of conscious mental life, are connected with the current theory of the conservation and correlation of physical energy. And here it is interesting to notice certain relations, both of similarity and of difference, between a prominent modern theory as to the mutual action of mind and brain and the now-abandoned views of Occasionalism and Pre-established Harmony. These views had regard to the reality and integrity of the soul, and respect for the ethical character of the Divine relations toward its activities and development. Modern science, on the contrary, raises most of its objections, against regarding the conditions of the central nervous system and the states of consciousness as connected by a real causal tie, out of a profound regard for matter and the laws of physics. The great value and significance of physical phenomena, and the regular modes of their recurrence, if not the independent and eternal existence of material beings, are taken for granted by this theory, whatever difficulties, fears, or hopes to the contrary may arise from the sphere of mind. Elements of material reality (called "atoms") are assumed to exist; the universal form of their relation is held to be the law of the conservation and correlation of energy. By "energy" we are to understand that which moves or tends to move the elementary atoms, or their aggregations into molecules and masses. The energy which is regarded as causing actual motion is kinetic; that which is to be regarded as tending to produce motion is stored or potential. But inasmuch as we have no test or suggestion of the presence of energy except motion, we seem compelled to consider the so-called "tendency" to move (potential energy) as motion that is beyond the sphere of the senses, because distributed over so vast a number of minute portions of matter whose amount of motion is too small to be discoverable. All physical elements and masses are, accordingly, always in motion, and the total *quantum* of this motion is invariable throughout the entire universe. All forms of energy must be classified, as respects quality, by the kind of their motion; and as respects degree, by the amount of their motion.

§ 19. It requires, however, only a brief and rather superficial examination of the conceptions of physical science, as they are popularly taken, and even as they are correctly and helpfully employed for purposes of scientific research, to discover how full they are of concealed figures of speech and of as yet unverifiable hypotheses. The known facts are of about the following order. Observed events in the elements and masses of the physical world make upon our minds impressions of more or less magnitude and intensity. Our experience, especially with respect to the correlations between our own mental strivings, feelings of effort or so-called "deeds of will," and the sequent changes in the bodily organism, and through this organism in material objects, begets and fosters the conceptions of "power," "force," "energy," etc. This power, force, energy, is conceived of as residing in "these objects," and as "passing over" from one to another of them; and so as being the *cause* of the interdependent, or mutually related, changes. But the causal conception is a distinctly metaphysical conception. For this vague and indeterminate idea of cause, therefore, the physico-chemical sciences very properly strive to substitute mathematical formulas which are designed to express definite relations in the amounts as measured by units of time and space, of these changes. Thus arises the theory of work, actually doing, or that may be expected to be done, by material masses and their elements. Between certain kinds of changes, either directly observed or capable of an approximately correct calculation, science has already established formulas which serve the purposes both of explanation and of prediction. Such are the formulas which give the equivalents of the kinetic energy of masses in terms of the energy called heat, or light, or electricity. Further, as a result of their experience, in general, with the quantitative correlations existing between the different material objects, the physico-chemical sciences have evolved an hypothesis of a more universal character. This is the hypothesis of the conservation of energy. It holds that any system of material elements or masses, so long as it can be kept "closed," or protected from dissipating its energy, and from receiving accessions of energy from the outside, will do only a fixed amount of work;—although this gross sum of energy may manifest itself in any of the various forms known to physical science, and may be distributed and redistributed among the different elements and masses of the system. Moreover, in the process of distribution and redistribution, the equivalents of the different kinds of energy will remain the same.

This hypothesis of the conservation of energy is still undergoing a process of experimental testing at the hands of the students of the physico-chemical sciences. Only in the case of certain pairs of the various recognized kinds of so-called energy have any definite, approximately exact formulas for their correlations been as yet discovered. In the world of man's experience there is no such thing as a "closed system." And wonderful new forms of energy, and of the doing, and the potentiality of work, on the part of the physical universe, are constantly being discovered. But slowly, and on the whole in a satisfactory way, some hypothesis corresponding in general to that called by the title—"The Conservation and Correlation of Energy"—seems to be gaining support by the sum-total of human experience with material things.

§ 20. How far, now, can such an hypothesis as the foregoing be applied to the nervous system of man? That this system is a mechanism and like every other mechanism dependent for the amount of work which it can do, upon resources of energy, either stored within itself or derived by accessions from outside itself, there can be no manner of doubt. All the various kinds of automatic and reflex, or sensory-motor activity illustrate and enforce this truth. In these activities the various kinds of energy recognized by physical science as kinetic energy of masses, quantity of heat, electrical energy, and chemical energy, take part. And so far as the laws of their conservation within the nervous system are known they appear to confirm the general hypothesis in question. It is true, however, that the work done by the nervous mechanism cannot as yet be fully explained—not to say, even correctly stated—in terms of other forms of energy. And thus far, the need of assuming a very special and, indeed, unique form of energy, to be called "nervous," does not seem to be in the least degree diminished. This is only to say: What the nervous mechanism does, considered as having the power to store, to transmit, and to distribute, its own resources for doing its own work, cannot as yet be explained in terms that are *mere* modifications or combinations of the formulas derived from a study of other forms of energy, employed in other kinds of work. But this fact by no means disproves the assumption that the general principle implied in the phrase we are discussing applies somehow to the peculiar functioning of the nervous mechanism.

§ 21. So, too, if we consider the external relations of man's nervous system, we find it dependent on energies outside of itself for the amounts, whether stored or kinetic, of its own peculiar way of doing work. This dependence is of two principal kinds. The nervous system must have nutriment; otherwise it cannot build itself up; cannot store energy; cannot acquire the material to be transmuted into its own form of work. In its metabolic processes, therefore, it is constantly illustrating a species of the law of the conservation of energy. It is true that we cannot at present give the exact equivalents, in the potentiality or kinetic energy of the nervous mechanism, for the different food products; whether they are considered apart from the whole organism, or as carried to the nervous system in the blood. The problem of food-supply as related to neural energy is immensely complicated—not only as a chemical and physiological study, but also as having a large mixture of obscure or totally unknown psycho-physical and mental factors. It is conceivable, however, that mathematical formulas may at some time be discovered for stating the quantitative relations between the energies stored in the blood supplied and the energies, stored or kinetic, of the nervous mechanism—including its own peculiar form of so-called "nervous energy."

The second form of the more obvious correlations between external forms of energy and the energy of the nervous system is realized every time any appropriate stimulus is applied to the end-organs of this system. How far we know of formulas that state in mathematical terms this kind of correlation has already been sufficiently discussed. Indeed, the whole science of psycho-physics involves the attempt to deal with these correlations.

Let us suppose, then, that all the functions of the nervous mechanism, and all their relations to the various forms of energy which act upon it, and upon which it reacts, have become so well known as to form a theory of the conservation of energy completely adapted for application to this mechanism. We should then be able to explain *in terms of quantity* the successive redistributions of work actually done: between the different parts of the nervous system of man; between it as a whole and the other organs of the body; and between it and the physical world as it affects the body. But the explanation would be couched *in terms of quantity only*. The mystery of the quality, or kind, of the energizing of the nervous mechanism might remain as great as before. And the mystery of its correlations with the phenomena of the mental life would not be changed, or its prospective better solution even approximated. For the popular conception of energy as a sort of entity that can actually be split up, and distributed, or passed over, is, of course, especially absurd when considered as applied to the relations of the body and the mind. That varying amounts of the activity of the central nervous system are correlated with somewhat comparable changes in the intensity of our consciously felt experiences, is a statement sufficiently warranted by a numerous class of observed facts and of reasonable inferences from facts. But all this scarcely touches the point at issue.

§ 22. The entire conception of the conservation and correlation of energy, as it is made fruitful use of in the physical and chemical sciences, and even as it hopes to be introduced into the biological sciences, is, therefore, essentially and utterly inappropriate to express those peculiar relations which are matters of experience between the body and the mind. This is as true of the brain, with all its complicated structure and subtile forms of functioning, as it is of any of the more massive and grosser forms of the bodily organism. The so-called " mind " is not the kind of an existence in which physical energy can be stored, or to which it can be transferred, or from which it can be derived. The utmost that could possibly be claimed on the valid ground of experience, would be statable only in terms somewhat like the following: The brain, considered as that part of the nervous mechanism which has the most intimate and important relations with the phenomena of conscious mental life, is itself subject to the principle of the conservation of physical energy. The felt intensity of some of the mind's experiences varies in some sort of dependence upon the amounts of the energy expended by the brain; and, possibly, upon the particular portions of the brain in which these changes of stored into kinetic energy take place. But if this relation is to be looked upon as *causal*—and we hold that it is, in a defensible and rational meaning of the word " causal "—it is a quite different kind of causal relation from that which maintains itself between material objects. And, in truth, even for the latter kind of relation, all that the principle of the conservation of energy at its best can do, is to give formulas applicable to the quantitative aspect of physical changes only. But this kind of quantitative formulas, and its mathematics, have no valid applications to the phenomena of consciousness, as such.

§ 23. To go over the ground again in a somewhat different way: On attempting to account for the whole world of phenomena in terms of motion, kinetic or potential, under the law of the conservation of energy, we are met with insuperable difficulty as soon as we enter the domain of consciousness. States of consciousness are not modes of motion. If they were, the general theory of physics would compel us at once to attempt a strict mathematical correlation between physical and mental phenomena. Just as the kinetic energy of masses can be expressed, with a tolerable approximation to exactness, in terms of heat as a mode of motion, so would some formula be conceivable for indicating what amount of chemical changes, or nerve-commotion, in the matter of the brain, is the mathematical equivalent of the conception of home, of the sense of obligation, or of the idea of God. In other words, it seems impossible to regard any amount of physical energy as abstracted from the brain, so to speak, and expended or stored up in consciousness. Energy is stored by the process of nutrition in the nervous elements of the brain; it becomes kinetic in connection with the phenomena of consciousness. But between the mind, whether regarded as merely the formal subject of consciousness or as a real unit-being whose faculty or power it is to be conscious, and the physical basis of mind in the brain, no correlation, in the sense of a passing back and forth of physical energy, can occur.

The entire circuit of the transmission and distribution of energy is, therefore, complete within the brain itself. Not a single atom enters its substance that does not come forth unchanged, with all its forces inherent in it. No atom is transferred from brain to mind, as all the atoms are transferred from the blood to the nervous substance of the brain. Not the most infinitesimal amount of energy exists, stored in the constitution of the molecules of this substance, which is not either used up there or returned to external nature in connection with the constitution of the molecules separated from this substance. The stricter we make our application of the law of the conservation of energy within the physical realm, the more impossible does it become to apply it at all to the relations of body and mind.

It is not surprising that, in the estimate of one who is unaccustomed to regard with favor any explanation of phenomena which does not come under the most general law of all physics, the case of the mind and the brain should seem to demand the most extraordinary treatment. In any event, the facts of consciousness, as facts, cannot be denied. Whether we can explain them or not, they are equally plain and persistent. Men perceive, and imagine, and remember, and reason, and believe in the invisible, and choose, etc. All this they do, as possessed of a body—and, particularly, of a nervous mechanism, the activities of whose central portion are related in some special and unique way with the doing of all this. And yet sure, beyond doubt—it is argued—is the existence of the atom, with

its host of inherent energies; and supreme is the law of the conservation and correlation of these energies regarded as modifications of
one fundamental form.   But here the whole conception becomes a
figure of speech so vague and evanescent that it loses all definable
meaning when the attempt is made to render it into terms of actual,
matter-of-fact experience.

§ 24. When freed, then, from a physical hypothesis which, of its
very nature, has no valid application to the subject in hand, the conception of causal influence, and of reciprocally dependent relations
under terms of this influence, between the nervous mechanism and
the phenomena of mental life, meets with no objection to itself in
a scientific study of the facts.   In a word, we may affirm anew that
kind of dualism, which holds that some, at least, of our conscious
states are *caused* to be such and no other, by the antecedent or accompanying functions of the nervous system; and, on the other hand,
that some, at least, of the changes which occur in the bodily states are
caused through the nervous system, by the antecedent or accompanying functions of the mental life.   This is—as has already been repeatedly said—the popular view.   Science has nothing to adduce
against it; but much to confirm it.   So far may we carry the theory
of the natural correlations between body and mind, by a direct appeal to the experienced facts.

§ 25. But the facts also compel us to admit that neither one of these
forms of functioning wholly explains the other.   What goes on in
the nervous mechanism does not completely account for what goes
on in consciousness; what goes on in consciousness does not completely account for the activities in the nervous mechanism.   Indeed, the very nature of the two series of occurrences is as unlike
as it is conceivable that different classes of phenomena should be.
The behavior of radium under the influence of radio-active energy,
is not so unlike that of the star Sirius under the influence of the force
of gravity, as is the simplest conscious sensation from the nerve-commotion which caused it.   Moreover, the brain has always something
to say as to what it will do, when under the most determined and
strongest influence from the mind.   And the mind has always
something to say as to what its own behavior shall be, even when
under the strongest of influences from the brain.   There is, however,
nothing unique about all this, so far as the propriety of any application of the conception of a causal relation is concerned.   For there
is no material thing so mean that it does not have a "nature" of its
own; and that nature determines, in the most powerful and practical way, what it shall be *caused* to do by its entering into all sorts
of relations with other things.   And there is no psychic existence
which has not a similar claim to a nature of its own.

In what sense we may assert any reality or unity for the subject of the mental life is not the question at the present time. But all our scientific research, as directed toward this particular kind of correlations, assumes that, in some valid meaning of the word, there *is* a being to be called the Mind. On the other hand, no one can cross the threshold of the science of physiological psychology, or psycho-physics, without assuming the existence of the body; and of the nervous system and brain, as portions of this body. The two existences, body and mind, may not be identified by the science which investigates their correlations; for they have markedly different ways of functioning; the phenomena which research both assumes and discovers, and so assigns to them, are characteristically unlike. They are, however, dependently connected. Each stands in causal relations to the other; although this dependence appears to be by no means complete. Body and Mind, changes in the nervous processes and the changing processes of the conscious mental life, cannot be identified. Neither can be stated with scientific precision, or in any other than a convenient figure of speech, in terms of the other.

§ 26. In the more particular description of the connection between the mind and the brain, it may be said that all intercourse between material objects and the subject of consciousness involves three processes—a physical, a physiological, and a psychical. In these processes the perceived object and the perceiving subject mutually condition each other. This fact, however, does not destroy the necessity, under which all scientific investigation finds itself, of assuming that both object and subject exist as real beings. The physical process consists in the action of the appropriate modes of physical energy upon the nervous end-apparatus of sense. The bringing of such modes of energy to bear upon the apparatus is accomplished through mechanical contrivances—such as the means for forming an image on the retina in the eye, and for conveying the modified acoustic impulses to the organ of Corti in the ear.

The second process consists in transmuting the physical energies, in part at least, into a physiological process, a nerve-commotion within the nervous system; and in propagating such nerve-commotion along the proper tracts and diffusing it over the various areas of this system. Inasmuch as the physiological process is also a physical process—that is, a mode of the motion of material molecules, accompanied by chemical and electrical and other changes—it must be conceived of as standing in certain relations of quality and quantity to the first, or more distinctively physical, process. That the law of the conservation of energy, as formulated for much simpler cases of the relations of forces between inorganic bodies, applies to the relations of the nervous system and its stimuli, or within the different parts of the nervous system itself, we are not yet able to affirm with confidence. But we have valid grounds for the belief that something of the sort is true.

The third process is psychical; it is a process which is a psychical event, a forth-putting of the energy of mind. It is directly correlated with the physiological process only when the latter has been realized in certain cerebral areas. It is not to be explained as a resultant of the cerebral physiological process, but as an action of the mind which is conditioned upon that process. So, also, are we entitled to say that, when certain psychical processes, by way of feeling, ideation, and volition, take place, then, and as conditioned upon these processes, certain corresponding physiological processes occur in the brain; the physiological processes, being propagated from the central nervous system, end in physical processes returning energy to the world outside of the body.

When the mental process is a perception of some object, called an "external" object, it is no less truly a *psychical* process. The mind creates its own objects; presents itself with its own presentations of sense; acts to bring forth that which it knows as not itself. But it does all this as dependent upon the processes which take place outside of itself, and with the assumption of extra-mental realities as existing, to which it stands in the relation of cause and effect.

Finally, then, *the assumption that the mind is a real being, which can be acted upon by the brain, and which can act on the body through the brain, is the only one compatible with all the facts of experience.* There is nothing which we know about the nature of material beings and the laws of their relation to each other, or about the nature of spiritual beings and their possible relation to material beings, or about the nature of causal efficiency whether in the form of so-called physical energy or in that of activity in consciousness, which forbids the aforesaid assumption. And no other assumption, substantially different from this, is compatible with the facts of experience.

§ 27. A distinctive feature of modern science is its endeavor to satisfy inquiry into the *nature* of the objects of its investigation by a detailed description of their *development*. In answer to the inquiry what a thing *is*, we are invited to listen to an account of how it *became* what it is. The history of the egg explains the bird even more than the nature of the bird explains the egg. Indeed the universal process of "Becoming" has been almost personified and deified so as to make it the true ground of all finite and concrete existences. There can be no doubt as to the great fruitfulness and value of this historical and genetic way of studying everything. Let us, then, now consider the most general relations, or correlations, of body and mind, from the point of view of their dependent development.

Undoubtedly, both of the two subjects, with whose correlations Physiological Psychology deals, require for their most satisfactory understanding to be studied by the genetic method. The structure of the nervous system, as we saw in the earliest chapters of this treatise, appears in a new light when regarded as the result of a process of evolution. Beginning with the impregnated ovum, by propagation of cells of living protoplasm, by segmentation of larger sections of these cells, by proliferation of cells and separation into layers, the one portion of the germ from which the mechanism of nerve-fibres and nerve-cells is to unfold itself becomes differentiated from the other portions. By vital processes kept up through nutrition and resulting in the growth of some areas beyond others, and by mechanical influences at work to crowd forward here or push back there, to fold and tuck and cause to dip or curve, etc., this epiblastic portion develops the system of end-organs, central organs, and connecting tracts of nerves.

Psychology, also, has felt strongly the same impulse. It has been forced to confess that its real task is but begun when it has, by introspection, examined and classified the phenomena of adult conscious life. All the mental phenomena undoubtedly have, as respects their genesis and order, a truly vital connection. Those of the present have their roots in those of the past. The so-called faculties of the mind are neither hard and fixed lines drawn to exclude from internal relation the various modes of its behavior in consciousness, nor are they kinds of activities that spring up, full-formed at once, at different intervals in its entire history. Perception itself is a result of development; for " things " are not ready-made products existing, as they appear, outside of the mind, but resultants of mental activities that have to be performed anew so often as the things appear. It is in the evolution of the mind that we find our means for understanding its true nature. Moreover, the characteristics which distinguish one mind from another are to be understood as largely resulting from the order and relative prominence of different activities in the development of each.

So far as the connection of mental phenomena with the increasing complexity of the nervous activities, and with the stored energies and hardening *habitus* of the nervous elements, affords any explanation of the development of the mind, we have already said all that is necessary. The growth of the mental life in the acquirement and arrangement of sensations, in the recalling of ideas, in the forming of judgments about objects of sense, etc., is plainly dependent upon the evolution of the bodily members. But the real nature of the relation which exists between the mental phenomena and the nervous mechanism, so far as this can be learned by studying the development of both, furnishes us with another question. Upon this question, also, the same conflict of view as that to which we have already drawn attention may arise.

§ 28. There can be no doubt of a general correspondence between the two developments, of the body and of the mind. Nervous system and mental condition are both immature in infancy; both develop with great rapidity in early childhood, and then more slowly on into adult life; both—it is claimed—remain comparatively stationary through the period of man's highest maturity; and as old age advances, both, in some respects at least, customarily keep pace in their decline. Moreover, cases of arrested development of brain are cases of arrested development of mental capacity. Idiots are frequently microcephalic; many of them have brains weighing less than thirty ounces. Degeneracy of the tissues of the cerebral hemispheres is commonly connected with increasing degeneracy of the mind. As the tides of molecular nerve-commotion rise and fall in the nervous mass, so rise and fall the tides of mental vigor.

On the other hand, attempts to account for the orderly increase in complexity and comprehensiveness of all the mental phenomena by tracing the physical evolution of the brain are wholly unsatisfactory to many minds. We have no hesitation in classing ourselves among this number. That something more than an absolutely dependent and physically conditioned development is implied in the history of each individual mind may be argued on two principal grounds. In the first place, it may be shown that the stages and laws of mental development do not fully correspond to those which are observed on tracing the evolution of the nervous system. It may also be shown that certain elements necessarily enter into the development of mind, which have nothing like them, or strictly correlated with them, in the evolution of the material mechanism. Any being may be dependent on other beings for its starting, as it were, and for certain factors that enter into its growth or furnish the indispensable conditions of its growth; and yet this fact gives us no right whatever to refuse to such a being all title to take rank among other real existences as having a complex nature of its own. No existence loses or impairs its claim to reality by being dependent on other existences for its development. The mind, on the contrary, most indubitably establishes such a claim, because the stages and laws of its unfolding, and some of the factors which necessarily enter into this unfolding, are peculiar to itself (*sui generis*).

§ 29. That the words, "development of the mind," stand for something real and verifiable, there can be no reasonable doubt. The sum-total of the conscious experience of each individual is far more than a mere series of states of consciousness. No difference in degrees under the same kind can be conceived of which is greater than the difference between the most mature and highly developed mental performances and those inconceivably simple activities with which the mental life begins. So far as the character of the phenomena of consciousness is concerned, the mind of the adult Newton or Kant is much farther removed from the mind of the infant Newton or Kant than the latter is from the mind of one of the lower animals. There is no doubt, also, that the incomparable improvement of the mental processes which distinguishes the adult from the infantile human being is a true development. Each stage of this improvement is dependent upon preceding stages. The changes are all in some sort according to a plan. Thus the life of every individual's mental experiences is capable of being made into a *history*. A certain tolerably uniform order in the relative development of the different faculties is discernible. At first the senses are awakened to a lively and varied activity; then memory and imagination become more prominent; and, finally, judgment and the reasoning powers assert their sway. Gradually, things become known and conduct shaped under principles which are assumed to have a universal validity as so-called general laws. The history of the mental life of every human being, from the cradle (or even from its embryonic existence) to the grave, has all these marks of unfolding itself in a regular order, in which every characteristic event happens in due sequence and in dependence upon what has preceded. This is the very essence of a true development.

Can this mental development be explained as merely the resultant or expression of the physical evolution of the nervous system—the latter being regarded as situated in the rest of the bodily environment, and surrounded by the more extended environment of the world of active physical energies outside? Against an affirmative answer to this inquiry stand many facts and laws of all such mental development. In spite of certain striking correspondences between the evolution of the bodily organism and the development of the mental powers, it must be held that there are marked divergences as well. At certain epochs of life the evolution of the brain seems to stand far in advance of the mind; at others, the mind appears to have overtaken and passed by the stage reached by its physical substratum. During a long period of life the growth of mental powers is constant and solid, while the growth of the physical basis has nearly ceased, and such changes as are taking place in it appear quite inadequate to serve as correlates for the mental growth. Moreover, the most distinctly typical features in the development of the mind remain the same when malformation or disease or accident have largely changed the physical evolution of the brain.

§ 30. We have no sufficient means for deciding how far the mental life of the human embryo keeps pace with its organic evolution. We do not even know beyond doubt that the embryo has a mental life, in the only tenable meaning of the words—that is, a life of *conscious* states. It is probable, however, that its antenatal movements are not all purely reflex, but are accompanied and directed by conscious sensation, feeling, and volition. But the mental life of the embryo, if it exist at all, can hardly be more than an irregular and fitful succession of the lowest and least complex of conscious processes. Taste, smell, hearing, and sight are, of course, not to be thought of as entering into such a mental life. Touch, as we understand the word to express the localized sensations of pressure which arise through the practised organ of the skin, is scarcely more likely to belong to the human embryo. Obscure feelings arising from changes in its relation to the surrounding tissues and fluids of the mother, or from disturbances in its own internal organs, and resulting equally obscure feelings of position and motion, as its limbs are moved, must constitute the greater part, if not the whole, of its experiences. As yet there is no *experience*, properly so called; no perception of things, no feelings of self, no discrimination of ego and state. Yet long before the child is born it possesses a wonderfully elaborate nervous mechanism, far surpassing in its grade of evolution the nervous system of the most intelligent adult animals. Previous to birth this nervous mechanism must also be constantly in action in a highly complicated way; it is engaged in supervising the processes of nutrition, and in the reflex and automatic activities which are expressed by the changes of the child's position within the womb of the mother. The mind, however, is as yet unawakened; this is not because the nervous mechanism is not complex and active enough to serve as the physical basis of a rich mental development, but because the kinds of sensation—visual, tactual, auditory, etc.— which start and furnish and direct this development have not yet been supplied. The mental life cannot then be said to have kept pace before birth with the evolution of the brain, or with its distinctive activities. On the contrary, it is far behind the stage already reached by its physical support. *It waits to be aroused* and set to its own work of combining and interpreting those sensations which are to serve as its chief means of early culture.

For the first few weeks of infancy the embryonic relation between the relative developments of the body and soul of the child seems to be maintained. Both are subjects of a rapid growth, but the former is still much in advance of the latter. The newly born infant is, in respect to the condition of its nervous system, much the most highly organized and fully equipped of all young animals; but as judged by the number and quality of its volitions and perceptions, many other young animals are less stupid and insensate. If we may represent its mental condition by anything conceivable through the adult imagination, the human infant is in a dreamless sleep occasionally interrupted by instants of unlocalized and unmeaning sensations.

The cavity of the infant's tympanum is filled with a fluid, the place of which is only gradually taken by the air. Sensations of sound, if they arise at all, must be at first only occasional and faint. Binocular movements of the eyes in the direction of bright objects take place early; and it is through sensations of light and color that the first activities of the mind in perception are chiefly aroused and controlled. But for some weeks there are only sensations and impressions, without true perceptions; there is as yet no knowledge of any "Thing." This earliest relation of mind and brain, with respect to the degree and rate of their development, is not favorable to any form of the materialistic theory. It rather favors the view that the mental phenomena belong to another principle than any material substratum. The dependence of the mind on the brain is indirect and *through* the sensations (chiefly of sight and touch) which must somehow be furnished as the primary factors in its development. The halt in the development of mind at first, and its distinct backwardness with respect to the relative stage it has reached, are due to a lack of *such* sensations as have the characteristics of spatial series, and so are able to stimulate the mind, and to afford it the requisite material for the construction of true presentations of sense.

§ 31. Within a few months after birth the child has undergone an enormous mental development; it has become a mind, in some inchoate way recognizing itself as the subject of states, and perceiving a surrounding world of objects of sense. It has also begun to attend to the objects presented in consciousness, and to direct its attention by voluntary choice. The mind's relating activity has been aroused; and acts of memory, discrimination, and judgment, as the basis for those concepts which require articulate language to express them, are repeatedly taking place. And soon, the assumptions of reason, as involved in all human experience of things, and of their action and reaction upon each other, are found to be shaping the growth of the mental powers.

As accompanying and forming the ground for this sudden blos-
soming of the mind in the use of its conscious powers, there is a
continuous and yet diminishing monthly increase of the substance
of the brain.   No new organs are formed within the cranial cavity;
but those which have been formed previous to birth are further
developed under the changed conditions of nutrition.   In respect to
the quantity and arrangement of its molecules, the nervous mechanism certainly undergoes no development during the first year of
the child's life which at all corresponds to, or accounts for, the development of the child's mind.

It may be claimed, however, that the most important development of the nervous mechanism has been overlooked in the foregoing description.   This development does not consist so much in
the increased quantity of the brain's substance, or in the more
intricate arrangement of its elements with relation to each other;
but, the rather, in the forming of what have already been referred
to as "dynamical associations" among the existing elements.   The
statement that such is the nature of the developing activities of the
nervous mechanism, and the assumption that such activities are an
indispensable physical condition for the growth of the mind, must
be taken for granted.   But even then the argument is far from complete upon which the development of mind as a real being, with a
nature of its own, and with a history controlled by its own laws,
can be denied.   The formation of so-called "dynamical associations" among the molecules of the nervous mass furnishes no adequate account of the development of mind.   This development is
not in the direction *simply* of associating together states of feeling,
each one of which has an exact physical correlate in a physical association among the minute parts of the nervous substance.   It is
rather a development which for its very existence requires something
different from such associations.   The child might go on forever
merely associating together affections of its own mind in correspondence to dynamical associations among the nervous molecules, and
yet have no growth of experience such as it actually attains.   The
fact is that within a single year, or within two years, the child has
learned to know "Things," to attend to some in preference to others,
to refer its states in some crude way to itself, to form concepts and
judgments by the mind's relating activity, and to underlay the world
of its sensuous experience with another world of assumption respecting certain non-sensuous realities.   To account for this bound-
less expansion of the activities of consciousness, with its surprising
new factors and mysterious grounds of synthesis and assumption,
by proposing an hypothesis of "dynamical associations" among
the particles of nervous substance in the brain, is a deification of

impotency. So far as we really *know* anything about the development of both brain and mind, we are compelled to say that the latter, when once started by the sensations furnished through excitation of the former, proceeds to unfold its activities with a rapidity and in an order for which no adequate physical causes can be assigned.

§ 32. During the period of young manhood, or young womanhood, the dependence of the development of the mind on that of the body is most strikingly seen in the influence over the emotions and imagination from the sudden unfolding of certain bodily organs and powers. The indirect influence of these acts of feeling and imagination upon the more purely intellectual progress of the mind is, of course, correspondingly great. But the dependence of mind on body is by no means such as to favor the view that there is no ground in a real being, other than the brain, for the order and rate of the mental development.

This same statement is emphatically true of the long period of maturity which constitutes what we call the "middle life" of man. During this time the nervous matter undergoes scarcely any discernible development. Nothing that microscope or electrometer can detect distinguishes the brain characteristic of the man of twenty-five from that of the man of fifty. A few grams of weight have perhaps been added to it during this long period of years. Any one is at liberty to speculate as to the immense development of so-called "dynamical associations" which has taken place during the same period. We are far from denying the possibility of such development. But the fact that a large development of mind may have taken place during the same period cannot be denied. If it be true that large numbers of mankind remain mentally stationary for most of their adult life, this truth in no way favors a materialistic view of the development of mind. Most observing persons will rightly find the chief account of the failure of mental growth in precisely those kinds of mental activity which least admit of being explained by physical analogies. It is from want of mental curiosity, attention, careful and comprehensive judgment, sound moral purpose, etc., that most men fail to develop during adult life in their mental powers. And these are mental activities for explaining which no one as yet has been able to conjecture any analogous or corresponding class of cerebral changes.

Many minds, however, not only make vast acquisitions, but also experience a large unfolding of mental capacities during the period of middle life. How mature and wide-reaching do the judgments of some men then become! How profound the insight into the most abstract and difficult speculations comes to be! What cerebral evolution shall be conceived of as being the only true cause, and the exact physical correlate, of the mental development of Kant during the years preceding the appearance of the "Critique of Pure Reason," or of Newton while he was unfolding the calculations and conjectures of the "Principia"? To hold that the changing molecules of the brain substance of these thinkers were the sole subjects, really being and acting in the unrolling of these great dramas of human speculation, involves an astonishing credulity. On the contrary, we seem compelled to affirm that no important activity, or law, or fact, in the order of such mental development, fails to demand the assumption of a real and non-material unit-being, unfolding its powers according to its own nature, although in dependence upon certain elements and conditions furnished through the brain.

§ 33. Advancing old age is doubtless, as a rule, characterized by a simultaneous decline both of certain mental and of certain bodily powers. In this period of life, however, the correspondence between the changes in the character of the phenomena of consciousness and the altered vigor and quality of the nervous mechanism is not such as to suggest that the two have an altogether common basis. In healthy normal old age the course of the organic life is distinguished chiefly by the dropping out or diminished action of certain factors that are relatively prominent in youth. The circulation is slower; the vital energy is declining; the muscles are less promptly and completely under the control of the volitions; the end-organs of sense are less sensitive under impressions; and certain emotions and passions whose physical basis is of the most obvious sort become greatly modified or disappear. As to the marked effect of these bodily changes upon the mental development there can be no doubt; and if the previous mental development has been chiefly along lines indicated by organic activities the apparent decay of mental vigor when the physical basis begins to fail is, of course, also most plainly marked.

On the other hand, there are many other cases, where no notable difference can be detected, or even fairly assumed, in the course of the psychical evolution down to the "feebleness" of old age; where the course of mental development continues substantially undisturbed in all its most important features. The mind of the cultivated old man, with calm and broad judgment, with refined kindliness and fixed moral principles, is not to be spoken of as suffering a decline which keeps pace with the failing of his physical powers. It may justly be claimed that the final period of human life, on the whole, favors that theory which regards the mind as by no means wholly conditioned upon the brain for the character, order, and laws of its development.

§ 34. The same general view of the development of mind, which is most consistent with the facts of the different stages of life, is also favored by considering those sudden checks or changes in the course of this development that are caused by disturbing or destroying considerable portions of the nervous matter. The phenomena which follow experimental extirpation of the substance of the brain in the lower animals, and loss of it by serious lesions in the case of man, do not favor a theory which completely identifies the two developments, or one which makes the unfolding of the mental life nothing more significant than a dependent expression of the evolution, maturing, and decay of the nervous mechanism. Extensive losses in certain areas of the cerebral hemispheres are often followed by no appreciable disturbance even of any sensory or motor activity. When lesions are followed by such disturbance, their effects may in time wholly or partially disappear. When such disturbance is permanent it is not necessarily connected with loss in the power of judgment, in the higher intellectual, æsthetic, and ethical activities of feeling, intellect, or will. Even where aphasia is so severe as to include the loss of all power to utter or understand articulate language, the patient may still show a good degree of mental acuteness by ability to make calculations or play games of skill.

On the other hand, a much more serious interruption or complete loss of mental development may occur when no adequate explanation can be detected in the disturbance or arrest of cerebral development. It is, of course, natural to conjecture that, in all this latter class of cases, more accurate information would show us some diseased condition of the brain as the physical antecedent of the mental defects. We know that subtle changes in the character of the blood-supply, such as we have no physical means whatever for detecting, are often the causes of most profound changes—either temporary or more permanent—in the train of ideas. None the less, however, do both classes of cases above mentioned favor the theory we are advocating, rather than the so-called materialistic theory of mind.

§ 35. Several references to the second argument for our view of the development of mind have already been made. This argument is based upon the fact that certain indispensable elements enter into the development of mental life which have nothing similar to them, or strictly correlated with them, in the evolution of the material mechanism. The mind can, indeed, undergo no development except as conditioned upon these elements. But the elements themselves are of such a nature that they cannot be regarded as the expression in consciousness of merely physical causes, or as flowing necessarily from more primitive activities of the mind which may possibly be regarded as the expression of such causes.

If we accept for the moment the customary classification of modern psychology, we may say: All of those fundamental forms of activity which are recognized in the threefold division of conscious processes —namely, acts of feeling, acts of knowledge, and acts of will—necessarily enter into the development of the mind. Its development consists in increased capacity for these three classes of acts, in their mutual dependence and according to the laws which belong to them. Among each of these three great classes of acts there are certain kinds that defy all attempts whatever to correlate them with changes in the nervous mechanism, or to explain them as necessarily or actually arising out of such physical changes. Such are the feeling of moral obligation, the sentiment of justice, the love of truth, and certain of the higher æsthetic feelings. Among the acts of knowledge, such are the mind's relating activity, its use of the principle of reason and consequent in drawing deductions, its confident assumption that similar phenomena are signs of like realities, and that the world of sensuous individual experience is but the manifestation of an invisible world of real beings, with permanent properties and forces, acting and reacting under law. Such, also, are the acts of deliberate choice among courses of conduct, under the influence of moral considerations—the so-called acts of "free will" in the highest sense of the term.

Not one of the higher acts of feeling, knowing, or willing, so far as its sui generis character is concerned, admits of being correlated with, or represented under, any of the conceivable modes of the motion and relation of molecules of nervous substance. Certain sensations and perceptions connected with the rise and growth of the higher forms of feeling have, undoubtedly, a physical basis; but such basis is not assignable to the feelings themselves. Sensations and perceptions, which are the resultants (in some meaning of the word) of physical processes, are discriminated by judgment and made the basis of deductions and inductions. But admitting this does not one whit the better enable us to conceive of a physical process which can account for the sui generis character of the relating activity itself. Acts of "free will," so called, always take place under certain conditions of sensation and perception, as well as of desire; but the physical correlates of these conditions can in no respect be conceived of as being also correlates of the conviction that the choice is responsible and free.

Now, if such activities as the foregoing do actually constitute indispensable elements of mental development—and it is obvious that they do—this development cannot properly be accounted for by assigning it to a mass of nervous matter undergoing a physical process of evolution, after the manner of the growing human brain. Such development rather implies a being of another than the physical order. And this other being must be thought of as stimulated by the rise and recurrence of sensations and images of past sensations to unfold its own activities as conditioned by its own inherent powers. Like every other real being, the history of its unfolding is dependent upon the *relations* in which it is placed to other real beings; but it is nevertheless a history determined also by what the being *is*.

§ 36. More particularly, it may be said that perceptions are not merely developed forms of sensations which latter are products of the brain; they are rather advanced forms of a mental life developing under the experience of sensation—elaborate products of the synthetic activity of mind. Moreover, the knowledge of things by perception involves the development of mental life in the forms of memory and judgment. But acts of memory and judgment are not developments from perception; they are not merely modified forms of sensations as recurring or combined under the action of physical antecedents. All talk about the "image" of memory as though it were merely a faint or faded-out impression of sense is quite unavailing; it does not hit the real point of inquiry, and consequently does nothing to explain the mystery. The vital element in memory, that which makes it to be *memory*, is neither a sensation, nor a modified form of sensation, nor a development of sensation. It is the subject *Ego's* recognition of its own past history as belonging to the life of a mind.

The same statement is true of judgment. The relating activity of mind, the power to bring two objects together in the unity of consciousness, and, while keeping their ideas distinctly separate, to bind them into one under the mental affirmation of their likeness or unlikeness—this is a new and startling mode of the activity of mind as contrasted with merely being affected in sensation. Minimize it as we may, we cannot look upon this activity as a mere "resultant" of two sensations or images of sensations arising simultaneously in consciousness. We cannot consider judgment under the principle of the conservation of energy. To treat it as such involves the grossest misapplication of the laws which control the coincidence or conflict of physical forces. Nor are the different forms of the relating activity of the mind—concept, judgment, deduction, induction—to be regarded, strictly speaking, as developments from each other or from any one mental activity simpler than any of them. They may all, indeed, be considered as modes of the relating activity, because they involve discrimination, the discernment of likenesses and unlikenesses. But each one of them involves somewhat more than simple discrimination; each one involves other elements peculiar to itself. That a sentient being should simply judge, or affirm this or that, is not of itself a sufficient reason why it should also make inferences by syllogistic processes or arrive at general laws by induction. Indeed, the former may belong to many animals which are incapable of the latter.

We might, properly and almost indefinitely, continue the fore-going line of remarks into the consideration of the mind's most general activities. Modern psychology, we have seen, is accustomed to distinguish faculties of knowing, feeling, and willing as belonging to the mind. But if we adopt this division, it becomes emphatically true that no one of these three faculties can be regarded as developed from any other one, or from any two combined. That a being feels—that is, is affected with a state of consciousness more or less pleasurable or painful, and having a characteristic quality—is in itself no ground for explanation of its knowing "Things" through sense-perception and inference. Conversely, a being is conceivable with the knowledge of an archangel, but without experience of de-sire, emotion, or sentiment of attraction or repulsion. Such a being would, indeed, have to attain its knowledge in other ways than those open to us, and we find it difficult or impossible to imagine precisely what such knowledge could be like. But growth in knowledge is a different thing from the unfolding of mere feeling; and the former cannot be explained as arising out of the latter. Acts of will are, indeed, always actually dependent upon knowledge and feeling, and cannot even be conceived of as taking place without this de-pendence. But acts of will are not mere developments of those acts of knowledge and feeling on which they undoubtedly depend. The act of choice involves a new element, an element not to be neces-sarily evolved from the other activities of mind.

§ 37. The development of mind, therefore, cannot be explained after the analogy of the accretion of molecules within a germ, and the resulting division, multiplication, and advancing arrangement of the living cells into separate organs of the entire system. No real elements of the mind exist which can aggregate to themselves other elements by absorbing them as pabulum, or can grow by arranging the new material thus gained according to the energies inherent in the material already organized. The life of consciousness is a never-ceasing change of states. Yet the result of this change of states is an orderly history, a true development. Such development is not merely the expression of the evolution of the material basis of some of these mental states. For it does not follow precisely the same order or the same laws as govern the material evolution; and some of its most important factors cannot be regarded as having any physical correlate, or as evolved from other factors which have such a correlate. *The development of Mind can only be regarded as the progressive manifestation in consciousness of the life of a real being which, although taking its start and direction from the action of the physical elements of the body, proceeds to unfold powers that are* sui generis, *according to laws of its own.*

CHAPTER II

REALITY AND UNITY OF THE MIND

§ 1. In all the discussions of the previous chapter it was implied that we were dealing with two different existences—separable at least in thought, and apparently belonging to widely divergent species of existence. And yet these two existences are in every case related to each other in a peculiarly and even uniquely intimate way: they are so correlated that each furnishes to the other the conditionating antecedent, or cause, of its habitual behavior and characteristic development. For example: I have, or rather am, a body and also a mind; and you have, or rather are, another and different body and also a mind. *My* body and *my* mind are bound together with these peculiar ties of correlation; and the same thing is true of *your* body and *your* mind. The individuality of each of us as human beings is the joint product of the nature and development of the two, in this their naturally appointed form of being correlated. In some such way as this, the popular conceptions relating to the subject would have to be expressed; and as yet we have found nothing in psychological science, as pursued from the physiological and experimental points of view, to contradict or substantially to modify the popular conception.

Now, only an extreme form of scholastic idealism (sometimes called "subjective idealism" or "solipsism"), of which science can take no account, ventures to deny the reality of the human body, in the fullest meaning of that word which can apply to any material entity. A piece of quartz rock and the gold extracted from it, or a ton of steel, is not a bit more real, and truly a part of physical nature, than is the most delicately organized human body, including the wonderfully intricate and tenuous network of nerve-cells in the brain attached to that body. Nor would any one think of denying that the different parts of the body constitute a certain kind of organic whole; or that the brain, considered by itself, shows manifest signs of both an architectural and a functional unity. All this, and much more of the same sort, enters into all the sciences of biology, anatomy, histology, and physiology, in their several ways of dealing with the same material substance. All these assumptions,

668

however, are a naïve and uncritical but legitimate and scientifically productive form of metaphysics.

§ 2. When we come to deal with the claims of the subject of the conscious mental life to a reality and a unity of its own, similar assumptions are apt to be ruled out, on the ground that they *are* metaphysical, and that science ought not to have anything to do with *metaphysics*. But why this prejudice against claiming for the subject of the mental life and mental development a title to some sort of reality, and to some sort of unity; when both these claims are admitted without contest for the bodily organism with which this mental life and mental development are correlated? In answer to this inquiry, four considerations may be alleged. One of the chief reasons for such discrimination against the claims of the mind is just that lack of the critical analysis of metaphysical conceptions, to which reference has already been made. What, indeed, do we mean by calling things "real," and by speaking of them as having a certain kind of "unity"? Until we have fixed upon some at least provisional answer to this inquiry, how can we say whether any particular thing is entitled to be called real, or to be spoken of as one, two, or any particular number? Another reason is to be found in the peculiar characteristics which affirm the existence in reality of the so-called mind; and which are relied upon to demonstrate its unity. A third reason has operated to produce scepticism ending in a virtually materialistic conception, in a yet more powerful way. This is to be found in the vagueness and extravagance of those who, in the supposed interests of morals and religion, have presented what they were pleased to regard as a "spiritual" conception of the human soul. And, finally, a reason is to be found, in many individual cases, in a hardened and highly prejudiced attitude on the part of the observer, against admitting anything that does not easily accord with a purely mechanical and materialistic conception of nature and her processes. In the opinion of such minds, nothing can be real that cannot be perceived by the senses, that cannot be weighed and measured in the laboratory or in the field; and nothing can have a real unity that does not admit of having its elements physically or chemically combined and separated for future combination with other elements. Each one of these four considerations will now be examined in the order just given.

§ 3. As to its conceptions of "reality" and "unity," modern psychology may properly claim to be following the lead of the chemico-physical sciences. These conceptions are now, more than formerly, of the "dynamical" and less of the statical order. No physical reality—not even the ancient atom—is to be fitly conceived of as an unchanging mass or unalterable tiny bit of material substance.

To have its claim entered in the world of real beings, every individual thing must prove this claim by continually doing something and by having something done to it. What kind of a reality any particular thing is to be proved to be, depends upon what it is able to do to other things and to have done to it by other things. In a word, *it is action which demonstrates reality—both that it is, and what it is.*

In somewhat similar manner, what gives unity to any particular thing is not the fact that it is a solid and indissoluble mass, or an unanalyzable, tiny bit of substance; but its unity is gained for it by the co-operation of its various elements, in their action and in their development. Or, to say the same thing in other words: Every reality becomes "one" through the continuous action and reaction of its elements in definite ways upon one another and upon all the other things which constitute its particular environment. This is true even of so loosely constituted a unity as a heap of sand; the different grains form *one* heap, only so long as they are held together in one place by the forces of gravity and cohesion. But there are different kinds of unity, and different degrees of being united, corresponding to these different kinds. In general, the more complex and unstable the unity, the higher it is in kind. According to modern physics, as respects its elements there is no more rapidly and subtly alterable unity than is the atom; and yet the atom, as the very word signifies, was formerly regarded as the most stable and unalterable of all conceivable unities. In the case of all *living* forms, the unity which they possess is the oneness that is attained by a process of development. And here, in general, the original elements are comparatively few in number and simple in arrangement; but they become more and more numerous and highly complex in arrangement, as this process goes forward. Indeed, by certain theories it would seem to be held, that to give a simple descriptive history of this progressive complication of elements is a sufficient explanation of the process itself. Such theories would think to account for the development by describing it as an increase in "aggregation," "differentiation," "integration," etc.; and would regard the unity resulting from the process as having no more reality than that which belongs to the process; and this is a never-ceasing, but ever restless, activity by way of action and reaction.

§ 4. If now we insist upon having some further and more satisfactory explanation of a unity which is achieved by a process of development that combines, even into a temporary oneness, a number of elements through the co-operation of a number of kinds of energy, we are obliged to introduce the conception of "plan." No unity of any kind or degree of complexity can be realized without giving evidence of some "indwelling" or "overruling" idea. In the case of such unitary beings as appear to our minds ready-made, as it were, the plan is thought of as already realized; while in the case of such beings as are found to be still in a process of development, the plan is thought of as in the way of being realized. Whether this manner of explaining the unitary nature of any physical thing is only a sign of the sort of necessity under which the human mind finds itself, and gives us no clue to the Nature of Reality, or whether it is also a trustworthy revelation of the essential character of the Being of the World, is a metaphysical inquiry which need not concern us at the present time.

It would seem, then, that if the phenomena of man's mental life give unmistakable signs of forms of energy, which act upon other real beings and are acted upon by them, and which arrange themselves according to some plan, then it is certainly permissible to claim reality and unity for the Subject of these phenomena—i. e., for the so-called soul or mind. At once, however, we are met by objections based upon the peculiar nature of these phenomena; and especially upon the well-known fact of their dependence—even to the point of not appearing at all, or of total disappearance—on the constitution and functioning of the bodily organism.

Now a certain very intimate, and in some respects seemingly absolute, dependence of all mental phenomena upon the integrity, condition as respects the character of its blood-supply, habitual ways of reacting, established "dynamical associations," "preoccupations," and concurrent sensory and motor nerve-commotions, etc., etc., of the brain, must be admitted. How intimate and far-reaching this dependence actually is, has occupied with its statement more than one-half of this entire treatise. It has been shown that the beginnings, the varying phases of intensity, the rise and fall below the so-called "threshold," and even the complete temporary cessation of the conscious states, are involved in this dependence. Here it is not necessary to repeat, however, what has been sufficiently insisted upon in the last chapter, and in numerous other places,— namely, that the phenomena which are ascribed to the nervous mechanism are also dependent for their existence and their character upon the reactions of the conscious mental life. But it is especially necessary at this point to remind ourselves that no kind of physical reality succeeds in escaping a similar condition of dependence. All the phenomena which material substances exhibit as signs of their reality are liable to vary in degree, in characteristic quality, and even to disappear and reappear, or cease entirely, in dependence upon internal changes and upon their relations to other material substances. The higher in the scale of complexity, expecially as a result of biological development, the living unity has come to be, the more significant, and yet, generally, the more unstable, is its unity apt to become.

§ 5. If now in the light of even so little criticism of the metaphysical conceptions involved, we examine anew the claims of the mind to reality and unity, we shall find it impossible not to accept them in a certain meaning of the words employed.   In some meaning of these words, the mind undoubtedly has an actual existence as a unitary being; it is *real* and it is *one*.   It has at least what Kant called a "phenomenal" reality; and it develops in time a "phenomenal" unity.   To establish so much of a claim we may appeal with confidence to every one's indisputable experience.   Both the reality and the unity of this sort are, indeed, a matter of degrees and of development.   But why should this fact diminish the trustworthiness or the value of the experience on which the claim is based?   Indeed, this kind of reality and unity is involved in the very conception of a *development*.   As a bare conception—not to speak of any corresponding facts in reality—no development can exclude the necessity of a process which is itself characterized by a certain kind of unity, and which has its result in a series of existences possessing a unitary character.   All this is conspicuously true of that organism with which the development of the mental life is especially correlated.   The human nervous mechanism, as was shown in detail in the opening chapters of the book, has resulted from a process which, in the case of each individual man, has followed a somewhat peculiar plan; and at every stage in this complex process, from the beginning of the faintest discernible traces of nerve-fibres and nerve-cells to the maturing of the adult brain, spinal cord, peripheral ganglia, end-organs of sense, etc., etc., this mechanism has exhibited all the signs of a "unitary being."   Indeed, were this not true, it could not properly be called either a "system," or a "mechanism."

§ 6. But to examine further the claims of the subject of the phenomena of the mental life, the so-called mind, to the titles of reality and unity: It was just now said that this claim can scarcely be combated, if we qualify the nouns by the adjective "phenomenal." By this it was meant that the phenomena present themselves to our inspection, whether we study them by the method of self-consciousness solely or also and chiefly by the methods of physiological and experimental psychology, as matter-of-fact experiences of a unitary character.   Many ill-advised attempts have recently been made to destroy or to minimize what used to be called "the authority of consciousness," and even to prove that no such experience as self-consciousness, properly so called, can possibly be had.   This, together with the loose use of such terms as "unconscious" and "subconscious" in application to the phenomena of mental life, has been the source of much obscuration of the entire problem. And when we add to this result the effect of the loose employment of such terms from the mathematics of physics as "double," "triple," etc., to human selfhood or personality, we have a state of affairs in which the plainest testimony of the most indubitable experiences is tolerably sure to be either sophisticated or totally overlooked. Surely, the consistent, tenable, and hopeful course, upon which to enter for the scientific definition of the existence and the nature of any thing, physical or otherwise, is not through the door of a denial of the actual facts of our experience with that particular thing.

§ 7. Now in the special case of man's mental life, its very essence consists in conscious activity, culminating in the achievement of perceptive consciousness (sometimes called "apperception"), or the knowledge of things, on the one hand; and in self-conscious-ness or the knowledge of Self, on the other hand. In this very process of development the mind not only constructs and affirms its own unitary being, but also constructs all the unities which it affirms of other selves and of material things. But when we speak of this reality and this unity as an *achievement,* we in no wise invalidate or diminish the truthfulness or the value of the claim. In fact nothing that is alive, especially no product of an elaborate process of development—and probably no inorganic physical reality even—has come into existence "ready made," as it were. On the contrary, each unity in nature has become one, through a process of self-making. Looked at from the purely objective and scientific point of view, Nature is constantly making and unmaking all those products, which appear to our minds to have a certain temporary unity, but which are in fact never wholly delivered from the necessity of ceaseless change. The rather must we say that the reality of their being at all consists in this actual process of change; and that their individual natures are defined to us by the character of the changes which take place in them and which they contribute to produce in other natural objects. But subjectively regarded, as the theory of perception already advanced has sufficiently made clear, all these same natural products are made to be one to us, through no process of merely copying-off, but by the constructive activity of our own minds.

§ 8. Now one essential thing about the activity of human consciousness, as the truth has all along been implied, is to affirm the actuality of the existence of the Subject of all the conscious states. *In a word, the reality, or actuality for the time being of this Subject of all the mental life is an indispensable implicate of all the phenomena of the same mental life.* The mind must do duty here; and there is nothing else which can by any possibility be supposed to take its place. Let the case be tried by making a beginning with that sort of testimony with which every one is most familiar. I know that I think, feel, will; that is to say, phenomena take place in my consciousness which there is no conceivable way of describing except by attributing them to the subject of all my consciousness—to the self-conscious "me" called mind. But because I cannot perceive this subject of all consciousness as an extended and external somewhat—a "Thing" so large, and shaped and colored in just such a manner, with a definitely hard or soft feel—that is to say, because I do not appear to myself in consciousness to be just such a kind of being as are some of the objects of my perception, I begin to raise the question whether this subject (the "I" that thinks, etc.) has any real being at all. May it not in fact be, I ask myself, that some "thing," or collection of things, like those which I have often seen and felt, is the subject to which the thoughts and feelings and acts of will that I have called "mine" should be attributed? Of course, if this question is to be answered in the light of modern physiology with even a provisional affirmative, the particular "thing,"to which such activities as those I am conscious of are to be attributed, is *my brain*. Nothing, surely, but my brain can think, and feel, and will —so to speak—for me.

But the inquiry may now be raised: How do we know that there is actually a brain, which may serve as the real substratum of the phenomena of consciousness? In view of the science of body *and* mind, it is as fair to ask this question in a sceptical way, as to ask the corresponding question about the mind. It scarcely need be said that no one has any evidence presented directly to the senses that such organ exists within his own cranial cavity. To be conscious, and at the same time to observe the substratum of one's consciousness, is an unattainable opportunity.[1] It may even be that the particular *ego* (the "I" of consciousness) which is engaged in the search for its own real being in a material substratum has never seen so much as a single human brain. Since there is such scarcity of direct ocular and tangible demonstration of a special relation between the brain and mental phenomena, it is plain that the testimony of experts must be summoned.

On the other hand, it must be confessed that no expert has any more direct evidence than every self-conscious ego has of the ex-

[1] After all, perhaps this opportunity is not forever in all respects "unattainable," for the most recent experiences with cerebral surgery without anæsthetics, leave it possible that an arrangement of mirrors might give one the rare sight of seeing his own brain exposed and operated upon to an hitherto inconceivable extent.

istence of a real material structure called brain, which may account, by its presence and activities, for his own mental phenomena. Nor can he offer any evidence peculiar to himself for his belief that the particular *ego* which he calls "himself" is connected with his brain. And how many soever other brains he may have seen, he only knows by a series of very indirect and complicated inferences that any individual whose brain he has not seen really possesses one. But whence these inferences? and, What are the grounds on which the confidence attached to them is based? To these questions only one answer is possible. The inferences themselves are acts of knowledge, modes of consciousness, phenomena of mind. The only possible grounds of confidence in them, as valid inferences, must be referred back to our inherent faith in the power of the mind rightly to infer, from its own phenomena, the real existence of beings the phenomena of which it has never perceived. Moreover, if the mind had perceived the phenomena of its own brain, there could be nothing in the phenomena themselves to account for the power to make inferences which belong to it as mind. On the ground, then, of an inferred reality called the brain, I am asked to dispense with my confidence in the reality of the being which makes the inference, and which, at the same time, makes a much more irresistible inference as to its own reality as an active inferring force.

§ 9. The case is, however, by no means so favorable as the statement just made would imply, for that phase of scientific materialism which refers the phenomena of consciousness to the brain as their *sole* cause. For it is not in the brain, as a mere mass of matter whose structure and mechanical functions can be made obvious to any intelligent observer, that the real substratum of mental phenomena must be sought. Considered as such a mass, this organ is no better than any other similar soft and pulp-like bulk. It is the wonderful molecular constitution, atomic play, and changing dynamic relations of the invisible particles of this mass, which are responsible for its unique functions. But the very existence of the atoms as real beings, capable of acting on each other and of being acted on—how shall this remote and obscure fact be ascertained? and how shall we learn what is the nature of these beings, so as to determine whether or not they are capable of performing the stupendous task of bringing forth the various mental phenomena?

In attempting to answer the last two questions we are in great danger of losing completely all that we have taken most pains to gain. It is to the all-powerful "atoms," with their potent forces, that we are now looking as the real subjects at once of the molecular changes in the brain-mass and of the phenomena of consciousness. From these real beings and their relations there must be derived, not only the activities which physiology ascribes to nervous matter, but also those which psychology is constrained to ascribe to conscious mind. And yet, how do we know that any real beings whatever called atoms exist? Certainly not by direct evidence of any of the senses. Not even the most pronounced advocate of the reality of physical things, and of the unreality of mind, would venture to affirm that he has seen or touched an atom, or can demonstrate its existence and nature to ordinary observation through the human senses. Atoms are *supersensible* beings. Moreover, they are hypothetical existences, or beings whose existence is inferred in an extremely roundabout way in order that we may be able to give to ourselves a rational account of the grounds on which certain classes of phenomena rest.

§ 10. Moreover, the best efforts of modern investigation to describe the nature of the atom appear, not only incomplete, but also, in certain particulars, self-contradictory. It is certain that the atom cannot be regarded as an independent reality. What it *is* can only be described by telling what it *does;* but in telling what *it* does we always find ourselves implying certain relations to *other* atoms. That is to say, we know nothing about the nature of any of the atoms which does not involve also complicated hypotheses concerning its mode of behavior as caused by the presence and mode of behavior of other hypothetical beings. In this way the reality of the atoms is made ultimately to depend on the reality of some law, or ideal force, that binds different atoms together, as it were, and makes them work to a unity of plan. But here, again, we are reminded that we can form no conception of a "plan" which is not a phenomenon of mind, and no conception of a "unity" that does not depend upon the unifying *actus* of the mind. Moreover, all ideas of "relation" are dependent upon mental activities that are quite without physical analogy. All "Things" are made into the units which they appear to be by the unifying action of the mind. Such action is implied in the most elementary and naïve perceiving of things; for the study of perception, from the physiological point of view even, has enabled us to show that no so-called "thing" is a ready-made material product, apprehended by mind in a form which is a copy of some extra-mental existence.

§ 11. Accordingly, the whole course of argument and the whole weight of conviction appear to be the reverse of what is assumed by the objector to the reality of mind. The material molecules of the brain are *not* beings about the reality and exact nature of which we have the most indubitable evidence—evidence so indubitable that we may venture to press it into the contradiction of the more immediate data of consciousness.   If these elements of all physical being are real, they come to us as inferences and hypotheses; they involve a vast amount of conjecture, indirect inference, and unsolved difficulties, or even contradictions.   And if we ask, On what authority are these inferences made? Whence comes the demand for any rational explanation whatever? Where do the conjecture, hypothesis, and sense of difficulty and seeming contradiction exist? then the only answer to be given to all these questions refers them to the Mind.   What atoms and forces and laws can be, or mean, without the being and activity of self-conscious mind, is even harder to conjecture than what a color can be which is not seen, a sound which is not heard, an odor that is not smelled.

Shall this, then, be the last word of science on the subject?— namely, that *the one being in whose active energizing all conceptions of all real being arise, feels justified in denying its own reality in the supposed favor of certain of its most remote and doubtful conceptions.*

§ 12. What is meant by affirming the reality of mind may now be made somewhat clearer by pursuing the following train of reflections: In the development of the mental life its phenomena come inevitably to divide themselves into two great classes.   As it appears to adult experience, not only the unfolding, but even the very existence of self-consciousness seems to involve the distinction between the ego and the non-ego—between the "I" with its states, and the "Things" which it knows with their manifold properties or attributes.   Each of these two classes of phenomena—the so-called subjective and the so-called objective—is inevitably attributed in consciousness to a different subject; the one to the "I" as its own states, the other to somewhat left undefined, except that it is not the "I," and is called "matter," "material substance," etc. (the unknown X which is not I).   It is only as involving all this mental process that any real being whatever, whether Mind or Thing, is known or believed to exist; but the mind in the development of experience inevitably completes the process, which involves the assumption that real beings do exist, and that all these real beings are either "things," such as I *know*, or myself and other conscious beings, such as I *am*.

§ 13. Peculiar and cogent reasons may be given, however, which further enforce and verify the assumption of a real existence for the Mind.   Repeated attention has been called to the fact that there is a class of so-called mental faculties, most important and distinctive, for the distinguishing characteristic of which no physical analogies or correspondences whatever can be discovered or imagined. This is true of memory as active reminiscence, of the unity of consciousness, of voluntary attention, and of the relating activity.   The existence of these modes of mental behavior requires the assumption of a characteristic real being, other than the molecules of the brain, to which they may be referred. Some of these modes of behavior are conspicuously unintelligible and meaningless without granting such an assumption. For example, an act of recollection involves the presence in consciousness of a state the very essence of which is that it claims to represent (or stand for) an absent past state of consciousness. No way of verifying this claim in any particular instance, which does not involve its acceptance in general, can possibly be devised. For *all* argument is valid, only if we accept the validity of *some* memory. But every present act of memory on my part is a process in *my* consciousness, and that which it claims to represent was also a process in *my* consciousness. To recollect the past state of another consciousness than my own involves an absurdity; to recollect a past state otherwise than as represented in a present state of my own consciousness also involves an absurdity. Of course, such reflection upon the nature of the act of memory affords no demonstration of the claim that the subject of the present state is one and the same real being with the subject of the past state. On the contrary, all demonstration itself rests on this assumption; for without accepting it as valid we could not reach the conclusion of any demonstration. The premises of every syllogism are connected with one another and with their conclusion in a living unity of thought, only on the assumption that one real being is the subject of each of the thoughts which constitute the syllogism. To "*be really*," and to be the one subject of changing states, are, therefore, but different ways of expressing the same truth. In this meaning of the words: the soul exists in reality, above all other kinds of being; because it alone, so far as we know on good evidence, knows itself as the subject of its own states; or, indeed, knows the states of which it is the subject as states belonging to itself.

§ 14. A similar train of argument leads us at once and irresistibly to an affirmation of the at least "phenomenal" unity of the developed human mind. In every act of self-consciousness its unity is achieved, as it were, by the very form of its own activity. Every act of memory is a further affirmation of the fact of some sort of unity between the *Ego* of the present and the *Ego* of the past. Memory, of the "recognitive" type, *recognizes* the oneness of the Subject of all the conscious states. All human business and social intercourse, all attribution of conduct and the moral ideas and sentiments of responsibility, all assignment and distribution of property rights, depend upon the significance and the value of the mind's unity. Even the much overworked and misunderstood phenomena of "double consciousness" confirm rather than confute the same view. Where the phenomena are not proofs of the unsuspected versatility, wealth of ideas and resources, and unexplored capacities, of the one mind, they are proofs of a mind disordered, disorganized, or even degenerate. The very conception of *the* mind at all is dependent upon this self-unifying *actus* of man's conscious mental life. In a word, *the experience upon which the conception of oneness is applied to the human mind is that of our actual unification, accomplished and recognized by the activity of the very subject, whose otherwise disparate states of existence, and phases of development, are, in fact, united.* A unifying of energies, that takes place more and more perfectly as the development of mind proceeds toward maturity and a certain characteristic type of the development of each individual mind—all this affords the indisputable basis for affirming the reality of the mind's unity.

§ 15. Of course, most of the terms applied to the unity of consciousness, when carefully examined, turn out to be figurative, and to have no meaning except as interpreted over from entities and relations of a material sort into terms of consciousness. By the "unity of consciousness" it cannot be meant that consciousness is some kind of an entity which remains one and unchangeable throughout, like those atoms which physical science formerly supposed to constitute the whole world of material reality. It will be found, however, that no conception can be formed of the unity which is supposed to belong to the atom without involving in it the unity of consciousness. We can, indeed, picture to ourselves a very little bit of extended matter, barely visible under the highest powers of the microscope, which never changes its shape or color, etc., and which always behaves itself in exactly the same way under precisely similar circumstances. But this mental picture would itself have any unity belonging to it only as it existed in the unity of consciousness. It is this unifying mental process which makes each "Thing" to be *one* thing; it is this unification which imparts to all else that is one whatever unity it may have.

When, then, we speak of the unity of consciousness we mean, first of all and chiefly, to call attention to the following primary fact of experience: All states of consciousness involve a reference of the state to an "I," as the subject of the state; and, in spite of the constant change of states which goes on, so that in reality the same state never recurs, and even the same thing is never twice known, all the states are somehow understood to be states of one and the same subject. This reference and this understanding enter into all our experience; they give conditions to experience and make it possible. Whatever changes experience may be conceived of as undergoing, they, as conditions of all possible experience, must be conceived of as remaining. To ask us to try to imagine a mental state or act not involving this reference and this understanding, with respect to the unit-subject of consciousness, is to ask us to try to be conscious and unconscious at the same time. The "I" may become unconscious; that is, the phenomena of consciousness in that connected development which characterizes the individual may cease to exist. But phenomena of self-consciousness cannot be conceived of without implying the actual and accomplished unifying of the self-conscious Subject—the *Ego*, the Mind.

§ 16. This kind of reality, and this kind of unity (call it "phenomenal," if you will), for the mind and for all things, is all that science can recognize, and all that it can prove. But this is a kind of reality, and a kind of unity, which science cannot refuse to recognize; or of which it cannot fairly deny the sufficient proof. Metaphysics, presuming upon its intimate relations to the "old psychology," has doubtless often made an unwarrantable use of the facts above mentioned. It has often declared that we have an immediate and indubitable knowledge of the mind as one and the same real being in all acts of consciousness. The facts have been interpreted as though the case stood as follows: I have the power to look within myself, and by thus looking I can discern what I really am. I immediately know (that is, know by the introspective act of self-consciousness) that "*I*" am always, however my states may change, one and the same real being. I am a real, self-identical entity; and if asked how I know that I am all this, my appeal is to the indubitable evidence of the act of self-consciousness.

The foregoing metaphysical statement of the case is by no means obviously correct; we believe it, on the contrary, to be exaggerated and incorrect. In thus overstating the case, there is liability that the case itself will be lost. *Consciousness carries with it no immediate knowledge of any real and self-identical being*—not even of that real being which we call Mind and, with good reason, assume to exist as the ground or permanent subject of mental phenomena. Metaphysics is the science which treats of those assumptions that underlie all of our experience with what we call "reality." But it treats of *assumptions* or beliefs such as we find do actually and inevitably enter into all our experience. The real existence of "Things," whether of the masses of matter we daily test by the senses, or of those hypothetical beings called atoms which physical science requires in order to account for the phenomena, depends upon such assumptions. If it be admitted that we cannot be immediately conscious of ourselves as real unit-beings, we are no worse off than we are with respect to our belief in the existence of any of the so-

called real beings of which all men suppose the world to be composed.

It can also be shown that the case of the mind or soul, with respect to its unity as a real being, is made no better by admitting
that an immediate consciousness of ourselves as such unit-beings is
possible. For let it be supposed that by concentrating all my attention upon the present state of consciousness I most clearly and
indisputably discern myself as one real being, forming the ground
of that state. Let it be supposed that every half-hour in the day I
repeat this mental act. It would still have to be *assumed*, as somewhat altogether out of consciousness, that the real being discerned
in any one of these acts of introspection is one and the same real
being as that discerned in all the rest. A real unit-being that
should last only while the difficult act of concentrated introspection was taking place would be of no value to serve as a self-conscious *mind*. In fact, such a unit-subject of the individual state
would have no claim to be considered as a real being at all.

§ 17. The question whether the mind is to be spoken of as non-
material or "spiritual" scarcely merits at the hands of psychological
science the grave and lengthy discussion to which it has often been
carried. Materiality, as predicated of any real being, is only a complex term including a number of so-called attributes, which are all
the subjects of experience only as belonging to individual things.
All real things are to be called material which have these attributes,
so called. Primarily, as has been frequently shown already, the
attributes are simply modes of the affection of the mind which we
have learned to localize and objectify as belonging to extra-mental
reality. But if we raise the question whether the Mind, too, is
known to itself as having those attributes which make up our complex, general notion of "materiality," no one would find it easy to
think of giving this question an affirmative answer. The mind attributes to "things" the qualities of extension, impenetrability, and
all the various subordinate modifications of these qualities. It perceives these things as colored, cold, hot, rough, smooth, etc. But
it does not attribute such qualities to itself; it can find nothing in
the modes in which it manifests itself to itself which would warrant
the application of similar terms to these modes of its own behavior.

Indeed, all the terms which do apply to the recognized qualities
of mind have to be understood as figurative when, having been
borrowed from physical relations, they are made to apply to psychical states. Even in those cases where the analogy seems almost
to amount to an identity, closer inspection shows that this seeming does not correspond to the actual fact. For example, we do
attribute *quantity* to sensations and feelings. But when the suffer-

ing from pressure becomes more intense, we do not regard the mind as actually passing, like some material thing, under a heavier load (*sub-fero*), against which it must either bear up or break, through the physical strain. Just so, movements of the mind are not to be defined as changes of its position with relation to other things in space. We are, then, surely warranted in affirming that, so far as the mind has any immediate information as to what qualities should be assigned to itself and what to "things"—which it always looks upon as not-itself—it is *compelled* to regard itself as *non*-material.

As has already been pointed out, there is no way of telling what is the real nature of any existence except by enumerating its qualities, or those modes of behavior which we attribute to it on account of its affecting our consciousness in certain definite ways. To attempt to regard the mind as material, when it manifests itself to itself as non-material, compels us either to use the word "material" in an unwonted and unauthorized way, or else to attribute to matter in general certain occult powers which it never manifests itself to the mind as possessing, and which make it really to be quite different from what its manifestation of itself would indicate.

The only way of maintaining the materiality of mind would then appear to be that of denying its real existence at all, and of attributing its phenomena to the material molecules of the brain as their real and material substratum or basis. But the untenable nature of this view has already been sufficiently indicated. Or perhaps a strong temptation may be again felt, at this point, to recur to the hypothesis of a third somewhat, a "two-faced unity," which is the ground of the phenomena of both body and mind. But such hypothesis can throw no light whatever on the inquiry whether the mind is material or non-material. The phenomena we call "mental," and attribute to the subject of consciousness, would remain just as radically unlike those which we call "physical," and attribute to matter, after making the hypothesis as before. And to the hypothesis itself the same objections would remain opposed.

The negative conclusion that mind is *non*-material is quite inevitable for every one who admits that mind is a real being with any nature whatever.

§ 18. It is not difficult, also, to show that we must make the corresponding positive statement, and affirm the *spirituality* of mind. This we can do with confidence, however, only so long as we mean by the term "spirituality" simply to sum up and express in one word the list of attributes which describe the known activities of mind. To perceive, feel, think, will—in brief, to be conscious in some one of the various forms of conscious life—this is to be positively spiritual, in the only sense in which science is entitled to affirm spirituality of mind as such.   As soon as we conceive of spirituality as some ethereal extension of thinking substance, we enter upon the vain effort to conceive of mind under terms of matter, and at the same time escape the consequences of so conceiving of it.   Nor can we hope to vindicate for the mind such spirituality as would be implied in its being freed from all relations to material things, or from dependence for the modes of its being upon the material substratum of the brain.   How spirit, in the sense of disembodied or unembodied mind, would perceive, and feel, and think, and will, is a question toward the answer to which we can make no beginning.   But to control the mental train as distinguished from being a passive member of a psycho-physical mechanism, to reason so as to deduce conclusions and make inductions to general laws, to recognize the call of duty, and to call up and classify in the consciousness the lofty and complex ideas of art and religion—these and other similar operations of the mind pre-eminently emphasize its spirituality.

§ 19. In somewhat the same way must it be admitted that the question of the *unity* of mind has given rise to much fruitless and by no means altogether pertinent debate.   The attempt to conceive of the mind as a unit-being, constituted after the analogy of those physical structures which we are accustomed to regard as unities, inevitably leads to confusion and error.   The important psychological fact is, that there is no one of these physical unities which does not derive its unity from the unifying *actus* of the mind.   This statement is true of each such so-called unity, whether it is perceived as one or is conceived of as one.   The unity which belongs to the percept finds its source in the synthetic activity of the perceiving mind; the unity of the conception, in the unifying activity of the mind's relating faculty.   It is sometimes supposed, however, that an atom which should have no parts, be perfectly homogeneous throughout, and so incapable of changes of its interior states, would be the highest possible type of a unity of real being.   Nothing could ever happen to disturb or destroy such a unity.   The temptation has therefore arisen to conceive of the mind after the analogy of a thinking atom.

§ 20. Now, it must be admitted that such a thinking atom would be in far less danger of suffering from the death of the physical basis of its thought than is the thinking man.   But two considerations of great importance are likely to be overlooked in the mere making of the hypothesis of such an atom.   Surely such an atom could hardly have any experience corresponding to what we call the unity of our consciousness; and if it had any unity of consciousness whatever, such unity could no more be explained as arising out of, or conditioned upon, the simplicity of the physical being of the atom than the unity of our consciousness can be explained as arising out of, or conditioned upon, the complexity of our physical being.

It is impossible to see how a unity of consciousness at all resembling what we understand by the term could find an adequate material substratum in a single rigid atom. In other words, if a spiritual being having a unity of consciousness were brought into special psycho-physical relations with a material being incapable of any interior changes, because possessed of no parts to undergo change, these relations would have to be totally different from any which we can conceive of as holding between the body and mind of man. For the very nature of the mind's unity is dependent upon that variety of experiences which is occasioned in the mind through the changing states of the brain. The physical basis of the human mind is undoubtedly an extremely complex system of interacting molecules. Certain relations can be traced between the character of these physical interactions and the character of the states arising in the mind. These states depend for their character, and even for their very existence, upon the occurrence of the corresponding material changes. A brain that is not in a ceaseless change of activities of the peculiar sort called "neural" is a dead brain, so far as its influence on the mind is concerned; such a brain could not serve as the substratum or physical cause of mental phenomena.

Moreover, comparative anatomy shows us that the greater the number of molecules, and the larger the variety and the size of the organs specially related to the mental processes, the richer in variety and nobler in quality the mental processes themselves become. So far as we can ascertain, the highest unity of consciousness belongs in connection with the greatest complexity of the material substratum. The animals which have the largest cerebral development appear to have, too, not only the most manifold and extensive mental life, but also, in the highest degree, the capacity for attributing the phenomena of that life to one subject. Those psychical activities which are connected with the physical interaction of the greatest number of material elements are the most numerous and significant; and they are, also, actually most perfectly harmonized into a higher unity of spiritual self-conscious being.

No information derived from the study of Physiological Psychology warrants us in affirming that a highly developed self-conscious existence must, from the universal necessities of the case, be united with a vastly complex material structure like the human brain. Such study does, however, compel us to affirm that *such* a unity in variety as is the human mind cannot be conceived of in dependence upon the movements in space of a single perfectly rigid and unchanging atom. The development of human experience is conditioned upon the arising in consciousness of many sensations of varied quantities, qualities, and orders in time; upon the synthesis of these sensations into presentations of sense; and upon the recall of the presentations in the form of representative ideas. What experience would be, if its basis were not laid in such rise and combination and recurrence of sensations, we cannot even conjecture. In the highest flights of imagination, in the profoundest explorations of reflection, we never wholly escape from the influences arising in this basis. The nature of this psychical basis of sensation and perception depends upon the nature of the physical basis of the living and acting brain. In other words, what sensations and perceptions constitute, at least in part, the "stuff" of all consciousness, depends upon what the molecules of the central nervous system are doing. We cannot even conceive of any other relations as possible between the mind, on the one hand, and the brain, on the other, than relations between a system of moving molecules and a corresponding change of conscious states.

Furthermore, the unity of a single indestructible and eternally unchanging atom would afford no explanation of a mental unity. In the case of man's mind and brain, the variety of the nervous changes in part explains the variety of the mental states; but nothing in the changing relations of the innumerable moving molecules throws any clear light on the origin of the unity of mind in consciousness. A material being absolutely without distinction of parts would be, for that fact, no better fitted to become conscious of itself as one. A series of states of consciousness can indeed be attributed by our imagination to such a being. From the purely psychological point of view we can conceive of the unit-atom as having an experience resembling our own. We, in our consciousness, can imagine such a being as the subject of states, and as attributing each of these states to one and the same subject—namely the "I" of the unit-atom—after the fashion of our customary mental behavior. But this is quite a different thing from explaining the consciousness of such an atom as arising, with respect to its unity, out of the material nature of the atom. By the very hypothesis, the material nature of this particular kind of atom can have no states; it never changes; it is always the same. But consciousness is always some particular definite state; and self-consciousness is always the being aware of some particular definite state. There is no consciousness in general; there is no consciousness which does not involve change of state. Indeed, change is a reality in human consciousness, if nowhere else in the universe of being. No particular state of consciousness, whether considered as involving an attribution of that state to a subject or not, could be explained by reference to the material nature or condition of such a unit-atom.

§ 21. The foregoing remarks have their value chiefly as a warning against supposing that the unity of the soul suffers any prejudice because it is not to be regarded or explained from a point of view furnished by physical analogies. To be one, as a rigid material atom may possibly be regarded as one, would be of no advantage to the soul. Or if it be admitted that, in case it had such unity, it could never cease to exist, it must also be admitted that we are unable to see how it could ever begin to exist as a self-conscious mind. If the unit-atom could never die, it could also never live—as a conscious psychical existence. And it is the unity which the mind plainly has in self-consciousness that is alone worth contending for. If the mind were really—that is, regarded as *out of* its own consciousness—one, and yet two or more *in* consciousness, it would be no better, but rather the worse off. If it were really one, but were obliged not to know itself as one, and could never be aware of its own states, or attribute them to the one "I" which is the subject of them all, it would surely be the worse off. To be one, in the only meaning of the word that is of real value, is to have and to keep the unity of consciousness. If this unity were really a mere seeming—a trick of nature to cheat the mind—the seeming would forever seem real, would, indeed, be the ground of all reality; the trick would be the kindest of all illusions, and one from which we should crave never to be set free. When, then, we have recognized the fact that all ordering and development of human consciousness implies this kind of unit-being as belonging to the mind, we have gone as far in vindication of the mind's rights as we have any psychological interest in going.

§ 22. It would seem, finally, as though our excursion thus far into the debatable field of metaphysical discussion, might commend itself to any unprejudiced and critical student of those phenomena, which we have called "correlations," existing as matter-of-fact experiences, between the human nervous mechanism and the human mental life. The conclusions warranted, in our judgment, by the phenomena, are by no means a final settlement of the metaphysical problems involved. As to the "ground" of these correlations, and as to how it is related to that Being of the World, which science is accustomed to speak of as Nature, and which the different schools of philosophy have conceived of in various ways, as to the first and last things of mind, psychology as studied from the physiological and experimental points of view finds itself unable to pronounce. It cannot, indeed, explain the entire being of the mind as arising out of the development of the physical germ from which the bodily

members unfold themselves. It knows no decisive reason against
the belief that such a non-material and real unit-being, as the mind
is, should exist in other relations than those which it sustains at
present to the structure of the brain. On the contrary, it discloses
certain phenomena which at least suggest, and perhaps confirm,
the possibility of such existence for the Mind. But, in general,
if it remain faithful to its own mission, within its own limits, it en-
trusts the full consideration of these questions, after it has cleared
the way from barriers of ignorance and prejudice, to Rational
Psychology, to Ethics, to Metaphysics, and to Theology.

INDEX

INDEX OF AUTHORS

ACH, 482, 484, 486 ff., 496
Alcmæon, 213
Aliotta, 379, 498
Allen, 505
d'Allonnes, 526
Alrutz, 344
Alsberg, 366
Angell, F., 569
Angell, J. R., 396, 486, 569
Angier, 409
Apáthy, 103, 106, 113
Aristotle, 214
d'Arsonval, 131
Atwater, 291
Aubert, 325, 331, 365, 370
Auerbach, 476, 491 ff.

BAILLARGER, 269
Bain, 505, 515
Bair, 568 f., 580
Baird, 335
Baldwin, 486, 501
Bang, 120
Barker, 100
von Bayer, 137
Bayliss, 151
Beaunis, 478
von Bechterew, 59, 88
Beer, 188
Beevor, 236
Bentley, 601
Benussi, 442, 451
Berger, G. O., 479
Berger, H., 509
Bergström, 580
Bernhardt, 118
Bernstein, 403
Bethe, 18 f., 21, 103, 106, 113, 288, 290
Beyerman, 262
Bidder, 475
Biedermann, 131, 133, 137, 363
Bielschowsky, 106, 265
Billings, 508
Binet, 401, 535, 577
Bingham, 530
Birge, 75
Blix, 344
Boll, 116,195
Bolton, 262
Bonnet, 597
Book, 556, 558 f., 561 f., 564, 569, 577

Boruttau, 140, 142
Bouguer, 369
Bouillaud, 255
Bourdon, 427, 429
Bourgery, 66
Bowditch, 136, 171 f., 453
Breese, 599
Breitwieser, 480, 486
Breuer, 210 f.
Broca, 227, 253 ff.
Brodhun, 370
Brodie, 136
Brodmann, 266, 270, 272
Brown, C., 210
Brown, E. M., 565
Brücke, 392
Brückner, 400
Bruner, 315, 368
Bryan, 556 ff., 561 f.
Buccola, 478
Budge, 227
Bühler, 601
Burch, 131
Burnham, 574
Byasson, 215

CAJAL, 41, 43 f., 47, 98, 102, 106, 109, 112, 116, 193, 265 ff.
Calkins, 573, 583, 592
Camerer, 372
Cameron, 318
Campbell, 240, 245, 261, 270 ff.
Cannon, 525
Caton, 230
Cattell, 132, 359, 371, 376, 478 f., 484, 489, 494, 496, 498, 537, 591, 597
Charpentier, 524
Chevreul, 310
Chodin, 432
Ciaccio, 183
Cline, 459 f.
Cole, 547
Conty, 524
Cook, 440
Coover, 569
Corti, 203 ff.
Cowling, 595
Cox, 643
Cramer, 124
von Cyon, 209, 524
Czermak, 402, 406

DANILEWSKI, 118, 230
Davies, 349
Davis, 565
Dax, 255
Dearborn, 461, 568
Debrou, 177
Deiters, 83, 95, 97
Dejerine, 84, 539
Delabarre, 409, 459
Delboeuf, 370, 378, 437
Descartes, 634
Despretz, 315
Dewey, 147, 603, 610
Diaconow, 123
Dobrowolsky, 329
Dodge, 457, 459 f.
Dogiel, 180
Dolley, 132, 478
Donaldson, 58, 60, 62, 102, 344, 404
Donders, 331, 432, 467, 470, 472, 476
Dubois, 35
Du Bois-Reymond, 130 f., 141 f.
Durig, 136
Duval, 289

Ebbinghaus, 378, 438 f., 502, 510, 572 ff., 579, 588, 604
Ebert, 566, 568, 574, 578, 582
Ecker, 27, 176
Eckhard, 116, 176, 227
Edelmann, 315
Edes, 136
Edinger, 26, 29, 31, 32, 59, 62, 63, 85, 108, 221 f.
Ehrenfels, 601
Einthoven, 131
Engelmann, 149, 178 f.
Ephrussi, 574, 578
Erb, 73
Eternod, 39
Eulenberg, 365
Ewald, 119, 150, 153, 207 ff.
Ewing, 105, 539
Exner, 167, 170, 214, 472 ff., 478 f., 483 f., 524

Fechner, 9, 356, 358, 360 ff., 366, 370 f., 373, 375, 377 f., 504, 565
Féré, 509, 533
Ferrier, 158, 228, 235 ff., 246, 251
Fick, 325, 327, 329 ff., 339, 342, 474
Filehne, 449
Fite, 396
Flateau, 539
Flechsig, 59, 224, ff., 248, 250 f.
Flourens, 208, 227 ff.
Flournoy, 486
Fowler, 305
Fracker, 567
Fränkel, 118, 121, 124
Franz, 263, 349
Fraser, 446 f.
Fraunhofer, 329
Freud, 585 f.
von Frey, 181, 344, 365, 400, 402
Fritsch, 228 f., 235, 255
Froeberg, 479 f.
Fullerton, 359, 371, 376
Funke, 399, 402, 517

Galen, 215
Gall, 227, 232
Galton, 315, 583
Gamble, 592
Gamgee, 123
Garten, 136
Gaskell, 149
Gaupp, 27
Gegenbaur, 184, 197, 203, 223
Gennari, 269, 271
Gerlach, 112
Gieke, 116
Gies, 121, 124
Gley, 508
Goethe, 521
Goldscheider, 344 ff., 349, 364, 366 f., 398 ff., 406, 477, 539
Golgi, 97, 103, 116
Goltz, 150, 152 f., 155
Gotch, 131, 133
Göthlin, 143
Griesbach, 401
Grünbaum, A. A., 601
Grünbaum, A. F., 228, 236 ff., 272

Haggerty, 547
Haines, 403
Hall, 404 f., 408, 453
Haller, 228
Halliburton, 118, 124, 136
Hamilton, F. M., 595
Hamilton, G. Van T., 554
Hamilton, W., 515, 597
Hammersten, 124
Hankel, 476
Hardesty, 75, 207
Harter, 556 ff., 561 f.
Haycraft, 308
Head, 148, 348 f., 401
Heidenhain, 524
Held, 59
Helmholtz, 132, 188 f., 194, 197, 199, 206 ff., 312 ff., 319, 322, 326, 328, 332, 339, 341, 370, 421, 423, 428 f., 434, 456, 462, 467, 540, 598
Henderson, 582
Henle, 71, 75, 114, 194, 197 f., 201 f.
Henmon, 360, 490
Henschen, 248 f.
Hensen, 205, 312 f., 317
Herbart, 511 f.
Hering, E., 285, 339, 341 ff., 346, 352, 363, 416, 421, 426, 432, 434, 445 f., 452
Hering, H. E., 148, 241
Hermann,, 140 ff.
Herophilus, 215
Herschel, 331, 369
Hillebrand, 427
Hippocrates, 214
Hirsch, 472, 476
His, 36, 40, 52 ff., 97 f., 112, 116
Hitzig, 228 f., 235, 255
Höber, 312
Hodge, 539
Hoffmann, 410
Hollingworth, 409
Holm, 347
Holmes, 240
Hooke, 326

Horsley, 236
Horwicz, 511, 513
Hough, 537
Howell, 129
Huey, 459, 461
Humboldt, 305

INGBERT, 75

JACOBS, 574
James, 211, 403, 525, 566, 569, 618
Janet, 535
Janssens, 240
Jastrow, 446, 448, 467, 480, 488
Jennings, 217, 544 f.
Jost, 573, 581
Joteyko, 538
Judd, 400, 402, 442, 445, 451, 459, 480, 569, 595
Jung, 509

KAES, 62
Kafka, 475
Kammler, 365
Kämpfe, 367
Kant, 524, 662, 672
Kastle, 312
Kennedy, 574
Keppler, 372 f.
Kiesow, 132, 312, 344, 346, 365, 477 f.
Kinnaman, 547, 549, 555
Kirkpatrick, 544, 574, 581
Klug, 406 f.
Koch, 119, 122
Kölliker, 102, 110, 116, 204, 265, 326
König, 370
Kopsch, 81
Kraepelin, 538
Kreidl, 208
von Kries, 196, 302, 331, 340, 476, 491 ff.
Krueger, 323
Kühne, 119, 195, 212
Külpe, 592, 601
Kundt, 438
Kunkel, 475
Kussmaul, 257

LADD, 243, 339 f., 410, 464, 466, 523, 525, 527, 531, 542, 579, 584, 597
Lange, C., 525
Lange, L., 484, 486
Lange, N., 600
Langelaan, 262
Langley, J. N., 150
Langley, S. P., 371
Leaming, 101, 266
Le Conte, 434
Lee, 538
Lehmann, 508, 510, 600
von Lenhossék, 98, 115
Leuba, 560, 569, 581
Lewis, B., 269
Lewis, E. O. 451
Liebreich, 123
Liepmann, 254, 259 f., 263
Lindemann, 366
Lindley, 534
Linnæus, 307
Lipps, 449
Listing, 421

Loeb, 409
Lombard, 171, 215, 532
Longet, 227
Lotze, 302, 317, 384, 398, 412, 432, 436, 456, 511
Löwit, 363
Luciani, 156

MACDONALD, 142
Mach, 210, 312, 475
Magendie, 227
Mandelstamm, 329
Marburg, 46, 83 f.
Margo, 212
Marie, 258 ff.
Marshall, 510
Martin, 602
Matteuci, 227
Mauss, 270
May, 240
McAllister, 460 f., 480
McDougall, 338, 475, 598, 611, 618 ff.
McMurrich, 78, 220
Mendelejeff, 308
Merkel, 489
Messenger, 402
Metzner, 400, 402
Meumann, 566, 568 f., 571, 574, 578, 582
Meyer, A., 258, 260
Meyer, M., 207, 510
Meynert, 227, 510
Mihalcovics, 49
Mill, J. S., 384
Möbius, 548
Moldenhauer, 478
von Monakow, 159, 242 f., 245 f., 248 f., 258, 260 f.
Montague, 610
Moore, A. W., 486
Moore, J. M., 537
Moore, T. V., 481
Morgan, 548
Mosso, 536
Moutier, 258
Müller, G. E., 317, 358, 361, 379, 573, 578 f., 582, 584 ff., 591, 602
Müller, J., 132, 284
Müller, J. J., 330
Müller-Lyer, 439, 441
Munk, 242, 246, 252
Münsterberg, 486, 532, 580, 610
Myers, 395 f., 403, 574

NAGEL, 208, 305, 307, 310
Nahlowsky, 522
Nelson, 510
Newton, 331, 340, 662
Nissl, 102 f.
Nothnagel, 366

OETTINGEN, 312
Ogden, 578
Ohms, 582, 584
Oppel, 437
Osthoff, 517

PARKER, 17
Pearce, 439 f., 442
Peckham, 545

Pentschew, 578
Peters, 588
Peterson, 509
Pfaff, 305
Pflüger, 139, 216
Pick, 254
Pierce, 445 f.
Piéron, 544
Pillsbury, 349, 569, 596, 603, 606
Pilzecker, 573, 584, ff., 591
Piper, 473
Plato, 214
Plutarch, 213
Pohlmann, 574
Porter, 547
Posner, 121, 124
Preyer, 312, 315, 317, 474
Purkinje, 194
Pythagoreans, 320 f.

RADOSSAWLJEWITSCH, 572, 576
Ranvier, 180
Rauber, 81
Rayleigh, 368, 395
Reid, 515
Remak, 97
Retzius, 23, 77, 182, 203 ff.
Reuther, 574
Richards, 312
Ritter, 305
Rivers, 348
Robertson, 440
Rosenheim, 124
Rosenthal, 148
Rouget, 212
Royce, 501
Ruediger, 461
Ruger, 554 f., 569, 605

SANDER, 475
Sappey, 87
Schaefer, 396
Schäfer, 63, 98 f., 107, 249, 479
Schenck, 187, 537
Schiff, 215, 227, 517
Schrader, 152, 158
Schröder, 240
Schroeder van der Kolk, 643
Schultze, 176 f., 190 ff., 194
Schumann, 573, 578 f., 582, 601 f.
Schuster, 262
Schwalbe, 68, 71, 79, 80, 82
Scripture, 537, 565
Sergi, 525
Shepard, 508, 526
Sherren, 348, 401
Sherrington, 147, 152, 154, 156, 159, 162 ff.,
    166 ff., 170, 181 f., 228, 236 ff., 241, 272,
    287, 289, 344, 365, 477, 524 f., 552, 599, 612
Sidis, 510
Slaughter, 600
Small, 547
Smith, S., 545
Smith, T. L., 565
Smith, W. G., 442, 480, 577
Sobotta, 78, 220
Solomons, 402
Sowton, 136, 442
Spalding, 157

Spaulding, 546
Spearman, 401
von Spee, 38
Spitzka, 61
Spurzheim, 227
Starch, 393, 395, 509
Starling, 151
Starr, 72, 101, 224, 266
Steele, 480
Steffens, Laura, 602
Steffens, Lottie, 578
Stein, 535
Steinach, 477
Stern, 591
Storey, 539
Störring, 606
Stout, 543
Stratton, 365, 455, 459, 461
Streeter, 50
Stricker, 317
Strong, 36, 63, 101, 266
Strümpell, 88
Stumpf, 312, 315 ff., 321 f., 378, 416, 510
Swift, 561
Symington, 63

TANZI, 477
Tarchanoff, 509
Tawney, 402
Tebb, 124
Tesla, 131
Theophrastus, 213
Thiéry, 449
Thorndike, 33, 537, 546 ff., 569, 573
Thudicum, 120, 122 ff.
Thunberg, 181, 344, 347, 403, 479
Titchener, 350, 358, 378, 471, 480, 502, 510,
    601
von Tobel, 537
Trautscholdt, 494
Treves, 537 f.
Triplett, 533, 547 f.
Trotter, 349
Turnbull, 315
Tyndall, 328

URBANTSCHITSCH, 600
Urstein, 591

VALENTIN, 305, 373 f., 392, 474
Valsava, 200
Van Biervliet, 574
Van Deen, 227
Van Gehuchten, 76, 103 f.
Veraguth, 509
Veratti, 108
Verworn, 15, 290
Vierordt, 329, 398 f.
Vigual, 116
von Vintschgau, 392, 475, 477
Voeste, 337
Vogt, C., 236
Vogt, O., 236, 248, 250, 267, 270 f.
Volkmann, 369 ff., 401, 565
Volkmann von Volkmar, 413, 470, 511
Volta, 305

WAGNER, 97, 523
Waldeyer, 112

Waller, 137
Ward, 584, 594
Warnecke, 38
Warren, 171 f.
Washburn, 544
Watson, 59, 62, 547
Watt, 494 f.
Weber, E., 509
Weber, E. H., 304, 326, 346 f., 360, 363, 366, 371 f., 394, 396 ff., 404 f., 474
Weigert, 264
Wernicke, 257 ff.
Whipple, 601
Wien, 368 f., 371
Wilson, 395
Winch, 571
Wirth, 596

Witasek, 582
von Wittich, 474, 476, 479
Woodworth, 157, 350, 535, 537, 552, 569, 594
Wright, 533
Wundt, 10, 274, 290; 338, 376, 384, 397, 410, 415, 421 ff., 425, 427, 432, 448, 456, 462, 476, 478 f., 481 ff., 501 f., 506 f., 516, 526, 594, 601, 610

Yerkes, 547 f.
Yoakum, 541
Young, 341

Ziehen, 511
Zinn, 228
Zoth, 421, 429
Zwaardemaker, 307 f., 374

INDEX OF SUBJECTS

ABSOLUTE PITCH, 317
Abstraction, 595 ff.; in perception, 596; in recall, 600 f.
Accommodation of the eye, 188, 325, 414, 417, 423, 427; to pitch, 200
Achromatopsia, 253
Action theory of consciousness, 610 f.
Action time, 333, 474 f.
Acuity, 357; of hearing, 368 f.; of muscle sense, 364, 409; of smell, 373 f.; of taste, 372 f.; of temperature sense, 365 f., 406 f.; of touch, 365, 397, 408; of vision, 326, 371 f., 427 ff., 461
Adaptation, 545 f., 570; of the retina, 195 f., 333, 337, 371, 378, 540; of other sense organs, 308, 346 f., 378, 540; of central organs, 540
Adjustment, 482 ff., 489, 491, 494, 551, 555, 569, 582, 589 f., 602, 605 f., 621 f.; neural mechanism of, 624
Adolescence, 661
Æsthetics, 504
Affection, 500 ff.
After-brain, 48 ff.
After-discharge, 166
After-image, 460, 475, 587; negative, 337, 343; positive, 338
Ageusia, 311
Agraphia, 254 f., 261
Alexia, 252
Alliance of reflexes, 169, 172 f.
Ambiguous figures, 594, 620
Amnesia, 253, 260, 544
Amœba, behavior of, 14 f., 64, 544, 612
Amphibia, brain of, 27, 29 ff.; intelligence of, 547
Ampulla, 201, 203 f., 210
Amputation, 218
Amusia, 250, 253
Analgia, 517
Analysis, 186, 302, 307, 310, 312 f., 319, 326, 330, 341, 343 f., 350 ff., 353, 380, 440, 450 ff., 458, 500, 551 ff., 569, 605 ff.; dependent on association by similarity, 589; in perception, 596 ff.; neural mechanism of, 624 f.
Anastomosis of branches of nerve-cells, 18, 21, 112 ff.; of nerves, 243, 285 f.
Anesthesia, 244 f., 464, 517, 526
Anesthetics, 120, 287, 289 ff.
Angle illusion, 442 ff.
Annelids, nervous system of, 20 ff.
Anosmia, 306, 308
Anthropoid apes, brain of, 33 ff., 228 f., 236 ff.; intelligence of, 552 f.
Anvil, 197 ff.

Aphasia, 253, 255 ff., 544, 663; varieties of, 256 ff.
Apoplexy, 93
Apperception, 380, 452, 483 ff., 487, 497, 673
Apprehension, 376, 436, 442, 444, 488, 491, 597
Apraxia, 253 f., 263
Aqueduct, 49, 78, 83 f.
Aqueous humor, 183 f., 186 f.
Arachnoid, 70
Archipallial system, 95
Archipallium, 31 f., 86, 219, 223, 250
Area, judgments and illusions of, 447 f.
Area of the cortex, functional, 235 ff.; histological, 268 ff.; auditory, 249 f., 272; of Broca, 255, 257 ff.; gustatory, 251; intellectual, 251, 262; motor, 228, 232, 235 ff., 254, 267 ff., 272; olfactory, 250 f.; prefrontal, 270 ff.; sensory, 244 ff., 267 ff; silent, 229, 244, 251; somesthetic, 244 ff., 403 f.; of speech, 227, 233, 255 ff.; striate, 271 f.; visual, 246 ff., 271 f.; of Wernicke, 257 ff.
Association, 402, 427, 429 f., 454 f., 466 ff., 493 ff., 502; by contiguity, 584, 617 ff.; by similarity, 588 f.; convergent, 624; controlled, 495, 586, 589, 623 f.; dynamical, 562, 579, 584, 616, 660 f.; formation of, 542, 544, 546, 549, 551 f.; 554, 570, 575 f., 577 ff., 617 ff.; free, 495, 586; neural mechanism of, 617 ff.; operation of, 583 ff.; principal and subordinate, 578 f.; remote, 579, 581, 619; serial, 578 f., 581, 620 ff.; subliminal, 584, 612
Association fibres, 58, 96, 223 f., 233, 246, 251 f., 269
Association time, 493 ff., 573, 585
Astereognosis, 253
Astigmatism, 187
Asymbolia, 252 f.
Atom, concept of, 676; reality of, 680; unity of, 679; the unity of the mind not atomic, 683 ff.
Attention, 401, 407, 435, 440, 450, 458, 483, 532, 541, 550, 556, 561 ff., 571 f., 582 f., 587, 596 ff.; centre for, 262, 274; cerebral conditions of, 609 ff., 618 ff.; definition of, 596 f.; determination of, 600; expectant, see Expectancy; feelings of, 214, 507; field of, 597, 609; fluctuation of, 599 f.; motor adjustments in, 249 ff., 507 f., 531; shifting of, 598 f., 611, 618, 620 ff., span of, 560, 597
Attraction, 442 f.
Auditory area, 249 f.

Auditory perception of space, 392 ff.
Auditory sensations, 312 ff., 367 ff., 475, 529 f., 659
Automatism, 64 f., 147 ff., 158, 485, 496, 533 ff., 559, 564, 610
Autonomic system of nerves, 150
Average error, 358 f.
Axis cylinder process, see Axon.
Axon, 74, 97, 100 ff.; central, 44; classes of, 44; conduction in, 111; function of, 109 f.; growth of, 41 ff., 98; motor, 42, 212; sensory, 42, 48, 177 ff.; sheaths of, 99, 142; structure of, 100 f.; types of, 104 f., 265; see Nerve-Fibre.

BAHNUNG, 170
"Baskets," 108 ff.
Beats, 322 f.
Beauty, 529 ff.
Behavior, of Amœba, 14 f.; of earthworm, 22; of jelly-fish, 17 ff.; of sponge, 17
Binocular vision, 414 f., 427 ff., 436, 458, 465; contrast, 452; rivalry, 452 f., 598 f.; mixture, 452
Birds, brain of, 29 ff.; intelligence of, 547
Blind, tactile sensitivity of the, 402 f., 411
Blind spot, 193 f.
Blocking of nerve impulses, 287, 289 f.
Bodily resonance of emotion, 525
Body, relations of, to mind, 629 ff.
Bone-conduction to the ear, 197, 393 f.
Brain, 66, 75; action of, on mind, 643 f.; chemistry of, 117 ff., 291; circulation in, 68, 70, 125, 215, 291, 643, 663; development of, 48 ff.; functions of, 213 ff.; of invertebrates, 24 ff.; of man, 33 ff.; as organ of mind, 636 ff.; as seat of mind, 213 ff., 632 ff.; a tube, 39, 48 f.; of vertebrates, 25 ff.; weight of, see Brain-weight
Brain-stem, 27 f., 77 ff., 155, 241; development of, 55 ff.
Brain vesicles, 48
Brain-weight, of idiots, 656; of mammals, 33 f.; of primates, 34 f.; of races of man, 35; as related to age, 59 ff., 660 f.; to intelligence, 33, 60 f., 216 f.; to sex, 60; to stature, 33, 60
Bridgman, Laura, brain of, 58
Brightness, 327, 329, 331, 333, 354 f., 370 f.
Bulb or medulla, 48, 66, 69, 75 ff.; development of, 56 f.; function of, 157 f.

CALCARINE region, 223, 248 f., 252, 268 f., 271
Callosum, 33, 54, 77 f.; 85 f., 222 ff., 254, 263
Calm, 501 f., 506, 508, 531
Carbon dioxide in nervous activity, 135, 137, 291; in respiration, 148; in fatigue, 538
Catabolism in nerve, 135 ff.; in brain, 215, 290 f.
Causal relations between brain and mind, 641 ff.
Cause, concept of, 647, 650
Cell, definition, 13 f.; chemistry of, 119 f.; gustatory, 178 f.; nerve, see Nerve-Cell, olfactory, 176 f.
Cell-body, 286 ff.
Cell membrane, 14, 119 f.

Central canal of the cord, 39, 45, 72
Central factors in illusions, 444, 447, 449 ff.; in reaction time, 481 f.
Centralization in the nervous system, 20 ff.
Cerebellar system, 95
Cerebellum, 66, 75 ff., 86 f., 108 ff., 221 f.; development of, 49, 54; function of, 156 f. 211 f.
Cerebral ganglion of invertebrates, 24 ff.
Cerebrin, 121
Cerebro-spinal fluid, 49
Cerebrum, 66, 76 ff., 156, 219 ff.; development of, 49 ff.; in different animals, 26, 31 ff.; influence of, on reflexes, 158 f., 171 f., 241, 505, 532 ff.; injury of, 215, 217 ff., 252 ff., 262, 274, 644, f., 663; localization of functions of, 213 ff., 235 ff.; as related to consciousness, 213 ff., 298, 609 ff., 618, 633 ff.; removal of, 158 f., 217; as seat of mental functions, 219, 281 ff.; see Brain
Character, 262
Chemical changes in retina, 195, 325
Chemical elements in brain, 118, 279
Chemical integration of the body, 151
Chemical senses, 28, 375, 479
Chemistry of nervous tissue, 117 ff., 279 f.
Chinese music, 320
Choice-time, 484, 488, 497
Cholesterin, 120 f.
Chorda tympani, 179
Choroid, 183 f., 194
Chromatolysis, 105, 240
Chromosome, 37
Ciliary muscle, 183, 188 f., 427
Circulation, in brain, 68, 70, 125, 215, 291, 526, 643 f., 663; during emotion, 505 ff., 523 ff.; as a means of co-ordination, 151; in nerves, 137
Clang, 313 f., 318 f., 369, 395
Classification of mental functions, 664, 666; of odors, 307; of sensations, 300 ff.; of sounds, 312 f.; of tastes, 310
Clearness, 597
"Climbing fibres," 109 f.
Cochlea, 200 ff., 280
Cochlear nerve, 82, 90, 203
Coelenterate, nervous system in, 17 ff.
Coenæsthesia, 350, 518 f.
Cold spots, 181, 344 ff., 366, 405
Collaterals, 42, 73, 88, 111, 265, 268
Collectors, 162, 240, 622 f.
Color blindness, 335 f., 343
Color mixture, 330 ff., 340, 343, 452
Color-tone, 327, 333, 337
Color triangle, 344
Color vision, 196, 324, 327 ff., 352, 475, 490; theories of, 340 ff.
Columns of the cord, 40, 46 ff., 71, 73 ff., 79 ff., 89 f.; of Clarke, 74, 90; of Goll, 75
Commissures, 40, 43 f., 71 f., 89
Comparison, 376, 440, 488, 601 ff.; mediate and immediate, 601; process of, 602 f.
Compensatory movements, 155, 209 ff.
Competition, between stimuli, 173; dynamogenic effect of, 533
Complementary colors, 332, 334, 339, 342 f.
"Complexes," 509, 586
Concatenation, 64, 280 f.

Concept, 466

Conduction, alterations of, 133, 139; in axon, 111, 133 ff., 279 f.; in gray matter, 111, 286 ff.; irreciprocal, 111, 290; in nerves, 127 ff.; in nerve-net, 19 f.; as primary function of nervous tissue, 16, 33, 143, 279 f.; rapid, due to long nerve-fibres, 20 f.; reversible, 133 ff.; at synapse, 111, 286 f., 290; velocity of, in nerves, 131 ff., 473; in other tissues, 132

Conductivity, 15 f., 127, 133

Conductor, 16, 65, 127 ff.; artificial, 139 ff.; indifferent, 284 f.

Cones of the retina, 190 ff., 325 f., 352

Confluxion, 441, 444, 447, 451

Conjunctiva, 180 f., 184

Consciousness, 651, 666, 685; centre of, 483, 564, 597; cerebral conditions of, 609 ff., 618, 635; double, 679; elements of, 500 f., 511; field of, 431, 483, 597, 618; intensity of, 597, 609 f., 650; limits of, 430 f.; relation of, to learning and habit, 496, 563 f.; to bodily movements, 145 f.; seat of, 213 ff., 633 ff.; theories of, 610 f.; unity of, 679, 684 ff.

Conservation of energy, 646 ff.; inapplicable to relations of mind and body, 650 f., 665; within the nervous system, 648 ff.

Consonance, 321 ff., 529

Constant errors, 409, 437 ff.

Contours, prevalence and rivalry of, 452

Contrast, in perception of space, 439, 441, 443, 447, 451; in taste, 311; in temperature, 347; in vision, 339 f., 343, 435, 452

Convergence, of the eyes, 189, 427; of nervous impulses, 93, 161 f., 171, 403, 622 ff.

Convolution, see Gyre

Co-ordination, as function of nerve-centres, 63 ff., 93, 281 ff., 285 f.; in movements initiated from cortex, 241, 254, 261 f., 562, 565, 622 ff.; in reflexes, 153, 155, 157 f., 169, 172, 241, 622; in sponge, 17; in worm, 24

Core conductor, 139 f., 284

Core model, 139 f.

Cornea, 181 ff., 186 ff., 346

Corpuscle, Pacinian, 180 ff.; tactile, 180

Correlation between the neural and the mental, 3, 6, 9 f., 124 ff., 213 ff., 281, 292 f., 298 f., 375, 381, 458, 483, 485, 592, 607 ff., 629 ff.; conception of, 629 ff.; limits of, 656 ff., 664 ff., 677 f.

Corresponding points, 248 f., 424 ff.

Cortex of cerebellum, 54, 86, 103, 108 ff.; of cerebrum, 31 ff., 104, 222 ff., 264 ff.; development of, 52 ff., 62; as seat of mind, 634

Covering points, 424

Crab, nervous system of, 24 f., 288; learning by, 546

Cross-education, 565

Crossing of nerves, 243, 285 f.

Cuneus, 222, 247

Curare, 136

Current of action, 134, 137 f., 230

Current of injury, 141 f.

Current of rest, 141 f.

Cutaneous senses, 179 ff., 244, 344 ff., 352, 363 ff., 473, 475 ff., 517

Deaf-mutes, 211

Deafness, 250, 316

Decerebrate animal, 152, 155, 158 f., 168 f., 525

Decussations, 69, 79, ff., 91 f., 247, 250

Deep sensibility, 181

Degeneration of nerve-fibres, 73, 87 f., 112 f., 239, 288

Dendrites, 42, 97, 101 ff., 265 f., 268; function of, 107 f., 161, 287 ff.; mobility of 289, 613

Departing station, 251

Depression, 501 f., 531

Depth, perception of, 413 f., 416, 423, 426 ff. 458, 465

Determining tendency, 495 ff.

Development, of the mind, 654 ff.; of the nervous system, in the individual, 36, 275, 279, 298, 655, 672; in the race, 13, 298; of space-perception, 381, 384 ff., 390 f., 410, 431, 458, 463 ff.

Diaschizis, 243

Dichromatic vision, 336, 340, 343 f.

Diencephalon, 48

Difference tone, 323

Diffusion, in living cells, 14, 290

Discrimination, 376 ff., 403 f., 410, 665; auditory, 315 ff., 369; as a factor in learning, 550, 554 f., 571; of intensities, 353 ff., 378 f.; olfactory, 374; tactile, 348, 396 ff.; time of, 360, 488 ff., 497, 571; visual, 326, 329, 331, 336

Disposition, 543, 583

Dissociation, 534 f.

Distribution of nervous impulses, 93, 159 f., 168, 622 ff.; of training, 581, 616

Divided space, illusion of, 438 ff., 448

Division of labor in animal economy, 15, 64 ff., 175, 351

Dizziness, 211, 350

Dorsal column, 40, 48, 80 f.

Dorsal horn, 46

Dorsal root, 40, 43 f., 46 ff.

Dot figure, 598, 618

Double contact, 411 f., 637

Double images, 414, 424 ff., 436, 465

Drainage theory, 611 ff., 618 ff.

Dreams, 587, 643

Dualism, 630, 640, 652

Ductus cochlearis, 202 f., 205

Duplex theory of vision, 196, 340

Dura mater, 70

Dynamogenesis, 532 f.

Ear, 196 ff.; an analytic organ, 206, 319; development of, 56; inertia of, 474, 476, 479; internal, 28, 155 f.

Ear drum, 197

Eccentric projection, 303, 384, 390, 411

Economy in learning, 577 f., 581 f.

Ectoderm, 38 ff.

Effector, 16, 65, 99

Eigenlicht, 325, 357, 369, 433

Einfühlung, 450

Einstellung, 602; see also Adjustment

Electrical excitation of cortex, 228 ff.; of nerve, 130 f.; of sense organs, 305, 309, 325

Electrical phenomena in cortex, 230; in

nerves, 137 ff.; in the retina, 138, 194; during emotion, 509 f.
Electrical theory of nerve impulse, 138, 140 ff.; of the synapse, 289 f.
Electrophysiology, 130
Electrotonic currents in nerve, 139 f.
Electrotonus, 138 f.
Elements of consciousness, 500 f., 511
Elimination by subtraction, 491, 497 f.
Embryo, 37 ff.; mental life of, 658
Embryology, 36 ff.
Eminent men, brain weights of, 60 f.
Emotion, 509, 521 ff., 661; bodily symptoms of, 523 ff.; central factors in, 522, 644; sensory factors in, 523, 644; suppression of, 586; theories of, 522 f., 525
Empiristic theory, 385, 418, 458 f.
End-brain, 31, 48 ff.
End-bulb, 180 f.
End-organs, 175 ff., 280, 299, 304, 351 f., 375, 473, 479
End-plate, motor, 100, 136, 212
Endoneurium, 99
Enlargements of the cord, 69 f., 74
Entoderm, 38
Epicritic sensibility, 349
Epineurium, 99
Equally tempered scale, 320
Equilibrium, 157, 209, 282
Erect vision, 453 ff.
Eustachian tube, 197 f., 200
Excitability, see Irritability
Excitation, method of, 228 ff., 244, 249 ff.
Excitement, 501 f., 506, 508, 531
Exercise, nutritive effects of, 59, 62, 581, 616
Expectancy, 480, 502, 507, 556, 602; physiology of, 621 f.
Experience, 380, 418, 458. 468, 542, 549 f., 563, 593 f., 646, 657 f., 679, 685
Extensity, 383, 418 f.
Extent, perception of, 364, 371, 409, 431 f., 440, 467 f., 490
External ear, 196 f., 394
External meatus, 196 f.
Extirpation, 229 ff., 238, 241, 262 f., 663
Eye, axes of, 420 ff.; development of, 49, 56; fixation of, 420, 448 f., 459 f.; movements of, 185 f., 189, 246 ff., 269, 414 f. 417, 420, 427, 447 ff., 454, 457, 459 ff., 530, 659; muscles of, 185 f., 420 f.; nerves of, 189, 191; nerve-centres of, 25, 30, 56, 83, 92, 158, 189, 237, 246 ff.; perceptions of, 413 ff.; positions of, 421 f., 465; rotation of, 420 ff.; structure of, 182 ff.; torsion of, 421 ff.

FACILITATION, 170 ff., 511, 584, 590, 599, 612
Faculties, 255, 274, 391, 566, 571, 581, 655, 666; development of, 657
Fatigue, causes of, 538 ff.; curve of, 536, 538; feelings of, 350, 536, 538 f.: level of, 537; mental, 401, 537 f., 541; of muscle, 536 ff.; of nerve-centres, 538 ff., 611 ff.; of nerve-fibres, 136; products of, 538 f.; of sense organs, 308, 337, 453, 537; varieties of, 539 ff.
Fechner's law, 361, 377 ff., 480
Feeling, 302, 373, 496, 500 ff., 564 f., 567, 658, 666; æsthetic, 505, 513 f., 528 ff.,

664; classification of, 512 ff., 526; common, 518 f.; complex, 518 f., 521 ff.; content of, 514; definition of, 500; dimensions of, 501 f., 506 ff., 526; experiments on, 504; expression of, 505 ff.; intellectual, 502 f., 513 f., 527 f., 544, 584, 590 f.; intensity of. 514; moral, 513 f., 664; nature of, 500, 503, 511; neutral, 515 f.; number of, 501; physiology of, 504 ff.; rhythm of, 514 f.; sensuous, 513 f., 518 ff.; sthenic and asthenic, 524; teleology of, 527; theories of, 504 f., 510 ff., 522 ff.
Feeling of familiarity, 503, 544, 590 f.; of strangeness, 544
Feelings of innervation, 407 f.
Feeling-tone of sensations, 502, 512, 515 ff.. 519 ff., 633, 635
Fenestra ovalis, 198, 205
Fenestra rotunda, 198, 205
Fibrillar theory, 114
Field of touch, 396 ff.; of vision, 415 ff., 436, 438, 456 ff., 461 ff.
Fillet, lateral, 82 f.; mesial, 81, 83 f., 90, 246
Filum terminale, 69 f., 72
Fishes, brain of, 27, 29 ff.: intelligence of, 217
Fissure, calcarine, 222, 247 ff.; central, 220 ff., 236 ff., 244 f., 271; of cerebellum, 86; of cerebrum, 33, 51 ff., 220 ff.; cingulate, 222; of the cord, 45, 69 ff., 79 f.; intraparietal, 221; longitudinal, 52; parieto-occipital, 220, 222, 247; postcentral, 221; precentral, 221; of Rolando, 220 ff., 236 ff., 244 f., 271; of Sylvius, 51 ff., 75, 86, 220 f., 249 f.
Fixation of the eye. 420, 448 f., 459 f.
Flatworm, 20
Fore-brain, 31
Fore-dog, 153, 155
Fore-period, 480, 482 ff., 489
Forgetting, 546, 573 ff.; curve of, 575 ff.
Fornix, 77 f., 85 f., 95, 219, 223
Fovea centralis, 193, 195, 247 f., 334, 420, 459 f.
Fraunhofer's lines, 327 ff.
Free nerve-ending, 180 f.
Functions, fundamental of animals, 14; intellectual, 219, 224, 251 ff., 273 f.
Fundamental system, 26 ff., 47, 56 f., 94, 96
Fundamental tone, 319
Fusion, 321 ff., 403 f., 410, 450 f., 599

GANGLION, cerebral, 24; in invertebrates, 20 ff.; spinal, 26, 42 ff., 50, 56, 73 f., 104, 106; spiral, 203
Genetic theory of space perception, 386
Geniculatum, 78 f., 84 f., 91 f., 96, 246, 248, 250
Geometrical illusions, 437 ff.; theories of, 447 ff.
Geometrical senses, 352, 383, 390, 410, 418
Germ layers, 38
Gestaltqualitäten, 601
Golgi net, 113; Golgi stain, 103, 112, 264 f., 267, 269
Gray matter, 45, 53 f., 73, 102, 106, 118, 222, 226; conduction in, 110, 286 ff.
Ground bundle, 47, 94
Growth of the brain, 59 ff.; of the nervous system, 57 ff.

Gyre, 221; angular, 221, 246 f.; dentate, 219; frontal, 221; fusiform, 222; lingual, 222, 247; occipital, 222; parietal, 221 f.; postcentral, 220 ff., 235 ff., 244 ff.; precentral, 220 ff., 235 ff., 245 f., 261, 268 ff.; supramarginal, 221; temporal, 221; sigmoid, 235

HABENULA, 78, 95
Habit, 263; formation of, 545 ff.; orders of, 556 ff.; law of, 615 ff.
Hair-receptors, 179 f., 346
Hallucinations, 306, 436, 644
Hammer, 197 ff.
Harmony, 321 ff., 529
Head, 25, 28; receptors of, 25, 27 f.
Hearing, acuity of, 368 f.; end-organ of, 196 ff., 351 f.; pathway of, 82, 90 f., 203, 250; sensations of, 312 ff., 367 ff.; space-perceptions of, 392 ff.; theories of, 205 ff.
Heart, beat of, 149, 262, 505 ff.; nerves of, 157, 163
Heat, sensation of, 347 f.
Hemianopsia, 247 f., 253
Hemiplegia, 263
Hemispheres, cerebral, 51 f., 213 ff.; predominance of the left, 263, 565
Heredity, 37, 520
Higher units, 498, 559 f., 562, 569, 578 f., 583, 597, 621; neural mechanism of, 622 ff.
Hind-brain, 48 ff.
Hind-dog, 153, 155, 174
Hippocampus, 95, 223
Hood or tegmentum, 83 ff.
Hormones, 148, 151
Horn of Ammon, 220
Horns of the cord, 46, 72 f., 79 f., 89
Horopter, 426
Hypermetropia, 187
Hypophysis, 76 ff.
Hysteria, 535, 544

IDEAS, 512, 593; learning by, 553 f., 563; physical basis of, 638
Identical points, 424, 426
Idiocy, 656
Illusion, 339, 409, 430, 434 ff., 519, 544; angle, 442 ff.; of area, 447 f.; confluxion, 441, 444, 447, 451; of divided space, 438 ff., 448; geometrical, 437 ff.; of Hering, 445 f.; of motion, 453; of Müller-Lyer, 440 ff., 448, 450 f.; one-dimensional, 438 ff.; of Poggendorf, 440, 444, 446, 451; theories of, 447 ff., 456; of time, 440; of touch, 440: twisted-cord, 446 f.; vertical-horizontal, 437, 447 ff.; of Zöllner, 444, 446 f.
Imagery, 583
Imagination, 219, 243, 253, 274, 589, 661
Incus, 197 ff.
Index of refraction, 186 f.
Indifference point, 346 f., 365 f., 468, 514 ff.
Indifferent conductor, 284 f.
Individual differences, 60 ff., 187, 221,232, 306, 314 ff., 326, 331 f., 335 f., 338, 368, 398, 438, 456, 471 f., 476, 491, 537, 542, 554 f., 571, 583, 591, 600, 655
Inertia of the senses, 471 473 ff., 479
Infancy, mental life in, 658 ff.

Inhibition, 148, 162 ff., 170 ff., 262, 274, 287, 507 f., 511, 532, 539 f., 551, 562, 572, 579 f., 584 ff., 590, 599, 612 f.
Injury of the brain, 215, 217 ff., 252 ff., 262, 274, 644 f., 663; of the cord, 218; of the nerves, 218, 306, 348 f., 400 f.
Instinct, 146, 542, 550, 600
Insula, 52
Intellect, 219, 224, 251, 259 f., 262, 435, 527
Intelligence of animals, 33, 216 f., 545 ff.
Intensity of sensations, 300, 302, 353 ff.; of consciousness, 597, 609 f., 650
Interaction, 640 ff., 654
Interbrain, 48 ff., 76, 78 f., 83 ff., 91 f., 223 248, 250; in different vertebrates, 30 f.
Interference, 496 f., 534, 540, 551, 570, 579 ff., 584 ff.; associative and reproductive, 580, 585; see, also, Inhibition.
Internal capsule, 52 f., 85 f., 93, 223
Internal ear, 200 ff., 350
Interval, 316 f., 320 f., 323
Introspection, 5, 7 ff., 307, 430, 463, 500, 551, 559, 594, 608, 672, 681
Intuition, 385
Iris, 183 f., 188 f.
Irradiation of impulses, 169
Irritability, 15 f., 64 f., 127, 129 ff., 133, 175, 228 f., 539, 545, 585, 587, 612, 615, 619
Island of Reil, 52, 85 f., 221, 250, 262
Itch, 347

JAPANESE music, 320
Joint-sense, 182, 349
Judgment, 593, 601 ff., 665 f.
Jump of the eye, 459 ff.
Just noticeable difference, 358, 361 ff., 432; just noticeable interval, 473 ff.

KEPHALIN, 122
Kinesthetic sensations, 317, 349 f., 407 ff., 414, 417, 423, 427, 431 ff., 447 ff., 454 f., 486
Knee jerk, 167, 171 f., 532 f.

LABYRINTH of the ear, 200 ff., 350
Language, 252 ff.
Lapses, 585, 623
Latent time, 166, 287, 290, 473 ff., 479
Lateral line in fishes, 27
Layers, of cortex, 265 ff.; of embryo, 38; of neural tube, 40 ff., 45, 53; of retina 190 f.
Learning, 542 ff.; as a function of the nervous system, 35, 96, 113, 145, 147, 159, 216 f., 254, 262 ff., 282, 286 f., 615 ff.; curve of, 548 ff., 556 f., 560 ff., 568, 575; in animals, 544 ff.; in man, 555 ff.; relation of consciousness to, 563 f.
Lecithin, 122
Le Long, case of, 256
Lens of the eye, 183 f., 186 ff., 427
Life, mechanics of, 290, 292
Limit, physiological, 557; of the scale of intensities, 356 ff., 362, 364 f., 368; of the scale of tones, 314 f.; of the visible spectrum, 328
Line of regard, 420
Lipoids of the brain, 118 ff.; function of, 119, 280
Listing's law, 421 f., 459

Lobe, 220 ff.; frontal, 51, 85 f., 220 ff., 227, 255, 257, 259 ff., 262 ff., 274; limbic, 222, 268; occipital, 85, 92, 220 ff., 246 ff., 252 f., 274.; olfactory, 31 f., 50, 158, 219, 250; optic, 30, 103; parietal, 220 ff., 245, 252 f., 262; pyriform, 95, 250, 268; temporal, 51, 85 f., 220 ff., 249 f., 252 f., 257 ff., 262, 272, 274
Local sign, 384, 388 ff., 394, 398 f., 401, 405 ff., 410, 414, 422, 431, 433, 456 f., 464, 614
Localization of sensations, 384, 390, 467, 511, 633, 635; auditory, 392 ff., 492 f.; cutaneous, 348, 396 ff., 406 f., 410; gustatory, 392; olfactory, 392; visual, 414
Localization of functions, 74, 152 ff., 219 ff.; history of, 227 f., 234, 235 f., 255, 257 f., 264; in human brain, 238 ff., 298, 614, 634; methods of, 87 f., 223, 228 ff., 273
Locomotion, 155, 157 f., 209, 242, 254
Logic, 593, 603
Lustre, 453

Macula lutea, 191, 193 f.
Malleus, 197 ff.
Mammillary body 76 ff., 86, 95 222
Mammals, brain of, 29 ff.; intelligence of, 547
Man, nervous system of, 33 ff.; intelligence of, 549, 553 ff.
Map of the cortex, 224 ff., 233, 264
Masson disk, 370
Materialism, 631, 640 f., 669; criticism of, 659, 663, 674 ff.
Materiality, concept of, 681; inapplicable to mind, 681
Maturity, 661 f.
Maze-test, 547
Mean gradations, 359, 376
Meaning, as aid to memory, 577, 579; recall of, 601
Measurement of sensation, 356 ff., 377 f.
Mechanism, concept of, as applied to the nervous system, 3, 63 ff., 96, 275 ff., 562; of association, 617 ff.: of attention, 611 ff.; of co-ordination, 159 ff., 622 ff.; of discrimination, 403, 624 f.; of habit, 615 ff.; of life, 290, 292; of memory, 615 ff.; of nerve-centres, 159 ff., 286 ff., 660; of perseveration, 587; of thought, 555, 589 f., 606, 623 ff.: of trial and error, 551 f.; of varied reaction, 611 ff.
Median longitudinal bundle, 83 f., 89, 94
Medulla oblongata, 48, 66, 69, 75, 157
Medullary sheath, see Myelin
Membrana tympani, 197 ff.
Membrane, basilar, 202 ff., 206 ff.; of brain and cord, 68, 70; of Reissner, 202 f., 205; semi-permeable, 14, 119 f.; tectorial, 205; tympanic, 197 ff.
Memorizing, 542, 566 f., 570, 577 ff.; economy in, 578, 581 f.
Memory, analysis of, 542 ff.; associative, in animals, 546; centre for, 274; disturbances of, 544; experimental study of, 572 ff.; feelings of, 502 f.; neural mechanics of, 286 f., 615 ff.; span, 574, 577; training of, 566 ff., 570
Mental work, 291, 507, 509, 537 f., 541, 590; elements, 382; products, 382, 458, 463,

512, 641, 654; processes, time of, 470 ff., 497, 614; life, in embryo, 658; in infancy, 658 ff.; in adolescence, 661; in maturity, 661; in old age, 662
Mesencephalic system, 94 f.
Mesencephalon, 48
Mesoderm, 38
Metabolism, in brain, 215, 290 f., 649; in nerve, 135 ff.; in retina, 342
Metaphysics, its place in psychology, 6, 629 f., 669, 686 f.
Metazoa, 13, 16, 545 ff.
Metencephalon, 48
Method, comparative, 13, 88, 216, 219, 231 f.; of expression, 504; of impression, 504; introspective, see Introspection; of localization of functions, 87 f., 223, 228 ff., 273; of physical science, 278; of physiological psychology, 7, 13, 297 ff.; of psychophysics, 357 ff.; of studying animal intelligence, 547 ff.: of studying memory, 572 ff.; of tracing tracts, 87 f.
Mid-brain, 77 ff., 90, 92, 103, 189; in different vertebrates, 30; development of, 48 ff.
Middle ear, 197 ff.
Mid-dog, 153, 155, 174
Mind, 2, 10, 468 f., 483, 625; action of, on brain, 642 ff.; dependence of, on brain, 215 ff., 643, 671, 685; development of, 644 ff.; immateriality of, 681; independence of, 652 f., 668 ff.; nature of, 385, 632, 652; reality of, 653 f., 668 ff.; relations of, to body, 629 ff.; to brain, 632 ff.; seat of, 631 ff.; spatia relations of, 632 ff.; spirituality of, 682 f.; unity of, 672, 678 ff.
Mixture, of colors, 330 ff., 340, 343, 452; of cutaneous stimuli, 347 f.; of odors, 308; of tastes, 311
Modifiability, 35, 217, 286 f., 542 ff., 615 ff.
Molecules, 275 ff.
Mollusks, nervous system of, 20
Monkey, brain of, 33 f., 235 ff.; intelligence of, 547, 549
Monocular vision, 413 ff., 423, 430
Motifs of perception, 413 ff., 433, 436, 464
Motility, 14 ff.; of dendrites, 289
Motor area, 228, 232, 235 ff., 254, 267 ff.
Movement, automatic, 485, 496, 533 f., 559, 564, 610 f.; compensatory, 155, 209 ff.; expressive, 504 ff., 523 ff., 528 ff., 534, 637; forced, 157, 210; ideomotor, 535; involuntary, 534; learned, 145, 147, 159, 242, 254 f., 262 ff.; perception of, 211, 364, 387 f., 404 f., 433 f., 453; reactive, 480 f., 484; reflex, 145 ff.; rhythmical, 149, 164 f.; skilled, 242, 254 f., 262 ff.; unconscious, 145; voluntary, 147, 535, 538, 645
Müller-Lyer illusion, 440 ff., 448, 450 f.
Muscle sense, 317, 349 f., 363 f., 374, 407 ff., 440; centre for, 244 f., 253; end-organs of, 181 ff., 349; pathway of, 90; theories of, 407 f.; in visual perception, 414, 417, 423, 427, 431 ff., 447 ff., 454 f., 466
Muscle spindle, 181 ff.
Music, feelings aroused by, 521 f., 529 f.; intervals in, 316 f., 320 f., 323, 521; scale of, 316, 320 f.

Myelencephalon, 48
Myelin, 26, 45, 58, 119 ff.: myelin sheath, 26, 45, 58, 99 f., 119, 142 f.
Myelinization, 58 f., 223 ff., 246
Myopia, 187

Narcotics, 120, 287, 289 f.
Native powers, 146, 386, 419, 457 f., 464, 600
Nativistic theory, 385, 418 f., 457 f.
Near-sightedness, 187
Neopallial system, 96
Neopallium, 31 ff., 86, 219, 266
Nerve, 67, 98 ff.; abducens, 55, 87; accessory, 56, 87; auditory, 55 f., 82, 87, 90, 202; blood supply of, 137; cochlear, 82, 202 f.; conduction in, 127 ff., 473; cranial, 55 f., 76, 79; development of, 39, 42 ff.; excitation of, 129 ff.; facial, 55, 87; function of, 21; glosso-pharyngeal, 55, 87, 178; hypoglossal, 56, 87; intermediate, 87, 179; oculomotor, 55, 79, 189; olfactory, 55 f., 79, 106 f., 177, 306; optic, 30, 55 f., 79, 191, 193; physiology of, 127 ff.; quickness of, 130 ff.; spinal, 42, 66; trigeminus, 27, 55, 79 ff., 87, 90, 178, 306, 518; trochlear, 55, 79; vagus, 55, 81, 87, 157, 163, 178, 524 f.; vestibular, 82, 95, 155 f., 202 f.
Nerve-cell, 97 ff.; basket, 108 ff.; branches of, 24 f., 41 f., 97, 286; central 23 f., 27 f., 33, 65, 67, 159 ff., 165, 167, 241; chemistry of, 105, 124, 280; in coelenterates, 18; of cortex, 265 ff.; development of, 41 ff., 57 ff., 97 f., 104; function of, 286 ff.; giant, 240, 268 f., 271; of Golgi type, 97; multipolar, 103; pigment in, 106: Purkinje, 101, 103 f., 109 f.; pyramidal, 102, 104, 240, 265 ff., 269; of retina, 190 ff.; size of, 103; stellate, 269; unipolar, 43 f.; in worms, 21, 23
Nerve-centre, 28, 67, 74, 226 ff., 281; auxiliary, 242; catabolism in, 291; fatigue of, 538 ff.; intellectual, 251, 262; of invertebrates, 20; mechanics of, 286 ff.; motor, 235 ff., 253 f.; perceptual, 252 f.; respiratory, 28, 157; sensory, 244 ff.; speech, 255 ff.; of vertebrates, 25 ff.
Nerve-fibre, 98 ff.; association, 58, 96, 223 f., 233, 246, 251 f., 269; catabolism in, 135 ff., 283; central, 24, 28, 33, 56; a concentration cell, 142; in cord, 75; a core conductor, 140 ff.; in cortex, 266 ff.; electrical properties of, 134, 137 ff.; fatigue of, 136; function of, 16, 20, 22, 35, 65, 127 ff., 154, 223, 279 ff., 284 ff., 304, 473; long and short, 20 f., 25, 27 f., 33 56 f., 94; motor, 42, 46, 56, 73, 100, 128, 132 f., 151, 154, 212, 279; in nerves, 98 ff.; nodes of, 99 f.; number of, 75, 101: of olfactory nerve, 26, 56, 107; projection, 223, 242, 251; sensory, 22, 26, 73 f., 110, 128, 132 f., 176, 178, 182, 191, 203, 285, 348 f., 398; size of, 75, 100: structure of, 98 ff., 141, 279; unmedullated, 99 f., 128, 132, 136
Nerve impulse, 127 f., 165, 277, 279, 283 ff.; blocking of, 287, 289; in different nerves, 284 f.; speed of, 131 f., 473; theories of, 135 ff., 143 f., 283 f.

Nerve-muscle preparation, 128 f.
Nerve-net, in coelenterates, 18 ff.; in higher animals, 20, 112
Nervous elements, 97 ff., 279 f.
Nervous system, of annelids, 22; of coelenterates, 17 ff.; of crustaceans and insects, 24: development of, 38 ff., 275, 279, 298; elements of, 97 ff.; evolution of, 35, 298; of flatworms, 20; function of, 13, 16, 33, 63 ff., 282 f., 287: fundamental and accessory, 26 ff.; growth of, 57 ff.; a mechanism, 3 f., 63, 96, 275 ff.; of mollusks, 20; plan of, 63 ff., 96, 127, 175, 280 f.; simplest form of, 17; structure of, 63 ff.; types of, 20, 22, 25; of vertebrates, 25 ff.
Neural crest, 39 f., 42 ff.
Neural groove, 38
Neural tube, 38 ff., 49
Neurofibrils, 18, 21 f., 41, 101, 106, 113 f., 265
Neuroglia, 40 f., 46, 52, 71, 97, 101, 110, 114 ff.
Neurokeratin, 119
Neurone, 100, 112, 160
Neurone theory, 98, 112 ff., 286 f.
Nissl granules, 105
Nissl stain, 103, 105, 264
Noises, 312 ff.
Nonsense syllable, 572, 577, 579
Nucleus, of the cell, 14, 100, 105, 288; caudate, 52, 78, 85 f., 223; of cranial nerves, 80 ff.; of Deiters, 83, 95; of the dorsal columns, 79 ff., 89; lenticular, 52, 85 f., 223, 259 f.; olivary, 80 ff., 95; pontine, 83, 86, 95; red, 84 f., 95, 223; terminal, 93 f.
Nutrition dependent on exercise, 59, 62, 581, 616 f.

Object of sense, 310 ff., 380 ff., 654
Object blindness, 252, 263
Occasionalism, 646
Odors, classification of, 306 ff.
Old age, brain-weight in, 61 f.; mental life in, 544, 662
Olfactometer, 374
Olfactory bulb, 31, 50, 56, 79, 107, 177
Olfactory lobe, 31, 50, 158
Olive, 69, 76 f., 79 ff., 86
Olive, superior, 90
Optic chiasm, 56, 76, 91, 222, 247
Optic lobes, 30, 103
Organ, concept of, 636 f.
Organ of Corti, 203 ff.
Orientation, 247, 253
Ossicles of the ear, 197 ff.
Osmosis in living cells, 14, 119 f.
Oral or snout sense, 27, 31
Otoliths, 203, 211
Overlapping, 498 f., 556, 558 ff., 562
Over-learning, 572, 576
Over-tone, 314, 319 f., 322 f., 369
Ovum, development of, 36 ff.; fertilization of, 36 f.
Oxygen consumption of brain, 125, 215, 291; of nerves, 137

Pacinian corpuscle, 180 ff.
Pain, 179, 181, 245, 302, 344 ff., 348, 477, 516 f., 532, 539 f.

Pain spots, 181, 344 ff., 477, 517
Paired associates, 573, 578
Pallium, 31, 86, 219; development of, 51 ff.
Papilla, of skin, 180; of tongue, 178, 310, 372
Paracentral lobule, 222
Paradoxical sensation of cold, 346, 348
Parallax, 427, 429, 458
Parallelism, 607, 631, 682
Paralysis, 238 f., 241 f., 245, 254, 263
Paramecium, behavior of, 545, 612
Paraphasia, 253, 260
Paraxon, 98
Parietal organ, 30 f.
Path, auditory, 82, 90, 203, 250; branching, 159 ff., 168 f., 611 ff.; cerebellar, 95; converging, 161 f.; cutaneous, 89 f.; gustatory, 90; kinesthetic, 90; motor, 239, 251; olfactory, 92, 107, 250; optic, 91 f., 246, 269, 479; reflex, 22, 89, 92; sensory, 81, 89 f., 246, 267; of voluntary reactions, 478, 485, 487
Pathological method, 231, 252 ff., 594
Peduncles, of cerebellum, 78, 82 ff., 86; of cerebrum, 76 ff., 84 f., 223
Perception 301 ff., 347, 375 ff., 403, 435, 440, 442, 449 ff., 458, 466, 483 f., 593 ff., 665, 673; centres for, 245 ff., 249 f., 252 ff., 260; of differences, 358 ff., 601 ff.; errors of, 434 ff.; in learning, 551 f.; mediate and immediate, 593; of movement, 211, 364, 387 f., 404 f., 433 f., 467; process of, 594 f.; of relations, 555, 664, f.; selection in, 596 ff.; of space, 380 f., 413 ff.; time of, 483 ff., 497
Perineurium, 99
Perseveration, 586 f., 615
Personal identity, 678, 680 f.
Personality, 262, 519, 673
Perspective, 429 f., 449
Phenomenal reality, 672, 680
Phosphene, 325, 417
Phosphorus of the brain, 121
Photo-chemical substance, 190
Photo-chromatic interval, 333
Phrenology, 227, 232
Physiological psychology, 1 ff., 13, 297 ff., 629; assumptions of, 653; limitations of, 469, 625; method of, 7 f., 13, 297 ff., 356, 380, 468
Physiological time, 472
Physiology, 3 ff.; method of, 7
Pia mater, 70 f.
Pineal gland, 78, 634
Pitch, 206 ff., 313 ff., 490, 492
Pithecanthropus erectus, 34 f.
Plane of regard, 421
Plasticity, 35, 217, 544, 581
Plateau in the curve of learning, 561 f.
Pleasantness, 501 ff., 508 ff., 515 ff., 526, 532, 552, 564 f., 567, 583
Plexiform layer, 266, 268, 273
Plexus in cortex, 267 f., 273
Poggendorf illusion, 440, 444, 446, 451
Point of regard, 420, 422
Pons, 66, 75, 76 ff., 82 ff., 222; development of, 49, 57
Posture, 157, 162, 173, 209
Practice, 401 ff., 451 f., 455, 471, 480 f., 488, 496, 499, 534, 542, 556 ff., 595

Practice curve, 548 ff., 556 f., 560 ff., 568, 575 f.
Precuneus, 222
Pre-established harmony, 646
Preparation for reaction, 480, 482 ff., 489, 491, 493 ff., 590, 602
Presentations of sense, 301 ff., 380 ff., 413 ff., 613 f., 659
Primary position of the eye, 421 f.
Primates, brain of, 34 f.; intelligence of 33, 547, 549, 551 f.
Product, concept of, 641
Projection fibres, 223, 242, 251
Projection of sensations, 303, 384, 390, 393, 411, 414, 633
Proprioceptors, 154, 156
Protagon, 123 f.
Proteid or protein, 14, 118; in brain, 118 f.
Protopathic sensibility, 349
Protoplasm, composition, 14
Protozoa, 13, 544 f.
Psalterium, 85 f.
Pseudoscopic vision, 428, 430
Psychic blindness, 247 ff., 252 f.; deafness, 250, 252 f.
Psycho-analysis, 586
Psycho-galvanic reaction, 509
Psychology, 1, 7, 264, 273; comparative, 14 ff., 216 f.; experimental, 4, 629, genetic, 381, 655; introspective, 381; physiological, see Physiological psychology
Psycho-physics, 6, 9, 353 ff., 649; methods of, 357 ff.
Pupil of the eye, 183 f., 188 f.
Purkinje cell, 101, 103 f., 109 f.
Purkinje phenomenon, 196, 333
Purposiveness of reflexes, 153 f., 216, 527
Pursuit movement of the eye, 460 ff.
Puzzle test, 555 f., 605
Puzzle-box test, 548 f., 551, 553
Pyramids, 69, 76 f., 79 ff.

QUADRIGEMINA, 30, 49, 77 f., 83 f., 90, 92, 95, 189
Quality of sensation, 302 ff., 324 ff., 353 ff., 408, 614
Quantity of sensation, 300, 302, 324, 353 ff., 614

REACTION, general concept, 15; anticipatory, 217; instinctive, 146; learned, 145, 147, 545 ff., 569; mental, 583, 594; unconscious, 145; varied, 545, 547 f., 550, 555, 563, 569, 595, 598, 600, 604 ff.; voluntary, 147
Reaction time, 166, 472 f., 476 ff.; analysis of, 473, 483 ff.; associative, 493 ff.; complex, 487; discriminative, 488 ff., 497; experiment in, 481; movement in, 480 f., 489; muscular, 485 ff., 489; reduced, 473, 483; sensorial, 485 ff., 489, 491; simple, 472, 476 ff., 497; to stimuli of different senses, 476 ff.; of different intensities, 479 f.
Readiness, 483, 485 ff., 489, 493, 495 ff., 503, 580, 584, 612
Reading, 252, 257, 461, 498 f., 560, 595
Reality, conception of, 656, 669 f., 677; of atoms, 675 ff.; of the mind, 653, 656, 662, 667, 668 ff.

Reasoning, 603 ff., 664 ff.; deductive and inductive, 605; mediate and immediate, 606
Rebound after inhibition, 164 f., 173, 599, 612 f.
Recall, 503, 543 f., 550 f., 563, 582 ff.; difficulties of, 585 f.; factors determining, 583, 600; partial or selective, 582 f., 600 f.; threshold of, 584
Receiving station, 246, 248, 250 f., 253, 260, 272
Receptive field, 161, 168
Receptor, 16, 65, 99, 127, 175 ff., 280, 304, 341 ff., 351 f., 375, 477; distance receptor, 25, 217; simplest type of, 176
Receptors, of annelids and arthropods, 25; of jelly-fish, 18; of vertebrates, 27 f.
Reciprocal innervation, 162
Recitation, value of in memorizing, 582
Recognition, 543, 590 ff., 665, 678; false, 544; feelings of, 590 f.; mediate and immediate 592, 593
Rectus internus, etc., 185 f.
Reflex, 128, 145 ff.; clasp, 153; compound, 169 ff.; duration of, 166; extensor thrust, 154, 164, 168, 173; flexion, 153, 161, 164, 167, 169, 171, 173; force of, 167 f.; local, 22 ff., 94, 146, 154; in man, 155; mental influences on, 532 f.; patellar, 167, 171 f., 532 f.; postural, 162, 173; protective, 153, 155, 173, 532; pupillary, 92, 145 f., 161, 168, 188 f., 248; scratch, 155, 161, 164, 167, 172 f.; simple, 146 f., 170; spread of, 168 f.; stepping, 154, 164; winking, 164, 167; wiping, 154
Reflex action, 145 ff., 281, 538; cerebral influence on, 158 f., 171 f., 241, 262; characteristics of, 159 ff.; fatality of, 173; interpretation of, 154; in man, 155; variability of, 174
Reflex arc or path, 22, 89, 92, 145 f., 154, 159 ff.
Reflex preparation, 151 ff.
Reflex time, 166 f., 287, 472; reduced, 167
Refraction in the eye, 183, 186 ff.
Refractory period, 131, 164 f., 540, 615
Reinforcement, 170 f., 532 f.
Relations, perception of, 555, 601
Relativity, law of, 375 f.
Relay station, 92 f., 151
Relief, 501 f., 506 ff., 531
Relearning, 572, 577
Reproduction, in protozoa, 14, 36; in metazoa, 16, 36 f.; of associations, 543, 582 ff.; see Recall
Reproductive tendencies, 493 ff., 583 ff., 605 f.; selection among, 590
Reptiles, brain of, 29 ff.; intelligence of, 547
Residual defects, 261
Resistance in gray matter, 287, 289 f.
Respiration, automatism of, 148; centre for, 81, 125, 148, 157, 262; in emotion, 505 ff., 525
Restitution of function, 241 ff., 259 ff., 663
Restlessness, 501
Retention, 542 ff., 545 f., 572 ff.; curve of, 575; loss of, 546, 574 ff., 585, 616 f.; partial, 573; physiology of, 286 f., 615 ff.
Reticular formation, 79 f.

Retina, 183 f., 186, 189 ff., 280, 325 f., 438; layers of, 190 f.; periphery of, 326, 334; projection of, upon cortex, 248 f.
Retinal field, 415 ff.
Retinal image, 186 f., 189, 382, 415 f., 419, 453 ff.
Retinal light, 325, 357, 369, 433, 463
Retraction of dendrites, 289, 613
Reward and punishment, 547 f.
Rhythm as a source of feeling, 529; as an aid in memorizing, 578 f., 584
Rhythmical movement, 149, 164 f.
Right and wrong cases, 359
Right-handedness, 263 f., 565
Rivalry, 308, 311, 392 f., 452 f., 598 f.
Rods of the retina, 190 ff., 325 f.
Roots of the nerves, 40, 42, 44, 47, 50, 56, 73 f., 134
Rotation, sensation of, 210 ff., 350; of the eye, 420 ff.

Saccule, 201, 203, 208, 211
Salts of the brain, 118
Saturation of color, 324, 327, 337
Saving method, 573
Scala tympani, 201 ff.
Scala vestibuli, 201 ff.
Scale, of colors, 328, 330 f., 344; of extensity, 383; of intensity, 356 f., 362; of tones, 314 ff., 318, 320 f.
Sclerotic, 182, 184, 194
Segments of the nervous system, in annelids, 22 ff.; in vertebrates, 25, 74
Selection, neural mechanism of, 623 f.; in the process of learning, 547, 549 ff., 564; in perception, 596; in recall, 590; in thought, 606
Self, 511, 519, 571, 658 f., 665, 668 ff.
Semicircular canals, 155, 200 f., 203 f., 208 ff., 350
Sensations, 16, 282, 285, 297 ff., 381 f., 639; classification of, 300; feeling-tone of, 502, 512, 515 ff.; measurement of, 356 ff., 377 f.; pure, 391, 594, 596, 659; quality of, 302 ff., 324 ff., 353 ff., 405, 408; quantity of, 300, 302, 324, 353 ff.; simple, 302 f., 327, 341, 351, 380, 391; subjective, 306; unit of, 361, 377 f.; visceral or organic, 350, 518 f., 525 f.
Sensation-circles, 397 ff., 405
Sense-organ, 67, 175 ff., 299, 473 ff., 479; development, of, 38, 56; see Receptor.
Sensitivity, 175, 345, 357, 364 f., 368 f., 371 ff.; see also Irritability; differential, 358 ff., 392, 404, 431 f.
Sensorium, 213 f., 284
Sensus communis, 214, 350, 518 f.
Series of sensations, 356 f., 383, 386 ff.
Sheath, medullary or myelin, 26, 45, 58, 99 f., 142 f.; primitive, 99
Shock of difference, 403
Sight, see Vision.
Skill, acquisition of, 555 ff., 565
Skin, senses of, 179 ff., 244, 344 ff.
Sleep, 113, 291
Smell, 27, 158, 175 ff., 219, 250 f., 304 ff., 351, 372 ff., 392, 475, 478
Snout sense, 31, 219
Solipsism, 668

Somesthetic area, 244 ff., 403 f.
Soul, 1 f., 10, 215 f., 625, 686; see Mind
Sounds, 312 ff.
Space-form, 383, 418 f., 466
Space-perception, 245, 364, 371, 380 ff., 413 ff.; theories of, 385 f., 418 ff.
Span of attention or apprehension, 560, 597; of immediate memory, 574, 577
Spatial series, 383, 386 ff., 406 f., 419, 422, 659
Spatial quality, 418 f.
Specialization of organs, 15 f., 18 f., 22, 36, 64 f., 175
Specific energies of nerves, 284 ff., 304, 350 ff., 389 f., 418, 420; of parts of the brain, 284 f., 614
Spectrum, 327 ff., 341
Speech, centres for, 227, 233, 255 ff.; disturbances of, 253, 255 ff.
Spider, learning by, 545 f.
Spider cell, 114 f.
Spinal cord, 25 ff., 66, 69 ff., 226, 241; consciousness in, 216 f.; development of, 39 ff., 59
Spinal dog, 153 ff.
Spinal frog, 152 ff.
Spinal ganglia, 26, 42 ff., 73 f., 103, 106
Spinal preparation, 151 ff.
Spirituality, concept of, 682 f.
Sponge, behavior of, 17
Spreading of reflexes, 169
Stable colors, 334 f., 337, 340, 344
Stains of nervous tissue, 101, 103, 124, 264; fibril, 103, 106, 265; Golgi, 103, 264 f.; Nissl, 103, 105, 264; osmic acid, 87; Weigert, 72, 264
Staircase effect, 536, 538
Staircase figure, 594, 618
Stapedius muscle, 198, 200
Stapes, 197 ff., 205
Stentor, behavior of, 544 f., 612
Stereognosis, 253, 410
Stereoscope, 427 f., 598
Stereoscopic vision, 414, 427 f., 430
Stimulation, method of, 229 f.
Stimulus, 4, 6, 14 f., 282, 303; adequate, 175, 304 f., 307 ff., 311, 324, 327 ff., 332, 341, 346 ff., 367; general, 17, 129 f., 175, 305, 309 ff., 324 f., 346; mixed, 308, 311, 330 ff., 340, 343, 347 f., 389, 452; in reaction time experiments, 471, 476 ff.; and sensation, 357 ff.
Stirrup, 197 ff., 205
Striatum, 31, 51, 78 f., 86, 219
Stripe of Baillarger, 269
Stripe of Gennari, 269, 271
Strychnine, 147, 160, 619
Subconsciousness, 2, 672 f.
Subcutaneous senses, 181, 348 f., 363 ff.
Sub-excitation, 485 ff., 580
Subjective idealism, 668
Suggestion, 402, 535
Summation of stimuli, 170 f., 612
Surface of separation, 14, 65, 119 f., 289 f.
Surprise, 602
Suspensory ligament, 184, 188
Sympathetic system, 66 f., 74, 99; development of, 44 f.; function of, 150, 189
Sympathetic vibration, 206 f.

Synapse, 107, 111 ff., 266, 287 ff., 479, 609 ff., 619
Synthesis, 93, 302 f., 383 f., 391, 407, 410, 419, 422, 435, 466, 468, 665, 683

Talbot's law, 474
Taste, 28, 306, 309 ff., 351 f., 372 f., 392, 475, 477 f.; centre for, 251; end-organs of, 178 f., 307; pathway of, 90, 178 f.
Taste-buds, 178 f., 307, 309 ff., 478
Tectal system, 94 f.
Tegmentum, 83 ff.
Telegraphy, learning of, 556 ff., 561, 621
Telencephalon, 48
Temperature sense, 179, 181, 245, 344 ff., 365 f., 406 f., 477
Tendon spindle, 182
Tension, feeling of, 501 f., 506 ff.
Tension theory of consciousness, 610 f.
Tensor tympani, 197 f., 200
Tentorium cerebelli, 68, 70
Terms of the judgment, 593
Testimony, reliability of, 589
Thalamus, 30, 49, 51 ff., 77 f., 84 ff., 90, 92 f., 96, 246; in different vertebrates, 30 f.
Things, 299 f., 303, 381 f., 422, 512, 633, 655, 658 ff., 666, 673 f., 676 f., 679 ff.
Third dimension, perception of, 413 f., 423, 426 ff., 449, 458, 465
Thomson's law, 453
Thought, 555, 589 f., 593 ff.
Threshold, of consciousness, 2, 458, 463, 671; of difference, 358 ff.; of excitation, 357, 478; of recall, 584; of spatial discrimination, 326, 396 ff., 565
Tickle, 347
Timbre, 314, 318 f., 369, 395
Time, illusions of, 440; of mental processes, 470 ff., 497, 614
Time-form, 470, 514
Tone-color, 314, 318
Tones, 312 ff.; difference, 323; end-organs for, 206 ff.; scale of, 314 ff., 318, 320 f.; simple, 313
Tonus, 155, 209, 211, 325
Touch, analysis of, 179, 306, 310, 344 ff.; centre for, 244 ff.; illusions of, 440; inertia of, 473 ff., 476; pathway of, 81, 89 f.; perceptions of, 391, 396 ff., 466 ff., 492
Touch compasses, 396, 401
Touch-corpuscle, 180
Touch-spots, 132, 179 f., 344 ff., 365, 398 ff.
Tract, 81 ff., cortico-spinal or pyramidal, 47, 73, 83 f., 88 f., 93, 232, 239 f., 242, 269; development of, 47; direct cerebellar, 95; list of tracts, 89; methods of tracing, 87 f.; naming of, 88 f.; olfactory, 50, 79, 92; optic, 91. See Path.
Training, 401 ff., 542, 547 f., 565 ff.
Transference of training, 402, 550, 563, 565 ff., 581, 588, 605
Treffermethode, 573
Trial and error, learning by, 550 ff., 582, 617, 620; in perception, 594 f.
Twilight vision, 196, 333, 335, 340
Twisted cord illusion, 446 f.
Two-point threshold, 396 ff., 565
Tympanic membrane, 197 ff., 367

Tympanum, 197 ff.
Typewriting, learning of, 558 ff., 576 f., 621

UNCONSCIOUS movements, 145
Unicellular animal, 13, 14
Unit, of perception, 442 ff., 597, 623; of reaction, 498, 558 f., 562, 569, 578 f., 584, 621 ff.; of sensation, 361
Unity, conception of, 670 f., 676; of consciousness, 679, 684 ff.; of the mind, 672, 678 ff.
Unpleasantness, 348, 501 ff., 508 ff., 515 ff., 526, 532, 552, 564 f., 567, 585 f.
Utricle, 201, 203, 208, 211

VARIABILITY, of brain-weight, 60; of perception, 359, 376; of reflexes, 174; of reaction time, 476, 481; of voluntary effort, 537
Varied reaction, 545, 547 f., 550, 555, 563, 569, 595, 598, 600, 604 ff., 615; physiological theory of, 611 ff., 620
Ventral horn, 46, 151, 154
Ventral root, 40 ff.
Ventricles of the brain, 39, 49, 51, 77 ff., 81, 86
Verbal amnesia, 253, 260
Vermis, 86 f.
Vertebrates, nervous system of, 25 ff.
Vertical-horizontal illusion, 437, 447 ff.
Vestibular nerve, 82, 95, 155, 203
Vestibule, 200 ff., 208, 211, 350
Vicarious function, 242
Visceral sensation, 350
Vision, acuity of, 326, 371 f.; æsthetics of,

530 f.; binocular, 414 f., 423 ff., 436, 458, 465; clear, 420, 457, 459 ff.; erect, 453 ff.; indirect, 326, 334, 422, 461; inertia of, 474, 476, 479; monocular, 413 ff., 423, 430, 466; peripheral, 326, 334 ff.; sensations of, 324 ff.; stereoscopic, 414. See Eye, Color vision.
Visual area, 246 ff., 285
Visual perception, 413 ff.
Visual purple, 125, 195
Visual sensations, 285, 324 ff., 369 ff.
Visual size, 430
Vital force, 279, 291
Vitreous humor, 183 ff., 187

WARMING-UP, 536, 538, 545, 615
Warmth-spots, 181, 344 ff., 366, 405
Weber's law, 361 ff., 432; interpretations of, 374 ff.
Weigert stain, 72, 264
Weight, perception of, 363 ff., 601 f.
Wernicke's region, 257, 259 f.
White matter, 45, 53, 74, 101, 118 ff., 223
Will, 243, 483 ff., 496, 645, 664, 666; will to learn, 582
Will-time, 484, 488, 497.
Word-blindness, 252, 257, 263
Word-deafness, 250, 253, 257, 260, 263
Writing centre, 254 f., 257, 261

YELLOW spot of retina, 191, 193 f., 326, 333, 371, 465

ZÖLLNER illusion, 444, 446 f.
Zones of the retina, 334 ff., 343